GRAS OF THE BRITISH ISLES

B.S.B.I HANDBOOK No. 13

TOM COPE & ALAN GRAY

Illustrated by
MARGARET TEBBS

Edited by
PAUL ASHTON

Botanical Society of the **British Isles**

Botanical Society of the British Isles
London
2009

PLANTS PEOPLE
POSSIBILITIES

ISBN Softback 978-0-901158-420
ISBN Hardback 978-0-901158-413

Published by the Botanical Society of the British Isles
c/o Department of Botany, The Natural History Museum,
Cromwell Road, London, SW7 5BD

Designed by Paul Westley, Norwich

Printed by Henry Ling Limited, Dorchester

CONTENTS

ACKNOWLEDGMENTS

The number of people willing to give assistance on this book has been legion, and we could not begin to thank them all individually. There are some, however, without whose help the book would not have been possible and to these we give our special thanks.

From TAC:

Alan Gray for agreeing to be my co-author and for sharing with me his huge expertise in grassland ecology, and **Margaret Tebbs** for giving up so much of her time to prepare the illustrations.

Eric Clement, Bruno Ryves and **Ron Payne**, the 'Aliens Committee,' for freely giving of their vast stores of knowledge of alien grasses, for guiding me in the final selection of aliens and for taking a constant and unflagging interest in the entire project.

Arthur Chater (formerly of the Natural History Museum, London) for his original invitation to write the book.

Philip Oswald (BSBI Publications) for constantly reminding me of agreed, but seldom met, deadlines and his successor on this project, **Paul Ashton**.

Gren Lucas (formerly Keeper of the Herbarium, Royal Botanic Gardens, Kew) for allowing me private access to the Kew grass collections and **Simon Owens**, his successor, for consenting to allow the project to become a significant part of my official Kew duties.

Mary Briggs (BSBI) for asking me to become British grass referee in place of the late Charles Hubbard and thereby setting me on the road that ultimately led to this book, and to **Derek Clayton** and **Steve Renvoize**, my erstwhile colleagues in the grass section at Kew, for their constant support and encouragement (not least by declining their own invitations to be the new grass referee).

The late **Charles Hubbard** for his inspiring conversations and guidance in my early days of grass taxonomy.

Clive Stace (University of Leicester) who first set me on the road to taxonomy in the days when we were both at Manchester University, me as a research student and he as my supervisor, and for his constant interest in the project.

Laurie Spalton (Budleigh Salterton, Devon) and **Jack Oliver** (Marlborough, Wilts) for their interest in *Bromus* and *Brachypodium* respectively, and for their willingness to keep me informed of progress in their private research.

Peter Thomas (Weybridge, Surrey) for his help in trying to unravel the complexities of *Festuca* taxonomy, for providing specimens and for collaborating in the final draft of the account. Peter in turn acknowledges the help he received from **Colin Taylor** who willingly translated texts from the original French.

Barry Phillips (RHS Wisley) for several inspiring field excursions and his constant interest in the project.

And to those many BSBI members who, since 1979, have sent me material for refereeing, thereby ensuring that I was constantly on my toes and fully aware of current taxonomic problems.

From AJG:

Tom Cope for being an agreeable and authoritative co-author and **Margaret Tebbs** for so beautifully capturing the essence of each species.

For their help and inspiration, botanical friends no longer with us who were always willing to guide and advise me as a small boy in Lincolnshire (**Verdun Wray, Joan Gibbons**) and in later years as a student of the grass family (**Charles Hubbard, John Trist, Paul Bowman**).

For me this book has been, in its true sense, an amateur's enterprise which I finally completed following retirement, but I am immensely grateful to have had the privilege of a lifetime's research in plant ecology and genetics – actually for one organisation which began as The Nature Conservancy and became respectively the Institute of Terrestrial Ecology and the Centre for Ecology and Hydrology. My thanks go to the many colleagues and students from whom I learned so much in the course of our research on grasses (especially **Paul Adam, Helen Ambrosen, Paulina Benham, Colin Ferris, Rebecca Mogg, Roger Parsell, Alan Raybould, Joanna Rihan, Richard Scott, John Thompson** and **Liz Warman**).

I am pleased to acknowledge the specific help of **Arthur Chater, Maria Scholten** and **John Valentine** (*Avena*) and **Jim Martin** (*Hordeum secalinum*).

Finally, for her constant support and encouragement throughout this project (and others), I am delighted to thank my wife **Sue Gray** and, for their forbearance, my children **James, Lisa, David** and **Katie** whose childhood holidays invariably involved searching for, counting or measuring some grass or other.

Both authors and editor would like to thank David Pearman for significant help in bringing the project through to publication. Gratitude is also due to Victoria Annis, Chris Boon, Sarah Watson-Jones and Mike Wilcox for assistance in the latter stages of the book.

6

INTRODUCTION

It is probable that anyone who has ever taken a serious interest in British grasses has owned Charles Hubbard's *Grasses* (Hubbard 1954, 1968, 1984). This has been the standard text on grasses of the British Isles for more than half a century and it is difficult to conceive of anything that might surpass it in either breadth or depth of content. It went to a second edition in 1968 and needed yet another in the post-*Flora Europaea* era once the final volume of that work had been published in 1980. This was the year that Charles Hubbard died and it fell to his son, John Hubbard, to see the third edition through to its publication in 1984. It is a pity that the publishers gave the younger Hubbard such limited scope for making changes; the most significant they allowed were the addition of one more species, *Agrostis castellana* (but without illustration and out of sequence), an account of the subspecies of *Festuca rubra* (edited from the elder Hubbard's extensive notes, but an account already superseded by a new treatment of the genus presented in *Flora Europaea*) and the addition of the latest accepted names for taxa, albeit in the form of footnotes. With no other changes accommodated (even the index was not reset despite the numerous additions that threw the column heads out of phase with the columns) the book has sadly lost some of its authority, a situation exacerbated, for example, by the retention of both *Agropyron caninum* and *Agropyron donianum*, each with full description and illustration, but each with the modern accepted name of *Elymus caninus*.

If there was a weakness with 'Hubbard' it was the general key to species. With no way of suspecting that anything may have gone wrong until the final statement was reached the user was compelled, in the event of failure, to begin again from the start with no guarantee of a better result. TAC, who was brought up in a culture of writing tropical grass Floras where tribe and genus are just as important as species, began to toy with the idea of writing keys to British grasses that would have this 'tropical' flavour. They would employ both tribe (and subtribe where appropriate) and genus as working units; the key to tribes would be relatively short, and keys to genera within tribes equally short. This would give the user an opportunity to take a rest and to check the specimen against a tribal description before moving on to genus, and against a generic description before moving on to species. This repeated routine would, in time, reinforce tribal and generic concepts and enable the user to recognize the tribes, and so cut out one key, and then the genera, and so cut out another (but not necessarily in that order since the tribes would be new to most users but the representative genera, in the British Isles at least, may already have been quite well known). With 'Hubbard,' unfortunately, knowing the genus did not help to short-cut the key since the latter was not constructed in a 'natural' way and related species could not be relied upon to come out in proximity.

With the need to present the user with more workable keys and to take account of the great strides forward in grass taxonomy that were inspired by Clayton & Renvoize's *Genera Graminum* of 1986, the time seemed right to think about preparing a new guide to the grasses of the British Isles to supplement 'Hubbard.' It was at about this time that the BSBI approached the present authors with the idea of a new addition to their series of Handbooks.

The Grass Handbook was to be an ambitious project, partly because it would be difficult to write anything that could ever truly replace 'Hubbard' and partly because, with 220 species to be dealt with in one way or another, it was destined to be the largest handbook the BSBI had ever attempted. Furthermore, it was to be illustrated with all new plates. TAC has always maintained that since no-one out in the field equipped with just a handlens and a ruler will ever see the individual parts of a grass spikelet lined up like a squad of soldiers on parade there is little to be gained by illustrating them in such a way. In a guide to identification – rather than an encyclopaedia which is, to all intents and purposes, what 'Hubbard' is – the illustrations should be diagnostic and show the parts as the user would see them in the field with a handlens, sometimes dissecting them a little for clarity. We were lucky to secure the artistic services of Margaret Tebbs who has built up a reputation for cleanliness of line, simplicity of portrayal and an ability to bring herbarium specimens to life in her drawings. To simplify the illustrations further, those parts of the grass spikelet of no diagnostic value (for example the lodicules and flower) have largely been omitted.

In line with the illustrations the text has also been simplified. One of the lessons learned from *Flora Europaea* (Tutin *et al*, 1980) was that of how to be economical with words; the hardest part of writing any description is knowing how much can safely be omitted. One extreme view on description-writing was held by Otto Stapf who, in the earlier part of the twentieth century, was Hubbard's head of section at Kew. Stapf believed that one should be able to draw a portrait of the plant from its description and consequently all his descriptions in the grass volume of *Flora of Tropical Africa* are extraordinarily long. If key characters were missing from a specimen then two closely related species might be distinguished by just a few other well chosen words but these could only be found by painstakingly comparing the descriptions phrase by phrase. The modern view is that the less said the better since the reader tends to be discouraged by long descriptions. Many words can be saved by not repeating in a generic description any characters that apply to the whole tribe, since the tribe itself will already have been fully described. Likewise, there is no place in a species description for characters common to the genus. Species descriptions should be a combination of diagnostic characters and any other features that help generate a mental image of the plant. Height of plant, width of leaves and overall inflorescence-form may not be diagnostic, but they provide the canvas on which the important characters can be painted. On the other hand, details of flower (other than the anthers), lodicules and caryopsis are not only seldom diagnostic but sometimes (in the case of lodicules) extremely hard to find; there seems little point in including such characters in a book designed for naming plants if they contribute neither to the taxonomy nor to the process of identification. A good illustration will, as it were, complete the picture.

The descriptions that follow, we hope, will fulfil the required task of confirming a determination in the fewest possible words, with those of species within genera, subgenera or sections being comparable on every included character. We chose not to go down the road of '*x* differs from *y* mainly by its longer anthers' since this can easily conceal other characters that might be of assistance (the exception being with certain aliens with abbreviated entries). Short descriptions allow more space for discussion of ecology and distribution, and for general points about relationships and hints on how to recognize the plant in the field. Every species has been thoroughly reworked with all appropriate characters remeasured from the rich collections at Kew, many gathered by Hubbard himself over his long career and many contributed by his contemporaries. To do this may seem like reinventing a wheel that Hubbard had already perfected but, it has to be said, there were some surprises in store for us and the project took much longer than anticipated.

The authors have tried, wherever possible, not to depart too far from accepted and familiar taxonomy; they are, nevertheless, well aware of the mixed feelings with which this book will be received and that the treatment of British grasses offered will not be to everyone's taste. Some decisions were hard to take but we decided to adopt a pragmatic approach and not offer to the user any taxa that we could not confidently identify ourselves. We worked on the assumption that most users will not have access to facilities for investigating anatomy (from counting sclerenchyma girders to distinguishing Kranz and non-Kranz syndromes), cytology (from simple chromosome counting to karyotyping) or gene sequencing. Several segregate taxa that are dependent on chromosome number for part of their circumscription have often been subsumed into one at a higher level when reliable supporting morphological characters could not be found; we chose not to make distinctions when differences could not clearly be demonstrated. The aim of the book is to enable the user, whether amateur or professional, experienced or inexperienced, to put names to grasses and sometimes taxonomic minutiae have had to be sacrificed at the altar of pragmatism. The format of the text leaves little scope for detailed discussion of infraspecific variation or classification and most of the variation is accounted for in the species descriptions without further elaboration.

A similar principle of parsimony has been adopted in descriptions of the distribution, ecology and status of each species, the aim being to capture the main characteristics of each species and to lead those who may wish to go further to the literature. The contents of the paragraphs covering these aspects are described below in the section 'HOW TO USE THE BOOK'.

THE GRASS PLANT

The grass family, *Poaceae* (*Gramineae* is permitted by the International Code of Botanical Nomenclature but now seems old-fashioned), ranks fifth in order of size behind *Orchidaceae, Fabaceae (Leguminosae), Asteraceae (Compositae)* and *Rubiaceae* but ranks first in order of importance. It provides the grasslands which occupy a third of the world's land surface and the cereal crops upon which much of the world's human population depends for its food. The grasses are an extraordinarily successful group and their success has been based on three recurring themes: (1) their ability to adapt to changing environments; (2) their ability to coexist with man and his grazing animals; and (3) their possession of a very distinct life-form that remains faithful to a single architectural idea but which has almost endless, and often very ingenious, variations. Grass taxonomists today generally recognize about 6 subfamilies, 40 tribes, 700 genera and 11,000 species, but as our expertise in molecular studies (particularly at the level of the gene) has increased, the phylogeny – and thus the classification – of grasses has come under increasingly close scrutiny; already there have been suggestions of major restructuring of the grass family (e.g. Grass Phylogeny Working Group, 2001), but none of these have yet achieved universal acceptance.

For an expanded treatment of what follows see Clayton & Renvoize (1986).

Root, stem and leaf

In most grasses, and our own in particular, the life-cycle is strongly seasonal. Perennials spend the winter in a dormant condition, allowing much, if not all, of their foliage to wither after the extraction of any useful nutrients, but truly deciduous grasses are very rare (*Molinia caerulea* is one example). Annuals, on the other hand, overwinter as seed, allowing the parent plant to die completely. Grasses do, however, have a tendency to be relaxed about the finer distinctions between annual and perennial and it is not uncommon for some annuals to survive a mild winter without any significant pause in their growth (e.g. *Poa annua*). In contrast, some perennials can only be described as 'short-lived,' lasting just two or three years, and these can be difficult to distinguish from annuals (e.g. *Bromus carinatus*). In general, perennials may be recognized by the presence of buds or sterile shoots at their base, and almost any grass that produces rhizomes is likely to be a perennial; the presence of stolons is a much less reliable indicator. In the tropics, perennial grasses can often be recognized by a basal tuft of old sheaths each with a burnt tip indicating that the plant was present during the previous season's bush fires.

The stem of a grass is usually (but by no means always) a hollow tube interrupted at intervals by a transverse septum of vascular tissue at a position referred to as the *node*; the length of stem between adjacent nodes is termed the *internode*. The node can often be detected by the presence of an external swelling, but this is often derived from the leaf-sheath and may not be a feature of the node itself; a node that is exposed beyond the mouth of the uppermost sheath is more likely to be seen as a contraction than as a swelling, and is often dark-coloured. The nodes tend to be closer together at the base of the stem than they are in the upper part.

The root system of grasses is fibrous and relatively shallow; it seldom penetrates for much more than a metre into the ground and often much less. All roots have their origin at a node.

The main branching system of the plant and its perennating buds occur just above ground level in tussock grasses, at ground level in stoloniferous and mat-forming grasses, and just below ground level in rhizomatous, turf-forming grasses. It is relatively inaccessible to grazing (and its man-made counterpart, mowing) and readily produces new shoots (*tillers* or *innovations*) to replace any aerial parts that may be lost by cropping. Tillers are produced from a ring of tissue at each of the nodes called the *intercalary meristem*. Those tillers that grow up within the subtending leaf-sheath are termed *intravaginal innovations* (and give rise to densely tufted grasses), and those that penetrate the base of the sheath and develop outside it are termed *extravaginal innovations* (and give rise to loosely tufted and turf-forming grasses). Adventitious roots are also produced from the nodes and each tiller is eventually supported by its own independent root system. Adventitious roots may also develop from any node that comes into extended contact with the ground; any stem that is lodged by heavy rain or trampling can take root and such rooted nodes can, by differential growth of the meristem, restore the stem to an upright stance. In a few species one or more of the basal internodes can develop into a swollen food-storing corm-like structure. Stems that bear an inflorescence are usually termed *culms*; the non-flowering shoots, which will bear inflorescences in the following season or later in the same season, are the tillers.

The leaves of a grass are arranged distichously – in two alternating rows – on the stem (though this arrangement is not always obvious, and there are rare exceptions) and follow the normal monocotyledonous pattern of division into *sheath* and *blade*. This division is so highly developed in grasses that it contributes much to their characteristic life-form. The most obvious manifestation of this is the way in which stem and sheath are combined into a single structural unit; the participating stem is often so weak that it could not maintain itself in an upright posture without the mechanical support of the enveloping sheaths. In the early stages of development of the stem the nodes are densely packed behind the apical primordium and the primordium itself is protected in a nest of tightly concentric sheaths. The internodes then elongate from the intercalary meristems and the tip of the stem is extruded from the supporting sheath. The sheath begins at the node and is wrapped firmly or loosely around the internode; it varies in length from shorter to much longer than the internode. Its margins often overlap, but sometimes they are contiguous and occasionally they are fused to form a cylinder. The blade is typically linear and flat, but has the ability to roll or fold under desiccation. At its base, in a zone known as the *collar* (visible as a pale or yellowish band on the abaxial side of the sheath at its junction with the blade), is a *plate meristem* from which the tissues of the blade originate; the cells of the young blade near the collar are shorter than those towards the tip of the leaf and as the blade is cropped it can appear to regrow by continued elongation of the basal cells. An uncropped leaf will only reach a certain length and further lost matter cannot be replaced, but the movement of the cut end of the leaf away from the collar during cell elongation gives a misleading impression of replacement. At the junction of sheath and blade, on the adaxial side, is the *ligule*, represented by a membrane or a line of hairs. Exactly what the ligule is for is still a mystery, but it may possibly act to deter either insects or water from entering the sheath. It is a novel structure in grasses that has no homology with any other known organ. It can be a useful aid in tribal recognition but is prone to unexpected variation (including complete absence). On occasion the base of the blade is expanded laterally into a pair of ear- or sickle-shaped structures termed *auricles*. Other vegetative characters are of little taxonomic use, but will be mentioned in the text as appropriate.

The first leaf of any axillary branch is adaxial and highly modified, and is termed a *prophyll*. It is a membranous, 2-keeled, scale-like structure on the basal branches but linear on aerial branches. It is difficult to find and seems to be of little practical importance, but it is of interest in establishing homologies, especially within the spikelet (see below).

Inflorescence

The inflorescence of a grass is a modified branch system in which subtending leaves have been suppressed. Its design is that of a simple or compound raceme with the *spikelet* (see below) as the basic unit but homologies at this point are not precise. The main forms it can take, with examples, are:

1. Single raceme, with spikelets on one side of the axis (the *rhachis*) (*Nardus*), on opposite sides (*Lolium*), or all around (no examples in the British Isles). Sometimes a distinction is made between racemes (spikelets pedicelled) and spikes (spikelets sessile), but the pedicel is often so slight as to be barely visible (*Brachypodium*), and in some members of tribe Andropogoneae (not in our area) it is highly confusing.

2. Panicle, either open and spreading (*Poa*) or contracted and spike-like (*Alopecurus*). In some cases the contraction has proceeded to the point where the branches are physically fused to the main axis (some *Phleum*).

3. Multiple racemes, arranged digitately (*Cynodon*) or scattered along an axis (*Spartina*). Since these are compound racemes they are technically panicles, but it is more helpful to retain the distinction.

Terminology of the grass inflorescence is sometimes rather strained and it is clear that it is technically inaccurate. It is derived from the assumption that its basic unit, the spikelet, is analogous to the normal petaloid flower. Difficulties arise when the inflorescence suffers modification generated by outside influences, such as a panicle so sparse as to resemble a very loose raceme (typical of many species of *Bromus* growing in dry or barren places) or where it is simply of a kind that does not quite conform to the three classes described above. An example of the latter is found in *Hordeum* where the lateral branches of the panicle are so short that the spikelets regularly occur in triads at each node of the rhachis, with the three pedicels connate below; the inflorescence in this case is termed a false (or quasi-) raceme to distinguish it from both a spike-like panicle and a true raceme.

Despite these difficulties the terminology of the grass inflorescence follows well established conventions and recent attempts to introduce a new, more precise system (Vegetti & Anton 2000) have been met by agrostologists with a singular lack of enthusiasm, not to say indifference.

The type of inflorescence is often very characteristic of a tribe and is so accessible that it is difficult to avoid using it. It can, however, mislead and artificial keys that are heavily reliant on inflorescence structure often bring quite unrelated grasses together and confuse rather than clarify taxonomic relationships.

Spikelet

The spikelet appears to be more or less what its name implies: a little spike. It consists of a series of scale-like bracts borne distichously on an axis (the *rhachilla*) and is supported, usually, on a long or short stalk, the *pedicel*. The two lowermost scales are empty and serve to protect the immature spikelet; these are the *glumes*: the lower, or outer, is the *lower glume* and the upper, or inner, is the *upper glume*. The majority of grasses regularly have both glumes, but inevitably there are exceptions or modifications. *Lolium* is missing the lower glume in all spikelets but the terminal, in *Nardus* the glumes are minute and in *Leersia* they are missing altogether; in *Parapholis* they are placed side-by-side and in *Hordeum* they are not only collateral but also reduced to little more than bristles.

Above the glumes is a series of one to several (or many) bracts, the *lemmas*, each of which is opposed by another bract, the *palea*. Lemma and palea together enclose the flower, the whole forming a unit known as a *floret*. The term floret is based on functional analogy rather than morphological homology and interpretation of homology is very much a matter of dispute. The glumes and lemmas are generally accepted as being derived from leaf-sheaths, but the origin of the palea is less certain. One suggestion, which at least has the merit of aiding understanding of spikelet structure, is to view the palea as the modified prophyll of a diminished axillary branch. The spikelet can thus be seen as a complete inflorescence in the form of a highly modified panicle (not, after all, a spike as the name 'spikelet' implies). The imprecise nature of the terminology of the grass inflorescence therefore has its roots in the simple fact that the 'inflorescence' is really no such thing; it is a highly modified branch system bearing, at the summit of each branch, a small, equally modified inflorescence. Terminology of the branches has also shifted, with the axis of the 'inflorescence' termed the *rhachis* and that branchlet bearing the spikelet termed the pedicel (strictly the latter is a peduncle but this term is employed by agrostologists for the culm-internode bearing the 'inflorescence'). Leaves and prophylls at the branching points have been suppressed because they would impair wind pollination (they do, however, reappear in some of the more modified members of tribe Andropogoneae which do not naturally occur in our area). The base of the spikelet or floret may be hardened to some degree into a knob or short stalk (or sometimes just a rim) termed the *callus*.

The flower itself is greatly reduced and typically comprises 2 minute scales called *lodicules*, 3 stamens and 2 plumose stigmas atop a single-celled ovary. From the morphological point of view these are all fairly uniform although the stamens are subject to variation in number. The stamens comprise a long slender filament supporting a versatile anther that mostly dehisces by means of a longitudinal slit, sometimes by a terminal pore.

The lodicules are usually interpreted as a vestigial perianth which swells to open the floret for anther emergence and then allows it to close again until the stigmas are ready for extrusion. In cleistogamous and protogynous florets they are usually missing. In grasses retaining some of the more primitive characters (the bamboos, for instance), there may be 3, or even 6, lodicules, thus betraying the trimerous origin of the grass flower. Some authors consider the palea and the 2 lodicules together to represent the trimerous nature of the flower, others that the palea comprises two fused outer perianth segments – the third being the lemma – and the lodicules two of the three inner perianth segments (the third being aborted), but these are very much minority views.

In many instances the lemmas (and sometimes also the glumes) may bear on their back or at their apex a stiff bristle termed an *awn*. This is usually a continuation, beyond the apex, of the mid-nerve but sometimes the nerve emerges below the apex and the awn is then variously termed, depending on position, sub-terminal, dorsal or basal. In many species the awn is little more than a straight apical whisker (e.g. *Vulpia*), but in others there is a degree of elaboration. In *Bromus* it is subapical, straight or curved, often flattened below; in *Arrhenatherum* one floret bears a tiny straight subapical bristle while the other bears a dorsal, geniculate awn. The latter type is very common in grasses and is divided into two parts: the lower, proximal part is termed the *column* and is usually twisted to some degree (it is often described as spirally twisted, but a spiral is a two dimensional figure like a watch spring and is not what is intended; it is not even a helix, this being a three-dimensional structure like an old-fashioned bedspring), while the upper, distal part, termed the *limb*, is untwisted and usually divergent at an angle so that the awn resembles a leg with a flexed knee (hence geniculate). Simple awns probably do little more than catch in the fur of a passing animal and thus passively contribute to dispersal. Geniculate awns, on the other hand, are much more active. With changing humidity the column can untwist or twist up again causing the limb to thrash from side to side driving the attached lemma, tightly wrapped around the fruit, across the soil surface, albeit randomly, until a suitable niche is found that will provide just the right degree of light and moisture for germination (in the shade of a stone, down a crack in the soil etc.). Wild oats are extremely good at this. In some species of the tropical and subtropical genus *Aristida* there are three straight awns connate below into a single twisted column and the floret has a pungent callus with upwardly directed barbs behind the tip. The fallen floret lands on a tripod comprising the callus and two of the awns. As the column untwists and increases in length the awns brace the floret in position and the callus slides forward. As the column twists up again and shortens, the barbs on the callus catch in the soil and hold their position while the awns slide forward. Thus the floret moves in a straight line across the soil until it finds a suitable niche. In some species of *Stipa* the awn is extremely long (up to 30 cm) and the limb is densely hairy. The detached floret can float away on the wind on a kind of parachute akin to that found in dandelions. The awn of *Corynephorus* (q.v.) has the most extraordinary structure.

Reproduction and breeding behaviour

The majority of grasses are chasmogamous and the majority of those are protandrous. Wind pollination is the norm for such grasses and copious amounts of pollen are produced. Only when the pollen has been shed do the stigmas mature and emerge. A spread of flowering over a period of time is therefore essential for successful pollination; flowering begins at the base of the spikelet and progresses upwards, but at the tip of a raceme and progresses downwards. Bees and other insects have been seen visiting grasses and feeding on their pollen, but with the exception of a few tropical forest species they make no contribution to pollination. Although the pollen grain is structurally unique in the grasses it is so uniform that its taxonomic value beyond family level is almost negligible. It is the shortest-lived of all angiosperm pollen and is viable in the open air for only a few hours; furthermore, it does not travel more than a few tens of metres in a viable condition. The florets remain open only for a brief period – just two or three hours – probably to reduce the chance of trapping destructive fungal spores, but whatever the reason grasses display an amazing degree of seasonal and diurnal synchronization.

Of the dozens of species of grass (and non-grass) that probably contribute to the pollen captured by a single floret only that of its own species is generally going to be effective in fertilization. Selection of this individual involves a whole spectrum of antigens in the pollen. Unfortunately, many of these antigens have allergenic properties, something that hay-fever sufferers are only too well aware of. Anemophily can lead, as Clayton & Renvoize (1986) so picturesquely put it, to 'incestuous promiscuity' and this has generated complex incompatibility systems to ensure outbreeding. In its extreme form this has led to monoecy and dioecy, but there are no native representatives of these strategems in our area (cultivated maize, however, is monoecious).

A means of countering the uncertainties of anemophily is by way of self-fertility or cleistogamy. Some 300 species of grass worldwide are reported as having cleistogamous spikelets in which self-fertilization occurs in the unopened floret. There are several types of cleistogamy. The most difficult to detect is that in which fertilization occurs on an exposed panicle but within spikelets that fail to open; this requires almost no modification of the spikelet. The commonest form of cleistogamy, however, is where the inflorescence or spikelets remain within the uppermost sheaths during fertilization, but may be exserted later. These spikelets are usually smaller than normal and may have fewer stamens. Sometimes the plant will produce normal chasmogamous spikelets in the panicle but modified cleistogamous spikelets (*cleistogenes*) within the lowermost sheaths. Rarely, highly modified spikelets (*rhizanthogenes*) are produced on specialized underground rhizomes (but not in our area).

Grasses also employ various cytogenetic systems and make extensive use of polyploidy (which occurs in approximately 70% of all wild grass species) and facultative apomixis; polyhaploidy – the reversion of polyploids to the diploid condition – has been reported in several genera, among them *Bromus, Spartina* and *Dactylis*. Chromosomes are of limited taxonomic interest; the karyotype is relatively constant and the chromosome count, though variable, shows little correlation with the classification (a problem found in modern treatments of the tribe Triticeae, q.v.). We cannot be sure of the evolutionary history of the chromosomes but it seems likely that the primitive basic number was 12, with 10 and 9 derived from it. The more advanced tribes have large chromosomes with a basic number of 7.

All of these processes, taken together, have produced systems of great flexibility that are capable of responding to the exigencies of selective pressure. They can proliferate segregate populations which, nevertheless, retain some capacity for gene exchange, and have thus often created polymorphic complexes of mind-numbing taxonomic difficulty (for example in *Dactylis*).

Vivipary and proliferation

True vivipary – the early germination of seed while still attached to the parent – is unusual in grasses but the term is often applied, incorrectly, to other processes. One of these, in which the plant propagates by means of the development of plantlets formed by the vegetative proliferation of the spikelets, is commonly seen in Arctic-alpine species (in the British Isles it is regularly seen in late-flowering *Dactylis*, and is normal practice in some species or subspecies of *Festuca, Poa* and *Deschampsia*). It involves the reversion of the glumes and lemmas to their ancestral role of leaves by the development of distal blades; adventitious roots are formed in the usual way from the basal nodes of the proliferous spikelet and the plantlets so-formed are capable of independent existence once detached from the parent. The process is sometimes referred to as pseudovivipary.

Fruit

The grass fruit, typically, has a thin pericarp firmly adherent to the seed and is thus correctly termed a ***caryopsis***. Commercial 'grass-seed' is not seed at all but caryopses; sometimes the caryopsis is attached to the adherent palea, sometimes even to the whole floret. It is not uncommon, except in British grasses, to find the pericarp free or at least easily separable from the seed. If the separable pericarp is soft, the fruit is a ***utricle***, but if it is hard the fruit is an ***achene***. At the point of attachment of the ovule to the pericarp wall there is a visible scar, the ***hilum***, whose shape can be of some taxonomic value.

The bulk of the seed is endosperm. This contains the starch and proteins that provide the initial food supply of the seedling. There are some taxonomic correlations in the sugar and amino-acid chemistry, but these are of limited practical value.

The embryo has a flat haustorial cotyledon (known as the ***scutellum***), and a special outer sheath (the ***coleoptile***) protecting the plumule during soil penetration. The relationships of these and other embryo structures (***epiblast, mesocotyl, scutellum cleft, coleorhiza***) are shown in the illustration (right). Numerous attempts have been made to establish precise homologies with foliage leaves, but it seems just as likely that these are novel organs evolved to meet the special needs of germination. They occur in various combinations, mostly of interest only to the taxonomist, the epiblast being particularly prone to erratic variation. The following conventional scheme defines the major groups of grasses:

Mesocotyl present (P) or absent (F)
Epiblast present (+) or absent (-)
Scutellum cleft present (P) or absent (F)
First leaf rolled (P) or folded (F)

and the groups so defined are:

Bambusoid	F+PP	Arundinoid	P-PF
Oryzoid	F+FP	Chloridoid	P+PF
Pooid	F+FF	Panicoid	P-PP
Centothecoid	P+PP		

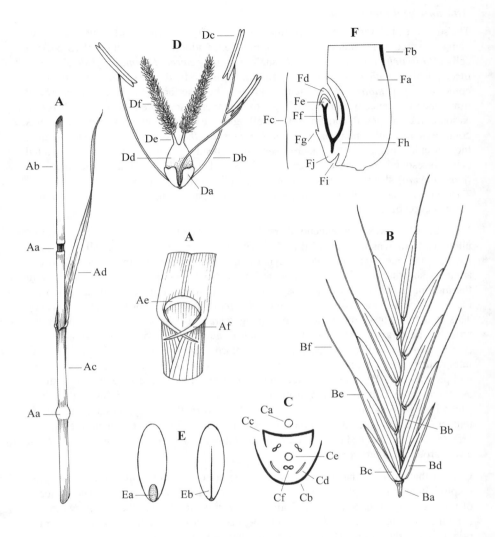

A. Culm and leaf: Aa, node; Ab, internode; Ac leaf-sheath; Ad, leaf-blade; Ae, ligule; Af, auricle.

B. Spikelet: Ba, pedicel; Bb, rhachilla; Bc, lower glume; Bd, upper glume; Be, floret; Bf, awn.

C. Floret, in section: Ca, rhachilla; Cb lemma; Cc, palea; Cd, lodicule; Ce, gynoecium; Cf, androecium.

D. Flower: Da, lodicule; Db, filament; Dc, anther; Dd, ovary; De, style; Df, stigma.

E. Caryopsis from both sides: Ea, embryo; Eb, hilum.

F. Caryopsis in longitudinal section: Fa, endosperm; Fb, hilum; Fc, embryo; Fd, coleoptile; Fe, plumule; Ff, mesocotyl; Fg, epiblast; Fh, scutellum; Fi, scutellum cleft; Fj, coleorhiza.

17

Anatomy and metabolism

The structure of a grass leaf is determined by the longitudinal vascular bundles, its tissues being arranged as a module around each bundle. In addition to the chlorophyll-bearing cells (*chlorenchyma*), these tissues usually include *sclerenchymatous girders* to give mechanical strength, and a number of colourless thin-walled cells (*bulliform cells* in the epidermal layer; *motor cells* in the mesophyll). The function of the latter is obscure but it may be to enhance penetration of light to the innermost chlorenchyma cells. It is not, as sometimes supposed, concerned with rolling of the leaf. The photosynthetic apparatus comprises the chlorenchyma cells of the *mesophyll*, and two sheaths surrounding the vascular bundle. The inner (*mestome*) sheath comprises small thick-walled cells corresponding to an endodermis and derived from the vascular tissue; the outer (*parenchyma*) sheath consists of large thin-walled cells originating in the mesophyll. The various manifestations of these tissues form part of the basis of the subfamily classification of grasses.

Most British grasses (the exceptions being *Cynodon* and *Spartina*) have C_3 or normal photosynthesis which is reflected in the anatomy of the leaf in what is called the *non-Kranz* syndrome. Here the chlorenchyma is irregular, with more than 4 cells between adjacent sheaths; both bundle sheaths are present; and starch is formed principally in the mesophyll. This form of photosynthesis begins with the diffusion of CO_2 into the mesophyll where it is taken up by a ribulose diphosphate (5-carbon) acceptor molecule. This then splits into 2 molecules of phosphoglycerate, a 3-carbon compound (hence the term 'C_3 pathway'). There follows a complex sequence of molecular rearrangements (the *Calvin Cycle*) that has the capacity to return more acceptor than it receives – an important requirement in allowing for the growth of the plant – and to manufacture the end-product. The latter tends to accumulate during daylight and is temporarily stored as starch pending translocation at night; it is easily detected by staining with iodine. The whole process takes place in the mesophyll. Normal photosynthesis is the rule in temperate grasses. The rate of photosynthesis is enhanced by higher temperatures but the effect is counterbalanced by a decrease in solubility of CO_2. Tropical grasses have found a way around this problem.

Grasses that grow in the tropics, where temperatures and light intensities are higher, employ an alternative photosynthetic mechanism termed the C_4 pathway. The presence of this pathway is reflected in the leaf anatomy in what is called the *Kranz* syndrome. Here the chlorenchyma has only 2–4 cells between adjacent sheaths and starch is formed principally in the sheath. There are several types of Kranz anatomy:

PS (parenchyma sheath) type. The chlorenchyma is strongly radiate and surrounds bundles of roughly equal size. Both sheaths are present, but only the parenchyma sheath forms starch. There are two variants:

i. Chloroplasts centripetal in sheath cells

ii. Chloroplasts centrifugal in sheath cells

MS (mestome sheath) type, The chlorenchyma is irregular or only weakly radiate and surrounds bundles of often widely differing sizes. Only one sheath is present, apparently derived from the mestome sheath, and starch is formed here.

18

The photosynthetic pathway associated with the Kranz syndrome (the **Hatch-Slack pathway**) involves an extra loop in the system. CO_2 is initially taken up in the mesophyll by phosphoenol pyruvate (a 3-carbon compound) to form a 4-carbon compound (hence 'C_4 pathway'). This migrates to the bundle sheath where, after removal of its CO_2 by a decarboxylating enzyme, it is fed into the Calvin cycle. There are several versions of the C_4 pathway which have been found, up to a point, to match the variations in the Kranz anatomy. Interestingly, C_4 photosynthesis takes up the isotopes ^{12}C and ^{13}C in almost atmospheric proportions, whereas C_3 photosynthesis discriminates against ^{13}C.

The epidermis is composed primarily of elongate **long cells** which may or may not be interspersed with equidimensional **short cells**. Two zones can usually be detected, the **intercostal zone** and the **costal zone**. The costal zones are narrow tracts overlying the vascular bundles and their associated sclerenchyma. They are characterized by the presence of opaline **silica-bodies** which, regardless of the shape of the cell containing them, assume characteristic shapes according to the different tribes; unfortunately, there is so much intergradation that their diagnostic value is low. The intercostal zones are usually much broader than the costal zones and may contain, in addition to the long and short cells, stomata, **microhairs** and silica-containing cells. Intercostal silica-bodies are not of any characteristic shape. The stomata are of an unusual kind in which the two guard cells are each supported by a subsidiary cell. Microhairs are fragile, microscopic, 2-celled hairs of unknown function (and are not to be confused with macrohairs of visibly hairy leaves).

CLASSIFICATION

The classification of grasses into subfamilies is very much the realm of the theoretical taxonomist. It depends almost entirely on cryptic characters that are quite inaccessible to all except those with adequate laboratory facilities. The category is, therefore, seldom utilized although it is of passing interest.

Clayton & Renvoize (1986), in their ground-breaking classification of grass genera, recognized 6 subfamilies whose characteristics are as follows:

Bambusoideae

A rather heterogeneous group of mainly forest grasses which are usually tall trees, shrubs or climbers commonly with lanceolate, tessellately-nerved leaf-blades. Some species, exceptional in their small stature, herbaceous stems and broad leaf-blades, inhabit the dim forest floor or moist clearings, while others, with narrower leaves, inhabit tropical swamps.

The spikelets are 1- to many-flowered, usually with awnless, 1- to many-nerved lemmas. Although relatively simple in their basic structure the spikelets may be assembled in extraordinarily complex inflorescences. The leaf-blade anatomy is characterized by large fusoid cells in the mesophyll and somewhat irregularly arranged chlorenchyma cells with invaginated walls (arm cells); photosynthesis is of the C_3 type. Two-celled microhairs are present on the epidermis and the chromosomes are small. The embryo is either bambusoid (F+PP, rarely F-PP) or oryzoid (F+FP).

The subfamily is best defined by the distribution of fusoid cells whose specialized nature is indicated by the fact that only the grass family has them. They are plate-like with a very narrow lumen and lie transversely in the mesophyll. The reason for their peculiar shape is unknown. Another bambusoid peculiarity is the occurrence of chlorenchyma cells with deeply invaginated walls projecting into the lumen (arm cells). Fusoid and arm cells are not always present so the subfamily must be diagnosed on a suite of supplementary characters which occur frequently in the Bambusoideae but only sporadically in other subfamilies: epidermal papillae, a tendency to trimerous floral symmetry and a bambusoid or oryzoid embryo.

The Bambusoideae are mainly tropical in Asia and America, with a few in Africa; they scarely impinge upon the British flora. The cultivated woody bamboos (tribe Bambuseae) are not native in the British Isles although several persist in neglected gardens. The herbaceous Cut-grass (*Leersia*, tribe Oryzeae) is an extremely rare species of southern England and is related to cultivated Rice of tropical Asia.

Pooideae

A very large subfamily containing most of the familiar cereal and pasture grasses of the temperate northern hemisphere.

The spikelets are 1- to many-flowered, all the florets are fertile (with one or two exceptions; and there is usually a decline in fertility of several-flowered spikelets towards the summit of the spikelet), and the spikelets usually disarticulate above the persistent glumes. The lemmas are mostly 5-nerved. In the leaf-blade the chlorenchyma cells are irregularly arranged, indicating C_3 physiology. The epidermis lacks 2-celled microhairs and the chromosomes are usually large. The embryo is pooid (F+FF), but the epiblast is sometimes absent (F-FF); in a few genera the embryo is oryzoid.

Pooideae are non-Kranz grasses lacking microhairs and having a pooid embryo. The ligule is always membranous. The inflorescence and spikelets are unspecialized and rather limited in their range of variation compared with other subfamilies. This may indicate a youthful stage of adaptive radiation, or it may indicate that selection pressures have been directed at internal physiology rather than external morphology. The subfamily is virtually confined to the temperate zones of both hemispheres, although numerous species bridge the tropics on the tops of high mountains. The physiological thrust therefore seems to be towards adjusting to a cold climate. A well-marked secondary thrust has been the proliferation of annual genera adapted to a Mediterranean-type winter rainfall regime. Virtually all grasses in the British Isles, except those few genera mentioned under other subfamilies, belong to the Pooideae.

Centothecoideae

A small subfamily just about held together by the embryo structure (centothecoid, P+PP) and certain features of leaf anatomy. The members are usually herbs with broad leaf-blades, membranous ligules and panicles or racemes of 1- to many-flowered laterally compressed spikelets. The lemmas are 5- or more-nerved.

The chlorenchyma forms a palisade layer below the upper epidermis but is otherwise irregular; the bundle sheaths are double and the lateral cells of the outer sheath are enlarged. This is the palisade variant of non-Kranz (C_3) anatomy. Two-celled microhairs are slender with an oblique joint between the cells, and the chromosomes are small.

The subfamily resembles the herbaceous bamboos in external appearance but its lodicules ally it to the Arundinoid line. Its members, few in number, are specialized forest grasses, mostly found in the New World.

Arundinoideae

This subfamily includes the spectacular Pampas Grass (*Cortaderia*) and our own common reed (*Phragmites*) as well as conventional tufted and tussocky grasses (e.g. *Molinia* and *Danthonia*).

The spikelets are 1- to many-flowered and break up above the persistent glumes. They are usually arranged in small to very large panicles, very rarely in narrow spikes. The lemmas are herbaceous or membranous and may be entire at the tip or divided into 2 or 3 lobes, with or without an awn from between the lobes. The ligule is almost always a line of hairs rather than a membrane. Leaf anatomy is typically non-Kranz. The epidermis has slender 2-celled microhairs and the chromosomes are generally small. The embryo is arundinoid (P-PF, rarely P-FF).

The origin of the subfamily is obscure, and possible links with both Bambusoideae and Pooideae are speculative. It is thought to represent the basic stock from which the

21

tropical savanna grasses evolved. The fragmentation of the principle tribe Arundineae, a phenomenon well known to agrostologists, is consistent with a subsequent history of decline. The spikelets intergrade with those of subfamily Chloridoideae, but a boundary can be set at the transition from non-Kranz to Kranz anatomy. While somewhat arbitrary, this boundary is supported by microhair and embryo differences. The boundary with subfamily Panicoideae is reversed: leaf anatomy is indistinguishable from non-Kranz representatives but the spikelets – supported by the embryo – provide a sharp distinction.

Although distributed throughout the world this subfamily is characteristic of subtropical and temperate regions of the southern hemisphere, generally growing in savanna and fairly dry, open situations. All three British genera belong to tribe Arundineae.

Chloridoideae

These herbaceous grasses are generally tufted or stoloniferous and often bear tough, spiny leaf-blades. Many have specialized in harsh, stressful habitats and it is likely that physiological differences may often outweigh the morphological distinctions between genera.

The spikelets are 1- to many-flowered, often arranged in single or multiple spikes, less often in panicles. Lemmas are usually 3-nerved. Leaf-blade anatomy is characterized by the oblong chlorenchyma cells arranged radially around the vascular bundles, indicating C_4 physiology. Bundle sheaths are double and the secondary and tertiary bundles are similar in size. Two-celled microhairs are short and stout and the chromosomes are small. The embryo is chloridoid (P+PF) although a few rare exceptions are centothecoid and others are arundinoid.

The subfamily is characterized by its well developed, uniform Kranz anatomy, distinctive swollen microhairs and usually 1- to 3-nerved lemmas. It probably shares a common ancestry with subfamily Arundinoideae and sometimes demarcation between the subfamilies is problematic. There may also be a direct link with subfamily Centothecoideae.

The Chloridoideae are mostly tropical and subtropical often in the arid zones or on saline soils. The only native British genus is *Spartina*, but the (probably) introduced *Cynodon* also belongs here (both in tribe Cynodonteae).

Panicoideae

A vast tropical subfamily whose spikelets are nearly always 2-flowered with the lower floret male or sterile and the upper fertile, the two florets usually disarticulating as a unit that also includes the glumes. Leaf-blade anatomy is characterized by (usually) radiate chlorenchyma and the bundle sheaths may be single or double, indicating mostly C_4 physiology, but non-Kranz, Kranz MS and Kranz PS syndromes are all represented. The epidermis bears 2-celled microhairs and the chromosomes are small. The embryo is panicoid (P-PP).

The subfamily comprises numerous tribes clustered about the two main ones, Andropogoneae and Paniceae. The two groups of tribes share the same embryo and dimorphic florets, but differ in the relative induration of the glumes and lemmas.

Members of the subfamily dominate throughout the tropics, extending into warm temperate regions. None occurs as a native in the British Isles although several are common as weeds, some quite persistent. The only member of the subfamily at all common in our area is Maize (*Zea mays*, tribe Andropogoneae) but this is barely suited to our climate and produces a worthwhile crop only in the longest and hottest summers; it fares better as a fodder grass.

Synopsis of classification

In the systematic section of this book genera are assigned to tribes and the first dichotomous key is to these tribes. The subfamily affinities of the tribes will not be evident from the key since the subfamilies are circumscribed mostly on cryptic characters. The classification of British grasses at these higher levels is therefore summarized below.

Subfamily I:	Bambusoideae
Tribe 1:	Oryzeae
Subfamily II:	Pooideae
Tribe 2:	Nardeae
Tribe 3:	Stipeae
Tribe 4:	Poeae
Tribe 5:	Hainardieae
Tribe 6:	Aveneae
Tribe 7:	Meliceae
Tribe 8:	Brachypodieae
Tribe 9:	Bromeae
Tribe 10:	Triticeae
Subfamily III:	Arundinoideae
Tribe 11:	Arundineae
Subfamily IV:	Chloridoideae
Tribe 12:	Eragrostideae
Tribe 13:	Cynodonteae
Subfamily V:	Panicoideae
Tribe 14:	Paniceae
Tribe 15:	Andropogoneae

Classification at tribal level is largely based on gross morphology – ligule form, inflorescence form and spikelet form being the most important characters – and should present few difficulties to the beginner. The more common tribes have a very distinctive look about them making it possible for the practiced eye to recognize them with little more than a cursory glance.

Recent studies in molecular-based phylogeny have suggested the need for a total rethink of the classification of grasses. However, much of the work is still in progress and conflicting results have frequently emerged. Some changes that have been proposed are the amalgamation of Poeae, Aveneae and Hainardieae into an enlarged Poeae with numerous subtribes; the separation of Danthonieae from Arundineae, even to the extent of placing them in separate subfamilies; the amalgamation of Eragrostideae with Cynodonteae (of passing interest only to British taxonomists) though leaving *Eragrostis* itself (a genus of 360+ species) as *incertae sedis*; and placing Brachypodieae once more adjacent to Triticeae even though earlier studies had indicated otherwise. Considerable modification in the number and circumscription of subfamilies has also been proposed.

Until molecular phylogeny studies are further developed and a consensus is reached the revisions to grass classification that utilise molecular work are likely to be transient and of little practical use. The authors therefore have followed the system of Clayton & Renvoize (1986) which offers sensible taxonomic delineation and is widely adopted.

SCOPE OF THE BOOK

The grasses of the British Isles can conveniently be divided into five categories, the first four following Preston, Pearman & Dines (2002):

1. Natives and probable natives
2. Archaeophytes
3. Neophytes
4. Casuals
5. Bamboos

All species in categories 1 (113 species), 2 (10 species) and 3 (50 species) have been fully described and illustrated, but we have had to be very selective about which of those in category 4 to include. We decided to exclude most wool-aliens on the understanding that those that have become established are already in the main list under category 3. Those that have not become established are probably now extinct or extremely rare since the practice of fertilizing fields with imported shoddy has virtually ceased. Most of these species do not survive our winters and must be regularly re-introduced if they are to remain on the British list. Species that have not managed to integrate themselves into local ecosystems are unlikely to persist and are of passing interest only. They are not dealt with in this book, but a comprehensive account of them, including many illustrations and keys to species, can be found in Ryves *et al.,* (1996). We have, nevertheless, included 47 regularly introduced casuals, bringing the total species count for the book to 220.

Grasses in category 5 – bamboos – have been excluded partly because of the immense identification difficulties they present, partly because they seldom escape beyond the parks and gardens in which they were originally grown and partly because of the authors' lack of expertise. Identifying and classifying bamboos is almost wholly dependent on inflorescence and spikelet structure and many bamboos are very shy of flowering, especially in our area. Bamboo taxonomy is, at best, unsettled with very little general agreement, especially on generic limits. In many cases the name of a bamboo is temporary pending the occasion that the species should flower and its taxonomic affinities finally be revealed. For an account of bamboos grown in Great Britain see Chao (1989). This will provide a name for the plant, using vegetative characters, but the name may no longer be that accepted by many bamboo taxonomists.

HOW TO USE THE BOOK

Formal description (Paragraph 1)

Values for length or width of parts of the grass plant are subject not only to natural variation, often beyond the generous limits set in this book, but also to variation in the manner in which they are measured. The results achieved will depend upon which particular part was measured and how it was measured. A very large proportion of available material has been sampled for this Handbook; all measurements were plotted as frequency histograms and sampling was reduced or stopped only when the shape of the histogram had clearly settled into a stable normal distribution (although some taxa were too poorly represented for this to happen; in this case the full range of measurements was used to compile the descriptions.) Unless otherwise stated in particular instances the following conventions apply throughout the book in both keys and descriptions.

Height of plant. From ground level to the tip of the uppermost internode of the inflorescence. Awns and terminal spikelets are ignored, as are non-flowering stems. Problems will arise with plants that are geniculately ascending from a prostrate base; care must be taken to measure the *height* and not the *length* of the culm. In practice, height of plant is seldom of taxonomic value. Measurements have been rounded up to the nearest 1cm for smaller grassses, and the nearest 5cm for the larger.

Ligule. The leaf should be peeled back, flattened across the finger and the ligule measured from base to tip at the point midway between the leaf-margins. In the descriptions it is the intact ligules that are described; as they age many become torn and ragged and their shape can become obscure. The ligule selected, unless otherwise required, should be on the second or third leaf from the top of the culm; that of the uppermost leaf is often at variance with the rest. Shape of ligule is often as important as length, sometimes more so.

Leaf-blade. Flat leaves are measured from margin to margin in their lowest third; inrolled leaves are measured across their diameter. In the former case the description will say leaf-blade so many mm *wide*; in the latter, so many mm *across*. Leaves that are folded should be measured from midrib to margin and the value doubled (except in *Festuca*, q.v.).

Inflorescence. From the lowest node to the tip of the uppermost internode of the main axis. Spikelets and awns are ignored. This may appear to under-value the lengths of some panicles, especially those with big spikelets; for example, that of *Bromus diandrus* can appear to be under-valued by up to 5cm, but the shortfall can be accounted for by the terminal spikelet which may be orientated vertically when young but horizontally when older (thereby deducting its own length from the overall length of the panicle).

Spikelet. From the base of the lower glume to the tip of the uppermost lemma (except in *Festuca* q.v.); ignore all awns. The spikelet selected should come from the middle part of the inflorescence.

Glumes and lemma. Both the lower glume and the lowermost lemma are measured in the intact spikelet from the *base of the lower glume* (the upper glume can be measured from its own base). The extra increment this appears to add to the actual length of the lemma is seldom significant and the technique dispels the need for awkward dissections to be undertaken in the field, sometimes in trying conditions (and it also prevents destructive sampling of valuable herbarium material). Ignore mucros and any awns unless they form a continuation of the body of the glume or lemma without any obvious point of transition, in which case they should be included in the measurement. The description will indicate the approximate proportion of the glume or lemma that is 'awn' but the distinction is arbitrary and often quite meaningless.

Palea. Knowledge of the exact length of the palea will rarely be needed. Usually its length relative to that of the lemma or caryopsis is all that is required.

Awn. The awn of the second or third lemma should be measured (except where there is only one floret or where the florets are markedly dimorphic; the text will make it clear). It should be measured from its apparent point of attachment to the lemma (which may be some way below the apex) to its tip; geniculate awns should either be straightened or the limb and column measured separately and then added together. Occasionally only the length of the awn beyond the lemma tip or glume tips matters (again the text will make it clear what to do). *Elymus* can present difficulties because it can be almost impossible to tell where the body of the lemma ends and the awn begins, but on the whole this is not too much of a problem in the species dealt with in this book.

Anthers. These must be fully grown. Immature anthers can be considerably smaller than mature ones. Dehisced anthers are often suitable, but they can eventually become crumpled and difficult to measure. Thin, underdeveloped, indehiscent anthers in what appears to be a normal spikelet are often an indication of hybrids or apomicts. Under these circumstances they can still be usefully measured. It is seldom necessary to wet the anther to allow it to stretch to its full length. All measurements are taken from dried herbarium material and may under-value the anther length when compared with fresh material, but anther length is often variable even within a single spikelet and seldom critical (given the limitations that exist on accurate measurement in the field).

Caryopsis. This must be mature and on the point of being shed. In those genera where it has a terminal appendage (e.g. *Bromus*) the appendage is not included in the length. When the caryopsis remains attached to part of the floret – usually the palea – it is best measured in a mature floret (that is, one that has just dropped from the spikelet, not one that had to be pulled out; the latter would not be quite mature in most instances), on the adaxial side from the base of the palea.

Flowering & fruiting. Information on flowering and fruiting was derived from the herbarium collections at Kew. The time of collection of each relevant specimen was noted (each month was divided into 'early' (1st – 10th), 'mid' (11th – 20th) and 'late' (21st – end) giving 36 units for the year) and plotted in a histogram against frequency. While not wholly accurate, these histograms do to a reasonable extent reflect the periods in which species are flowering and fruiting. No account could be taken of seasonal variations year by year, so it is only a rough guide, but since records stretch back for over one hundred years and the histograms invariably showed normal distribution, whatever the time of year, it was felt that the information was not entirely without meaning. Anthesis may only occupy the first week or two of the season, but this will vary from year to year. No attempt was made to assess whether or not the specimen was at anthesis when collected.

Specimens that were so mature as to be disintegrating were ignored, as were those that had obviously been collected before anthesis. It was assumed, probably quite rightly, that plant collectors are active throughout most of the year and that those times during which plants were not collected accurately reflected their absence in a flowering or fruiting condition.

In the following text, plant names in **bold** are those recommended for acceptance. Names given in *italics* are synonyms, references to names accepted elsewhere in the text or names in current usage that are not accepted by the present authors.

Distribution and habitat (Paragraph 2)

The second paragraph of each species account deals with where to find it. It includes the grass's geographical distribution in Great Britain and Ireland, its major habitat-types, the soils in which it grows and its main plant associates.

When this project was first conceived we intended to include a set of distribution maps, at least for a selected range of species. The publication in 2002 of the superlative *New Atlas of the British and Irish Flora* (Preston, Pearman & Dines 2002) made this unnecessary and allowed us to produce a considerably thinner book! The page in the New Atlas (or the CD) on which the species map appears is given for each species, along with a (usually) brief description of its geographical distribution and general abundance. Our grasses have widely varied distribution patterns from the very widespread and abundant to the very rare. Of the 23 plant species in the New Atlas which have been recorded from more than 90% of the 10km squares mapped in Great Britain and Ireland 7 are grasses. These are, in order, *Holcus lanatus, Cynosurus cristatus, Poa annua, Festuca rubra, Agrostis stolonifera, Anthoxanthum odoratum* and *Lolium perenne*. The first of these, Yorkshire-fog, is, by this criterion, the fifth most widespread plant species in Britain and Ireland after *Plantago lanceolata, Trifolium repens, Bellis perennis* and *Cerastium fontanum*. By contrast, other native grasses have very restricted distributions and may be confined to a single area (e.g. *Koeleria vallesiana* in the Mendips, *Milium vernale* on Guernsey) or, in the case of *Calamagrostis scotica*, a single location. One species, *Bromus interruptus*, is no longer actually found in the wild. Between these extremes other species may be widely scattered, have distinctive regional distributions (e.g. *Festuca vivipara* in the northwest, *Agrostis curtisii* in the southwest, *Hordeum marinum* in the southeast) or quite disjunct ones (e.g. *Deschampsia setacea, Festuca longifolia*).

Similarly, our native (and introduced) grasses vary enormously in respect of the range of habitat-types they occupy. Some, such as *Agrostis stolonifera* and *Festuca rubra*, have extremely wide ecological amplitudes, occurring across very different habitats from intertidal saltmarshes to high mountain pastures. Others are more or less restricted to a single type of habitat (e.g. *Elymus farctus* on foredunes, *Hordelymus europaeus* in woods, *Spartina maritima* on saltmarshes) and even to specific narrow niches within habitats (e.g. *Corynephorus canescens* in areas of slightly mobile sand, *Deschampsia setacea* on the margins of seasonal pools). One or two species occupy two or more very different habitats (e.g. *Festuca longifolia* on acid heathland and sea cliffs, *Poa nemoralis* in woodland and rock ledges on mountains), whilst *Anthoxanthum nitens* is a wetland grass found in several remarkably different types of habitat including base-rich fen, raised bog, lakeside carr and saltmarsh. Yet other species are largely restricted to man-made habitats (e.g. *Bromus lepidus, Poa compressa*) or to cultivated land (*Alopecurus myosuroides*).

Most grass species occur in a characteristic range of soil types and of soil pH, a range of which is given for those species where it is known. These include calcicoles (found only, or almost only, on calcareous soils) such as *Brachypodium pinnatum, Bromus erectus* and *Gastridium ventricosum*, and calcifuges (almost always on acidic soils) such as *Deschampsia flexuosa, Holcus mollis* and *Nardus stricta*. Other species appear to tolerate a wide pH range (e.g. *Anthoxanthum odoratum, Holcus lanatus*) and some, such as *Danthonia decumbens* and *Molinia caerulea*, are distinctly bimodal, although only *Festuca ovina* has large populations in both strongly calcareous and highly acidic sites.

Many accounts list other plant species which are characteristically found growing alongside the species in question, described here as associates. These are included where it is thought that they may help the reader to locate the grass species or where they typify a habitat-type. They are based on the authors' experience and are in no sense formal prescriptions (i.e. part of a community classification). It was decided to exclude reference to National Vegetation Classification (NVC) types mainly because these require the reader to be familiar with a specialist methodology based on a large and separate body of literature. Finally, most accounts, where it is of interest, quote the altitudinal range of the species including the location of the highest record. These are taken directly from the New Atlas.

Biology and ecology (Paragraph 3)

Grasses display a great variety of life styles. These, the subject of Paragraph 3, range from short-lived plants which germinate, grow and produce seed very quickly, often exploiting seasonal gaps in their environment, to very long-lived plants which are maintained principally by vegetative growth and, although they may flower several times (are polycarpic), establish from seed relatively rarely. Among the former group is the smallest grass in the world, *Mibora minima*, capable of producing viable seed on plants 1.5cm tall, whilst the latter group includes our tallest non-woody native plant, *Phragmites australis*, reaching 3.5m in height.

In the British Isles our short-lived species are often winter annuals (e.g. *Aira praecox, Vulpia fasciculata*) which germinate in the autumn, overwinter as small plants and flower and set seed before the drier days of high summer, but we have one or two summer annuals (e.g. *Setaria pumila, Vulpia unilateralis*) and several species in which flowering individuals are produced from both autumn and spring germination (e.g. *Bromus sterilis, Catapodium rigidum*). Other species have a variety of life histories, the most remarkable being *Poa annua* which can produce several generations of short-lived annuals per year (from seed to seed in less than 6 weeks) or can, despite its name, be perennial and polycarpic.

Our perennials include species that have populations in which one can find extremely long-lived individuals, tens or hundreds of years old (e.g. *Festuca ovina, Holcus mollis*). Several dominate and change their environment to such an extent that they can be regarded as ecosystem engineers (e.g. *Ammophila arenaria, Spartina anglica*), whilst grasses such as *Phalaris arundinacea* and *Phragmites australis* even create their own reedbed habitat-type. These last two species expand as a phalanx of vegetation in contrast to others such as *Poa pratensis* or *Spartina maritima* which 'forage' by means of rhizomes to exploit gaps or nutrient-rich sites in dense or species-rich vegetation. There is, in fact, a wide range of strategies among perennial grasses from the dominant and aggressive (e.g. *Arrhenatherum elatius, Brachypodium pinnatum*) and those which have a subordinate or 'companion' role in grassland (e.g. *Festuca pratensis, Poa trivialis*) to species which avoid competition by being able to grow in nutrient-poor, shaded, droughted, saline or other stressful environments (e.g. *Danthonia decumbens, Melica uniflora, Phleum phleoides* and *Puccinellia maritima* respectively).

The contrast between relatively short-lived plants which produce many seed and longer-lived, predominantly vegetative plants can be seen in closely related members of the same genus (e.g. *Holcus lanatus* (seed) versus *H. mollis* (vegetative), *Elymus caninus* (seed) versus *E. repens* (vegetative)) and also within the same species, especially those such as *Dactylis glomerata, Lolium perenne* or *Phleum pratense* where the natural range of variation has been exploited by the plant breeder to produce short-lived 'stemmy' types for hay and longer-lived 'leafy' types for pasture. Variation in these traits in natural populations is often habitat based and heritable. In some species intraspecific variation is recognized and delimited in the form of infraspecific taxa (e.g. *Agrostis stolonifera*) but in others (e.g. *A. capillaris*) it is not.

Our grasses also exhibit variety in the regenerative and dispersal phases of their life cycle. As mentioned previously, whilst all chasmogamous species are wind pollinated (and mostly protandrous) the extent to which they are self-fertile, and hence tend to be inbreeding, varies hugely between species (and between populations or varieties of some species). As a general rule, annual species tend to be inbreeding and perennials tend to be self-incompatible and outbreeding, but there are exceptions, at least one of which has an intriguing mechanism to control genetic recombination (see *Mibora minima*, a self-incompatible annual). Seed may be produced asexually by apomixis (e.g. *Calamagrostis purpurea, Poa compressa*), by self-fertilization, sometimes in unopened florets (cleistogamy) (e.g. *Danthonia decumbens, Vulpia ciliata*) and almost exclusively by cross-pollination between different individuals (e.g. *Agrostis curtisii, Bromus erectus*). Many species have mixed systems (e.g. *Calamagrostis canescens, Poa nemoralis*).

However they are produced, seed may be dispersed in several ways. (Here we adopt the ecologist's convention of using the word 'seed' rather loosely. In grasses this is the caryopsis, which is sometimes attached to the adherent palea and sometimes even to the whole floret). In many grasses there is no obvious dispersal mechanism whilst those with awns (e.g. *Bromus sterilis, Helictotrichon pratense*) are frequently dispersed by furry animals, and others are dispersed by waterfowl (e.g. *Glyceria fluitans, G. notata*) or by ants (e.g. *Danthonia decumbens, Melica uniflora*). The seed of some species are dispersed by wind (e.g. *Deschampsia cespitosa, Phragmites australis*) or water (e.g.

Glyceria maxima, Phalaris arundinacea), and the dispersal of seed of *Bromus secalinus* and *Bromus lepidus* by man is enhanced by their mimicry of cereal grain and small-seeded forage grasses respectively. Once dispersed, grass seeds may germinate almost immediately and have little or no persistent seed bank (e.g. *Briza media, Bromus hordeaceus*) or have delayed germination and in some cases a very long-lived seed bank (e.g. *Phleum bertolonii, Polypogon monspeliensis*).

Grasses have other ways of getting about. Some produce small plantlets instead of spikelets by the process of 'proliferation' (notably *Festuca vivipara* but several other species such as *Poa alpina* and *P. bulbosa*). These plantlets may disperse and establish new plants. Other forms of vegetative spread include establishment from detached fragments of stolons (e.g. *Agrostis canina*), rhizomes (e.g. *Elymus repens*) or shoots (e.g. *Agrostis stolonifera*) whilst *Poa bulbosa*, and to a lesser extent *Alopecurus bulbosus*, produces swollen bulb-like basal internodes which can disperse many metres to establish new plants. Dispersal by such vegetative fragments may be as important as dispersal by seed (e.g. dispersal by rhizome fragments and by seed are of equal importance in foredune *Elymus farctus*) and its relative importance is likely to vary within species between different habitats. For *Glyceria ×pedicellata*, a sterile hybrid, vegetative dispersal is its only, but apparently successful, option.

The accounts of species biology and ecology are based on a wide range of sources and the data available for each species varies greatly in quantity. Thirty-six species have been covered in the *Biological Flora of the British Isles*, a series of comprehensive and detailed autecological accounts of British plants in the *Journal of Ecology*. Of these species, 22 are also included, along with a further 25, in Grime, Hodgson & Hunt (2007), *Comparative Plant Ecology* (CPE). Thus there is extensive and reliable published information for more than 60 species. Somewhat less detailed accounts of 23 species are given in Stewart, Pearman & Preston (eds.) (1994), *Scarce Plants in Britain* (SPB) and of 12 species in Wigginton (ed.) (1999), *British Red Data Books 1. Vascular plants, ed. 3* (RDB). Reference to these four sources (as Biol. Flora: Author(s), CPE pp, SPB pp. and RDB pp.) is given for all relevant species. Other data sources have included electronic databases such as the Ecological Flora of Great Britain, many literature sources, personal communications and the authors' own notes, experiments and experiences. All but the latter are acknowledged in the text.

Status and wider distribution (Paragraph 4)

As mentioned above, just over half of the species covered in this book (113) are native or probably native in the British Isles, and of those which have been introduced and naturalized in the wild 10 are archaeophytes (naturalized before 1500 AD) and 50 are neophytes (introduced and/or naturalized since 1500 AD). The remaining 47 species are casuals. The status of some species is uncertain (see, for example, *Apera spica-venti* or *Gaudinia fragilis*) and several are possibly represented by a mixture of native and introduced populations (e.g. *Bromus madritensis, Cynodon dactylon*). We have 3 British endemic grasses, *Bromus interruptus* (now almost certainly extinct in the wild), *Calamagrostis scotica* and *Spartina anglica*. The story of the birth and spread of the last of these species following hybridization between the (probably) native *Spartina maritima*

31

and the accidentally introduced *S. alterniflora* (from N America) is a remarkable and well-documented example of evolution involving allopolyploidy (see these species accounts). Introductions to the British Isles have arrived here from all five continents but include a large proportion from the Mediterranean region. Some are encountered as temporary escapes from cultivation and may, like *Secale cereale* or *Zea mays*, only be known in cultivation. The origin of introduced and casual species, where known, is usually given in paragraph 4. Further details of many of these species can be found in Ryves, Clement & Foster (1996), *Alien Grasses of the British Isles*, which is cited throughout as AGB, sometimes with a page reference. Dates of cultivation and observation as wild plants generally follow the New Atlas.

The wider distribution of our native, and some other, plant species outside Great Britain and Ireland has been classified by Preston & Hill (1997) (P&H), and this classification is included in the New Atlas and repeated here. It defines floristic elements in terms of the major terrestrial biomes in which the species occurs as a native combined with the eastern limits of its distribution. Our grasses, not unexpectedly, mostly have native distributions centred either in the Temperate Zone (33 species) or equally in the Temperate and Boreal Zone (28 species) or the Temperate and Southern (Mediterranean) Zone (24 species). The largest category based on eastern limits is European *sensu* Preston & Hill (40 species) with an eastern limit west of 60°E, although several species are limited to W Europe (Oceanic; 7 species) or W and C Europe (Suboceanic; 8 species) and others have much wider native distributions, 17 extending further east to between 60 and 120°E (Eurosiberian) and 25 having circumpolar distributions. The largest single element, as with other native plants, is the European Temperate group of grasses.

Changes in the abundance and distribution of our grass species, usually discussed in this paragraph, are almost invariably a result of human activity and particularly agriculture. The changes in arable cultivation have seen winners such as *Alopecurus myosuroides* and *Bromus sterilis* whose populations are favoured by minimum tillage and year-on-year autumn-sown crops such as winter wheat; and conversely, losers in such intensive agriculture include *Bromus interruptus* and the arable biotypes of *Gastridium ventricosum*. Changes in pastoral agriculture have also favoured certain species at the expense of others, grasses such as *Brachypodium pinnatum* and *Bromus erectus* on chalk grassland and *Nardus stricta* on moorland flourishing when sheep grazing is reduced or abandoned. The advent of myxomatosis in the 1950s also allowed some species to flourish, not only in grassland but in other habitats too (e.g. *Elymus athericus* on saltmarshes, *Vulpia fasciculata* on sand-dunes). Many more species have been affected by the drainage of wetlands such as water-meadows and coastal grazing marshes, especially the lowering of water tables and the infilling of ponds and ditches (e.g. *Calamagrostis canescens, Leersia oryzoides*) whilst others which rely on regular disturbance to create open sites for colonization have also lost out when the traditional maintenance of such habitats is changed (e.g. *Puccinellia rupestris, Hordeum marinum*). At least two grasses from this latter group, *Puccinellia distans* and *Hordeum marinum* (and more recently *Catapodium marinum*), have been able to exploit the open, disturbed and periodically saline habitats along the edges of our roads, joining a small but increasing British roadside flora (which includes exotic aliens such as *Hordeum jubatum*).

Until recently the extent of a species' distribution in Britain was used to assign national conservation status. The rarest species, those with the most restricted distribution, were listed in the three editions of the vascular plant *Red Data Book* (Perring & Farrell, 1977, 1983; Wigginton, 1999) with *Scarce Plants in Britain* (Stewart *et al*., 1994) covering the slightly less rare species, While the accounts in Wiggington (1999) and Stewart *et al*, (1994) contain much of interest (RDB and SPB respectively) the conservation status designations in these texts have been superseded by the Red Data List (or simply Red List) of Cheffings & Farrell (2005). Based upon IUCN criteria, the Red Data List utilises both distribution and the rate of decline to allocate species to one of five classes of conservation importance from **Critically Endangered**, through **Endangered**, **Vulnerable** and **Near Threatened** to **Least Concern**. Additionally Cheffings & Farrell (2005) found that some species were impossible to assign to one of the above categories. These were placed into one of three groups: the **Waiting List**, species lacking population, distributional or taxonomic data; the **Parking List**, which contains previously listed taxa now considered neophytes or having a lower rank than subspecies or **Data Deficient**, where there is insufficient information on a species.

Additional information (Paragraph 5 and following)

A great majority of the full species accounts, and several of the short accounts of casuals etc. (which by and large follow the same sequence: distribution and habitat, ecology, status and origin) include additional information in a fifth and sometimes further paragraphs. Broadly covering 'hybrids, hints and history' these deal with the presence and identification of hybrids, unique features of the species and/or ways of distinguishing them from close relatives, unusual morphological features, important nomenclatural changes and taxonomic problems, aspects of their use and cultivation and various other miscellanea which we hope will interest the reader.

Key to Tribes

1. Plant monoecious; male spikelets in an ample terminal panicle; female spikelets in rows on axillary woody cobs (cultivated maize, *Zea*) .... **XV. Andropogoneae**
+ Plant not monoecious as above, at least some spikelets bisexual 2

2. Spikelets dorsally compressed, 2-flowered, falling entire, borne in pairs on short racemes in an open panicle, one of the pair sessile and bisexual, the other smaller, pedicelled and male or barren; glumes as long as the spikelet; upper (fertile) lemma of sessile spikelet hyaline, awned .... **XV. Andropogoneae**
+ Spikelets not as above 3

3. Spikelets dorsally compressed or somewhat turgid, 2-flowered, falling entire, borne singly in open or contracted panicles, in digitate or subdigitate racemes or in spiny or bristly burs, if paired then those of a pair identical; lower glume shorter then the spikelet (rarely absent); upper (fertile) lemma coriaceous to crustaceous, awnless .... **XIV. Paniceae**
+ Spikelets not as above, if falling entire then either 2-flowered but strongly laterally compressed or 1-flowered 4

4. Spikelets sunk in hollows in the internodes of a fragile cylindrical raceme, covered by the collateral glumes (rarely a single glume) .... **V. Hainardieae**
+ Inflorescence not as above, the spikelets not sunk in hollows 5

5. Spikelets with 1 fertile floret, with or without male or barren florets below or a clavate mass of barren florets above 6
+ Spikelets with 2 or more fertile florets 14

6. Glumes quite absent; spikelets strictly 1-flowered with 1-keeled palea, in a loose panicle (this seldom fully exserted except in a long hot summer); leaf-blades very rough on the edges and on the midnerve below, easily lacerating the skin .... **I. Oryzeae**
+ Glumes, or at least one of them, present or if apparently absent then spikelets in a pectinate raceme (*Nardus*); palea 2-keeled 7

7. Inflorescence a panicle 8
+ Inflorescence composed of racemes 11

8. Ligule reduced to a line of hairs .... **XII. Eragrostideae**
+ Ligule a membrane 9

9. Fertile floret succeeded by a clavate mass of sterile lemmas .... **VII. Meliceae**
+ Fertile floret solitary or with male or barren florets below it 10

10. Lemmas terete to dorsally compressed, firmly membranous to coriaceous, usually enfolding the palea; spikelet strictly 1-flowered; awn terminal or absent .... **III. Stipeae**
  + Lemma not indurated and enfolding the palea or if so then fertile floret accompanied by 1 or 2 sterile florets, these longer than the fertile or vestigial; awn dorsal or absent .... **VI. Aveneae**

11. Raceme single, the spikelets edgewise to the axis, ± pectinate; glumes minute .... **II. Nardeae**
  + Racemes several, or if single then a quasi-raceme with several spikelets at a node or a simple raceme with the spikelets broadside to the axis, not pectinate; glumes well developed 12

12. Lemma 3-nerved; racemes several to many and either digitate or disposed along an elongated axis .... **XIII. Cynodonteae**
  + Lemma 5- or more nerved; raceme or quasi-raceme single 13

13. Dwarf annual; raceme unilateral (*Mibora*) .... **VI. Aveneae**
  + Annual or perennial; raceme or quasi-raceme bilateral .... **X. Triticeae**

14. Inflorescence of several racemes .... **XII. Eragrostideae**
  + Inflorescence a panicle or a single raceme or quasi-raceme 15

15. Ligule a membrane 16
  + Ligule a line of hairs 21

16. Inflorescence a panicle, rarely spike-like or capitate with paired dimorphic spikelets (*Cynosurus*) or with 2 scarious bracts at the base (*Sesleria*), if reduced to a raceme then lemma with geniculate awn (*Gaudinia*) or lower glume absent (*Lolium*) 17
  + Inflorescence a single raceme or a quasi-raceme with up to 3 spikelets at a node; awn not geniculate; lower glume always present 20

17. Upper glume far exceeding the adjacent floret, or awn dorsal, or awn geniculate .... **VI. Aveneae**
  + Upper glume shorter than the adjacent floret or scarcely exceeding it, if longer then lower glume absent; lemma with or without a straight or curved, terminal or subterminal awn 18

18. Ovary surmounted by a lobed fleshy hairy terminal appendage, the styles arising from beneath it .... **IX. Bromeae**
  + Ovary hairy or glabrous at the summit but without an appendage; styles terminal ... 19

19. Leaf-sheaths open, their margins overlapping, if fused almost to the top then lemma awned; florets all fertile or the upper progressively reduced .... **IV. Poeae**
  + Leaf-sheaths cylindrical, their margins fused; lemmas awnless; uppermost florets sometimes reduced to a clavate mass of sterile lemmas .... **VII. Meliceae**

20. Inflorescence a simple raceme with shortly pedicelled (pedicel c.1 mm) subterete spikelets .... **VIII. Brachypodieae**
+ Inflorescence a spike-like raceme or a quasi-raceme, the spikelets or spikelet-groups quite sessile .... **X. Triticeae**

21. Tall, densely tufted (*Cortaderia*) or reed-like (*Phragmites*) perennials with large plumose panicle .... **XI. Arundineae**
+ Smaller herbaceous annuals or perennials; panicle not large and plumose 22

22. Glumes as long as the spikelet, 3- to 9-nerved, or if shorter and 1- to 3-nerved then basal internodes of the culm swollen and leaf-blades deciduous from their sheath .... **XI. Arundineae**
+ Glumes shorter than the spikelet, 1- to 3-nerved; basal internodes of the culm not swollen nor leaf-blades deciduous from their sheath .... **XII. Eragrostideae**

Tribe I. Oryzeae

Ligule membranous. Inflorescence a panicle, occasionally with simple, raceme-like primary branches, the spikelets all alike (in our species) or the sexes separate. Spikelets 1-flowered (in our species), or 3-flowered with the 2 lower florets reduced to sterile lemmas, without rhachilla-extension, mostly laterally compressed, disarticulating above the glumes; glumes absent or just discernible as obscure lips at the tip of the pedicel; lemma membranous to coriaceous, 5- to 10-nerved, entire, with or without a straight awn from the tip; palea resembling the lemma, 3- to 7-nerved; lodicules 2; stamens often 6; stigmas 2, plumose. Caryopsis linear to ovoid, rarely with a free pericarp.

Genera 13; species c.70. Tropical and warm temperate regions.

The anatomy of the tribe points to a relationship with the bamboos, but all of its members are herbaceous. There are three very characteristic features of the tribe involving modification of the spikelets: the reduction of the glumes to obscure lips at the tip of the pedicel; the two barren florets below the fertile reduced to tiny scales or bristles (absent in our species); and the multi-nerved palea with central keel.

The only genus .... **1. Leersia**

Tribe II. Nardeae

Ligule membranous. Inflorescence a unilateral spike-like raceme, the spikelets all alike and borne edgeways on to the axis with the lemma opposed to a shallow hollow in the tough rhachis but not embedded. Spikelets 1-flowered without rhachilla-extension, dorsally compressed, disarticulating beneath the floret; lower glume reduced to a cupular rim on the rhachis, the upper suppressed or almost so; lemma abaxial, 3-nerved, with a weak dorsal keel and two strong lateral keels, subcoriaceous, awned from the tip; palea 2-nerved, shorter than the lemma; lodicules 0; stamens 3; stigmas 1, puberulous. Caryopsis fusiform; embryo 1/6 its length; hilum linear.

Genus 1; species 1. Europe.

An odd little tribe whose unusual spikelets give no clue to its origin or affinities. The embryo structure, embryo length and ligule are all pooid, but it has the slender microhairs characteristic of bambusoids and arundinoids; the absence of lodicules, which would have provided essential information, clouds the problem even further.

The only genus .... **2. Nardus**

Tribe III. Stipeae

Ligule a membrane; leaf-blades mostly inrolled or filiform. Inflorescence an open or contracted panicle, the spikelets all alike. Spikelets 1-flowered without rhachilla-extension, terete to laterally or dorsally compressed, disarticulating above the glumes; glumes persistent, usually longer than the floret, hyaline to membranous, 1- to 7-nerved, mostly acute to long-acuminate; lemma rounded on the back, 5- to 9-nerved (3-nerved in some *Oryzopsis*), membranous to crustaceous, terete to lenticular and often enclosing the palea, awned from the entire or shortly 2-toothed tip or awnless; palea usually about as long as the lemma, hyaline to membranous or coriaceous, mostly without keels, usually acute; lodicules usually 3, sometimes 2. Caryopsis usually fusiform; hilum linear.

Genera c.8; species c.530. Temperate and warm temperate regions.

A distinctive tribe circumscribed by its single indurated floret without rhachilla-extension, and terminal awn. The rounded palea and 3 lodicules can be traced back to a bambusoid origin though the highly specialized spikelets and complex cytology are anything but primitive. The tribe has a single large genus (*Stipa*, c.420 species) and a number of imperfectly separated satellite genera. It can be difficult to distinguish from 1-flowered members of Aveneae, but the terminal (rather than dorsal) awn and indurated (rather than hyaline or membranous) lemma are distinctive enough in the British Isles. The placing of *Milium* in this tribe is controversial since some authors consider it a member of Aveneae, and others place it in its own tribe Milieae. For now, the indurated lemma is deemed adequate to place it in Stipeae as a more or less awnless equivalent of *Piptatherum*, but its systematic position needs to be reviewed. *Milium* has only two lodicules, much like members of Aveneae, but *Piptatherum* may have either two or three.

Key to genera

1. Floret terete; lemma with bigeniculate awn .... **5. *Stipa neesiana***
+ Floret laterally or dorsally compressed; lemma with straight or flexuous awn or awnless 2

2. Lemma awnless .... **4. Milium**
+ Lemma awned 3

3. Lemma dorsally compressed, coriaceous and bony .... **3. Piptatherum**
+ Lemma lightly laterally compressed, membranous ...... *4. Anemanthele lessoniana*

Tribe IV. Poeae

Ligule membranous; sheath-margins mostly free, sometimes connate. Inflorescence a panicle, or sometimes a single bilateral raceme with the spikelets edgewise to the axis, the spikelets all alike, rarely dimorphic. Spikelets (1)2- to many-flowered, the uppermost florets usually imperfect, laterally compressed, disarticulating below each floret (a few exceptions); glumes persistent, mostly not or scarcely exceeding the lowest lemma, usually membranous; lemmas membranous to coriaceous, 5- to 7(13)-nerved, rarely 3-nerved, with or without a straight or curved awn from the tip or between apical teeth; ovary sometimes hairy, but not with a lobed appendage; lodicules 2; stigmas 2. Caryopsis mostly ellipsoid; hilum linear or round; endosperm soft in some genera.

Genera c.50; species c. 1200. Temperate and cold regions.

Poeae are largely unspecialized grasses with simple spikelets bearing short glumes and several florets with 5-nerved lemmas. It contains a number of large genera with numerous small satellites whose recognition is often controversial. Separation from Aveneae has recently been questioned, but with minor adjustments to the boundary between them there is no practical reason for abandoning the distinction. The short membranous glumes similar to the lemmas and terminal straight awn of Poeae contrast well with the long papery glumes thinner than the lemmas and dorsal geniculate awn of Aveneae. *Koeleria* is often difficult to place because of its short glumes and lack of awn but it has obvious affinities to *Trisetum* and clearly belongs in Aveneae; it does, however, persistently key out to Poeae and appears in the key below.

Key to genera

1. Spikelets dimorphic, fertile spikelets intermixed with sterile spikelets .... **8. Cynosurus**
    + Spikelets all alike 2

2. Inflorescence an open to contracted panicle or an elongated raceme 3
    + Inflorescence a capitate to spiciform panicle 14

3. Inflorescence a bilateral raceme, the spikelets edgewise to the axis and lower glume absent (except in the terminal spikelet) .... **6. Lolium**
    + Inflorescence a panicle 4

4. Plant perennial 5
    + Plant annual 10

5. Lemma rounded on the back, at least below 6
    + Lemma keeled throughout, sometimes weakly so but then orbicular to oblate 7

6. Tip of lemma firm, acute to awned; hilum oblong or linear .... **5. Festuca**
    + Tip of lemma thinly scarious to hyaline, obtuse or acute, ± erose; hilum round to oval .... **9. Puccinellia**

7. Lemmas orbicular to oblate with broad membranous margins, appressed to the lemma above .... **10. Briza**
    + Lemmas narrower, the margins less distinct and often inrolled 8

8. Lemmas prominently 3-nerved, broadly obtuse to truncate .... **13. Catabrosa**
+ Lemmas 5-nerved 9

9. Lemmas acuminate, spinulose on the keel; panicle secund, lobed, the spikelets gathered in 1-sided clumps at the tips of the branches .... **12. Dactylis**
+ Lemmas obtuse to acute; panicle not as above, the spikelets evenly distributed .... **11. Poa**

10. Lemmas awned .... **7. Vulpia**
+ Lemmas awnless 11

11. Lemmas rounded on the back 12
+ Lemmas keeled 13

12. Lemmas membranous .... **9. Puccinellia**
+ Lemmas coriaceous .... **14. Catapodium**

13. Lemmas orbicular to oblate with broad hyaline margins .... **10. Briza**
+ Lemmas lanceolate to ovate with inconspicuous narrow hyaline margins ... **11. Poa**

14. Lemma rounded on the back, not shiny; panicle subtended by a pair of scarious bracts .... **15. Sesleria**
+ Lemma keeled, shiny; panicle not subtended by bracts .... see 22. *Koeleria*

Tribe V. Hainardieae

Ligule membranous, glabrous. Inflorescence a single cylindrical bilateral raceme, tough or fragile, the spikelets alternate in 2 opposite rows, sessile and ± sunk into the hollowed axis, mostly broadside on. Spikelets all alike, 1- to 2-flowered, with or without a minute rhachilla-extension; glumes appressed to the axis, subequal and side by side (except *Hainardia* where there is only one), usually exceeding and covering the floret, coriaceous, strongly 3- to 7-nerved, obtuse or acute; lemma usually hyaline, 3- to 5-nerved, entire and usually awnless; stamens 3; stigmas 2. Caryopsis narrowly oblong, the hilum round to narrowly oblong; endosperm sometimes soft.

Genera 6; species c. 10. Mediterranean region and N America.

A small tribe of equally small genera in which the axis of the inflorescence is progressively integrated with the spikelet. The main feature of the tribe is the fragile cylindrical inflorescence with collateral glumes (except for one genus) although this pattern is repeated in other unrelated genera (not in the British Isles). Recent molecular studies suggest that the tribe should be amalgamated with Poeae, along with Aveneae, but its distinctive morphology is sufficient to justify its separate status.

Glumes 2, collateral .... **16. Parapholis**
Glume 1 .... *61. Hainardia cylindrica*

Tribe VI. Aveneae

Ligule membranous. Inflorescence a panicle (a raceme, or several racemes, in *Gaudinia, Mibora,* and sometimes in *Helictotrichon*), the spikelets all alike (except sometimes in *Phalaris*). Spikelets with one to several fertile florets, the one fertile floret often accompanied by male or barren florets, or rudiments, below it (rarely with a single male floret above it), laterally compressed, disarticulating below each floret (though with a number of exceptions; spikelets with 1 fertile floret accompanied by reduced florets breaking up above the glumes only; spikelets falling entire in *Holcus*; raceme-axis fragile in *Gaudinia*); glumes persistent, usually longer than the adjacent lemmas and often as long as the spikelet (some exceptions, notably *Koeleria*), commonly membranous with thin hyaline margins; lemmas hyaline to coriaceous, often with thin shiny margins, 5- to 11-nerved (3-nerved in some species of *Agrostis, Calamagrostis, Koeleria, Phleum*), typically with a dorsal awn, this often geniculate with twisted column; lodicules 2; stigmas 2, plumose. Caryopsis mostly ellipsoid; hilum usually round or oval; endosperm sometimes soft, occasionally liquid.

Genera 57; species c. 1050. Temperate and cold regions.

The tribe is normally an easy one to recognize, especially in our area, having the classic combination of thin papery glumes enclosing the whole spikelet and lemmas with dorsal geniculate awn. The long, thinly membranous glumes contrast well with the short herbaceous or firmly membranous glumes of tribe Poeae, although there is some variation in glume length within the tribe. The geniculate awn is also fairly characteristic, but unfortunately it is not always present nor necessarily obviously dorsal when it is; in Poeae the awn, if present, is invariably straight and terminal. The genus that causes most problems is *Koeleria* which has short glumes and awnless lemmas; it nearly always keys out into Poeae, but the thin shiny margins of its glumes, and its obvious relationships to *Trisetum* and *Rostraria*, are the best indication of its membership of Aveneae.

There is a progression from several-flowered to 1-flowered spikelets with the extremes and the intermediates usually accommodated in subtribes (formerly tribes, but not necessarily with the same boundaries as the modern subtribes). Recent molecular studies have suggested that the tribe be amalgamated with Poeae, but the few problematic genera scarcely justify such an extreme measure.

Key to subtribes

1. Spikelets with 2 or more fertile florets, the florets all alike (but the uppermost rudimentary or replaced by a short rhachilla-extension), sometimes the spikelet 2-flowered with the florets slightly dimorphic, one of them fertile and the other male .... subtribe 1. **Aveninae**
+ Spikelets with 1 fertile floret, sometimes with male or barren florets below it, these often reduced to rudiments, but in any case morphologically quite different from the fertile 2

2. Spikelets with the fertile floret accompanied by 2 (rarely 1) male or barren florets below .... subtribe 2. **Phalaridinae**
+ Spikelets strictly 1-flowered .... subtribe 3. **Alopecurinae**

Subtribe 1. **Aveninae**

Spikelets with 2 to several fertile florets plus an apical rudimentary floret or rhachilla extension, rarely strictly 2-flowered with one floret male and the other fertile, breaking up below each floret (except *Holcus*, falling entire); glumes equal or unequal, the upper sometimes a little shorter than the lemma and seldom enclosing the spikelet.

Before *Genera Graminum* was written this subtribe was more or less the equivalent of the old tribe Aveneae. For some reason *Anthoxanthum* was included in this tribe even though it is structurally more similar to *Phalaris* (see below). Both *Holcus* and *Arrhenatherum* have a single fertile floret, but in each case this is accompanied by a single male floret. Occasionally *Arrhenatherum* has spikelets with 2 fertile florets, as well as the male, and then its affinity to *Helictotrichon* is very obvious. In *Holcus*, unusually, the spikelets fall entire while in *Gaudinia* the raceme-axis is fragile (the raceme itself is unusual in the tribe although in *Helictotrichon* the panicle is sometimes reduced to a loose raceme).

Key to genera

1. Inflorescence a fragile bilateral raceme fracturing at the base of each internode .... **20. Gaudinia**
+ Inflorescence a panicle, if reduced to a loose raceme this with a tough axis and the spikelets disarticulating above the glumes 2

2. Plants annual 3
+ Plants perennial 5

3. Panicle large and loose with pendulous spikelets over 15 mm .... **19. Avena**
+ Panicle small, loose or contracted, the spikelets not pendulous and not over 10 mm 4

4. Lemmas keeled; spikelets more than 2-flowered, the florets separated by short but distinct internodes .... *74. Rostraria cristata*
+ Lemmas rounded on the back; spikelets 2-flowered, the florets arising at about the same level .... **26. Aira**

5. Awn with a ring of hairs at the junction of column and limb ...... **25. Corynephorus**
+ Awn without a ring of hairs, or spikelets awnless 6

6. Lemmas keeled 7
+ Lemmas rounded on the back 8

7. Lemmas dorsally awned .... **21. Trisetum**
+ Lemmas awnless .... **22. Koeleria**

8. Spikelets strictly 2-flowered, the florets slightly dimorphic, not accompanied by a rhachilla-extension 9
+ Spikelets more than 2-flowered, or if 2-flowered then the florets alike and accompanied by a rhachilla-extension 10

9. Spikelets disarticulating above the glumes; lower floret male .. **18. Arrhenatherum**
+ Spikelets disarticulating below the glumes and falling entire; upper floret male .... **24. Holcus**

10. Spikelets more than 10 mm; lemmas firmly membranous to subcoriaceous, stoutly awned, well exserted from the glumes .... **17. Helictotrichon**
+ Spikelets not more than 7 mm; lemmas thinly membranous, inconspicuously awned, seldom much exserted from the glumes .... **23. Deschampsia**

Subtribe 2. **Phalaridinae**

Spikelets 3-flowered (rarely 2-flowered), the two lower florets (rarely just one) male or barren, the uppermost fertile, disarticulating above the glumes (except some species of *Phalaris*) but not between the florets; glumes, or at least the upper, usually enclosing the florets.

This is almost the equivalent of the old tribe Phalarideae but with the addition of *Anthoxanthum*. In each case the fertile lemma is cartilaginous and usually glossy, and much firmer in texture than the glumes.

Key to genera

Lower florets well developed and exceeding the fertile floret; tissues smelling of coumarin .... **27. Anthoxanthum**
Lower florets rudimentary, reduced to small chaffy scales or minute fleshy stumps (sometimes one of them absent); tissues not smelling of coumarin .... **28. Phalaris**

Subtribe 3. **Alopecurinae**

Spikelets strictly 1-flowered; glumes commonly enclosing the florets.

The equivalent of the old tribe Agrostideae, the change of name being enforced by the rules of botanical nomenclature which require that the earliest available name at the appropriate taxonomic level should take priority over all others.

Key to genera

1. Inflorescence a single unilateral raceme .... **35. Mibora**
+ Inflorescence a panicle 2

2. Spikelets falling entire 3
+ Spikelets disarticulating above the persistent glumes 5

3. Spikelets shed with a basal stipe apparently comprising the pedicel or part of it
   .... **36. Polypogon**
+ Spikelets shed without a basal stipe 4

4. Lemma dorsally awned (rarely awnless); glumes connate along their opposite
   margins at least at the base; lemma margins fused below; palea absent
   ....**37. Alopecurus**
+ Lemma awnless; glumes not connate; lemma margins not fused; palea present
   .... **38. Phleum**

5. Plants annual 6
+ Plants perennial 8

6. Glumes villous and awned; panicle white and fluffy .... **33. Lagurus**
+ Glumes glabrous, awnless; panicle not white and fluffy 7

7. Glumes swollen below; lemma with inconspicuous dorsal geniculate awn or
   awnless .... **32. Gastridium**
+ Glumes not swollen below; lemma with conspicuous subapical flexuous awn
   .... **34. Apera**

8. Spikelets 10 – 15 mm; lemma strongly laterally compressed and keeled; leaf-blades
   inrolled, rigid and pungent .... **31. Ammophila**
+ Spikelets up to 7 mm; lemma rounded on the back; leaf-blades not as above 9

9. Floret with glabrous or pubescent callus .... **29. Agrostis**
+ Floret with bearded callus, the hairs at least half as long as the lemma
   .... **30. Calamagrostis**

Tribe VII. Meliceae

Ligule membranous; leaf-sheaths with connate margins. Inflorescence a panicle or raceme,
the spikelets all alike. Spikelets of 1 to many fertile florets, with one or more imperfect
florets above, these similar to the fertile or gathered into a clump of rudimentary lemmas,
laterally compressed, mostly disarticulating below each floret; glumes persistent, usually
not exceeding the adjacent lemma, often papery; lemmas herbaceous to coriaceous,

prominently 5- to 9(13)-nerved, rounded on the back, awnless (in our genera); lodicules 2, usually connate, short, fleshy and truncate. Caryopsis ellipsoid to terete; hilum linear.

Genera 8; species c. 130. Temperate regions.

The external morphology of the tribe is rather variable, but the genera are united by their connate sheath margins, peculiar lodicules and atypical chromosome number (basic number 9 or 10 rather than 7).

Key to genera

Florets alike except for the rudimentary uppermost in each spikelet; upper glume 1-nerved .... **39. Glyceria**
Fertile floret(s) quite different from the sterile, the latter gathered into a terminal clump of vestigial lemmas; upper glume 3- to 5-nerved .... **40. Melica**

Tribe VIII. Brachypodieae

Ligule membranous. Inflorescence a raceme, the spikelets all alike and diverging from the tough axis on extremely short pedicels. Spikelets cylindrical or slightly laterally compressed, straight or curved, with several to many florets, the florets all alike and fertile or the uppermost imperfect, disarticulating between the florets; glumes persistent, unequal, distinctly 3- to 9-nerved, shorter than the the lowest lemma; lemmas herbaceous, rarely becoming coriaceous, 7- to 9-nerved, rounded on the back, obtuse or extended into a straight awn at the tip; lodicules 2, ciliate. Caryopsis ellipsoid with linear hilum and hairy terminal appendage.

Genus 1; species 16. Temperate Eurasia, extending southwards on tropical mountains; also in Mexico and Bolivia.

The affinities of *Brachypodium* are uncertain. The genus has been allied to Triticeae and also bears some resemblance to Bromeae, but is anomalous in both tribes despite sharing the peculiar hairy terminal appendage to the ovary. Cytologically the genus is a mixed bag with basic chromosome numbers of 5, 7 and 9 (and one species with $2n = 38$). The chromosomes are much smaller than those of the other two tribes and point to an affinity with Meliceae. The sugars in the endosperm are laevulose rather than saccharose which is the rule in other pooid tribes including Triticeae and Bromeae.

The only genus .... **41. Brachypodium**

45

Tribe IX. Bromeae

Ligule membranous. Inflorescence a panicle, the spikelets all alike. Spikelets of several to many fertile florets with imperfect florets above, laterally compressed, disarticulating below each floret; glumes persistent, shorter than the lowest lemma, entire; lemmas herbaceous to coriaceous, 5- to 13-nerved, ± 2-toothed at the tip, with a straight or recurved subapical awn; lodicules 2, glabrous; ovary capped by a hairy lobed appendage bearing 2 subterminal stigmas. Caryopsis narrowly ellipsoid to linear, hollowed on the hilar side.

Genera 3; species c.150. Temperate regions.

Bromeae are very similar to Poeae, the main justification for their separation lying in their unusual starch grains. In almost all other grasses the starch grains in the endosperm are compound or angular and too variable to be of much taxonomic value, but in Bromeae (and also in Brachypodieae and Triticeae) they are of a peculiar simple rounded form. Other studies have revealed a close association between Bromeae and Triticeae, but Brachypodieae still stand apart despite their superficial resemblance to Triticeae.

The best morphological distinction between Bromeae and Poeae is the former's possession of an ovary appendage which is visible even in young plants.

The only genus .... **42. Bromus**

Tribe X. Triticeae

Ligule membranous; leaf-blades often auriculate. Inflorescence a single bilateral raceme or false-raceme, the spikelets alternate in two opposite rows, single or in groups of 2 – 3 at each node, broadside to the axis and usually sessile, all alike (some exceptions); rhachis tough or fragile and then disarticulating at the base of the internode (some exceptions). Spikelets 1- to many-flowered with the apical florets smaller, laterally compressed (dorsally if 1-flowered), disarticulating below each floret if rhachis tough; glumes persistent, rarely deciduous, shorter or narrower than the lemma leaving much of the latter exposed (some exceptions), usually coriaceous, sometimes awn-like; lemmas coriaceous, 5- to 11-nerved, with or without a straight or recurved awn from the tip; ovary tipped by a small fleshy hairy appendage. Caryopsis ellipsoid, hollowed on the hilar face.

Genera 18 (or more depending on criteria, see below); species c.330. Temperate and warm temperate regions, mostly in the northern hemisphere.

The tribe as a whole is plagued with taxonomic uncertainties, difficulties of identification and rampant hybridization both within and between genera. There is no general agreement on circumscriptions of genera, and estimated numbers that should be recognized vary from 18 (Clayton & Renvoize 1986) to 36 (Löve 1984). One school of thought is that genera should be defined not in terms of their morphology but of their genomic constitution. Almost 40 different haploid genomes or genome combinations have been identified, all of them accorded rank of genus at one time or another. Unfortunately, the genera so circumscribed can rarely be determined until the species have been indentified and therefore have limited practical value. Should the genomic circumscription be preferred for the Triticeae of the British Isles several genera would have to be split: *Hordeum* into *Critesion* (genome H) and *Hordeum* (genome I); *Triticum* into *Gigachilon* (genome AB) and *Triticum* (genome ABD); and *Elymus* into *Elymus* (genome HS), *Elytrigia* (genome EJS) and *Thinopyrum* (genome J). It is not uncommon for *Elymus* and *Elytrigia* to be recognized by British authors, but since the basis for this split is as valid as that for *Triticum* and *Hordeum*, either the two segregates should be re-amalgamated or *Triticum* and *Hordeum* should be divided and *Elytrigia* itself further divided. Anything else would be an unsatisfactory compromise.

Key to genera

1. Spikelets borne singly at each node of the rhachis 2
+   Spikelets borne in groups of two or more at each node of the rhachis 4

2. Plant perennial; wild grass .... **43. Elymus**
+   Plant annual; cultivated cereal or escape 3

3. Lemma pectinately spinulose on the keel; glumes acuminate, 1-nerved .. **47. Secale**
+   Lemma glabrous or pilose but not pectinate; glumes obtuse to 2-toothed, several-nerved, the outer nerves separated at the tip .... **48. Triticum**

4. Spikelets sessile and paired at each node of the rhachis .... **44. Leymus**
+   Spikelets with their pedicels connate in triads at each node of the rhachis 5

5. Rhachis tough; awn of lemma 1.5 – 2.5 cm, slender .... **45. Hordelymus**
+   Rhachis fragile, or if tough then awn of lemma up to 18 cm, stout .... **46. Hordeum**

Tribe XI. Arundineae

Ligule apparently a line of hairs (but in fact a very short, barely visible membrane with long-ciliate margin). Inflorescence a panicle, sometimes spike-like, often large and plumose, the spikelets all alike (except in 50. *Cortaderia*). Spikelets usually several-flowered, the uppermost florets imperfect, laterally compressed, disarticulating above the glumes and between the florets, the callus short and obtuse, rarely linear, usually bearded; glumes persistent, usually membranous, acute to acuminate; lemmas usually rounded on the back, 3- to 11-nerved, hyaline to coriaceous, entire or 2-lobed at the tip, with or without a straight or geniculate awn from the tip or sinus; palea well developed; lodicules 2, fleshy, truncate. Caryopsis usually ellipsoid, sometimes with a free or separable pericarp; hilum narrowly oblong to linear.

Genera 40; species c. 300. Cosmopolitan but best developed in the southern hemisphere.

A controversial tribe comprising two elements that were once considered tribes in their own right, Arundineae (*Phragmites* and *Cortaderia*) and Danthonieae (*Danthonia* and *Molinia*). The tribe is extremely heterogeneous and rather difficult to circumscribe morphologically, and efforts to define the limits of the two components have repeatedly failed. On the other hand, recent DNA analyses have suggested, despite a lack of morphological support, that not only should the component tribes be reinstated, but that they should be raised to subfamily level; furthermore, *Cortaderia* would be moved from Arundineae to Danthonieae.

The tribe is best distinguished from Poeae by the ligule. *Molinia* superficially resembles *Eragrostis*, but apart from the anatomical characters that would distinguish their respective subfamilies, the best distinction is *Molinia*'s deciduous leaf-blades and swollen lower internodes.

Key to genera

1. Plant reed-like with cauline leaves and large plumose panicle .... **52. Phragmites**
+ Plant tufted with mostly basal leaves 2

2. Plant over 2 m tall, with large plumose panicle and harsh leaves .... **50. Cortaderia**
+ Plant much less than 2 m tall; panicle not plumose and leaves soft 3

3. Lower glume shorter than the lowest lemma; lemmas 3- to 5-nerved; panicle with many small (3 – 7.5mm) spikelets .... **51. Molinia**
+ Lower glume longer than the lowest lemma; lemmas 7- to 9-nerved; panicle with few (6 – 12) larger spikelets (6 – 12mm) .... **49. Danthonia**

Tribe XII. Eragrostideae

Ligule membranous or a line of hairs. Inflorescence a panicle or of tough unilateral racemes, these digitate or scattered along an axis, the spikelets all alike. Spikelets 1- to several- or many-flowered with the lower florets fertile and the uppermost ± reduced, usually laterally compressed, commonly disarticulating below each floret but with a wide variety of other abscission modes; glumes persistent or deciduous, usually membranous, 0- to 1-nerved and shorter than the lowermost lemma, entire; lemmas membranous to coriaceous, 1- to 3-nerved, entire or 2-lobed, with or without a straight or flexuous terminal awn. Fruit sometimes with a free pericarp.

Genera 77; species c.1000. Tropics and subtropics.

A very large tribe of grasses that by and large have unspecialized, usually many-flowered spikelets with (usually) 3-nerved lemma. It could be confused with either of two large temperate tribes, Poeae and Arundineae. The former are distinguished by their (usually) 5-nerved lemma, and the latter by the (usually) thinner texture of the lemma. In our area, however, confusion is unlikely although *Molinia* can only be distinguished from *Eragrostis* by minor vegetative characters (the genera are, however, fundamentally different in both their leaf anatomy and their physiology). In general Eragrostideae, on one hand, and Poeae and Arundineae, on the other, are seldom sympatric and their morphological overlaps are rarely a problem.

Key to genera

1. Inflorescence an open or contracted panicle 2
+ Inflorescence composed of digitate, subdigitate or scattered racemes 3

2. Spikelets several-flowered .... **54. Eragrostis**
+ Spikelets 1-flowered .... *183. Sporobolus africanus*

3. Inflorescence composed of digitate or subdigitate racemes .... **55. Eleusine**
+ Inflorescence composed of racemes scattered along an elongated axis
   .... **53. Leptochloa**

Tribe XIII. Cynodonteae

Ligule a short membrane with ciliate margin, but often one or other of these components predominating. Inflorescence of tough unilateral racemes, these single, digitate or scattered along an axis, often deciduous, the spikelets all alike. Spikelet with 1 fertile floret, with or without additional male or barren florets, cuneate to subterete, laterally or dorsally compressed, disarticulating below the fertile lemma, sometimes falling entire; glumes usually persistent, herbaceous to membranous, 1- to 3(5)-nerved, shorter than the floret or enclosing it; lemma membranous to coriaceous, 3-nerved, often ciliate on the nerves, entire or 2- to 3-lobed at the tip, with or without 1 – 3(5) terminal or subapical awns, these usually straight; callus usually very short and obtuse. Fruit sometimes with free pericarp.

Genera 59; species c.300. Tropics, extending to the N American prairie.

The tribe is very close to Eragrostideae and differs mainly by the reduction of the spikelet to a single fertile floret. Members of the tribe are mainly tropical but one group has penetrated temperate N America and *Spartina* has extended into cool marine habitats. They are less weedy and xerophytic than Eragrostideae and commonly occur in seral and disclimax communities. Several recent authors have amalgamated Cynodonteae with Eragrostideae on the basis of molecular data, but this conceals a fundamental difference in their structure.

Tribe XIV. Paniceae

Ligule a combination of short membrane and long ciliate fringe, but of variable proportions (absent in *Echinochloa*). Inflorescence an open to spikelike panicle or of unilateral racemes (these digitate or scattered along a central axis), the spikelets all alike (in our species), sometimes in pairs but those of a pair similar, when racemose the lower glume usually turned away from the rhachis (abaxial). Spikelets 2-flowered without rhachilla-extension, usually dorsally compressed, falling entire, rarely awned; glumes membranous or herbaceous, the upper often as long as the spikelet, the lower usually shorter and sometimes rudimentary; lower floret male or barren, its lemma usually membranous or herbaceous and as long as the spikelet, with or without a palea; upper floret bisexual, the lemma and palea indurated.

Genera >100; species c. 2000. Mostly in the tropics.

The hallmark of the Paniceae is the indurated upper floret which tightly encloses the caryopsis. This modification is presumed to be protective and thus diminishes the role of the glumes which are usually thin and the lower often rudimentary. The lower floret is likewise reduced, often to an empty lemma. With the lower glume often greatly reduced, the upper glume can be visualised as replacing it and the barren lemma thus assumes the role of the upper glume. The degree of reduction is of little taxonomic significance above species level, but the glumes and lower lemma all contribute to the 'fruit' since the spikelet is usually shed as a whole from the tip of the pedicel.

4. Upper lemma with flat margins covering most of the back of the palea
    .... **64. Digitaria**
+   Upper lemma with inrolled margins exposing most of the back of the palea 5

5. Ligule absent .... **59. Echinochloa**
+   Ligule present 6

6. Upper lemma distinctly mucronate, the mucro enclosed in the cuspidate spikelet tip
    .... **61. Urochloa**
+   Upper lemma not mucronate and the spikelet not cuspidate 7

7. Upper lemma rugose .... **60. Brachiaria**
+   Upper lemma smooth .... **62. Paspalum**

Tribe XV. Andropogoneae

Ligule usually a membrane, sometimes with ciliate fringe. Inflorescence composed of fragile (rarely tough) racemes, these sometimes in a large panicle, but usually single, paired or digitate, terminal on the culm or axillary and numerous. Racemes bearing the spikelets in pairs (but usually terminating in a triad) with one sessile and the other pedicelled, these sometimes alike but usually dissimilar, the sessile being bisexual and the pedicelled male or barren. Sessile spikelet 2-flowered without rhachilla extension, usually dorsally compressed, falling entire at maturity with the adjacent pedicel and internode (unless the raceme tough), the pedicelled spikelet usually falling separately; glumes enclosing the florets and ± hardened, the lower facing outward, the upper usually boat-shaped and fitting between internode and pedicel; lower floret male or barren, the lemma membranous or hyaline and awnless, the palea usually suppressed when floret barren; upper floret bisexual, its lemma membranous or hyaline, with or without a geniculate awn, its palea short or absent. Pedicelled spikelet commonly male or barren, awnless, smaller than the sessile or even vestigial (sometimes larger); rarely the pedicel absent or fused to the internode.

Genera 85; species c. 960. Throughout the tropics and extending into warm temperate regions.

The most characteristic feature of the tribe is the fragile raceme bearing paired spikelets. Not all genera follow this pattern and *Zea* is quite exceptional in having tough racemes with the sexes in separate inflorescences. In common with Paniceae the spikelets are 2-flowered and fall entire (except in *Zea*) but the resemblance ends there. Both glumes are well developed (in Paniceae the lower glume is usually reduced) and both lemmas are thin and membranous (in Paniceae the lower is glume-like, the upper hardened). The few representatives in our area are distinctive: *Zea* is monoecious while *Sorghum* follows the standard pattern for the simpler members of the tribe in having short racemes in an ample panicle and the dimorphism of the spikelets is very apparent.

Key to genera

Spikelets unisexual, the male in an ample terminal panicle, the female in rows on thick woody axillary cob, the latter enclosed in several leaf-sheaths (husks) and the long silky stigmas protruding from the apex .... **67. Zea**

Spikelets, or at least one of each pair, bisexual, in short racemes in an open panicle .... **66. Sorghum**

1. Leersia Sw.

Annual or perennial (ours perennial). Panicle branches sometimes simple and raceme-like. Spikelets 1-flowered without vestiges of sterile florets, strongly laterally compressed, not or shortly stipitate; lemma chartaceous to coriaceous, 5-nerved, awnless or rarely awned (ours awnless); stamens 1, 2, 3 or 6 (3 in our species).

Species 18; tropical and warm temperate regions.

The genus closely resembles *Oryza* L. (Rice) but lacks the sterile florets below the fertile. Recognition of the genus can be problematical because in Britain in all but the warmest seasons the panicle remains partially or even wholly enclosed in the uppermost leaf-sheath and the hidden spikelets are cleistogamous. There are, however, distinctive vegetative characters that can be used (see species account).

The only species .... **1. L. oryzoides**

2. Nardus L.

Tufted perennial with filiform leaf-blades. Description otherwise as for tribe.

Species 1; Europe.

The only species .... **2. N. stricta**

3. Piptatherum P.Beauv.
Oryzopsis auct. non Michx.

Perennial; leaf-blades flat or inrolled. Floret narrowly lanceolate to ovate or obovate, dorsally compressed, the callus very short and obtuse; lemma coriaceous to bony (but conspicuously 3-nerved in our species), pallid to brown, the margins not overlapping and the back of the palea thus visible; awn readily deciduous, straight, not twisted (rarely persistent and geniculate in the New World); palea coriaceous, 2-nerved but without keels, mostly acute; lodicules 2 or 3.

Species 35; temperate and subtropical regions of the northern hemisphere, especially SW Asia.

Related to, but not easily confused with *Stipa*, the short obtuse callus, dorsally compressed floret and exposed palea being the main distinguishing features.

The only species .... **3. P. miliaceum**

4. Milium L.

Annual or perennial; leaf-blades flat. Floret narrowly to broadly elliptic, dorsally compressed, the callus very short and obtuse; lemma coriaceous, the margins not overlapping, awnless; palea coriaceous, 2-nerved but without keels, obtuse; lodicules 2.

Species 4; north temperate regions of the Old World and in eastern N America.

Despite having only 4 species, *Milium* has basic chromosome numbers of 4, 5, 7 and 9. Its placement in tribe Stipeae is controversial (see the tribal account).

Key to species

Perennial; culms mostly erect, sometimes ascending; panicle loose and open
....**6. M. effusum**
Annual; culms prostrate; panicle contracted .... **7. M. vernale**

5. Festuca L.
Schedonorus P.Beauv.

Perennial; occasionally dioecious (but not in our area); leaf-blades sometimes flat, occasionally with cross-nerves, but mostly folded and sometimes filiform, rarely pungent. Panicle open or contracted. Spikelets (2)4- to 9(10)-flowered; glumes membranous to herbaceous, the lower 1-nerved, the upper (1)3-nerved; lemmas membranous to thinly coriaceous, rounded on the back (at least towards the base), 5-nerved (rarely 3-nerved), acute to awned; awns mostly short, sometimes long, terminal or rarely minutely subterminal; floret callus and rhachilla glabrous; palea-keels scaberulous; stamens 3; ovary sometimes hairy at the top. Hilum linear, rarely oblong.

Species c.450; temperate regions throughout the world, extending through the tropics on mountain tops.

A large and variable genus for which no overall treatment is yet available although at the higher levels of the classification our species present few problems. The following simplified key illustrates how our species are arranged.

Leaves with falcate auricles .... Subgen. *Schedonorus*
Leaves without obvious auricles:
  Lemma 3-nerved .... Subgen. *Drymanthele*
  Lemma 5-nerved .... Subgen. *Festuca*
    Lemma translucent; leaves pungent .... Sect. *Eskia*
    Lemma green; leaves not pungent:
      Sheath margins on tillers fused to the top; tillers mostly extravaginal . Sect. *Aulaxyper*
      Sheath margins on tillers overlapping; tillers all intravaginal .... Sect. *Festuca*

Subgenus *Festuca* presents the most difficult problems although Sect. *Eskia* is distinct enough. The remainder comprise the fine-leaved fescues and these are commonly broken down into two principal groups, those centred on *F. rubra* (Sect. *Aulaxyper*) and those centred on *F. ovina* (Sect. *Festuca*). These two groups are very different and it is vital that a specimen be assigned with certainty to one or the other before proceeding with the key. In Sect. *Aulaxyper* the tillers are almost all extravaginal and the plant is inclined to form an extensive turf, less often loose tufts or circular patches. In addition, the leaf-sheaths have their margins fused for most of their length and old sheaths on drying tend to be reddish or brownish in colour. In contrast, in Sect. *Festuca* the tillers are always intravaginal and the plant forms dense tufts; the leaf-sheaths are open with the margins overlapping for most of their length (they may be fused below) and the old sheaths on drying tend to be whitish.

Special techniques are required for identifying members of the subgenus, particularly in Sect. *Festuca*. For the purposes of this Handbook the following conventions have been adopted:

Pedicel length. From the lowest branch of the panicle that has at least 3 spikelets, and measured from the second spikelet up on this branch. Terminal spikelets should always be avoided, and those that are borne singly on lateral branches in the upper part of the panicle should also be treated with circumspection. In both cases the pedicel is continuous with – and indistinguishable from – the branch axis that bears it and will give misleadingly long measurements as a result.

Spikelet length. Choose a spikelet from the middle region of the panicle. Measure in a straight line from the base of the lower glume to the tip of the fourth lemma, ignoring the awn. In rare instances there may only be 3 florets in the spikelet or the fourth floret may be conspicuously under-developed. In either case, measurement should be taken to the tip of the third lemma and an increment equivalent to the difference in length between measuring to the tips of the first and second lemmas added to this.

Lemma length. Choose the second lemma in the spikelet and measure from the base of the callus to the tip of the lemma-body, ignoring the awn.

Awn length. This varies considerably from floret to floret even within a spikelet. An average from numerous measurements can be used, but in this Handbook the awn of the third lemma of a spikelet is taken as the standard. There are sometimes practical problems associated with recognising where the tapering lemma-body ends and the awn begins, except when the awn is clearly – but minutely – subterminal; inevitably the point chosen is often somewhat arbitrary.

Leaf width. In flat leaves this is measured from margin to margin but in those leaves that are folded it is taken from the midrib to the visible margin (the true margin may be inrolled slightly).

Leaf anatomy. There has been a long tradition of reliance on internal leaf anatomy and length of stomatal guard cells for delimiting taxa but since these are mostly inaccessible to all except those with laboratory facilities they have been avoided as far as practicable in this Handbook. It is possible, just, with a sharp pair of scissors and a ×20 handlens to detect the sclerenchyma as pale patches within the otherwise greenish ground tissue; a leaf from a tiller should be used and cut across as neatly as possible near the middle. Islets of sclerenchyma always occur below the midrib and along each margin, with variable numbers of islets between. The aspect of the folded leaf-blade in transverse section varies according to internal anatomy and number of islets, and the following main types can be recognised from observation of the outer surface without the need of cutting sections:

Type 1. Smoothly oval or U-shaped in section. The sclerenchyma forms a continuous ring between the nerves and the lower epidermis and on drying of the leaf there is no contraction of the surface; none of the nerves can therefore be discerned.

Type 2. Slightly unevenly U- or Y-shaped in section. The sclerenchyma is usually discontinuous although the islets are of low profile; they often tail off towards the edges and may be contiguous to their neighbours. On drying, the leaf surface contracts very slightly between the islets – especially on either side of the midrib – and the surface is undulating but not obviously ribbed. There may be a blunt rounded keel formed by the midrib.

Type 3. Triangular or polygonal in section. The sclerenchyma forms discrete islets below the nerves; they do not tail off and are always quite distinct. On drying, the leaf-surface contracts markedly between the islets and the leaf is clearly angular in section. The midrib may form a narrow, acute keel.

Sclerenchyma above the nerves is usually very sparse and cannot be detected without cutting leaf-sections and using a compound microscope.

Chromosome numbers and sometimes stomatal dimensions are noted in the accounts but neither can be used in the keys due to their inaccessibility to most users. There is supposed to be a correlation between ploidy level and stomatal dimensions but this is poorly expressed and occasionally very unconvincing. In *F. ovina* in particular there is no reliable way of predicting ploidy level from the morphology. In many cases there is no way of discriminating between taxa without knowledge of chromosome number and leaf anatomy, and in these cases the practical value of the taxa must be called into question.

Subgenus *Schedonorus* hybridizes with *Lolium* and subgenus *Festuca* sect. *Aulaxyper* with *Vulpia*. The hybrids generally show very low fertility.

Key to species

1. Base of blade extended on either side into a pointed clasping auricle (Subgen. *Schedonorus*) 2
+ Base of blade without auricles or with short rounded auricles not clasping the culm 4

2. Lemmas with awn longer than the body; exposed nodes of the culm dark violet-purple ....**8. F. gigantea**
+ Lemmas awnless or with awn much shorter than the body; exposed nodes of the culm green, sometimes tinged with purple 3

3. Auricles glabrous; lowest 2 panicle nodes each with 2 unequal branches, the shorter with 1 – 2(3) spikelets .... **9. F. pratensis**
+ Auricles usually fringed with minute hairs (often few, wearing off with age); lowest 2 panicle nodes bearing 2 subequal branches, each with (3)4 – many spikelets .... **10. F. arundinacea**

4. Blades flat, >4mm wide; lemma 3-nerved, awnless (Subgen. *Drymanthele*) .... **11. F. altissima**
+ Blades folded, <4mm wide; if flat and >4mm wide then lemmas 5-nerved and usually awned (Subgen *Festuca*) 5

5. Ovary obovoid, free from the palea, with pubescent apex; most of the lemma width translucent; blades all folded and with pungent apex; ligules 0.5 – 1mm (Sect. *Eskia*) .... **12. F. gautieri**
+ Ovary ellipsoid to oblong, adherent to the palea, usually glabrous, if with pubescent apex then blades of culm-leaves flat; most of the lemma width green, not translucent; blades without pungent apex; ligules not more than 0.5mm 6

6. Young leaves with sheath margins fused almost to the top; some or all tillers extravaginal (Sect. *Aulaxyper*) 7
+ Young leaves with sheath margins not fused near the apex but overlapping; all tillers intravaginal (Sect. *Festuca*) 8

7. Ovary and caryopsis with pubescent apex; blades of culm leaves and tillers markedly different, the former flat, 2 – 4mm wide and with 5 – 9 nerves, the latter folded, not more than 0.6mm from midrib to edge and with 3(5) nerves .... **13. F. heterophylla**
+ Ovary and caryopsis glabrous; blades of culms and tillers similar, all with 5 – 9(11) nerves .... **14. F. rubra**

8. Leaf-blades junciform, the upper surface with 4 or more grooves defining at least three ribs; lemmas with conspicuous awn often over 1.5mm; spikelets not proliferous ... 9
+ Leaf-blades slender, rarely junciform but then the upper surface seldom with more than 2 grooves defining a single rib; lemma with awn generally less than 1.5mm, sometimes absent, or spikelets proliferous 10

9.   Pedicels 0.6 – 1mm; sheaths mostly quite glabrous; blades usually very glaucous
     .... **15. F. longifolia**
+   Pedicels 1.3 – 3(3.5)mm; sheaths usually pubescent; blades scarcely glaucous
     .... **16. F. brevipila**

10. Spikelets all or mostly proliferating (some sexual florets usually present at the base
     of the spikelet) .... **17. F. vivipara**
+   Spikelets not proliferating 11

11. Spikelets mostly less than 7.5mm; blades usually less than 0.55mm across;
     widespread 12
+   Spikelets mostly greater than 7.5mm; blades usually more than 0.55mm across;
     Channel Islands only 13

12. Blades filiform, usually less than 0.4mm across; spikelets mostly less than 5.5mm;
     lemmas usually awnless or mucronate .... **18. F. filiformis**
+   Blades broader, usually more than 0.4mm across; spikelets mostly more than 5.5mm;
     lemmas usually awned .... **19. F. ovina**

13. Panicles well exserted from the sheath at anthesis; blades usually not glaucous;
     culms erect; usually on dunes .... **20. F. armoricana**
+   Panicles not completely or only just exserted from the sheath at anthesis; blades
     often slightly glaucous; culms erect to procumbent; usually on cliffs .. **21. F. huonii**

6. Lolium L.

Annual or perennial (sometimes biennial); leaf-blades often auriculate, those of the
tillers either folded (in perennials) or convolute (in annuals) when young. Inflorescence a
stiff spicate raceme; spikelets alternate in opposite rows with one edge sunk in a hollow
in the continuous rhachis. Spikelets several- to many-flowered, the uppermost floret(s)
rudimentary; lower glume absent except in the terminal spikelet; upper glume abaxial,
shorter than the lemmas to longer than them, coriaceous; lemma rounded on the back,
membranous to coriaceous, with or without a subterminal awn; palea as long as or nearly
as long as the lemma. Hilum linear.

Species 8; temperate Eurasia but widely introduced elsewhere for fodder.

For ease of description the length of the spikelet given for *Lolium* does not include the
glume; it is therefore possible for the glume to be longer than the spikelet.

The role of the missing lower glume is fulfilled by the hollowed internode of the
rhachis, except in the terminal spikelet which consequently has both glumes. The spicate
inflorescence is unusual in Poeae and may give rise to confusion with species of *Elymus*,
but these have their spikelets broadside to the axis and both glumes are present in all of
them.

Lolium is essentially an annual derivitive of *Festuca* sect. *Schedonorus*, with a narrower geographical amplitude in southern Europe, Southwest Asia and North Africa. The habit, and inflorescence and spikelet structure form a very distinctive suite of characters fully justifying distinction at generic level. However, *L. perenne* occupies an intermediate position, bridging the gap between the genera by combining the inflorescence and spikelet structure of *Lolium* with the perennial habit and wider geographical range of *Festuca*. Furthermore, it freely hybridizes with members of *Festuca* sect. *Schedonorus* and with other members of *Lolium*, but the habit and behaviour of this one intermediate species are scarcely sufficient to justify the realignment of existing generic boundaries. Some authorities have advocated the partitioning of *Festuca* into *Festuca* and *Schedonorus* with *Lolium* being subsumed into the latter, but this introduces an anomalous annual element into a genus otherwise exclusively perennial.

Because of hybridization within *Lolium*, boundaries between the species can sometimes be hard to locate and as a result there will always be specimens whose identity is in some doubt.

Key to species

1. Fruit turgid at maturity, not more than 3 times as long as wide; lemmas becoming hard at maturity ....**25. L. temulentum**
+ Fruit not turgid at maturity, more than 3 times as long as wide; lemmas not hardening at maturity 2

2. Plant perennial; leaf-blade folded when young .... **22. L. perenne**
+ Plant annual; leaf-blade convolute when young 3

3. Spikelet usually more than 11-flowered; lemma usually awned; axis of raceme scabrid on the back as well as along the edges .... **23. L. multiflorum**
+ Spikelet seldom more than 11-flowered; lemma usually awnless; axis of raceme smooth or faintly scaberulous throughout .... **24. L. rigidum**

7. Vulpia C.C.Gmel.
Nardurus Bluff, Nees & Schauer

Annual (very rarely perennial; not in our area). Inflorescence a sparsely branched ± secund panicle or a raceme. Spikelets several-flowered, the uppermost florets sterile, disarticulating below each floret and sometimes also below the pedicel, this clavate or slender; glumes very unequal, the lower sometimes minute, the upper 1- to 3-nerved, acute to awned; lemmas thinly coriaceous, rounded on the back (rarely keeled), faintly (3)5-nerved, narrow, tapering to a long straight awn or sometimes only a short awn; palea about as long as the lemma-body; floret-callus usually obtuse and glabrous, rarely pungent and pubescent; stamens 1 – 3, often small and cleistogamous; ovary sometimes hairy. Caryopsis linear; hilum linear.

Species 22; temperate and subtropical regions of the northern hemisphere; introduced into the southern hemisphere but perhaps some S American species endemic.

A vary variable little genus that has absorbed several peripheral genera such as *Nardurus* and *Ctenopsis*. The species are mostly cleistogamous annuals and tend to occupy areas with a Mediterranean-type climate. Some of them manage to hybridize with species of *Festuca*, and the hybrids are always perennial. There are one or two species, intermediate between *Vulpia* and *Festuca*, that are either perennial or chasmogamous (or both), but they are not a serious problem for generic circumscription.

Relative glume length can vary considerably within the panicle and care must be taken to avoid measuring glumes from spikelets that are terminal on the raceme or branches as they tend to be atypical. The lemma passes imperceptibly into its awn making measurement of both extremely difficult. In this account the length of the body of the lemma is measured to the tip of the palea.

Key to species

1. Lemmas with bluntly pointed basal callus; ovary and caryopsis with minute apical hairy appendage; lemmas 7.5 – 10.5mm excluding the awn; upper glume 12 – 26mm including the awn .... **26. V. fasciculata**
+   Lemmas with rounded basal callus; ovary and caryopsis glabrous; lemmas 3.3 – 7(7.5)mm excluding the awn; upper glume 1.3 – 8.4mm including the awn, if present 2

2. Anthers 3, well exserted at anthesis .... **30. V. unilateralis**
+   Anthers 1(-3), 0.4 – 0.8(1.8)mm, usually not exserted at anthesis; lemmas 4 – 7.5mm; inflorescence a panicle (except in starved plants) 3

3. Spikelets with 1(2) bisexual and 3 – 6 distal sterile (but scarcely smaller) florets; lemma of fertile florets 3(5)-nerved .... **27. V. ciliata**
+   Spikelets with 2 – 5(6) bisexual florets and 1(2) distal much reduced sterile florets; lemma of fertile florets 5-nerved 4

4. Lower glume 3.2 – 5.3mm, 0.45 – 0.7(0.75) × the length of the upper; lemmas usually >1.3mm wide when flattened; inflorescence normally well exserted from the uppermost leaf-sheath at maturity .... **28. V. bromoides**
+   Lower glume 0.7 – 2.7mm, 0.2 – 0.45 × the length of the upper; lemmas usually <1.3mm wide when flattened; inflorescence normally not fully exserted from the uppermost leaf-sheath at maturity .... **29. V. myuros**

8. Cynosurus L.

Annual or perennial without rhizomes. Inflorescence a spike-like or capitate panicle, ± one-sided, bearing spikelets in pairs, the outer of each pair sterile and covering a fertile spikelet. Sterile spikelet reduced to a pectinate cluster of sterile lemmas, persistent on the panicle. Fertile spikelet (1)2- to 5-flowered, disarticulating above the glumes and between the florets; glumes subequal, narrow, sometimes exceeding the lemmas, 1-nerved; lemmas coriaceous, rounded on the back, 5-nerved, scaberulous above, acute, narrowly obtuse or minutely 2-toothed at the tip and muticous, mucronate or awned. Hilum oblong to linear.

Species 8; Europe, N Africa and SW Asia.

A rather odd genus in the tribe on account of its dimorphic spikelets, but the fertile spikelets have all the characteristics of Poeae. The genus itself presents two quite distinct facies, both represented in our flora, one with short-awned linear inflorescence, the other with long-awned ovoid or capitate inflorescence.

Key to species

1. Perennial; inflorescence narrowly oblong; fertile lemma with awn up to 1mm
.... **31. C. cristatus**
+ Annual; inflorescence ovoid; fertile lemma with awn up to 17mm ... **32. C. echinatus**

9. Puccinellia Parl.
Atropis Trin.
Pseudosclerochloa Tzvelev

Perennial, sometimes annual; leaf-sheath with free margins. Inflorescence an open or contracted panicle. Spikelets 2- to several-flowered; lower glume 1- to 3-nerved; upper glume 3- to 5-nerved; lemma membranous in the middle, scarious or hyaline at the tip, rounded on the back, weakly 5-nerved, smooth, obtuse or sometimes acute or erose at the tip, the callus and rhachilla glabrous but the base of the lemma sometimes pubescent. Hilum round to oval.

Species c. 80; temperate regions throughout the world, but mostly in Asia.

Puccinellia is allied to *Poa* but the lemmas are rounded, not keeled, on the back. It also resembles *Festuca* (but this has pointed lemmas and elongated hilum) and *Glyceria* (but this has a 1-nerved upper glume and connate sheath margins). The majority of species occur on saline soils on the coast or saline or alkaline soils inland; several grow in alpine grassland in the Himalaya. In our area they were once exclusively coastal, or found on saline soils inland, but several species are now beginning to spread inland along salted roads with other halophytes.

Because of its strongly nerved keeled lemmas and stiff 1-sided panicle *P. rupestris* is considered by some authors (e.g. Tzvelev 2004) to occupy a position intermediate between *Puccinellia* and *Sclerochloa* (southern Europe and SW Asia). A new genus has been described for it – *Pseudosclerochloa* Tzvelev – but for now it is retained in *Puccinellia*.

Key to species

1. Anthers large, greater than 1.5mm; lemmas greater than 3mm ...... **33. P. maritima**
+   Anthers small, not exceeding 1mm 2

2. Lemmas greater than 3mm; panicle ovoid with short stiff branches and pedicels; plants annual or biennial .... **34. P. rupestris**
+   Lemmas less than 3mm, if more then panicle loose with at least some branches bare of spikelets below; plants perennial 3

3. Panicle with most branches bearing spikelets to the base, the longer ones often bare of spikelets below but the naked portion concealed amongst the shorter branches; branches erect or spreading, rarely reflexed; lemmas narrowly obtuse to subacute, with obvious nerves, the central reaching the tip of the lemma and sometimes slightly excurrent .... **35. P. fasciculata**
+   Panicle with most branches bare of spikelets below, usually reflexed at maturity (except in Scotland north of the Firth of Forth); lemmas broadly obtuse, inconspicuously nerved, the central fading before reaching the tip .... **36. P. distans**

10. Briza L.

Annual or perennial. Panicle open to loosely contracted. Spikelets several- to many-flowered, oblong or ovate to rotund, laterally compressed or globose, disarticulating above the glumes and between the florets; glumes cordate to narrowly ovate; lemmas orbicular to oblate, folded or flattened, chartaceous to coriaceous with broad membranous margins in the upper half or all along, clasping the floret above and sometimes elaborated into basal auricles or lateral wings, gibbous on the back and keeled though sometimes indistinctly so, 5- to 11-nerved, obtuse, cuspidate or bilobed at the tip, with or without a mucro; palea sometimes much shorter than the lemma, lanceolate or orbicular; stamens 1 – 3. Hilum round to elliptic, rarely linear; endosperm sometimes soft.

Species 20; temperate Eurasia and S America.

The genus is remarkable for the shape of its lemma whose margins are appressed to the flanks of the lemma above.

Key to species

1. Perennial .... **37. B. media**
   + Annual 2

2. Spikelets 3 – 5.5mm, numerous .... **38. B. minor**
   + Spikelets 13 – 20mm, up to 7 per panicle .... **39. B. maxima**

11. Poa L.
Parodiochloa C.E.Hubb.

Annual or perennial, rarely dioecious (not in our area); basal leaf-sheaths occasionally thickened into a pseudobulb. Panicle open or contracted. Spikelets 2- to several-flowered, sometimes proliferous; lower glume 1- to 3-nerved, upper glume nearly always 3-nerved; lemmas herbaceous or membranous, often with hyaline margins, keeled throughout, the keel glabrous or ciliate, 5- to 7-nerved, obtuse to acute at the tip, awnless or very rarely awned; floret-callus often with a web of fine woolly hairs, the rhachilla glabrous; palea-keels scaberulous to stiffly ciliolate, rarely woolly-hairy and almost smooth in some annual species; stamens 3, rarely 1; ovary glabrous. Hilum round to oval.

Species c.500; cool temperate regions throughout the world, extending through the tropics on mountain tops.

Poa is a very uniform genus for which there is no satisfactory infrageneric treatment. It has facetiously been described as a genus of 500 identical species but this is uncomfortably close to being true. The matter is not helped by a dearth of useful discriminatory characters and the widespread occurrence of apomixis and introgression. The species in the British Isles are not, on the whole, too difficult but there are two apomictic complexes which will give some trouble.

Key to species

1. Plant annual, or if short-lived perennial then with stolons but not rhizomes; palea-keels woolly-hairy or rarely smooth and glabrous 2
   + Plant perennial; palea-keels scabrid or pectinate-ciliate below and scabrid above .. 3

2. Lower panicle-branches patent or deflexed after anthesis; spikelets with crowded florets; anthers 0.6 – 0.8(1)mm, at least twice as long as wide .... **40. P. annua**
   + Lower panicle-branches erecto-patent after anthesis; spikelets with rather distant florets; anthers 0.2 – 0.5mm, scarcely longer than wide .... **41. P. infirma**

3. Lemma awned; spikelet never proliferous .... **52. P. flabellata**
   + Lemma awnless; spikelet rarely proliferous 4

4.	Stems strongly compressed below, stout	**51. P. chaixii**
+	Stems not compressed, or if so then slender	5

5.	Base of stem bulbous	**42. P. bulbosa**
+	Base of stem not bulbous	6

6. Plant tufted without rhizomes, or if rhizomes present then spikelets proliferous ... 7
+ Plant rhizomatous; spikelets never proliferous 12

7.	Spikelets proliferous	**43. P. alpina**
+	Spikelets not proliferous	8

8.	Panicle-branches smooth	**44. P. flexuosa**
+	Panicle-branches scabrid	9

9.	Ligule of uppermost leaf 5 – 10mm, sharply pointed	**45. P. trivialis**
+	Ligule of uppermost leaf not more than 4.5mm, blunt	10

10.	Ligule 2.5 – 4.5mm; panicle large (10 – 30cm), subverticillate	**48. P. palustris**
+	Ligule seldom more than 2mm; panicle smaller (3.5 – 20cm), not subverticillate.... 11

11. Upper node of stem above the lower third, the uppermost leaf-blade emerging in the upper half of the stem .... **46. P. nemoralis**
+ Upper node of stem in the lower third, the uppermost leaf-blade emerging in the lower half of the stem .... **47. P. glauca**

12. Stem strongly compressed, especially above, the nodes exposed and often purple-tinged; lemma glabrous or sparsely hairy .... **49. P. compressa**
+ Stem terete, without purple-tinged nodes; lemma usually hairy on the nerves .... **50. P. pratensis**

12. Dactylis L.

Tufted perennial, the vegetative shoots strongly laterally compressed. Panicle contracted, lobed, 1-sided, the spikelets crowded in compact fascicles at the end of the main branches the lowermost of which may be long and patent. Spikelets 2- to 5-flowered, strongly laterally compressed, breaking up above the glumes and between the florets; glumes keeled; lemmas thinly coriaceous, keeled, 5-nerved, mostly spinously ciliate on the keel, entire or bidentate at the tip and mucronate to shortly awned. Hilum round; endosperm soft.

Species 1 or numerous; temperate Eurasia but widely introduced elsewhere.

A difficult genus that exemplifies the classic polyploid-pillar complex. It mostly comprises a single extremely variable tetraploid complex, supported by perhaps a dozen or more enclaves of diploids, particularly around the Mediterranean region. These diploids are variously recognized as varieties, subspecies or species but they are not well circumscribed (except in cryptic characters) and there is little agreement about how many there should be or what their distinguishing characters would be. It is likely, since they intergrade to an uncomfortable degree, that an infra-specific rank would be most suitable.

Key to species

Plant robust; lemmas pectinate-ciliate on the keel, usually mucronate or awned at the tip .... **53. D. glomerata**
Plant slender; lemmas smooth on the keel and usually awnless .... **54. D. polygama**

13. Catabrosa P.Beauv.

Perennial. Inflorescence an open panicle with whorled or clustered branches. Spikelets (1)2(3)-flowered, disarticulating above the glumes and between the florets; glumes unequal, both much shorter than the lowest lemma, obtuse to truncate at the tip; lemmas thinly membranous, becoming hyaline at the tip, keeled on the back, prominently 3-nerved with raised nerves, broadly obtuse to truncate and erose at the tip; floret callus glabrous. Hilum linear.

Species 2; North temperate regions and Chile.

A very distinctive member of the tribe with whorled panicle branches and 3-nerved lemma. Apart from the basic chromosome number of 10 it seems to have nothing in common with *Glyceria*. The latter has tubular leaf-sheaths whereas those of *Catabrosa* have overlapping margins. Some authors describe the lemmas as rounded on the back, but the prominence of the mid-nerve makes this rather hard to judge; because all three nerves are so prominent the lemma can even appear to be 3-keeled.

The only species .... **55. C. aquatica**

14. Catapodium Link
Desmazeria auct. non Dumort.

Annual. Panicle 1-sided with stiff short branches and usually branching in only 2 dimensions, or reduced to a raceme. Spikelets several- to many-flowered on short, stout pedicels; glumes subequal, the upper a little longer than the lower, coriaceous, 3- to 5-nerved; lemmas narrowly ovate in profile, coriaceous, rounded on the back at least below, glabrous, 5-nerved but the intermediate nerves sometimes inconspicuous, subacute at the tip. Hilum round.

Species 2. Europe and N Africa to Iran.

The genus is only marginally distinct from *Desmazeria* Dumort., with which it was once amalgamated, but its glabrous lemma rounded on the back is sufficient to distinguish them.

Key to species

Upper glume 2 – 3(3.4)mm; lemma 2.4 – 3.6mm; panicle racemose above, sparingly branched, if at all, below, the axis thick, flattened on the back, angular in the front .... **56. C. marinum**
Upper glume 1.4 – 2(2.3)mm; lemma 2 – 3mm; panicle mostly branched throughout, but often becoming racemose above, the axis slender, 3-angled .... **57. C. rigidum**

15. Sesleria Scop.

Perennial; leaf-sheaths with fused margins. Inflorescence a capitate or spiciform panicle, its base subtended by usually 2 scarious bracts. Spikelets 2- to 5-flowered, disarticulating between the florets; glumes shorter than or slightly exceeding the lowermost lemma; lemmas membranous, rounded on the back, 2- to 5-toothed at the tip, the teeth often produced into short awns; palea muticous or 2-awned; stigmas pubescent, terminally exserted. Hilum oval.

Species 27; Europe, especially in the Balkans.

An oddment in Poeae on account of the subtending bracts, and formerly placed in its own tribe Seslerieae. The fused sheath margins are also slightly odd in the tribe but can be found in one or two other genera.

The only species .... **58. S. caerulea**

16. Parapholis C.E.Hubb.

Annual. Inflorescence with fragile axis. Spikelets 1-flowered; glumes 2, collateral; lemma hyaline, 3-nerved with very short lateral nerves, awnless, orientated with its side towards the rhachis. Endosperm liquid.

Species 6; Mediterranean region and SW Asia, northwards along the Altantic coast of Europe to the Baltic.

The glumes are keeled and sharply inflexed on their outer edge, the infolded margin being extremely narrow. Sometimes there is an equally narrow wing along the keel, mimicking the membranous opposite margin of the glume. The axis of the inflorescence disarticulates below the spikelet and each spikelet falls with next axis-internode above.

Key to species

Culms and inflorescence usually stout and strongly curved; anthers 0.5 – 0.8(1.1)mm
.... **59. P. incurva**
Culms and inflorescence usually slender and straight; anthers (1.7)2.2 – 3.1(3.5)mm
....**60. P. strigosa**

17. **Helictotrichon** Schult.
Avenula (Dumort.) Dumort.

Perennial. Panicle usually narrow and erect, sometimes lax, rarely simple and racemose. Spikelets with 2 – several fertile florets and 1 – 2 reduced florets, disarticulating above the glumes and between the florets, the rhachilla pilose; glumes unequal, the upper usually shorter than the spikelet and often shorter than the adjacent lemma, hyaline to membranous, 1- to 5-nerved, with scaberulous keel; lemmas firmly membranous to coriaceous, rounded on the back or weakly keeled, glabrous, 2-toothed at the tip, dorsally awned from above the middle, the awn usually geniculate, rarely straight; palea enclosed by the lemma. Ovary hairy; hilum linear; endosperm sometimes liquid.

Species c.100; mainly in temperate Eurasia, but extending via tropical mountains to temperate regions throughout the world.

The genus has been subjected to partition on the basis of certain anatomical characters (see *Flora Europaea*). *Helictotrichon* has a ring of sclerenchyma surrounding the endodermis in the root, the leaves are distinctly ribbed above, the basal without distinct bulliform cells above or with several rows of distinct bulliform cells between the ribs. *Avenula* (Dumort.) Dumort., on the other hand, has no ring of sclerenchyma in the roots, the leaves are without ribs above, and the basal have 2 distinct lines of bulliform cells along the midnerve above. Such characters, besides being totally inaccessible to most people, especially in the field, are of highly dubious taxonomic value at generic level, and certainly do not divide the genus into two readily recognizable elements. Supporting morphological characters, such as number of nerves in the glumes and form of the column of the awn, seem equally valueless at generic level. The British species, transferred to *Avenula* in *Flora Europaea*, are therefore retained in *Helictotrichon* in this handbook, a move that now seems more popular than the alternative.

Key to species

Column of awn tightly twisted, the margins straight and parallel in silhouette; panicle full and conspicuously branched; spikelets 2- to 3-flowered; hairs at summit of rhachilla joint 3.5 – 5(7)mm; leaves soft and hairy; sheaths pilose with spreading or deflexed hairs .... **62. H. pubescens**
Column of awn loosely twisted, appearing like a string of beads in silhouette; panicle narrow and ± racemose; spikelets 3- to 5(8)-flowered; hairs at summit of rhachilla joint 1 – 2mm; leaves rather stiff, glabrous; sheaths glabrous .... **63. H. pratense**

18. Arrhenatherum P.Beauv.

Perennial; basal internodes sometimes swollen into globose 'corms'. Panicle moderately dense. Spikelets 2-flowered, with or without an additional rudiment, the lower floret male and stoutly awned, the upper bisexual and weakly awned or awnless (rarely a few spikelets with both florets bisexual and alike), disarticulating above the glumes but not between the florets; glumes unequal, the lower shorter than the upper, the upper as long as the spikelet, 1- to 3-nerved, with scaberulous keel; lemmas firmly membranous to subcoriaceous, rounded on the back, bidenticulate, at least the lower geniculately awned from the back. Ovary hairy; hilum linear.

Species 6; Europe and the Mediterranean region to SW Asia.

A genus segregated from *Helictotrichon* on account of the dimorphic florets. However, the odd occurrence of spikelets with isomorphic florets indicates that the relationship is extremely close and the distinction just barely tenable.

The only species .... **64. A. elatius**

19. Avena L.

Annual. Panicle loose and nodding. Spikelets large (10 – 40mm), 2- to several-flowered, disarticulating below each floret or only above the glumes (not at all in cultivated species); glumes herbaceous to membranous, usually equal and as long as the spikelet, 3- to 11-nerved, rounded on the back, smooth; lemmas coriaceous, rarely membranous, rounded on the back, bidentate to biaristulate, the latter rarely with 2 additional awnlets, geniculately awned from the back (the awn often reduced or absent in cultivated species); floret callus, when floret deciduous, acute to pungent. Ovary hairy; hilum linear.

Species 25; mainly in the Mediterranean region and SW Asia, extending into northern Europe and widely introduced into other temperate regions; 2 species in Ethiopia.

A uniform genus distinguished from *Helictotrichon* by its annual habit and smooth glumes. It not only contains some of the world's most important cereals (Oats), but also one of the world's worst weeds (*A. fatua*; see *Alopecurus* for another).

Key to species

1. Spikelets non-shattering, the mature florets retained in the panicle 2
+   Spikelets variously breaking up at maturity 3

2. Lemma teeth acute, without bristles .... **69. A. sativa**
+   Lemma teeth each bearing a bristle 4 – 8mm long .... **66. A. strigosa**

3. Lemma teeth each bearing a bristle up to 10mm long .... **65. A. barbata**
+ Lemma teeth acute 4

4. Rhachilla disarticulating, the florets falling separately at maturity ....**67. A. fatua**
+ Rhachilla not disarticulating, the florets falling together at maturity as a unit
.... **68. A. sterilis**

20. Gaudinia P.Beauv.

Annual, biennial or perhaps short-lived perennial. Inflorescence a fragile bilateral raceme fracturing at the base of each internode, the spikelets sessile in opposite rows and broadside to the axis. Spikelets several-flowered, falling entire; glumes equal or unequal, shorter than the adjacent lemmas, herbaceous, with 3 – 7(11) prominently ribbed nerves; lemmas thinly coriaceous, weakly keeled, acute, with a dorsal geniculate awn. Ovary hairy; hilum round; endosperm liquid.

Species 4; mostly in the Mediterranean region.

The inflorescence is unusual in Aveneae, but the geniculate awn and compound starch grains exclude the genus from the only other likely tribe, Triticeae.

The only species .... **70. G. fragilis**

21. Trisetum Pers.

Perennial. Panicle moderately dense to spike-like, rarely open. Spikelets 2- to several-flowered, the rhachilla hairy; glumes mostly unequal and shorter than the spikelet; lemmas membranous to thinly coriaceous, strongly laterally compressed and distinctly keeled, bidentate or sometimes bisetulate, dorsally awned from below the middle, the awn geniculate or merely reflexed; palea gaping, silvery. Ovary glabrous; endosperm liquid.

Species c.70; throughout temperate regions of both hemispheres, but absent from Africa.

Closely resembling *Helictotrichon* but with glabrous ovary, keeled lemmas of thinner texture, and free palea. It belongs with *Koeleria* in a dense cluster of inter-related genera, none of which is all that clearly disjunct though each does have a recognizable facies; there will be no problems with distinguishing them in the British Isles since our species of *Koeleria* are awnless.

The only species .... **71. T. flavescens**

22. Koeleria Pers.

Perennial; basal sheaths sometimes swollen into 'bulbs'. Panicle spike-like, the branches hispidulous. Spikelets 2- to several-flowered, the rhachilla glabrous to puberulous; glumes unequal or subequal, usually shorter than the spikelet; lemmas membranous, strongly compressed and distinctly keeled, obtuse to acuminate, awnless or with a subapical mucro up to 1 mm; palea gaping. Ovary glabrous; endosperm sometimes liquid.

Species c.35; temperate regions throughout the world.

A genus still in need of taxonomic revision and apparently derived from *Trisetum*. It is an enigmatic genus that persists in keying out to tribe Poeae rather than Aveneae because of its lack of an obvious awn and its short glumes. It is most likely to be mistaken for *Poa*, but this genus never has a spike-like panicle, hispidulous panicle branches and glossy spikelets in combination.

Key to species

Stem bases thickened and clothed in a mass of reticulate fibres derived from the nerves of the sheaths .... **72. K. vallesiana**
Stem bases usually not thickened; basal sheaths remaining intact, or if disintegrating then doing so into parallel filaments .... **73. K. macrantha**

23. Deschampsia P.Beauv.
Lerchenfeldia Schur

Perennial. Panicle usually open. Spikelets 2(3)-flowered plus rhachilla extension, disarticulating below the florets, the lower floret sessile; rhachilla well developed and hairy; glumes subequal and as long as the spikelet; lemmas hyaline to polished-cartilaginous, rounded on the back, 4-toothed to denticulately truncate, with an inconspicuous or weakly geniculate awn from the base (rarely above the middle); callus pubescent to conspicuously bearded. Endosperm solid.

Species c.40; temperate regions throughout the world.

A uniform genus distinguished from *Helictotrichon* by its small delicate spikelets and slender awns, and from *Trisetum* by the rounded back of the lemma, the form of the lemma tip and the position of the awn. European species were at one time included in the related genus *Aira*, but this is now exclusively annual; some North American annuals, however, are retained in *Deschampsia*.

Key to species

1.   Leaves flat, 2 – 4(5)mm wide, or if loosely inrolled then not setaceous and more than 1mm in diameter, harshly scabrid above and on the margins .... **75. D. cespitosa**
+   Leaves tightly inrolled, setaceous, 0.2 – 0.6mm in diameter, smooth 2

2.   Florets distant by about 1/4 the length of the lower lemma or less; rhachilla extension c.0.5mm; ligule blunt, up to 3.5mm .... **76. D. flexuosa**

+   Florets distant by 1/3 – 1/2 the length of the lower lemma; rhachilla extension 1 – 1.7(2.6)mm; ligule narrow, sharply pointed, mostly 3.5 – 8mm .... **77. D. setacea**

24. Holcus L.

Annual or perennial. Panicle moderately dense. Spikelets 2-flowered, often with a short rhachilla extension, falling entire, the lower floret bisexual and usually raised upon a curved rhachilla internode, the upper male; glumes subequal, enclosing the florets, papery; lemmas polished-cartilaginous, rounded on the back, indistinctly nerved, obtuse to bidentate, the lower awnless, the upper with a geniculate, hooked or straight dorsal awn from the upper third. Endosperm sometimes soft.

Species 6; Europe, N Africa and SW Asia.

Holcus, in regions beyond the British Isles, intergrades with *Deschampsia* and the relationship between the genera is not unlike that between *Helictotrichon* and *Arrhenatherum*.

Key to species

Plant tufted, without rhizomes; stems and leaves softly hairy; nodes pubescent, not conspicuously bearded; awn of upper lemma hooked, projecting from the sides of the glumes .... **78. H. lanatus**
Plant mat-forming, with rhizomes; stems and leaves glabrous except for the conspicuously bearded nodes; awn of upper lemma geniculate, projecting from the tips of the glumes .... **79. H. mollis**

25. Corynephorus P.Beauv.

Annual or perennial. Panicle open or contracted. Spikelets 2-flowered plus rhachilla extension; glumes equal, as long as the spikelet; lemmas thinly membranous, rounded on the back, minutely bidenticulate, with a basal awn, this divided into a twisted column and a clavate limb with a ring of hairs at the junction. Endosperm solid.

Species 5; Europe and the Mediterranean region eastwards to Iran.

A small genus adequately circumscribed by its extraordinary awn (see under the species for more details).

The only species .... **80. C. canescens**

26. Aira L.

Annual. Panicle open or contracted. Spikelets 2-flowered, without rhachilla extension, the florets arising at about the same level; glumes equal, enclosing the florets; lemmas lanceolate, thinly coriaceous, scaberulous, rounded on the back, acuminately bilobed, with a geniculate awn from below the middle. Endosperm solid.

Species 8; Europe and the Mediterranean region eastwards to Iran.

Aira is now restricted to annual species; perennial species once included in the genus are now accommodated in *Deschampsia* which also differs in the blunt or denticulate rather than acuminately bilobed lemmas.

Key to species

1. Panicle contracted; spikelets 3 – 3.5mm; lemmas 2.7 – 3.1mm; sheaths quite smooth or faintly scaberulous .... **81. A. praecox**
+. Panicle loose and open; spikelets 1.5 – 3.1mm; lemmas (1)2 – 2.4(2.6)mm; sheaths faintly scaberulous to scabrid 2

2. Pedicels not more than twice as long as the spikelets; spikelets 2.4 – 3.1mm; lemmas (1.8)2 – 2.4(2.6)mm .... **82. A. caryophyllea**
+   Pedicels 2 – 5 times as long as the spikelets; spikelets 1.5 – 2.5mm; lemmas 1 – 2mm .... **83. A. elegantissima**

27. Anthoxanthum L.
Hierochloe R.Br.

Annual or perennial. Panicle open or contracted and spike-like. Spikelets 3-flowered, lanceolate, the 2 lower florets male or represented by empty lemmas, the uppermost bisexual, disarticulating above the glumes but not between the florets; glumes equal or unequal, at least the upper exceeding and enclosing the florets, weakly to strongly keeled; sterile lemmas as long as or longer than the fertile, membranous to coriaceous, acute to bilobed at the tip, the lower awnless or with a short straight awn from above the middle, the upper geniculately awned from below the middle; fertile lemma cartilaginous, the margins inrolled and covering the palea, emarginate; palea 1-nerved, without keels; lodicules 0 – 2; stamens 2 (3 in the male florets).

Species c.48; temperate and arctic Eurasia, temperate Africa, tropical African mountains and in C America.

The distinction between *Anthoxanthum* and *Hierochloe*, while presenting no problems in Europe, has always been suspect in Asia and the conclusion has now been reached that the distinction is artificial and can no longer be justified (see Schouten & Veldkamp, 1985).

The species are all sweetly scented with coumarin, and the common species, *A. odoratum*, is responsible for the smell of new-mown hay in freshly cut grassland.

Key to species

1. Annual .... **84. A. aristatum**
+   Perennial 2

2. Glumes very unequal; panicle contracted; lower florets barren ..... **85. A. odoratum**
+   Glumes subequal; panicle loose and open; lower florets male .... **86. A. nitens**

28. Phalaris L.
Digraphis Trin.

Annual or perennial. Panicle spike-like to capitate or merely contracted. Spikelets (2)3-flowered, ovate, the (1)2 lower florets reduced to rudimentary lemmas, the uppermost bisexual, disarticulating above the glumes but not between the florets (rarely the spikelets gathered into deciduous clusters of 1 fertile and up to 6 ± deformed sterile); glumes equal, exceeding and enclosing the florets, keeled, the keel usually winged; sterile lemmas usually subulate and up to 1/2 the length of the fertile, rarely chaffy or little fleshy scales; fertile lemma polished-coriaceous, the margins not overlapping, acute, awnless; palea coriaceous, 2-nerved, without keels.

Species 22; north temperate zone, but mainly in the Mediterranean region with a secondary centre in California; also in S America.

A very distinctive genus, with papery glumes and a glossy fertile lemma, that represents the ultimate stage in a line of reduction of the several-flowered Aveneae that was begun by *Anthoxanthum*. The sterile lemmas are sometimes barely discernible and one of them may be absent altogether. When reduced to small fleshy scales they look exactly like the callus of the fertile lemma and it is easy to mistake this for one of them.

Key to species

1. Perennial 2
+   Annual 3

2. Base of plant not bulbous; keel of glume wingless .... **87. P. arundinacea**
+   Base of plant bulbous; keel of glume winged .... **88. P. aquatica**

3. Spikelets in deciduous clusters of 6 or 7, only one of which is fertile
    .... **91. P. paradoxa**
+   Spikelets not in deciduous clusters, all fertile and breaking up above the persistent glumes 4

4.   Wing of glume toothed or erose; sterile lemmas linear-oblong with indurated base, less than half as long as the fertile .... **89. P. minor**
+   Wing of glume entire; sterile lemmas chaffy, at least half as long as the fertile .... **90. P. canariensis**

29. Agrostis L.
Vilfa Adans.

Annual or perennial. Panicle diffuse to contracted or rarely spike-like after flowering (always diffuse at flowering). Spikelets 1-flowered and usually without a rhachilla-extension, disarticulating above the glumes; glumes equal or unequal, as long as to much longer than the floret, membranous and glossy, 1-nerved (rarely 3-nerved), often scabrid on the keel, mostly acute or acuminate; lemma hyaline, thinner than the glumes, glabrous or hairy, rounded on the back, mostly 5-nerved but sometimes 3-nerved, truncate to 4-toothed at the tip and often with the nerves excurrent and the outer sometimes forming distinct lateral awns, with a geniculate dorsal awn or this much reduced or commonly absent; callus glabrous or minutely pubescent (the hairs in two lateral tufts), rarely (not in our species) with a beard up to half the length of the lemma; palea usually shorter than the lemma (always in our species), often vestigial, largely covered by the inrolled margins of the lemma. Endosperm sometimes liquid.

Species c.220; temperate regions throughout the world, and on tropical mountains.

The genus is a very difficult one to name to species, partly because of the practical problem of handling such small spikelets, especially in the field, partly because of high genetic plasticity in many species, and partly because some of the traditional characters are not as reliable as many texts would suggest.

It is essential to know the degree of development of the palea: whether it is vestigial and scarcely visible even under a microscope, or whether it is well developed and clearly visible if not with the naked eye then at least with a modest handlens. The best times to see the palea are at flowering, when the floret is wide open and lemma and palea make an obvious if asymmetrical V-shape, and at fruiting when it shines against the dull background of the ripe caryopsis (but beware: if the caryopsis should be shed the palea often goes with it).

The most variable aspect of almost any species of *Agrostis* is the awn. It can vary from geniculate with twisted column, arising from or near the base of the lemma and well exserted from the tips of the glumes, through straight and not twisted, arising from the median part of the lemma and scarcely exserted, to a minute subapical bristle. More often than not it is quite absent and even when present it is frequently only found in a minority of spikelets within a panicle. A complete range of awn-types, as listed above, can even be found in a single panicle, and any one plant may have any segment of the full range of variation. Occasionally awned and awnless panicles can be found on the same plant. Any key that relies on length, position or even presence of the awn will probably fail to work in most instances. Commonly, the awn is associated with a 5-nerved, rather than a 3-nerved, lemma, the former normally being found towards the tip of the branchlet, the latter lower down. The 3-nerved lemmas are very rarely awned and 5-nerved lemmas are frequently awnless. When the awn emerges from the back of the lemma below the tip, the body of the lemma is 4-nerved above this point.

Another very misleading character is the ligule. It is important to remember that ligules on the flowering culms may be considerably different from those on the tillers (they are usually longer). It is equally important to remember that on the culm the ligule of the uppermost leaf is often at variance with those lower down and the second ligule from the top is the one that should be considered. In the absence of tillers (a frequent occurrence in herbarium material) the lowest ligules on the culm should be observed since these would have been present when the culm was a tiller in the previous year.

The form of the panicle can also be deceptive. In all species it opens fully at flowering to allow the free passage of pollen both in and out, but what happens after flowering is more important. In some species it remains fully open, in some it partially closes, and in others it fully closes. Again, some texts are misleading and imply a regularity of behaviour that is not always observed.

Key to species

1. Palea vestigial, often scarcely visible and never more than 1/3 the length of the lemma; ligules bluntly or sharply pointed, always distinctly longer than wide (sect. *Agrostis*) 2
+ Palea well-developed, usually (2/5)1/2 – 3/4 the length of the lemma, ligules rounded or truncate (sect. *Vilfa*) 6

2. Anthers 0.2 – 0.6mm 3
+ Anthers 0.8 – 1.8mm 4

3. Spikelets (2)2.3 – 2.9mm; lemma 1.4 – 1.8mm; leaves flat or loosely inrolled, 1 – 3mm wide .... **92. A. scabra**
+ Spikelets less than 2mm; lemma 1 – 1.2mm; leaves setaceous, less than 1mm across .... **93. A. hyemalis**

4. Leaves bristle-like and mostly basal, seldom more than 0.3mm across; panicle always with ± erect branches; rhizomes and stolons absent .... **94. A. curtisii**
+ Leaves flat or inrolled but never bristle-like, mostly cauline, more than 0.6mm across even when inrolled (usually more than 1mm); panicle often with spreading branches after flowering; rhizomes or stolons usually present 5

5. Stolons 0; rhizomes usually present; leaf-blades firm; panicle usually contracted after flowering .... **95. A. vinealis**
+ Rhizomes 0; stolons usually present; leaf-blades soft; panicle usually remaining open after flowering .... **96. A. canina**

6.   Anthers 0.15 – 0.7mm; spikelet with or without a distinct rhachilla-extension 7
+   Anthers 1 – 1.7mm; spikelet without rhachilla-extension 8

7.   Anthers 0.15 – 0.45mm; spikelet with distinct rhachilla-extension ... **97. A. avenacea**
+   Anthers 0.4 – 0.7mm; spikelet without rhachilla-extension .... **98. A. lachnantha**

8.   Terminal lemma of each branchlet shortly hairy on the back, at least towards the margins .... **99. A. castellana**
+   Terminal lemma of each branchlet quite glabrous on the back 9

9.   Primary panicle-branches often bearing branchlets ± from the extreme base but sometimes bare in the lower 1/4 – 1/3; panicle tightly closed after flowering; plants usually extensively stoloniferous .... **100. A. stolonifera**
+   Primary panicle-branches bare of branchlets in at least the lower half; panicle open or only partially closed after flowering; plants usually without stolons but always with extensively creeping rhizomes 10

10. Ligule of tiller-leaves distinctly shorter than wide .... **101. A. capillaris**
+   Ligule of tiller-leaves as long as or longer than wide .... **102. A. gigantea**

30. Calamagrostis Adans.
Deyeuxia P.Beauv.

Perennial. Panicle contracted to spike-like or capitate, rarely open. Spikelets 1-flowered, with or without a rhachilla-extension, disarticulating above the glumes; glumes equal or unequal, usually as long as the spikelet (and often greatly exceeding the floret), firmly membranous, 1(3)-nerved, scabrid on the keel, acute to acuminate; lemma firmly membranous to coriaceous, sometimes thinly membranous but then the callus-hairs more than half its length (longer than it in our species), rounded or keeled on the back (3)5-nerved, bilobed to irregularly denticulate, sometimes with the nerves excurrent, with an inconspicuous straight (in our species) or geniculate dorsal or subapical awn, sometimes only mucronate or quite awnless; callus bearded with hairs from 1/5 as long as to much longer than the floret. Endosperm sometimes soft.

Species c.270; temperate regions worldwide and on tropical mountains.

Usually, but not always, distinguished from *Agrostis* by the presence of a beard on the floret-callus (though the distinction works well enough in our area). The genus was formerly divided into two (*Calamagrostis* and *Deyeuxia*), but the distinction often fails. The situation is currently under review and it is possible that *Deyeuxia* may have to be revived in order to sustain the distinction between *Calamagrostis* and *Agrostis*. The taxonomy of the genus is complicated by extensive interspecific hybridization and apomixis, even in our area (see Nygren, 1962).

1. Hairs at the base of the lemma not reaching the lemma-tip; lemma minutely scaberulous, with an awn arising from below the middle (sect. *Deyeuxia*) 2
+ Hairs at the base of the lemma exceeding the lemma-tip; lemma smooth, with an awn arising from above the middle (sect. *Calamagrostis*) 3

2. Spikelets 4.5 – 6mm; lower glume acuminate; ligule 1 – 2mm (if more than 3.5mm see C. ×*gracilescens*) .... **103. C. scotica**
+ Spikelets 3 – 4(4.5)mm; lower glume acute; ligule mostly 1.5 – 3.5mm
.... **104. C. stricta**

3. Anthers indehiscent and without pollen; ligule (7)9 – 10(14)mm ... **107. C. purpurea**
+ Anthers dehiscent and with good pollen (if all or some indehiscent then ligule less than 6 mm) 4

4. Upper surface of leaf sparsely pubescent to shortly pilose; ligule 1 – 4.5(6)mm
.... **105. C. canescens**
+ Upper surface of leaf scabrid, not at all hairy; ligule 5 – 12mm ..... **106. C. epigeios**

31. Ammophila Host

Rhizomatous perennial; leaves rigid, inrolled and pungent. Panicle spike-like. Spikelets 1-flowered with rhachilla extension; glumes equal, a little longer than and enclosing the floret, chartaceous, the upper 3-nerved, acute; lemma thinly coriaceous, sharply keeled, bidenticulate and with a subapical mucro; floret callus bearded.

Species 2; Europe and N Africa, and the east coast of N America.

A highly specialized genus adapted to a particular environment (drifting sand). It is not immediately obvious, because of its adaptations, that it is very closely related to *Calamagrostis* and, indeed, hybridizes with it.

The only species .... **108. A. arenaria**

32. Gastridium P.Beauv.

Annual. Panicle spike-like. Spikelets 1-flowered, with or without a minute rhachilla extension; glumes unequal, membranous above, indurated and gibbously swollen below to accommodate the much shorter floret, 1-nerved, acuminate; lemma cartilaginous, rounded on the back, truncate and denticulate, with a geniculate dorsal awn or awnless.

Species 2; Europe and N Africa eastwards to Iran.

One of a number of small genera peripheral to *Agrostis*, distinguished by the structure of the glumes.

The only species .... **109. G. ventricosum**

33. Lagurus L.

Annual. Panicle spike-like, ovoid. Spikelets 1-flowered, with rhachilla extension; glumes equal, longer than the floret, narrowly lanceolate, membranous, 1-nerved, white-villous, acuminate to a slender awn; lemma membranous, rounded on the back, 2-awned at the tip and with a geniculate dorsal awn from the upper third. Endosperm soft.

Species 1; Mediterranean region.

Another satellite of *Agrostis*, characterized by the fluffy white inflorescence, narrow glumes and 3-awned lemma.

The only species .... **110. L. ovatus**

34. Apera Adans.

Annual. Panicle open or contracted. Spikelets 1-flowered with rhachilla extension; glumes unequal, the upper as long as or longer than the floret and 3-nerved, hyaline to membranous and shining, acute to shortly awned; lemma firmly membranous, 5-nerved, rounded on the back, with a long flexuous subapical awn. Endosperm liquid.

Species 3; Europe to Afghanistan.

A derivative of *Agrostis*, but with a 3-nerved upper glume. Its most obvious feature, however, is the extremely long awn from just below the tip of the lemma.

Key to species

Panicle open and very diffuse, the whorled capillary branches naked below; anthers 1.2
– 1.7mm .... **111. A. spica-venti**
Panicle narrow, contracted, the branches spiculate from the base; anthers
(0.2)0.3–0.4mm .... **112. A. interrupta**

35. Mibora Adans.

Dwarf annual. Inflorescence a unilateral raceme. Spikelets 1-flowered without rhachilla extension; glumes longer than the floret, membranous, 1-nerved, obtuse; lemma hyaline, rounded on the back, hairy, obtuse; lodicules 0.

Species 2; western Europe and N Africa.

A rare and very distinctive genus circumscribed almost entirely by its annual habit and racemose inflorescence.

The only species .... **113. M. minima**

36. Polypogon Desf.

Annual or perennial. Panicle contracted to spike-like. Spikelets 1-flowered without rhachilla extension, falling entire together with the pedicel or apparently part of it; glumes equal, longer than the floret, chartaceous, ± scabrid, 1-nerved, entire to bilobed, often with a slender awn; lemma hyaline, 5-nerved, rounded on the back, the nerves sometimes excurrent from the ± truncate tip, awnless or with a subapical awnlet or a geniculate dorsal awn.

Species 18; warm temperate regions and on tropical mountains.

Extremely close to *Agrostis* with which it hybridizes. At one time it was circumscribed by its awned glumes, but it is now clear that a more natural division is formed by its deciduous spikelets with stipitate base (this latter appears to be the pedicel or part of it, but may be a downwardly extended callus; thus where the whole 'pedicel' falls with the spikelet, the spikelet may in actual fact be sessile, but the situation has not yet been satisfactorily resolved). As a result, *Agrostis semiverticillata* has moved to *Polypogon* where the epithet *viridis* takes priority (but it should also have taken priority in *Agrostis*).

Key to species

Glumes awnless .... **114. P. viridis**
Glumes awned, the awn up to 3 times the length of the body ...... **115. P. monspeliensis**

37. Alopecurus L.

Annual or perennial, rarely the lowest internode swollen and bulb-like. Panicle contracted and spike-like, cylindrical to ovoid, the branches free from the main axis. Spikelets 1-flowered without rhachilla-extension, strongly laterally compressed, falling entire;

glumes equal, about as long as and enclosing the floret, membranous to thinly coriaceous, 3-nerved, often connate along their opposite margins below, ciliate on the keel, obtuse to acute; lemma membranous, 4-nerved, the margins connate below, truncate to acute; awn dorsal, straight or geniculate, rarely absent; palea small or (in our species) absent; lodicules 0. Endosperm sometimes liquid.

Species c. 36; north temperate regions and S America.

A genus with a very distinctive facies, containing a useful pasture grass (*A. pratensis*) and one of the world's worst weeds (*A. myosuroides*). The flowers are strongly protogynous and the stigmas are pubescent rather than feathery.

Key to species

1.   Annual; glumes winged along the keel, connate for at least one third of their length; anthers more than 2.5mm .... **116. A. myosuroides**
+   Perennial; glumes not winged on the keel, connate only at the extreme base; if plants annual or biennial then anthers not exceeding 1.2mm 2

2.   Stems conspicuously bulbous at the base; glumes acute .... **117. A. bulbosus**
+   Stems not bulbous at the base, or if slightly swollen then glumes blunt 3

3.   Anthers orange or golden yellow, up to 1.2mm .... **118. A. aequalis**
+   Anthers brown or purplish, at least 1.5mm 4

4.   Glumes very blunt; hairs on the keel less than 0.5mm .... **119. A. geniculatus**
+   Glumes subacute to acute; hairs on the keel more than 0.5mm 5

5.   Lemma awnless, or if awned then the awn exceeding the tip of the lemma by 1 – 2mm; panicle oblong to ovoid (rare alpine) ....**120. A. ovatus**
+   Lemma with a conspicuous awn exceeding the tip of the lemma by 3 – 5mm; panicle cylindrical to broadly cylindrical (common) .... **121. A. pratensis**

38. Phleum L.

Annual or perennial, sometimes the lowermost 1-3 internodes swollen and 'bulb'-like. Panicle spike-like, cylindrical, the branches sometimes adnate to the axis. Spikelets 1-flowered without rhachilla-extension (in our species), strongly laterally compressed, breaking up above the persistent glumes; glumes equal, longer than and enclosing the floret, membranous, 3-nerved, not connate, strongly keeled and often ciliate on the keel, truncate to acute, the midnerve extended into a stout mucro or short stiff awn; lemma membranous 3- to 7-nerved, keeled, truncate to subacute, awnless (in our species) or mucronate; palea well developed; lodicules 2.

Species 15; north temperate regions and S America.

A tightly circumscribed genus distinguished from *Alopecurus* by its awnless lemmas, florets always with a palea, and spikelets disarticulating above the persistent glumes. The margins of the glumes and lemma are never connate.

Key to species

1. Annual .... **122. P. arenarium**
+ Perennial ....:............... 2

2. Panicle branches free from the main axis and panicle loosely cylindrical (sometimes the branches very short but then the panicle ovoid to broadly cylindrical) 3
+ Panicle branches adnate to the main axis and panicle tightly cylindrical 4

3. Panicle ovoid to broadly cylindrical, 1 – 3(5)cm × 8.5 – 12mm; spikelets 4.5 – 6mm including an awn 2 – 3mm; rare alpine .... **123. P. alpinum**
+ Panicle cylindrical, 2.5 – 6.5(9)cm × 5-7.5mm; spikelets 2.2 – 3.4mm including an awn 0.2 – 0.5(0.7)mm; common in the lowlands .... **124. P. phleoides**

4. Plant mostly >70cm; leaf >4mm wide; anthers >1.7mm; panicle >7mm wide; spikelet, including awn, >4mm; awn usually >1.2mm .... **125. P. pratense**
+ Plant mostly <70cm; leaf <5mm wide; anthers <1.7mm; panicle <7mm wide; spikelet, including awn, <4mm; awn usually <1mm .... **126. P. bertolonii**

39. Glyceria R.Br.

Perennial, often with rhizomes or stolons; leaves with cross-nerves in the larger species. Panicle copious, or narrow and almost raceme-like. Spikelets several- to many-flowered, disarticulating between the florets, the uppermost floret much reduced; glumes very small to almost as long as the adjacent lemma and of similar texture, 1(3)-nerved; lemmas herbaceous, membranous or thinly coriaceous except for the thin membranous tip, 5- to 11-nerved, acute, obtuse or 3- to 5-toothed; stamens 2 – 3.

Species c. 40; temperate regions throughout the world.

Glyceria could be confused with *Puccinellia* because of a superficial similarity in spikelet morphology, but can be distinguished by the cylindrical leaf-sheaths; in *Puccinellia* the sheath is open with overlapping margins.

Key to species

1. Palea not winged on the keels; spikelets 6 – 10mm, 4- to 9-flowered; culms to 250cm, erect and self-supporting .... **127. G. maxima**
+ Palea narrowly winged on the keels; spikelets 12 – 35mm, 7- to 15-flowered; culms up to 100(150)cm, decumbent to ascending, or if erect then not self-supporting 2

2.   Anthers indehiscent; spikelets not disarticulating at maturity .. **130. G. ×pedicellata**
+   Anthers dehiscent; spikelets disarticulating at maturity 3

3.   Lemmas 6 – 7.5mm; anthers 1.5 – 3mm .... **128. G. fluitans**
+   Lemmas 4.4 – 5.3mm; anthers 0.8 – 1.4mm 4

4.   Lemmas distinctively and sharply 3(5)-toothed at the tip, exceeded by the 2 sharply pointed apical teeth of the palea .... **131. G. declinata**
+   Lemmas inconspicuously and irregularly lobed to very bluntly toothed at the tip, not exceeded by the apical teeth of the palea .... **129. G. notata**

40. Melica L.

Perennial. Panicle loose and open or contracted, narrow and raceme-like. Spikelets 1- to several-flowered, with 1 – 3 fertile florets below and terminating in a clavate clump of 2 – 3 rudiments, disarticulating readily below the lowest floret and reluctantly between the florets; glumes shorter than the lowest lemma or as long as the spikelet, papery with hyaline tips, 3- to 5-nerved; lemmas mostly coriaceous, 5- to 9(13)-nerved; floret-callus glabrous.

Species c.80; temperate regions throughout the world except Australia.

A very distinctive genus recognized at once by the combination of tubular leaf-sheaths and clavate mass of sterile lemmas. The latter character is not consistent for the whole genus, but does occur in both of our species.

Key to species

Spikelet with 1 fertile floret (rarely 2); leaf-sheaths terminating in a distinctive bristle opposite the ligule .... **132. M. uniflora**
Spikelet with 2 or 3 fertile florets; leaf-sheaths not terminating in a bristle
.... **133. M. nutans**

41. Brachypodium P.Beauv.

Description as for tribe. Perennial or rarely annual.

Key to species

Plant tufted, only weakly rhizomatous; raceme usually nodding at the tip; lemma with an awn usually as least as long as the body .... **134. B. sylvaticum**
Plant strongly rhizomatous, scarcely tufted; raceme usually erect; lemma with an awn less than half as long as the body .... **135. B. pinnatum**

42. Bromus L.

Annual or perennial. Leaf-sheaths with margins connate for most of their length, usually hairy. Panicle open or contracted, ample or scanty. Spikelets ovate or oblong to cuneate and gaping; glumes herbaceous; lemmas herbaceous to subcoriaceous, often with membranous margins, entire or minutely 2-toothed to deeply 2-lobed at the tip, mucronate to long-awned, the awn subapical, sometimes minutely so, or arising from the base of the sinus; palea shorter than to as long as (rarely exceeding) the lemma; stamens usually 3.

Species c.150; temperate regions of both hemispheres but mainly in the north.

The genus is a relatively easy one to recognise although some species have a superficial resemblance to *Festuca* (especially *F. gigantea*); they can easily be distinguished by their (usually) hairy leaf-sheaths, subterminal awn and possession of a hairy terminal appendage on the caryopsis (visible even on the young ovary).

Bromus is morphologically extremely variable and several authors have been tempted to fragment it into a number of smaller genera. There is little to gain from this fragmentation since the characteristics the segregates share seem to be more important than those that separate them. There is no doubt that the segregates make perfectly good sections and they will be treated as such in this account.

Key to sections

1. Lemmas firmly laterally compressed and keeled .... Sect. **Ceratochloa**
+   Lemmas rounded on the back 2

2. Plants perennial .... Sect. **Pnigma**
+   Plants annual 3

3. Lower glume 1-nerved; upper glume 3-nerved; mature spikelets cuneate and gaping .... Sect. **Genea**
+   Lower glume 3- to 5-nerved; upper glume 5- to 7-nerved; mature spikelets lanceolate or ovate to oblong .... Sect. **Bromus**

Keys to species

Sect. **Ceratochloa** (DC. & P.Beauv.) Griseb. (*Ceratochloa* DC. & P.Beauv.)

1. Lemmas glabrous to scaberulous on the back 2
+   Lemmas pubescent on the back 3

2. Awns (5)7.5 – 12.5mm .... **136. B. carinatus**
+   Awns 0.5 – 4.5(5)mm .... **138. B. catharticus**

3. Lemmas 12 – 18(21)mm .... **137. B. marginatus**
+   Lemmas 8 – 10.5mm .... **139. B. stamineus**

Sect. **Pnigma** Dumort. (*Bromopsis* (Dumort.) Fourr.; *Zerna* auct. non Panz.)

1. Inflorescence very lax, the branches pendent or all swept to one side; leaf-sheaths with distinct pointed auricles at the apex .... **140. B. ramosus**
+   Inflorescence dense to fairly lax, the branches erect to erecto-patent; leaf-sheaths without or with short rounded auricles at the apex 2

2. Plant densely tufted, with short rhizomes; lemmas with awns (2)3 – 8mm; leaves of tillers usually folded or inrolled along the long axis .... **141. B. erectus**
+   Plant not densely tufted, with long rhizomes; lemmas awnless or less often with awns up to 3(6)mm; leaves of tillers usually flat .... **142. B. inermis**

Sect. **Genea** Dumort. (*Anisantha* K.Koch)

1. Lemmas 24 – 32mm .... **143. B. diandrus**
+   Lemmas 9 – 23mm 2

2. Panicle lax, with branches spreading laterally or pendent 3
+   Panicle lax or dense, with stiffly erect branches 4

3. Lemmas 16.5 – 23mm; inflorescence simple or the larger branches slightly branched and with up to 3(5) spikelets .... **144. B. sterilis**
+   Lemmas 10.5 – 13mm; inflorescence compound, the larger branches with 3 – 8 spikelets (except in depauperate plants) .... **145. B. tectorum**

4. Inflorescence lax, the axis thinly hairy to glabrous; upper part of rhachilla not twisted, the spikelets all in the same alignment .... **146. B. madritensis**
+   Inflorescence dense, the axis densely pubescent; upper part of rhachilla twisted, the uppermost florets out of alignment with the lower and the awns projecting in several different planes .... **147. B. rubens**

Sect. **Bromus** (*Serrafalcus* Parl.)

1. Caryopsis thick, with inrolled margins; lemma with margins wrapped around the caryopsis when mature, the lemma margins thus not overlapping the back of the next lemma above, but rhachilla ± exposed between the florets; rhachilla tardily disarticulating .... **148. B. secalinus**
+   Caryopsis thin, flat or with weakly inrolled margins; lemma margins not wrapped around the caryopsis, overlapping the back of the next lemma above and concealing the rhachilla; rhachilla readily disarticulating 2

2. Palea bifid nearly to the base; panicle with mostly subsessile spikelets densely clustered in groups .... **149. B. interruptus**
+   Palea entire to shortly bifid; panicle various but spikelets not obviously subsessile in groups 3

3. Lemmas subcoriaceous at maturity, the nerves embedded in the thick tissue and quite inconspicuous; panicle lax or dense, in the latter case usually drooping to one side 4

+ Lemmas papery at maturity, the nerves not embedded in the thin tissue, but prominent and conspicuous; panicle usually dense, sometimes lax 6

4. Anthers 3 – 4.5mm, not less than half as long as the lemma .... **150. B. arvensis**

+ Anthers 0.5 – 3mm, less than half as long as the lemma 5

5. Awn flattened below, usually curved or reflexed at maturity .... **151. B. japonicus**

+ Awn terete, usually straight .... **152. B. racemosus**

6. Spikelets relatively few in number, 20 – 50mm, with lemmas 12 – 20mm; awn arising c.4mm below the lemma-tip, conspicuously flattened below and usually strongly recurved or contorted at maturity .... **155. B. lanceolatus**

+ Spikelets relatively abundant, seldom exceeding 20mm, with lemmas not exceeding 11mm; awn arising less than 2mm below the lemma-tip or from the base of a deep apical sinus, usually terete, sometimes flattened below, straight or lightly curved .. 7

7. Caryopsis exceeding the palea, sometimes exceeding the lemma; lemma deeply bifid with the awn arising from the base of the sinus .... **153. B. lepidus**

+ Caryopsis shorter than the palea; lemma shallowly notched at the tip, the awn conspicuously subterminal .... **154. B. hordeaceus**

43. Elymus L.
Elytrigia Desv.
Thinopyrum Á.Löve

Perennial; leaf-blades soft or firm, green or glaucous, flat or inrolled. Inflorescence a true raceme, the spikelets sessile, borne singly (in our area; sometimes borne in pairs elsewhere) on a tough or fragile rhachis. Spikelets 3- to 9-flowered, clearly laterally compressed, disarticulating above the glumes and between the florets, sometimes tardily so; glumes persistent or deciduous, opposite, lanceolate to narrowly oblong, firmly membranous to coriaceous, distinctly 3- to 9-nerved, the nerves parallel or convergent and the body often keeled above, obtuse to shortly awned at the tip; lemmas coriaceous, 5-nerved, rounded on the back or keeled only above, obtuse, acute or minutely 2-toothed at the tip, muticous or awned.

Species c.150; temperate regions of both hemispheres, but most abundant in Asia.

The genus is contiguous to *Leymus* and separation of the two is rather contentious. The difference is clear enough in our area – single versus paired spikelets – but elsewhere this character breaks down and nervation of the glumes becomes paramount. *E. farctus* is unusual in having a fragile rhachis.

Cytotaxonomists have looked long and hard at *Elymus* and have reached various conclusions on how the genus should be treated; most agree that it should be subdivided, but not on its morphology; they chose to do so according to genomic constitution of individual species, and at least a dozen segregate genera have been proposed (of which Löve (1984) accepts 7 with a total of 17 sections). The view taken by Stace (1997) is that our species should be accommodated in two genera, *Elymus* and *Elytrigia*. The former is tufted and the latter rhizomatous. However, this brings two discordant elements together in *Elytrigia*, one with fragile rhachis (*E. juncea*) and the other with tough rhachis (*E. repens* and *E. atherica*). The genomes of these two elements are different and Löve has gone a step further in removing *E. juncea* (i.e. *Elymus farctus*) to yet another segregate genus, *Thinopyrum*. Three genera for four obviously closely related species seems excessive and inclusion of all four in a single genus, defined by overall morphology, is much the more practical solution, especially since members of both *Elytrigia* and *Thinopyrum* readily hybridize with one another, albeit with sterile progeny. A case could be made for segregating *E. caninus* because of its lack of hybridization with other species, but this is a very weak generic character, scarcely more convincing than that of presence or absence of rhizomes. Infrageneric status of the segregates of *Elymus* might be more reasonable, but since there is a subspecies of *E. farctus* in Asia that completely lacks rhizomes the value of any infrageneric break-up is extremely doubtful.

Great care must be taken when looking for cilia on the sheath margins. They are found on the outer, visible margin; the inner margin, which is covered by the overlapping outer, is glabrous. The one species that has these cilia sometimes grows in a wind-swept sandy environment where they may easily be worn away, especially by the end of the season. It is worth taking extra trouble to search diligently before concluding that they are absent. They are most likely to be found on the lower sheaths where wind action is ameliorated, or by peeling back the outer sheaths and looking at those within where they have been protected from damage. Cilia are usually present in *E. athericus* (and its hybrids) but are absent from the very similar-looking *E. repens* subsp. *arenosus* which also grows in a sandy environment. Difficulties in distinguishing these two taxa can be considerable.

Hybrids within *Elymus* are surprisingly abundant, but always sterile. However, not all sterile plants are necessarily hybrids since sexual reproduction can sometimes fail. Care must be taken with presumed hybrids to ensure that they show some degree of intermediacy between the parents. If a specimen seems convincingly to be one species or another, but is sterile, the chances are that it may not, in fact, be a hybrid. *E. repens* also hybridizes with *Hordeum secalinum* and the hybrid is sometimes fertile.

Key to species

1. Plant male-sterile; anthers undeveloped, containing imperfect pollen; not setting
    fruit .... *probable hybrid* (see separate key below and note above)
+   Plant fertile 2

2. Rhachis fragile, disarticulating at the base of each internode, this falling with the spikelet attached; anthers exceeding 4mm and lemma mucronate; nerves on upper surface of leaf pubescent .... **156. E. farctus**
+   Rhachis tough, the florets falling separately or in groups, if rhachis fragile then anthers not more than 3mm and lemmas usually long-awned; nerves on upper surface of leaf glabrous, scabrid or thinly pilose 3

3. Plant tufted, without rhizomes; florets falling separately above the persistent glumes but rhachis sometimes fragile; anthers not exceeding 3mm............ **159. E. caninus**
+   Plant with long rhizomes; florets often falling in groups, reluctantly falling separately, the glumes often falling as well; anthers exceeding 4mm 4

4. Outer margin of leaf-sheath ciliate or ciliolate, often sparsely so (but see note above); leaves usually glaucous, the blades inrolled and with thick, closely spaced, flat-topped, scabrid nerves on the upper surface .... **157. E. athericus**
+   Outer margin of leaf-sheath quite glabrous; leaves usually green, the blades flat with thin, round-topped, smooth or loosely pilose nerves on the upper surface, sometimes glaucous and inrolled with thick, closely-spaced nerves .... **158. E. repens**

Key to hybrids *

The following is only a rough guide; in general, a hybrid is intermediate between its parents in most characters, particularly readiness of rhachis to disarticulate, shape of nerves on upper surface of leaf, pubescence or scabridity of nerves and abundance of cilia on outer margin of leaf-sheath.

1. Glumes ± collateral, the back of the first lemma visible between them; rhachis tardily fragile .... ×**Elyhordeum langei** (*E. repens* × *Hordeum secalinum*)
+   Glumes not collateral, the side of the first lemma visible between them 2

2. Outer margin of leaf-sheath thinly ciliate or ciliolate; rhachis tough or tardily fragile 3
+   Outer margin of leaf-sheath quite glabrous; rhachis tardily fragile 4

3. Rhachis tough .... **E. ×oliveri** (*athericus* × *repens*)
+   Rhachis tardily fragile .... **E. ×obtusiusculus** (*athericus* × *farctus*)

4. Glumes and lemmas conspicuously awned
    .... ×**Elyhordeum langei** (*E. repens* × *Hordeum secalinum*)
+   Glumes and lemmas at most mucronate or apiculate ... **E. ×laxus** (*repens* × *farctus*)

* For a discussion of the problems of nomenclature of these hybrids, see Stace (2001).

44. Leymus Hochst.

Perennial; leaf-blades stiff, flat or inrolled, harsh, usually glaucous, ± pungent at the tip. Inflorescence a false raceme, the spikelets borne in pairs (rarely up to 6) on a tough rhachis. Spikelets 3- to 7-flowered, disarticulating above the persistent glumes and between the florets; glumes opposite or collateral, mostly over half the length of the lowermost lemma, typically 1-nerved, linear and awn-like, but sometimes narrowly lanceolate (as in our species) and then coriaceous and 1- to 3(5)-nerved, the nerves not raised, acute to shortly awned at the tip; lemmas not keeled or only so at the tip, acute to shortly awned.

Species c. 40; north temperate zone and 1 species in Argentina.

At the time that all of our species of *Elymus* were included in the broader concept of *Agropyron*, Old World species of *Leymus* were included in *Elymus*; the genus *Leymus*, in the modern sense, has been accepted in the New World for many years. The separation of *Leymus* from *Elymus* is contentious and is based on the nature of the glumes rather than the previously employed, but unsatisfactory, number of spikelets at the rhachis node. In *Elymus* the glumes have prominent rib-like nerves, while in *Leymus* the nerves are indistinct or the glume itself is 1-nerved and awn-like. However, the number of spikelets at a node works well for the species that occur in our area.

The only species .... **160. L. arenarius**

45. Hordelymus (Jess.) Jess. ex Harz

Perennial with short rhizomes. False raceme oblong to linear, bearing a triad of spikelets, rarely only a pair, at each node of the tough rhachis, these all sessile and fertile or the central sometimes male. Spikelets 1(2)-flowered plus conspicuous rhachilla-extension, disarticulating above the persistent glumes, dorsally compressed; glumes collateral, 1- to 3-nerved, awn-like, connate for a short distance above the base; lemma rounded on the back, 5-nerved, acuminate to a long slender awn.

Species 1; Europe and N Africa eastwards to the Caucasus.

An obvious relative of *Hordeum* but with tough inflorescence axis and all 3 spikelets at a node fertile (or occasionally the central male; in *Hordeum* it is the lateral spikelets that are reduced).

The only species .... **161. H. europaeus**

46. Hordeum L.
Critesion Raf.

Annual or perennial; leaves soft. Inflorescence a false raceme, the spikelets borne in triads on a fragile axis, the central spikelet fertile and the laterals male or barren, all pedicelled or the central sessile (the axis tough and all spikelets sessile in cultivated cereals). Spikelets 1-flowered plus bristle-like rhachilla-extension, dorsally compressed, not breaking up; glumes collateral, usually awn-like, occasionally narrowly lanceolate, weakly 3-nerved and flat, free to the base; lemma rounded on the back, obscurely nerved, acuminate to a conspicuous awn; lateral spikelets usually smaller than the central, sometimes reduced to a cluster of 3 awns.

Species c. 40; temperate regions throughout the world. *H. vulgare* is an important temperate cereal.

A familiar genus in which the fragile rhachis readily disarticulates at the base of each joint to produce a dispersal unit comprising the 3 spikelets in the form of a cuneate, aerodynamic 'dart' beloved of children. Some authorities contend that the bristle-like glumes are a split lower glume with the true upper glume suppressed.

Key to species

1. Inflorescence axis tough, eventually shedding the spikelets; cultivated cereal
    .... **166. H. vulgare**
 + Inflorescence axis fragile, the joints falling with the spikelets; wild grass 2

2. Glumes of lateral spikelets over 3cm, awn-like throughout, the floret reduced to an awn-like rudiment; awn of central floret over 5cm .... **165. H. jubatum**
 + Glumes of lateral spikelets less than 3cm, usually broadened at the base, the floret usually well developed; awn of central floret less than 5cm 3

3. Plant perennial .... **162. H. secalinum**
 + Plant annual 4

4. Glumes of central spikelet conspicuously ciliate on both margins; leaves with well developed falcate auricles .... **163. H. murinum**
 + Glumes of central spikelet not ciliate on the margins but merely scabrid; leaves with small rounded auricles .... **164. H. marinum**

47. Secale L.

Annual, biennial or perennial. Raceme oblong to linear, with single spikelets on a fragile rhachis (tough in cultivated forms). Spikelets 2-flowered plus a short rhachilla extension (sometimes this bearing a rudimentary floret); glumes linear, membranous, 1-nerved, sharply keeled throughout, acuminate or awned at the tip; lemmas sharply keeled, pectinate-spinulose on the keel, 3-nerved, tapering to an awn.

Species 4; eastern Europe to C Asia and in Spain and South Africa; 1 species widely cultivated.

A complex genus of unsettled taxonomy that is complicated by a host of ill-defined weedy intermediates between the wild *S. montanum* Guss. and cultivated *S. cereale* L. Many of these intermediates (at least 11) have been accorded rank of species, but the trend nowadays is to regard them as no more than subspecies.

The only species .... **167. S. cereale**

48. Triticum L.
Gigachilon Seidl

Annual. Raceme linear or oblong, bearing single spikelets on a fragile rhachis (tardily fragile or tough in cultivated species; those in our area all the latter). Spikelets several-flowered (rarely only one of the florets fertile); glumes oblong to ovate, shorter (rarely longer) than the adjacent lemmas, coriaceous, 5- to 11-nerved, asymmetrically 1- to 2-keeled (but sometimes becoming rounded below as the grain expands), obtuse, truncate or toothed at the tip, the lateral nerves diverging into the teeth, these mucronate or awned; lemmas rounded on the back or keeled near the tip, the tip similar to that of the glumes.

Species 10 – 20; native in the E Mediterranean region to Iran, but widely introduced as cereals throughout the world.

More than half the species in the genus are cultivated and wheat is the principal cereal of temperate regions. It was domesticated in SW Asia some time prior to 7000 BC. There are three ploidy levels with $2n = 14, 28$ and 42, and within each level selection has proceeded from wild species (except the hexaploids) through hulled cultivated species (in which the grain is difficult to separate from the lemma and palea) and thence to free-threshing naked species. Strictly speaking, only the diploids truly belong to *Triticum*, the others being intergeneric hybrids with *Aegilops* L. The tetraploids have assimilated a genome from *A. speltoides* Tausch and the hexaploids a further genome from *A. tauschii* Coss. Löve (1984), in his summary of Triticeae, disperses the species among three genera: the presumed wild diploid progenitor is placed in *Crithodium* (genome A); the tetraploids in *Gigachilon* (genome AB); and the hexaploids in *Triticum* (genome ABD).

90

1. Grain with a prominent hump or ridge along the back .... **170. T. durum**
+ Grain without a hump or ridge along the back 2

2. Glumes keeled only towards the tip, rounded on the back below .. **168. T. aestivum**
+ Glumes firmly and broadly keeled from base to tip .... **169. T. turgidum**

49. Danthonia DC.
Sieglingia Bernh.

Tussock-forming perennial; leaves flat or inrolled, mostly basal; ligule a line of hairs; cleistogenes usually present in the sheaths of the stem-leaves. Panicle open or contracted, of few spikelets and sometimes reduced to a raceme. Spikelets several-flowered, breaking up above the persistent glumes and between the florets; glumes as long as the spikelet, papery, 3- to 9-nerved; floret-callus short to narrowly oblong, blunt; lemmas firmly membranous, 7- to 9-nerved, hairy on the margins or all over, 2-toothed at the tip and mucronate (in the British Isles; otherwise bilobed and with a geniculate central awn).

Species 20; Europe and the Americas.

The genus is recognized by the combination of hairy ligule, basal tuft of leaves, many-nerved lemma and panicle with few relatively large spikelets. The lack of awn in the only representative in the British Isles is unusual but not so remarkable as to warrant generic segregation. The old generic name, *Sieglingia*, has been rejected for technical reasons and replaced by the conserved name *Danthonia*.

The only species .... **171. D. decumbens**

50. Cortaderia Stapf

Robust, densely tufted dioecious (separate male and female plants) or gynodioecious (separate female and bisexual plants) perennial, the two forms similar or not. Panicle usually large and plumose, rarely small. Spikelets 2- to 7-flowered, the rhachilla internodes usually hairy; glumes as long as the lowermost floret, 2/3 as long to as long as the spikelet, hyaline, narrow, 1(3)-nerved; floret callus linear, hairy; lemmas hyaline, 3- to 5(7)-nerved, hairy or glabrous, entire or 2-toothed at the tip, with or without a straight awn from between the teeth; palea hairy or glabrous; female plant with minute or well developed staminodes.

Species 24; mainly in S America, but 4 species in New Zealand and 1 in New Guinea.

The genus is best known for its large tussocks and handsome plumose panicles. Two species are widely cultivated in Great Britain and Ireland (Pampas-grasses) and both have become naturalized where planted or discarded.

Key to species

Leaf-blade with prominent midrib, best seen on the underside, and numerous closely spaced inconspicuous nerves, usually green below and glaucous above; sheath eventually curling up and fracturing horizontally into short segments; lemma tapering to a long tail; flowering August to November .... **172. C. selloana**
Leaf-blade with prominent midrib and several prominent nerves on either side as well as numerous closely spaced inconspicuous nerves, usually dark green on both sides; sheath remaining intact; lemma bifid with linear lobes and an awn in the sinus; flowering late June to August .... **173. C. richardii**

51. Molinia Schrank

Tufted perennial; culm internodes unequal, the lowest short, clavately swollen and persistent for several years, the intermediate reduced to a sequence of closely spaced leaf-bearing nodes, the uppermost comprising most of the culm; ligule a line of hairs; leaf-blades deciduous from the sheath. Panicle open or contracted. Spikelets 2- to 5-flowered, rarely a few spikelets 1-flowered, the rhachilla internodes usually 1/3 – 1/2 the length of the lemma; glumes shorter than the lemma, 1- to 3-nerved; floret callus short, truncate, glabrous (bearded in some species); lemmas membranous, 3(5)-nerved, glabrous; palea almost as long as the lemma; fruit with reluctantly free pericarp.

Species 2 – 4. Europe, western Russia and Turkey; China and Japan. Wet moors, heaths and fens.

The swollen basal internode of the culm serves as a food storage organ. The genus is otherwise remarkable for having deciduous leaf-blades which disarticulate from the sheaths in winter. It could be confused with *Eragrostis* but can be distinguished by the swollen culm-internode, the length of the rhachilla internodes (much shorter in *Eragrostis*) and the deciduous leaf-blades, but the two are seldom sympatric.

The only species .... **174. M. caerulea**

52. Phragmites Adans.

Tall rhizomatous perennial reed; leaves cauline with deciduous blade; ligule a very short membrane with long-ciliate margin. Panicle large, plumose. Spikelets with lowest floret male or barren; rhachilla internodes with long silky white hairs; glumes unequal, shorter than the lowest lemma, 3- to 5-nerved; floret callus linear, plumose; lemmas hyaline, 1- to 3-nerved, glabrous, long-caudate and entire at the tip; palea 2/3 the length of the lemma.

Species 3 – 4; cosmopolitan.

The genus is extremely uniform and the component species are barely distinguishable. It is remarkable in being the only genus of grass in the British Isles in which the spikelets mature on the panicle after its emergence from the uppermost leaf-sheath; in all others the spikelets mature before emergence of the panicle. The tall reed-like habit and cauline leaves with deciduous blades are unmistakable; *Phragmites* resembles no other British grass genus.

The only species .... **175. P. australis**

53. Leptochloa P.Beauv.
Diplachne P.Beauv.

Annual or perennial; ligule membranous, sometimes with a ciliate fringe. Inflorescence open, comprising several slender racemes arranged along a central axis. Spikelets laterally compressed or subterete, 2- to several-flowered; lemmas keeled or rounded on the back, glabrous or appressed-hairy on the nerves, obtuse or 2-toothed at the tip, rarely acute, sometimes mucronate, rarely with a short awn.

Species 40; throughout the tropics, and in warm temperate parts of America and Australia.

A large and very variable genus that can be relatively easily partitioned into two genera (*Leptochloa* and *Diplachne*) in the Old World, but whose component species fully intergrade in the New World. The one species found in our area belongs in *Diplachne* which is distinguished by its larger, subterete rather than compressed spikelets that are indistinctly secund in the racemes.

The only species .... **176. L. fusca**

54. Eragrostis Wolf

Annual or perennial; ligule a line of hairs, rarely a short membrane (not in our area). Inflorescence an open or contracted panicle. Spikelets 2- to many-flowered, orbicular to vermiform, variously disarticulating; glumes often deciduous, 1-nerved (rarely 3-nerved); lemmas 3-nerved but the lateral nerves sometimes very faint, keeled or rounded on the back, membranous to coriaceous, glabrous to asperulous or rarely hairy, entire, obtuse to acuminate, rarely with excurrent lateral nerves; palea keels rarely winged, often ciliate (but not in our area); anthers 2 – 3. Fruit usually a caryopsis, rarely with the pericarp free.

Species c.370; tropics and subtropics throughout the world.

A large and extremely variable genus usually recognized by the combination of paniculate inflorescence, 3-nerved lemma and hairy ligule, and most closely resembles *Poa* (5-nerved lemma, membranous ligule). The most useful characters for naming species involve the mode of disarticulation of the spikelet (see Cope, 1998 for a review). Unfortunately, many of the species introduced into Britain – especially the perennials, less so the annuals – fail to reach maturity in our climate; as a result the best characters are not always available and the species can be very difficult to identify. This account is restricted to the most common 6 (only 2 of which could be said to be naturalized) of the recorded 50 – 60 British aliens. It is not worth attempting to name any species of *Eragrostis* that is not in full flower; preferably it should be in fruit and the florets beginning to fall.

Key to species

1. Plants perennial (at least potentially) with the basal leaf-sheaths yellow and horny, closely and conspicuously ridged; anthers 0.8 – 1.1mm .... **180. E. curvula**
+   Plants annual; basal leaf-sheaths membranous, not ridged; anthers not exceeding 0.6mm 2

2. Leaf-margins with raised crateriform glands; pedicels and sometimes the midnerve of the glumes and lemmas similarly glandular 3
+   Leaf-margins without crateriform glands 4

3. Grain subrotund, 0.4 – 0.6mm in diameter .... **181. E. cilianensis**
+   Grain broadly oblong, (0.5)0.6 – 0.8mm long .... **182. E. minor**

4. Grain broadly oblong, with a ventral groove .... **179. E. mexicana**
+   Grain narrowly oblong to elliptic, without a ventral groove 5

5. Florets and grain readily deciduous at maturity; grain not turgid, 0.6 – 1mm; lemmas 1 – 1.6(1.8)mm .... **177. E. pilosa**
+   Florets persistent and retaining the mature grain; grain turgid, 1 – 1.2mm; lemmas 2 – 2.7mm .... **178. E. tef**

55. Eleusine Gaertn.

Annual or perennial; leaf-blades folded and the sheaths strongly keeled; ligule membranous and usually with a ciliate fringe. Inflorescence of digitate or subdigitate, rarely racemose, racemes, the axis usually shorter than the longest raceme. Spikelets disarticulating between the florets; glumes 1- to 3-nerved, persistent; lemmas 3-nerved, strongly keeled, sometimes the keel thickened and containing 1 – 3 closely spaced additional nerves, membranous, glabrous, obtuse or acute, sometimes mucronate. Grain with free pericarp.

Species 9; mostly in E & NE tropical Africa, but 1 widespread weed of warm climates and 1 species confined to S America.

A genus with a very distinctive facies, still undergoing active speciation in Africa and sometimes difficult to name to species. The two species regularly introduced into Britain were until recently considered by many authorities to be conspecific (although distinguished at subspecies level).

Key to species

Culms slender; ligule sparsely and minutely ciliolate; racemes 3 – 5.5mm wide; lower glume 1-nerved, 1.1 – 2.3mm; upper glume 1.8 – 2.9mm; lemmas 2.4 – 3.6(4)mm; grain obliquely striate and with very fine close lines perpendicular to the striae
.... **184. E. indica**
Culms moderately stout; ligule with a definite ciliate fringe; racemes 4 – 7mm wide; lower glume often 2- or 3-nerved, 2 – 3.2(3.9)mm; upper glume 3 – 4.7mm; lemmas 3.7 – 4.9mm; grain uniformly granular and obliquely ridged .... **185. E. africana**

56. Cynodon Rich.

Perennial, mostly rhizomatous or stoloniferous, or both, and sward-forming. Racemes digitate, with flat or semiterete rhachis, sometimes in 2 or more closely spaced whorls. Spikelets strongly laterally compressed, 1-flowered, with or without a rhachilla extension (this rarely bearing a vestigial floret); glumes narrow, herbaceous, very short to as long as the floret, divergent, acute; lemma keeled, firmly cartilaginous, entire, awnless. Caryopsis ellipsoid, laterally compressed.

Species c. 8; Old World tropics; 1 species pan-tropical and extending into warm temperate regions.

The genus is immediately recognizable by its mat-forming habit and star-shaped inflorescence. It is likely to be confused only with *Digitaria*, but this has dorsally compressed, 2-flowered spikelets, and those species found in the British Isles are all annuals.

Key to species

Plant with both rhizomes and stolons; ligule a membrane with ciliate margin, 0.2 – 0.3mm .... **186. C. dactylon**
Plant without rhizomes; ligule a hyaline membrane without ciliate margin, 0.4 – 1mm .... **187. C. incompletus**

57. **Spartina** Schreb.

Extensively rhizomatous perennials. Ligule a short membrane with long-ciliate margin. Racemes disposed along an elongated axis (rarely subdigitate), bearing appressed or pectinate spikelets on a triquetrous rhachis, this terminating in an elongate flattened bristle which often exceeds the terminal spikelet (sometimes the lower racemes reduced to a single spikelet subtended by this bristle or even to just the bristle; in the latter case it may look as though the next raceme is *subtended* by a bristle). Spikelets strongly laterally compressed, 1-flowered without rhachilla extension, falling entire; glumes unequal, the upper exceeding the floret, the lower shorter, firmly membranous, acute to shortly awned; lemma keeled, firmly membranous, acute; lodicules often absent. Grain fusiform, the pericarp reluctantly free.

Species c. 15; both coasts of the Americas and the Atlantic coasts of Europe and Africa, especially in temperate and subtropical regions; mainly intertidal mudflats but some species extend to coastal dunes and inland freshwater swamps.

The genus is easily recognized by the combination of 1-flowered spikelets in racemosely arranged racemes, and hairy ligule, and it is one of the few grass genera to inhabit intertidal mudflats. In the British Isles the genus comprises one rare native species, one rare introduced species, a sterile hybrid between the two, and a rapidly spreading spontaneous fertile amphidiploid derived from the hybrid (backcrosses and polyhaploids have also been reported although it is scarcely practicable to distinguish them in the field). The elements can be a little difficult to separate at first, but become easier with practice; care is needed to distinguish fertile (dehiscent) from barren (usually, but not always, indehiscent) anthers and a microscope is essential for distinguishing viable from inviable pollen.

Key to species

1.   Upper glume very scabrid on the keel, awned at the tip with an awn 3 – 8mm; inland
     species .... **193. S. pectinata**
  + Upper glume glabrous or ciliate on the keel, awnless; coastal species 2

2.   Anthers indehiscent, without good pollen; plant sterile .... **191. S. ×townsendii**
  + Anthers dehiscent, containing good pollen; plant fertile 3

3.   Glumes glabrous, or hairy on the keel, sometimes very sparsely hairy on the flanks
     .... **189. S. alterniflora**
  + Glumes softly pubescent on keel and flanks 4

4.   Ligule 0.3 – 0.8mm; terminal bristle of raceme 8 – 18(21)mm; anthers 3 – 5(6)mm
     .... **190. S. maritima**
  + Ligule (1)1.4 – 3.2mm; terminal bristle of raceme 18 – 50(57)mm; anthers 6.5 –
     10.5mm .... **192. S. anglica**

58. Panicum L.

Annual or perennial. Inflorescence a panicle, sometimes condensed about the primary branches. Spikelets dorsally compressed, usually symmetrical, glabrous; lower glume mostly shorter than the spikelet, sometimes as long, truncate to acute; upper glume as long as the spikelet, truncate to acute; lower lemma usually similar to the upper glume, male or barren, with or without a palea; upper floret sessile, its lemma coriaceous to bony with inrolled margins, obtuse to acute. Hilum round to oval, rarely linear.

Species c. 470; pantropical, extending to temperate regions of N America. Includes a number of minor cereals and important fodder grasses.

A very large genus with remarkably uniform spikelets but much variation in habit and leaf-form. Despite its size it is not readily partitioned into subgenera or sections. It lies at the heart of a difficult complex of interrelated neighbours. Some of these are rather minor and there is little agreement about the rank at which they should be recognized; there are always intermediates which effectively blur the lines of demarcation. *Brachiaria* is a particularly difficult genus to separate, at least in the tropics, although species of the two genera that are to be found in our area are not usually a problem.

Key to species

1. Lower glume more than 1/3 the length of the spikelet, if less then acute; leaf-sheaths with long spreading hairs 2
+ Lower glume obtuse, less than 1/3 the length of the spikelet; leaf-sheaths glabrous .. 3

2. Spikelets (4)4.5 – 5.5(6.5)mm; lower glume 1/2 – 2/3 the length of the spikelet
.... **194. P. miliaceum**
+ Spikelets 2 – 3.5mm; lower glume 2/5 – 1/2 the length of the spikelet
.... **195. P. capillare**

3. Spikelets 2 – 2.8mm, obtuse to subacute at the tip; lower floret usually male with a well developed palea more than half as long as the lemma .... **196. P. schinzii**
+ Spikelets 2.7 – 3.5mm, acute to acuminate at the tip; lower floret barren, with palea much reduced or absent .... **197. P. dichotomiflorum**

59. Echinochloa P.Beauv.

Annual or perennial; ligule often absent. Inflorescence of racemes along a central axis. Spikelets paired or in short secondary racemelets, typically densely packed in 4 rows, narrowly elliptic to subrotund, flat on one side, gibbous on the other, often hispidulous, cuspidate or awned at the tip; lower glume 1/3 the length of the spikelet, acute to acuminate; upper glume as long as the spikelet, acute to acuminate, rarely with a short awn-point; lower lemma male or barren, with or without a palea, often stiffly awned;

upper lemma crustaceous with inrolled margins, terminating in a short membranous, laterally compressed, incurved beak and the upper palea acute with its tip shortly reflexed and slightly protruberant from the lemma.

Species 30 – 40; tropical and warm temperate regions generally.

A difficult genus of numerous ill-defined, mostly self-pollinating elements for which there is no agreed treatment at species level. It can be recognized by its hispidulous, cuspidate or awned spikelets in 4 rows, but it can easily be confused with *Brachiaria*. The most reliable character in cases of doubt is the peculiar reflexed tip to the upper palea. The genus contains a number of minor tropical crops in India, China and Japan and a number of serious weeds. Perhaps the worst of these, *E. oryzoides* (Ard.) Fritsch (not in our area), is becoming a very troublesome weed of rice in southern Europe. Its resemblance to the crop plant is remarkable, making it difficult to eradicate even by hand.

Key to species

1. Racemes loose and ± distant, not forming a dense lanceolate head 2
+   Racemes crowded with plump spikelets, closely spaced to form a dense lanceolate head 3

2. Spikelets acuminate to awned, 3 – 4mm excluding the awn (itself up to 5cm), hispid; lower floret barren; racemes untidily 2- to several-rowed, the longest 2 – 10cm and usually with secondary branchlets below .... **198. E. crusgalli**
+   Spikelets acute to cuspidate, 1.5 – 3mm, pubescent; lower floret often male; racemes neatly 4-rowed, the longest seldom exceeding 3cm and simple .... **200. E. colona**

3. Spikelets yellowish-green or pallid, 2.5 – 3.5mm; lower lemma acute to subacute, sometimes minutely apiculate .... **201. E. frumentacea**
+   Spikelets dark green and slightly to deeply suffused with purple, 3 – 4mm; lower lemma acuminate .... **199. E. esculenta**

60. Brachiaria (Trin.) Griseb.

Annual or perennial. Inflorescence of racemes along a central axis, the rhachis filiform to ribbon-like. Spikelets single or paired, rarely in fascicles or on secondary racemelets, sessile or pedicelled, adaxial (the lower glume turned towards the rhachis), plump, glabrous; lower glume sometimes as long as the spikelet but mostly shorter than it; upper glume as long as the spikelet; lower lemma similar to the upper glume, male or barren, with or without a palea; upper floret sessile, its lemma coriaceous to crustaceous with inrolled margins, obtuse to acute, occasionally mucronate.

Species c. 100; mainly in the Old World tropics.

Intergrades with *Panicum*, the difference embodied in the distinction between open panicle and scattered racemes that can be very arbitrary in those species with secondary racemelets or long pedicels. There is also a body of opinion that views the distinction between most species of *Brachiaria* and *Urochloa* as untenable, retaining only a handful of species in the former. There is a case for retaining the genera intact, but if amalgamation must take place then the whole of *Brachiaria* should be subsumed into *Urochloa*.

The only species .... **202. B. platyphylla**

61. Urochloa P.Beauv.

Annual or perennial. Inflorescence of racemes scattered along a short axis, this ± triquetrous. Spikelets single or paired, abaxial (the lower glume turned away from the rhachis), plano-convex, cuspidate to acuminate, glabrous or hairy; lower glume shorter than the spikelet; upper glume as long as the spikelet; lower lemma similar to the upper glume, the floret male or barren with well developed palea; upper floret sessile, its lemma coriaceous with inrolled margins, obtusely rounded at the tip and with a long mucro enclosed within the spikelet.

Species 12; Old World tropics, mainly in Africa.

Distinguished from *Brachiaria* by the combination of abaxial spikelets and mucronate upper lemma. However, the orientation of the spikelet in both genera is obscured when the spikelets are paired, and the distinction then rests on the facies of the spikelet: plano-convex and cuspidate with mucronate upper lemma in *Urochloa*, but plump and ± obtuse with muticous upper lemma in *Brachiaria*. There are, unfortunately, several awkward intermediates and some authorities advocate wholly or partially amalgamating the two genera under *Urochloa*.

The only species .... **203. U. panicoides**

62. Paspalum L.

Annual or perennial. Inflorescence of single, paired, digitate or scattered racemes; rhachis flat, sometimes broadly winged, bearing single or paired abaxial spikelets in 2 – 4 rows. Spikelets plano-convex, orbicular to ovate; lower glume absent or rarely present as a minute scale; upper glume as long as the spikelet; lower lemma resembling the upper glume, as long as the spikelet, barren and with a minute palea; upper lemma coriaceous to crustaceous with inrolled margins, usually obtuse.

Species c. 330; throughout the tropics but mostly in the New World.

In our area the genus is best recognized by the plano-convex abaxial spikelets. In many parts of the world the most characteristic feature is the absence of a lower glume; unfortunately, in our species the glume is often present, though minute.

Key to species

Spikelets glabrous; racemes 2, conjugate (rarely up to 4 and subdigitate)
.... **204. P. distichum**
Spikelets with a ciliate fringe from the margins of the upper glume; racemes several,
scattered along a central axis .... **205. P. dilatatum**

63. Setaria P.Beauv.

Annual or perennial. Inflorescence a panicle, either spike-like or with the spikelets contracted about the ± spreading primary branches (the latter not in our area), the spikelets subtended by 1 or more scabrid, persistent bristles. Spikelets ± gibbous, glabrous; lower glume shorter than the spikelet, clasping; upper glume shorter than to as long as the spikelet; lower lemma as long as the spikelet, male or barren, the palea often well developed; upper floret sessile, its lemma crustaceous with inrolled margins, strongly convex on the back, smooth to rugose or corrugate.

Species c. 100; tropics and subtropics throughout the world.

A genus of variable facies, particularly with respect to leaf morphology, inflorescence form and upper lemma shape. The most obvious feature is the sterilization of the tips of the panicle branches and their modification into persistent bristles subtending the spikelets.

Key to species

1. Upper glume not more than 2/3 the length of the upper lemma, if longer then plant perennial; bristles usually more than 5 per spikelet cluster 2
+   Upper glume as long as the upper lemma and concealing it, rarely slightly shorter but then bristles fewer than 5 per spikelet cluster 3

2. Annual; spikelets (2.5)2.8 – 3.3mm .... **206. S. pumila**
+   Perennial; spikelets 2 – 2.5(3)mm .... **207. S. parviflora**

3. Bristles retrorsely barbed and tenaciously clinging (if antrorsely barbed then panicle untidily lobed) .... **209. S. verticillata**
+   Bristles antrorsely barbed, not clinging; panicle neatly cylindrical, usually not lobed 4

4. Spikelets disarticulating below the upper lemma leaving behind the persistent glumes and lower floret; bristles often scarcely exceeding the spikelets; upper lemma smooth .... **210. S. italica**
+   Spikelets falling entire leaving behind only the pedicel and bristles; bristles much longer than the spikelets; upper lemma finely rugose 5

5. Upper glume as long as the spikelet; panicle erect .... **208. S. viridis**
+ Upper glume c.3/4 the length of the spikelet; panicle nodding .... **211. S. faberi**

64. Digitaria Haller

Annual or perennial. Inflorescence of digitate or subdigitate racemes, the rhachis triquetrous to flat and ribbon-like. Spikelets in groups of 2 or 3 (or up to 5, but not in our area) on unequal pedicels, usually imbricate, puberulous to villous, the hairs usually in stripes between the nerves of the upper glume and lower lemma, rarely glabrous; lower glume minute or suppressed; upper glume variable, sometimes much reduced; lower lemma as long as the spikelet, barren and with reduced or suppressed palea; upper floret sessile, its lemma chartaceous to cartilaginous with flat hyaline margins, subacute to acuminate.

Species c. 230; tropical and warm temperate regions.

An extremely variable genus but with a relatively uniform spikelet-facies. It has variously been divided into several to numerous sections, depending on author, some of the sections being much more obvious than others. The three species found in our area are superficially rather similar, but represent 2 of the more important sections.

Key to species

1. Spikelets in groups of 3, at least in the middle part of the raceme; mature fruit dark brown or purple; hairs on upper glume and lower lemma verrucose (minutely warty) (sect. *Ischaemum*) .... **212. D. ischaemum**
+ Spikelets in pairs; mature fruit pallid or grey; hairs on upper glume and lower lemma simple, smooth (sect. *Digitaria*) 2

2. Upper glume 1/3 – 1/2 the length of the spikelet; nerves of the lower lemma minutely scabrid .... **213. D. sanguinalis**
+ Upper glume (1/2)2/3 – 3/4 the length of the spikelet; nerves of the lower lemma quite smooth .... **214. D. ciliaris**

65. Cenchrus L.

Annual or perennial. Inflorescence a cylindrical spike-like panicle, each spikelet or cluster of spikelets enclosed by a deciduous involucre of 1 or more whorls of bristles, those of the innermost whorl ± flattened and often spiny, connate at the base to form a disc or for some distance above the base to form a cup. Spikelets dorsally compressed; lower glume up to half the length of the spikelet, sometimes suppressed; upper glume a little shorter than the spikelet; lower floret as long as the spikelet, male or barren, the palea often well developed; upper floret with lemma firmly membranous to coriaceous, its thin flat margins covering much of the palea.

Species 22; throughout the tropics.

The genus is recognised at once by its prickly deciduous burs.

Key to species

1. Bur comprising a single whorl of connate, flattened spines surrounded by numerous smaller terete bristles .... **215. C. echinatus**
+   Bur comprising several whorls of flattened spines without additional smaller bristles 2

2. Inner spines broad at the base, usually fewer than 25; outer spines flattened; spikelets 3.5 – 6mm .... **216. C. incertus**
+   Inner spines slender, usually more than 30; outer spines usually terete and reflexed; spikelets 6 – 8mm .... **217. C. longispinus**

66. Sorghum Moench

Annual or perennial, mostly robust, with or without rhizomes; ligule membranous or scarious, rarely a line of hairs. Inflorescence a large terminal panicle with tough persistent branches bearing short fragile racemes (except in cultivated species), these with paired dissimilar spikelets, one sessile, the other pedicelled; internodes and pedicels filiform; sessile spikelet dorsally compressed with obtuse callus; lower glume coriaceous, broadly convex across the back, becoming 2-keeled and narrowly winged near the tip, usually hairy; lower floret reduced to a hyaline lemma; upper lemma hyaline, 2-toothed at the tip, with a glabrous awn in the sinus, or awnless; caryopsis obovate, dorsally compressed; pedicelled spikelet male or barren, linear-lanceolate to subulate, much narrower than the sessile, awnless.

Species c.20; Old World tropics and subtropics, 1 endemic in Mexico.

The genus contains several cultivated species one, *S. bicolor*, of major importance in the tropics of the Old World. It was probably first domesticated in or around Sudan about 3000 years ago. Also in the genus is a pernicious weed, *S. halepense*.

The genus is very unlike *Zea* despite being in the same tribe. It follows the normal pattern for the tribe in having paired dissimilar spikelets, the sessile fertile and the pedicelled male or barren. Sometimes the raceme is reduced to a single sessile spikelet and two terminal pedicelled spikelets.

Key to species

1. Rhizomatous perennial with deciduous spikelets .... **218. S. halepense**
+   Annual without rhizomes; spikelets persistent .... **219. S. bicolor**

67. Zea L.

Euchlaena Schrad.

Annual or rarely perennial; monoecious. Male inflorescence (the tassel) terminal, of digitate or paniculate racemes of persistent spikelets; internodes tough, narrow, bearing paired spikelets, one of them subsessile, the other on a slender pedicel; glumes equal, chartaceous; both florets male, awnless. Female inflorescence axillary, a single raceme wrapped in 1 or more spathes (husks); internodes much condensed and fused into a polystichous woody cob with paired spikelets at each node, both sessile (fragile, swollen, bearing single distichous sessile spikelets without trace of pairing in wild species). Spikelets 2-flowered, persistent, shallowly inserted on the surface of the cob, with short chaffy glumes exposing the grain (deeply immersed in and almost enclosed by the internode, and with crustaceous lower glume in wild species); lower floret barren, much reduced; upper floret well developed, awnless; style single, silky, those of the whole cob (the silks) pendulous from the tip of the inflorescence.

Species 4; C America.

Culitvated maize is so different in appearance from the three wild species that the latter were at one time accommodated in a separate genus, *Euchlaena*. On close inspection, however, the differences are seen to be slight and are under relatively simple genetic control.

The only species .... 220. **Z. mays**

1. Leersia oryzoides (L.) Sw.

Cut-grass New Atlas: 740

Slender, loosely tufted rhizomatous perennial up to 120cm; culms erect or ascending, often branched, hairy at the nodes; sheaths with short reflexed bristles, culminating in broadly to narrowly triangular auricles as long as the ligule; ligule a short truncate rim 0.7 – 1.8mm; blades flat, 5 – 11mm wide, rough on the surface, spiny on the midnerve below. Panicle enclosed in the leaf-sheath or partly or wholly exserted, contracted to very loose, (7)11 – 22cm, the primary branches naked in the lower half, bearing the overlapping spikelets on one side towards the summit. Spikelets semi-elliptic to oblong, (4)4.5 – 6mm; lemma coriaceous, fringed on the keel with stiff bristles, scabrid on the flanks, the lateral nerves near the margins, the tip abruptly pointed; palea as long as or slightly exceeding the lemma, stiffly bristly on the back; anthers 3, 0.4 – 2mm. $2n = 48$, 60. Flowering and fruiting early August to late October, but mostly late August to late September.

This very rare grass is known from a tiny handful of locations in southern England (currently 4 sites in the southeast). It occurs on the edges of rivers, canals and ponds and, in its British stronghold at Amberley Wild Brooks in W Sussex, thrives best in open vegetation on nutrient-rich mud fringing drainage ditches which have been dredged or cattle-poached. Not part of a characteristic 'community' as such, *L. oryzoides* may be found with a range of species that occupy the shallow water and seasonally drawn-down margins of these habitats. They include the grasses *Glyceria fluitans, G. maxima* and *Phalaris arundinacea* and herbs such as *Lythrum salicaria, Mentha ×verticillata, Stachys palustris* and the emergent aquatics *Alisma plantago-aquatica* and *Sparganium erectum*.

In most years, even when spring and summer are mild, the panicle rarely emerges more than part-way from the subtending sheath and the spikelets are cleistogamous with anthers not exceeding 0.7mm. Only in exceptionally warm years, usually with hot summers, does the panicle emerge fully; on those occasions the spikelets are likely to be chasmogamous with the extended anthers reaching 2mm. When no panicles are visible Cut-grass can be recognised by the combination of its distinctive yellow-green colour, the characteristic angle of the single terminal culm-leaf, the retrorsely bristly leaf-sheaths, finely-spined leaf margins and the coarsely spiny midnerve on the underside of the leaf. These last three traits have given the plant its vernacular name – the unwary botanist can be quite badly lacerated by the leaves of this plant.

L. oryzoides is native, occurring in suitable habitats through temperate Europe from southern Finland to Spain and eastwards to C and E Asia. It also occurs in N America. It is classified as an **endangered** species in the UK (Cheffings & Farrell, 2005), where it is fully protected, and has decreased markedly throughout Europe. The shy flowering, late seasonal growth and development (which may be swamped by summer cutting and clearing of water courses), and the tall vigorous

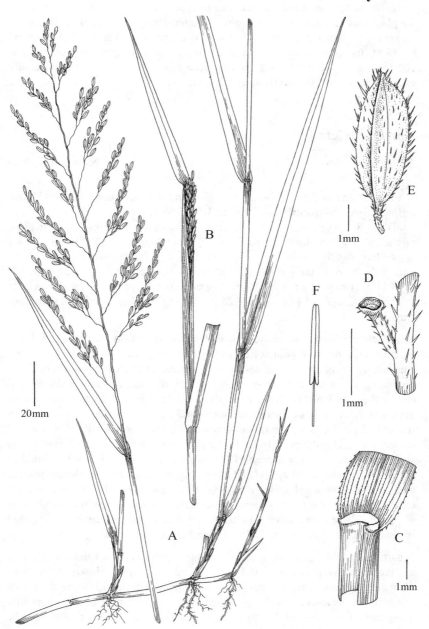

Leersia oryzoides: A, habit with chasmogamous panicle; B, cleistogamous panicle; C, ligule; D, segment of panicle branch with pedicel; E, spikelet; F, anther.

105

habit of many of its companions may have led to the plant being overlooked. However, former locations are searched regularly without success. For example, the plant was first discovered along the Taunton-Bridgwater canal in 1959 at 18 separate sites which had reduced to 8 by 1983, one in 1988 and had disappeared by 1990. Its recent discovery (or rediscovery?) at Richmond in Surrey some 200 years after the last record from the area suggests it may very occasionally establish new populations (Holloway, 2004).

2.   Nardus stricta L.

Mat-grass   New Atlas: 740

Densely tufted mat-forming perennial with short rhizomes; culms up to 40(50)cm, arising above a basal cushion of sheaths 1.5 – 4.5(6)cm deep; leaves mostly basal with usually just one on the culm; ligules of basal leaves blunt, 0.4 – 0.8mm, those on the culm-leaves bluntly pointed, usually much longer (1 – 2(2.3)mm); blades bristle-like, tightly inrolled, 0.4 – 0.6mm across, conspicuously grooved on the underside, hairy in the grooves or glabrous. Inflorescence 3 – 9.5cm; spikelets 6.5 – 11mm (including the awn); lemma gradually tapering above into an awn 1.5 – 3mm; anthers 2.9 – 4.2mm. $2n = 26$. Flowering and fruiting mid-May to mid-August.

N. stricta is widespread in the British Isles on moorland, heathland, hill and mountainside on base-poor, often peaty, soils of generally low fertility and, particularly in the north and west, may dominate extensive areas of moorland, producing characteristic slate-grey or whitish fibrous and unpalatable 'mats' (hence the name). Although most abundant in upland areas of high rainfall, it also occurs in the lowlands on sandy heathland and unproductive acidic grassland. A true calcifuge, it is absent from the predominantly calcareous soils of central and eastern England and central Ireland. The plant is more common on free-draining soils which are wet in winter and favours soils of pH <4.0. It is often found in species-poor habitats. In upland and montane grassland it may co-dominate large areas with the more palatable grasses *Agrostis capillaris* and *Festuca ovina* and can be found in dwarf shrub communities throughout its range. It is found from sea-level, where it can occur close to the upper limits of saltmarsh, to snow-bed habitats at high altitudes (to 1250m on Ben Macdui, S Aberdeen).

A particularly slow-growing species, Mat-grass produces new tillers in February and reaches a maximum in April. Individual tussocks expand slowly and isolated plants may appear at their edges as the old rhizomes decay. Rhizome fragments can also be detached, usually by sheep, and establish new plants, especially along trampled pathways. By contrast, seedlings are rare although they may be important in colonizing bare ground. Unusually, the flowers are protogynous and have just a single pubescent stigma that protrudes before the anthers are ripe. Many anthers appear to be indehiscent so it is likely that the species is at least

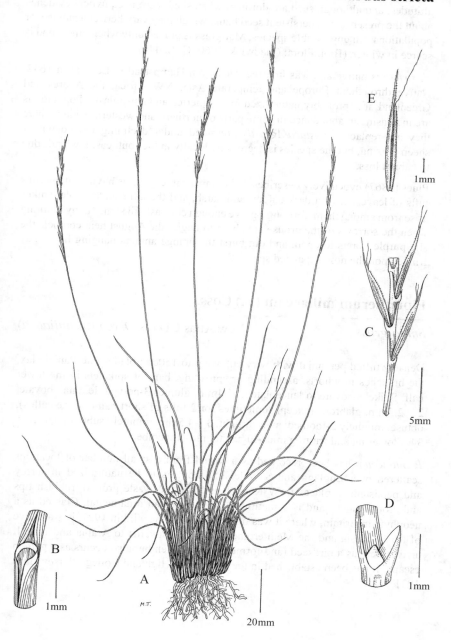

Nardus stricta: A, habit; B, ligule; C, segment of raceme; D, glumes; E, floret.

partially apomictic. Seed set may be low in poor summers, especially at high altitudes, and although seed are dormant when shed there is equivocal evidence about the presence of a persistent seed bank, which may vary between habitats or populations. An unpalatable species, Mat-grass is grazed only when other food is scarce in winter. (Biol. Flora: Chadwick, 1960; CPE: 446).

N. stricta is native and was first recorded from Hampstead in London in 1632. Native throughout Europe and temperate Asia, NW Africa, the Azores and Greenland, it is probably naturalized in N America and Australasia. Populations are increasing in abundance in some parts of northern and western Britain where they are replacing *Festuca/Agrostis* grassland under declining upland winter sheep grazing, but the species is decreasing locally in the southeast lowlands due to habitat loss.

Plues (1867) evocatively describes this unmistakable grass as having "numerous tufts of leaves … of a dark colour, and harsh, and the tall slender violet spikes arise from among them, forming a grave enough contrast, till some sunny morning when the sorrows of the grouse are about to begin, the August heat compels the shy purple florets to open, and out burst the orange anthers hanging like a gay fringe upon the now expanded spikelet".

3.   **Piptatherum miliaceum** (L.) Coss.

Smilo-grass   New Atlas CD (as *Oryzopsis miliacea*)

Densely tufted perennial with wiry culms up to 150cm; blades flat. Panicle lax, the branches in whorls, ascending or spreading, bare of spikelets in the lower half. Spikelets ovate to lanceolate, 3 – 4mm; glumes 3-nerved; lemma obovate, 2 – 2.5mm, glabrous (except sometimes for 2 tufts of short hairs on the callus), obtuse, minutely 2-toothed; awn straight, 3 – 4.5mm, minutely subterminal. $2n =$ 34. Flowering and fruiting mid-August to mid-November.

P. miliaceum has been recorded as a casual from a small number of locations scattered over England and S Wales and appears to be naturalized in Jersey and persistent in places in W Kent. It is found on waste ground, rubbish tips and around docks and is sometimes cultivated as an ornamental. Classed as a neophyte in Britain, where it was first recorded in the wild in 1927, it is a native of Macaronesia and the Mediterranean region eastwards to Arabia and Iraq. It arrives here as a birdseed (and formerly wool) alien but also occurs as a garden escape. It has been established in the grounds of Highland College, Jersey since 1931.

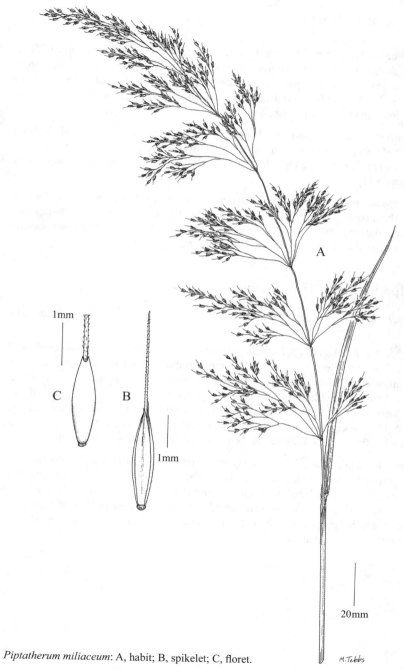

1mm

C

B

1mm

A

20mm

M.Tebbs

Piptatherum miliaceum: A, habit; B, spikelet; C, floret.

4.   Anemanthele lessoniana (Steud.) Veldkamp.

New Zealand Wind-grass

Densely tufted perennial up to 150cm. Panicle nodding, very lax, up to 75cm. Spikelets 2.5 – 3.3mm; glumes subequal, acute, the upper with an excurrent nerve; lemma, including the weakly developed, obtuse, conical, 0.15 – 0.2mm callus, 2 – 3mm, glabrous; awn minutely subterminal, straight or flexuous, not divided into column and limb; anther 1.

A native of New Zealand, it is becoming more popular in gardens and showing signs of becoming naturalized, especially in Ireland and parts of southern England (AGB: 11). For instance Oswald (2006) noted it successfully seeding along streets in Cambridge.

The species probably belongs in *Stipa* (where it has been known as *S. arundinacea* (Hook.f.) Benth.) but it also closely resembles *Piptatherum* from which it differs by its 3-nerved (rather than 5-nerved) membranous fruiting lemma that conceals at least the flanks of the palea, and single anther.

5.   Stipa neesiana Trin. & Rupr.

American Needle-grass   New Atlas CD

Tufted perennial up to 75(100)cm. Panicle spreading or ascending with appressed spikelets. Spikelets 12 – 18.5(22.5)mm; glumes subequal, lanceolate, long-acuminate-aristulate; lemma, including the 3 – 4mm pungent callus, (5.5)7.5 – 10.5mm, tuberculate on the body, hairy below and on the lower part of the midnerve, the tip with a corona 0.4 – 0.7(0.9)mm, this ciliolate on the margin; awn 4.5 – 10cm, bigeniculate, with hairy column and scabrid limb, those of a panicle often twisted together to form a tail at the summit of the panicle.

Recorded from a handful of widely scattered sites in Britain and persisting for several years in some locations in the south, *S. neesiana* has not been recorded recently. It occurred on waste ground and rubbish tips. Classified in the New Atlas as a neophyte, it was first recorded in the wild here in 1916 from Scotland. A native of S America, widely naturalized elsewhere, it was originally introduced to Britain as a wool alien.

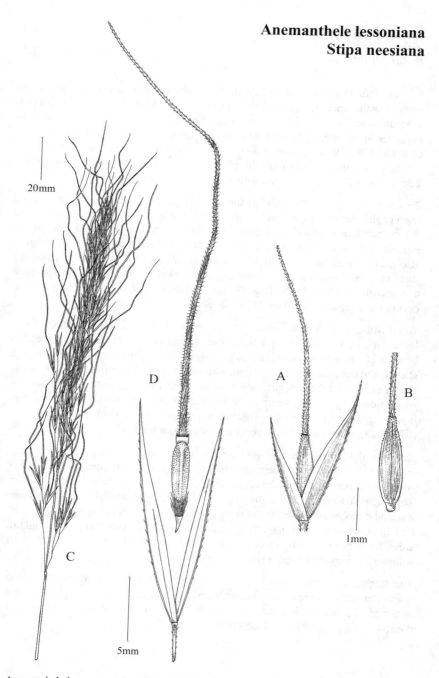

Anemanthele lessoniana: A, spikelet; B, floret.
Stipa neesiana: C, panicle; D, spikelet with floret separated from glumes.

6. Milium effusum L.

Wood Millet

New Atlas: 741

Loosely tufted perennial up to 130(160)cm; culms erect or ascending, slender to stout; sheaths smooth; ligules (3)4 – 9mm, obtuse to bluntly pointed; blades (4)6 – 15mm wide. Panicle 15 – 35cm, loose and open, nodding, the fine flexuous branches in clusters, spreading or deflexed. Spikelets narrowly elliptic to ovate, (2.8)3 – 3.7(4.3)mm; glumes subequal, scaberulous, 3-nerved; lemma (2.6)2.8 – 3.4mm, slightly shorter than the glumes, finely 5-nerved; anthers (1.5)1.7 – 2.3mm. $2n = 28$. Flowering and fruiting mid-May to mid-August.

This distinctive grass of woodlands and shaded places is found throughout England (except the Fens), and in lowland Scotland, but is sparse or absent in upland Wales, northern Scotland and Ireland. It is locally abundant in deciduous woods, especially those on damp, calcareous soils which are high in humus, although it also occurs on moist soils and over rocks. *M. effusum* may grow among shrubs such as *Rubus fruticosus* and *Lonicera periclymenum* and companions include a range of woodland herbs (e.g. *Oxalis acetosella* and *Digitalis purpurea*). It occurs from sea-level to 380m (W of Dockray, Cumberland).

Wood Millet is easy to recognize in flower and the broad smooth bright green leaves often stay green through the winter. Plants in more shaded woods tend to be tall with green florets whilst those from more open habitats are sometimes more stunted and have purple florets. There is limited vegetative spread but many seeds are produced and these persist in woodland seed banks. In southern populations where flowering is early, seeds germinate mostly in the autumn, whereas in later-flowering northern populations germination may be delayed until the spring (CPE: 428). Plants take 2 to 5 years to flower from seed.

Native to the British Isles, *M. effusum* has a circumpolar distribution, occurring in most parts of Europe except the Mediterranean, and in temperate Asia and N America. It has been introduced to Australasia. First recorded in Britain from Sandwich in Kent in 1597, the species is said to be an indicator of ancient woodland in Lincolnshire. At the same time it is known to colonize sites opened by felling or fire and appears to be spreading into newer woodland in some upland areas. It has been sown into woods to provide food for game birds. A variety with yellowish leaves ('Aureum') is a popular garden plant.

The toughened floret resembles that of *Piptatherum* but is awnless. It also resembles that of some species of *Panicum*, but in *Milium* the floret falls from the persistent glumes and is unaccompanied by a barren or male floret; in *Panicum* the spikelet is 2-flowered and falls entire.

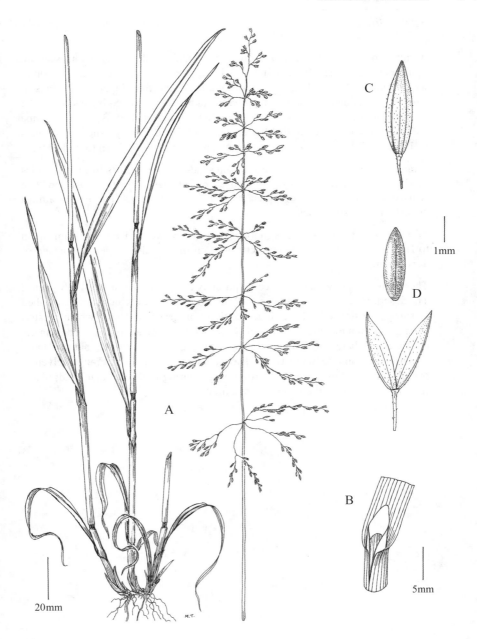

Milium effusum: A, habit; B, ligule; C, intact spikelet;
D, spikelet with floret separated from glumes.

7. **Milium vernale** M.Bieb.

Early Millet   New Atlas: 741

Annual up to 16(50)cm; culms erect or prostrate, slender; sheaths scabrid; ligules (1.5)2 – 3(5.5)mm, obtuse to bluntly pointed; blades 1.5 – 2(5)mm wide. Panicle 2 – 4(13)cm, open or contracted, the fine flexuous branches in clusters, spreading, ascending or appressed to the main axis. Spikelets ovate, 2.2 – 2.6(3.2)mm; glumes subequal, scaberulous to tuberculate, 3-nerved; lemma 1.7 – 2(2.6)mm, significantly shorter than the glumes, finely 5-nerved; anthers (1.1)1.2 – 1.5(1.8)mm. $2n = 8$. Flowering and fruiting early April to mid-May.

A rare species known only in short turf on sand-dunes and cliffs from 2 localities in Guernsey where it was discovered as recently as 1899 (but lost and then rediscovered in 1949). Inconspicuous and early flowering, it grows in almost closed turf on fixed dunes.

M. vernale is native, occurring along the coast of western Europe from Spain to Holland and reaching its northern limit on the Dutch Wadden Sea island of Terschelling.

The species is very variable and could possibly comprise at least 3 or 4 subspecies. The description above is based on material from Guernsey which is distinguished as subsp. **sarniense** D.C.McClint. mainly by its prostrate habit (which persists from generation to generation in cultivation) and contracted panicle. The panicle character is shared with many French and Dutch populations, but the habit appears to be unique to Guernsey. The extended morphological ranges given in parentheses are those of material from neighbouring France and Holland; plants from further away still are even more extreme.

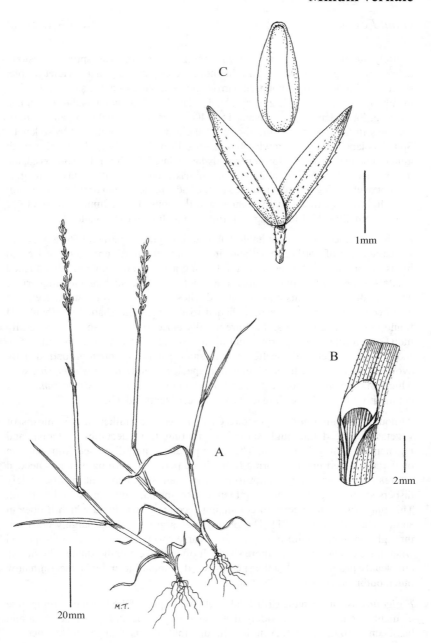

Milium vernale subsp. *sarniense*: A, habit; B, ligule, C, spikelet with floret detached from glumes.

8.   Festuca gigantea (L.) Vill.

Giant Fescue   New Atlas: 742

Loosely tufted perennial without rhizomes; culms erect or spreading, stout, unbranched, up to 140(165)cm, the nodes conspicuously dark violet-purple; sheaths glabrous, with pronounced narrow glabrous auricles at the summit; ligule a membranous rim (0.7)1 – 2(2.5)mm; blades flat, 7 – 15mm wide, glabrous. Panicle nodding, loose, lanceolate to ovate, 15 – 40cm; branches usually in pairs, bare of spikelets in the lower part, the shorter at the lowest node with 2 – 16 spikelets. Spikelets lanceolate to narrowly oblong, 10 – 17mm, loosely (2)4- to 8-flowered; glumes unequal, acute, the lower narrowly lanceolate 3.5 – 7mm, 1- to 3-nerved, the upper lanceolate, 4.5 – 8mm, 3-nerved; lemmas eventually with incurved margins and not overlapping, broadly rounded on the back, lanceolate in profile, 6.5 – 9mm; awn slightly subterminal, very slender and flexuous, 12 – 22mm; anthers (1.6)2 – 3(3.2)mm. $2n = 42$. Flowering and fruiting mid-July to early September.

F. gigantea is common in suitable habitats throughout mainland Britain except for large areas of northern Scotland. It occurs in the north and south of Ireland but is uncommon in the central plain. It is a grass of woodland and other shaded habitats, especially favouring open areas within woods such as clearings, rides and the edges of streams and drainage ditches, as well as woodland margins. It also occurs in hedgerows, scrub, shaded road verges and shaded riverbanks. If found in unshaded habitats, these are usually close to woods. Soils are generally moist and fertile, ranging from neutral to base-rich and mostly with a pH >5.0. Individuals are generally scattered or in small patches on open ground, usually avoiding areas of leaf litter. Companion species include *Bromus ramosus*, with which it is sometimes confused (see below) and *Brachypodium sylvaticum*. Most common in the lowlands, it reaches 370m near Nenthead, Cumberland.

Although perennial and polycarpic, Giant Fescue has rather limited means of vegetative spread (although sometimes rooting from decumbent stems), and regenerates mainly from seed. These are produced and dispersed from autumn onwards and germinate in spring following a period of chilling which is needed to break dormancy. They do not form a persistent seed bank but may be widely dispersed, the long awns enabling them to become entangled in fur and clothing. This may assist the species in colonizing secondary woodland which it does in some areas (Peterkin 1981). The plant remains green, though largely dormant, through the winter, with new growth in early spring extending into the period when the trees begin to cast more shade. It often flowers in the shade. The florets are weakly protogynous but the species is self-compatible and it is uncertain how much outbreeding occurs (CPE: 302).

F. gigantea is native in the British Isles where it is part of the European Temperate element in our flora. It is widely distributed in Europe and temperate Asia and has been introduced in N America. Its distribution has changed little since the 1962 Atlas, although the slight increase may reflect its ability to thrive in modern broad-leaved woodland.

Festuca gigantea: A, habit; B, ligule with auricles; C, spikelet; D, lemma.

Giant Fescue is recognized at once by its long slender awns, pronounced glabrous auricles and violet-purple nodes. It may perhaps be confused with *Bromus ramosus* but this has hairy sheaths and a hairy ovary-appendage. It hybridizes with both *F. pratensis* and *F. arundinacea*. In both cases the hybrids are sterile but see under the other respective parents for further details.

F. gigantea also hybridizes with *Lolium perenne*. The resultant hybrid (×**Festulolium brinkmannii** (A. Braun) Asch. & Graebn. resembles other ×*Festulolium* hybrids, especially those involving *L. multiflorum*, but has much longer awns and somewhat broader leaf-blades. Rather rare in England, Wales and Ireland.

9.   Festuca pratensis Huds.

Meadow Fescue   New Atlas: 741

Loosely tufted perennial without rhizomes; culms erect or spreading, slender to stout, unbranched, up to 100(125)cm; sheaths glabrous, with pronounced narrow glabrous auricles at the summit; ligule a membranous rim 0.3 – 1mm; blades flat, 3 – 8mm wide, glabrous and glossy below, often scaberulous above and on the margins. Panicle erect or nodding, loose, lanceolate to ovate and more or less 1-sided, 9 – 30cm; branches usually in pairs, sometimes solitary, the shorter of a pair with 1 – 2(3) spikelets only. Spikelets lanceolate or narrowly oblong, (10)11.5 – 17.5(20)mm, 5- to 10(16)-flowered; glumes unequal, narrowly lanceolate to oblong, bluntly pointed at the tip, the tip and margins membranous, the lower 2 – 4.5mm, 1-nerved, the upper 3.5 – 5mm, 1- to 3-nerved; lemmas overlapping, narrowly oblong to lanceolate-oblong in profile, 6 – 8.5mm, awnless or rarely with a minute awn-point to 0.3(0.8)mm; anthers 2.4 – 3.8(4)mm. $2n = 14$. Flowering and fruiting early June to early August.

F. pratensis is widespread and fairly frequent throughout the British Isles but is more scattered in the northern half of Scotland and SW Ireland. It is most common in water-meadows and other moist grassland habitats including hay-meadows and pasture, but can be found on road verges and waste ground. It often occurs as scattered tufts in grassland reaching its greatest density on fertile heavy or loamy neutral soils (above pH 5.0) which have high water-holding capacity. Hence it may also be found by rivers and ditches. Sown for grazing and hay, it can have a wide range of associates and in old grassland may occur in very species-rich communities. It is found from sea-level to 575m (Hartside, Cumberland) and exceptionally at 845m on Great Dun Fell, Westmorland.

Once very popular as a constituent of grass mixtures for pastures and hay-meadows, Meadow Fescue is essentially a 'companion' species, combining well with clovers and other grasses. It is highly palatable and was widely grown in long leys or permanent pastures where it was favoured for its good 'bottom' growth (a high ratio of leaf to stem) and the fact that it produced easily gathered seed.

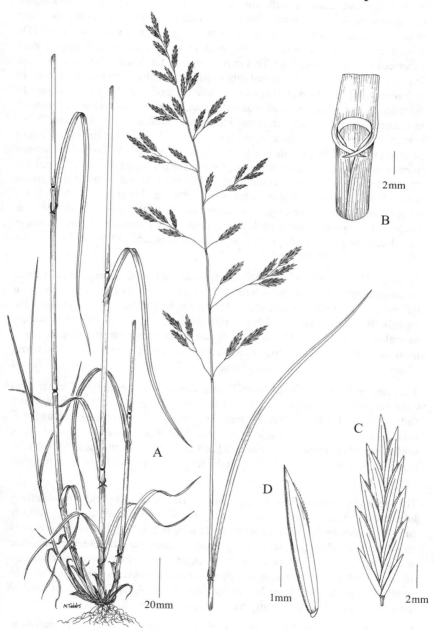

2mm

B

C

A

D

20mm

1mm

2mm

Festuca pratensis: A, habit; B, ligule with auricles; C, spikelet; D, lemma.

The species is highly cold tolerant, remaining green, and even growing slowly, over winter and recovers well from cutting. It spreads mainly by seed which can germinate in the autumn without pre-chilling, probably enabling the plant to colonize gaps in the vegetation following the hay crop. (Subsp. *apennina* (De Not.) Hegi from montane Europe dies back in winter and its seeds require cold treatment before germinating). This may explain its tendency to be more frequent in hay-meadows, as well as its inability to persist in either very tall or intensively grazed grassland. However, it is a quite variable species and has been subject to selection by plant breeders and many cultivars have been imported. *F. pratensis* is reported to be normally cross-pollinating although it has no incompatibility system. Its popularity as an agricultural grass has declined (in Britain in favour of Rye-grass and in the USA, where it was introduced, in favour of another introduction there, the heavier-yielding and more persistent *F. arundinacea*) but its cold tolerance, excellent combining ability and relatively slow development mean that it is often recommended for recreating flower-rich grassland, for wildlife buffer strips, for organic systems and for silage mixtures. In addition, modern plant breeders use hybrids with *Lolium* to investigate the genetic basis of useful traits in *F. pratensis*, such as winter hardiness, and to transfer these genes into new varieties. (CPE:306).

Although *F. pratensis* is native in the British Isles, it is difficult to be certain about its native range and it may be present in the north and west of Britain and western Ireland only as a relic of cultivation (for example, the New Atlas classifies the records from the Orkney and Shetland Islands as introductions). It is widely naturalized elsewhere and has a Circumpolar Boreo-temperate distribution. Apart from its decline as a sown species it may be decreasing here because of the loss of semi-natural areas such as water-meadows.

The species is distinguished from *F. arundinacea* by the glabrous rather than ciliate auricles, by having only 1 or 2 spikelets on the shorter branch of a pair and by the distinctly awnless lemmas. The two species hybridize; see under *F. arundinacea* for details. It also hybridizes with *F. gigantea*; the hybrid (**F. × schlickumii** Grantzow) is male-sterile ($2n = 28$) and is intermediate between the parents in morphology, particularly in the length of the awn. It has been reported very rarely.

The species hybridizes with *Lolium perenne* and the resultant hybrid (×**Festulolium loliaceum** (Huds.) P.Fourn.) is largely sterile though a low degree of fertility can sometimes be found and backcrossing may occur. The hybrid more closely resembles the *Lolium* parent in having a largely racemose inflorescence, but some branching may occur below and even when unbranched the lower spikelets are often pedicelled. Both glumes are present but the lower is very reduced. The auricles are glabrous and the lemma awnless; $2n = 14, 21$. Throughout most of the British Isles and forms easily when the parents grow together.

F. pratensis also hybridizes with *L. multiflorum*, and the hybrid (×**Festulolium braunii** (K.Richt.) A.Camus) is very similar to the above but has awned lemmas; $2n = 14$. Scattered in England, Wales and Ireland.

10. **Festuca arundinacea** Schreb.

Illustration, page 123

Tall Fescue

New Atlas: 742

Densely tufted or tussocky perennial without rhizomes; culms erect, slender to robust, unbranched, up to 165(200)cm; sheaths glabrous, with pronounced narrow ciliate auricles at the summit; ligule a membranous rim 0.6 – 1.6mm; blades flat, or becoming inrolled on drying, (3)4.5 – 10mm wide, scaberulous on both sides and on the margins, sometimes smooth below. Panicle erect or nodding, loose and open, lanceolate to ovate, or sometimes contracted and narrow, (10)15 – 40(50)cm; branches usually in pairs, each of a pair with 3 – 18 spikelets. Spikelets oblong to elliptic, 9 – 15mm, 4- to 8-flowered; glumes unequal, acute, the tip and margins membranous, the lower narrowly lanceolate, (3)3.5 – 5.5mm, 1-nerved, the upper lanceolate to oblong-lanceolate, 4 – 6.5(7.5)mm, 3-nerved; lemmas overlapping, lanceolate to oblong-lanceolate in profile, 6.5 – 9.5mm, blunt or pointed, awnless or frequently with a subapical awn up to 1.5(3)mm; anthers 2.8 – 4.5mm. $2n = 42$. Flowering and fruiting mid-June to early August, sometimes beginning in late May and lasting until late September.

F. arundinacea is widespread and common throughout most of the British Isles, except for northern Scotland where it occurs mainly near the coast. It can be found in a great variety of both established and disturbed habitat-types ranging from pastures and hay-meadows, chalk and limestone grassland, freshwater marsh, maritime cliff-tops and ledges and the upper reaches of tidal saltmarsh to waste ground, road verges, railway embankments and arable field margins. Additionally, it occurs in scrub, the edges of woods, coastal shingle and river gravel, disused railway tracks, riverbanks, coastal strandlines and the clay slopes of eroding sea cliffs. It is perhaps most easily recognized in relatively unmanaged habitats, such as estuarine marshes, unimproved grassland or waste ground, where it tends to form large densely-tillered tussocks, often on poorly drained or frequently flooded soils. In chalk grassland it tends to be found in the relatively less-grazed areas on deeper, moister soils. Across this huge variety of substrates, from clay to gravel, Tall Fescue occurs on neutral or basic soils, many around pH 7.0, which can vary greatly in fertility. It has a large number of associates; a full list of the communities in which it occurs, including those in continental Europe, is given by Gibson & Newman (2001). In Britain it is mainly a lowland grass, extending to higher altitudes (and northwards) especially along road verges. It reaches 430m near Alston, Cumberland.

Biologically, *F. arundinacea* shares many features with *F. pratensis* (some older texts group them together as *F. elatior*) in growing through the year and overwintering as a green plant, flowering and setting seed from June onwards and producing non-dormant seed which may be animal dispersed and largely germinate shortly after being shed (exploiting gaps in the autumn vegetation). Neither produces a persistent soil seed bank. Both have been exploited as forage species, Tall Fescue being much more popular for a wider range of uses in the

121

USA. However, *F. arundinacea* is generally a more robust and longer-lived plant, is often very deep rooted (giving it better drought-tolerance) and more persistent in a range of extreme habitats, has some degree of salt-tolerance (although largely found in fresh or brackish marsh), is coarser and less palatable (and of course taller!), and is mainly self-incompatible (although self-fertile inbred lines are known). As expected with a species of such wide ecological amplitude, Tall Fescue is extremely variable in size and morphology. This, as in other grasses, is probably widely affected by the presence of agricultural strains. For example, the most widely-grown cultivar in Britain, S170, was developed from plants originating in England, Wales, France and N & S America. Gibson & Taylor (2003) showed that the overall size of individuals in 16 English populations depended on the productiveness, rather than the ecological type, of their habitat, but the genetic basis of this variation was not analyzed (Biol. Flora: Gibson & Newman, 2001).

F. arundinacea is native in the British Isles, although in many areas it may only be a relic of cultivation (or a former wool alien). It is part of the Eurosiberian Southern-temperate flora and is widely naturalized outside this range where it has been introduced for agriculture (e.g. N & S America, Australia and New Zealand).

The species is rather similar to *F. pratensis* but is generally a taller, more robust plant often forming tussocks rather than loose tufts. The slightly shorter of the two inflorescence branches at a node bears several to many spikelets (never fewer than three) and the lemmas are more frequently awned. The most important diagnostic character, however, is the ciliate auricles but the cilia are fragile and are easily lost with age. The two species hybridize and the hybrid (**F. ×aschersoniana** Dörfl.) is male-sterile. It more closely resembles *F. arundinacea* but the influence of *F. pratensis* can just be seen in the lack of hairs on the auricles and the chromosome number ($2n = 28$). It has rarely been recorded but is likely to be more common than the records suggest. *F. arundinacea* also hybridizes with *F. gigantea*; again, the hybrid (**F. ×fleischeri** Rohlena) is male-sterile ($2n = 42$). The lemmas have awns of intermediate length and the auricles, unlike those of *F. gigantea*, are ciliate.

F. arundinacea hybridizes with *Lolium perenne* and the hybrid (×**Festulolium holmbergii** (Dörfl.) P.Fourn.) resembles ×*F. loliaceum* with the exception that the panicle is more freely branched, especially below, and the auricles are minutely ciliate; $2n = 28$. Scattered in southern England, the Midlands, Scotland and Ireland.

The species also hybridizes with *L. multiflorum*; the hybrid is similar to ×*F. holmbergii* but has awned lemmas; $2n = 28$. Very scattered in the southern half of Great Britain.

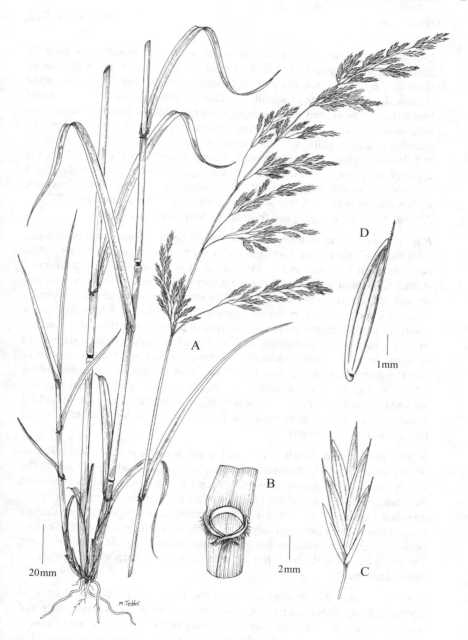

Festuca arundinacea: A, habit; B, ligule with auricles; C, spikelet; D, lemma.

11. Festuca altissima All.

Wood Fescue New Atlas: 742

Compactly tufted perennial without rhizomes; culms erect, slender to moderately stout, unbranched, up to 120(140)cm, clothed at the base by sheaths with reduced blade or the blade sometimes absent; sheaths glabrous, without auricles at the summit; ligule a truncate or broadly rounded erose membrane (2.5)3 – 5.5mm; blades flat, (4.5)6 – 15mm wide, scaberulous on both sides and margins, sometimes only on the margins. Panicle nodding, loose and open, (10)12 – 18(23)cm, the branches usually in pairs. Spikelets oblong or wedge-shaped, 5.5 – 8(9.5)mm, 2- to 5-flowered; glumes linear-lanceolate, 1-nerved, the lower (2)2.5 – 3.5mm, the upper (2.5)3 – 4(4.5)mm; lemmas not overlapping, lanceolate in profile, (4)4.5 – 5.5(6)mm, rounded on the back below, somewhat keeled above, 3-nerved, scaberulous to scabrid, finely acute but awnless at the tip; anthers (1.7)2.3 – 2.8mm. $2n = 14$. Flowering and fruiting late May to early August.

F. altissima occurs in scattered locations in NW Britain, north and west of a line from the Wye Valley to NE Yorkshire, and in the north of Ireland. There are outlier populations in E Sussex and in SW Ireland. It is a rather local plant of moist shaded habitats in and around woodland on rocky slopes, in rock crevices and on rock ledges, frequently occurring beside streams or waterfalls. It is typically found in wooded valleys, ravines or glens in conditions of high humidity, and is wholly or partially restricted to various types of primary woodland over much of its range, here and in continental Europe. It prefers slightly basic soils but can be found in woods over a variety of substrates, including limestone pavement (the E Sussex plants are on outcrops of sandstone). Associates include *Galium odoratum, Luzula sylvatica, Melica nutans, M. uniflora, Polystichum* spp. and *Sanicula europaea* (SPB: 170). Although geographically a grass of upland Britain, Wood Fescue occurs mainly at low altitudes from sea-level to 330m (at Haweswater, Westmorland).

A fairly distinctive grass with its flat leaf-blades and pale panicles, Wood Fescue often grows in large leafy tufts which may accumulate soil around them. The root system does not appear to penetrate deeply into the ground which may make the plant sensitive to drought at the soil surface and restrict it to humid or spray-drenched areas. Little appears to have been published on the species' reproductive biology and ecology although individual plants appear to be long-lived. Tests on Scandinavian plants indicate that germination, though high in laboratory tests, appears to be low in the wild. It is an interesting grass which would repay more detailed research.

A native species, *F. altissima* is part of the European Temperate element in our flora, being rather scattered across Europe from northern Spain, Italy and northern Greece to central Norway (and locally into C Asia). It is more frequent in Britain than suggested by the 1962 Atlas, as more thorough recent researches of its inaccessible habitats in northern England and Scotland have revealed.

124

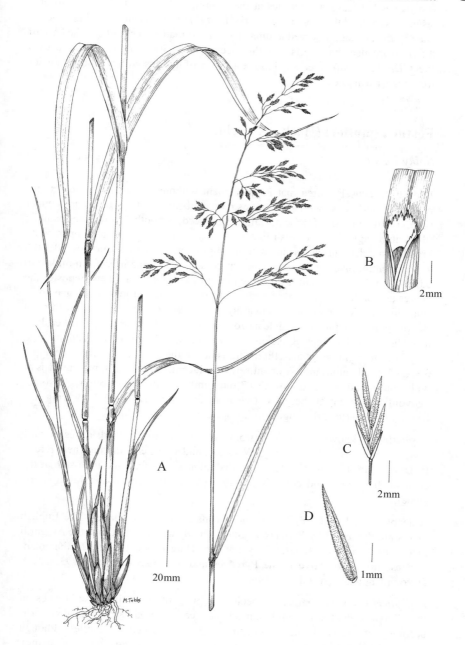

Festuca altissima: A, habit; B, ligule; C, spikelet; D, lemma.

Wood Fescue shares with section *Schedonardus* (species 8 – 10) the broad flat leaf-blades but lacks the auricles at the summit of the sheath. In this respect it resembles some of the more robust variants of *F. rubra* but can be distinguished at once by the unusual 3-nerved lemma. The almost bladeless sheaths at the base of the culm are also characteristic of the species. Its position in a section of its own (Sect. *Drymanthele*) is reflected in the absence of hybrids with any other species from the British Isles.

12. Festuca gautieri (Hack.) K.Richt.

Spiky Fescue   New Atlas CD

Loosely to densely tufted mat-forming plant without rhizomes, but sometimes pseudostoloniferous with the culms procumbent, rooting at their slender base; culms up to 45(55)cm, faintly grooved, smooth below the panicle; tillers intravaginal, each brush-like with numerous leaves; sheaths open, with broadly rounded auricles at the summit; ligule, including the auricles, (0.5)0.6 – 1.7(2.5)mm; blades green or glaucous, folded, 0.35 – 0.55mm from midrib to edge, 5- to 7-nerved, with sclerenchyma in discrete abaxial islets opposite the nerves and on the margins, or ± continuous (the leaf therefore either ribbed or ± smooth on the lower surface), outwardly curved, glabrous throughout, stiffly and sharply pointed at the tip. Panicle narrow, 3.5 – 7(9)cm, the branches scaberulous to scabrid, usually erect. Spikelets oblong to narrowly ovate, 9 – 12mm, 3- to 6(8)-flowered; glumes ovate-elliptic, translucent, the lower 3 – 4.4mm, the upper 3.8 – 5.2mm; lemmas mostly or entirely translucent, (5.3)5.5 – 7mm, muticous or with a subapical awnlet up to 0.5(0.7)mm; anthers (1.9)2.6 – 3.6mm. Caryopsis obovoid, pubescent at the apex, free from the palea. $2n = 14$. Flowering and fruiting in June (to early August in Europe).

F. gautieri is known in the wild from only 2 sites in England: a quarry near Aysgarth in the Yorkshire Dales (NW Yorks); and a road embankment near Exeter (S Devon). In its Yorkshire location it is colonizing a flat limestone slab at the edge of the quarry and comprises a single patch (which is probably a single clone).

A neophyte in Britain, Spiky Fescue is a native of the Pyrenees. The English plants are described by Fletcher & Stace (2000) who suggest that the Aysgarth plant was introduced at least 75 years ago. Here it occurs with 2 other plant species which are native in the Pyrenees and was discovered in 1993. The S Devon plant was first found in 1990.

F. gautieri is a very distinctive species; its pungent leaves in dense brushes on the tillers and the translucent lemmas have a certain ornamental appeal and it is becoming progressively more readily available from specialist nurseries (although it is possible that more than one species is being offered under the name).

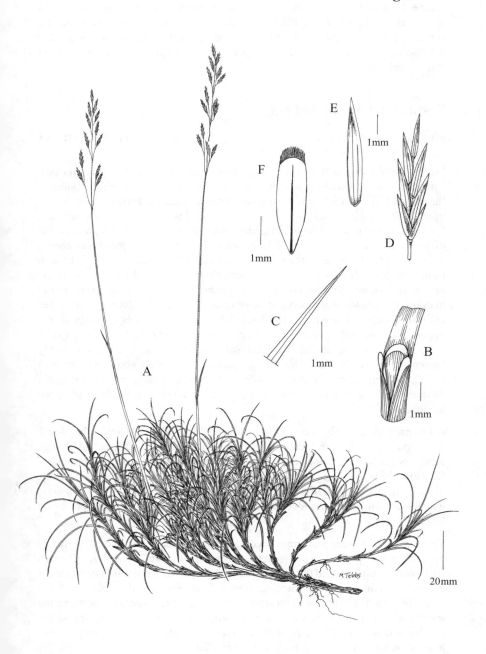

Festuca gautieri: A, habit; B, ligule; C, leaf tip; D, spikelet; E, lemma; F, caryopsis.

It is therefore quite likely that in the future it will feature more frequently as an escape from cultivation. Plants naturalized in England seem to be referable to subsp. **scoparia** (A.Kern. & Hack.) Kerguélen; this is usually defined as having spikelets not more than 9(10) mm and by being a calcicole, but in practice the morphological distinction is rather vague. Subsp. **gautieri** has longer spikelets and is a calcifuge.

13.   Festuca heterophylla Lam.

Various-leaved Fescue   New Atlas: 743

Densely tufted plant without rhizomes; culms up to 100(120)cm, faintly grooved, smooth below the panicle; tillers intravaginal; leaves markedly dimorphic; sheaths fused, those of the culm with conspicuous broadly rounded auricles, those of the tillers with inconspicuous auricles; ligule of culm leaves, including the auricles, 0.4 – 1(1.5)mm, those of the tillers seldom exceeding 0.3mm; blades green, those of the culm usually flat, 1.5 – 3.5mm wide, 7- to 9-nerved, pubescent above, glabrous beneath, those of the tillers folded-triangular, (0.2)0.3 – 0.45(0.5)mm from midrib to edge, 3-nerved, with sclerenchyma in 5 small islets opposite the nerves and along the margins, glabrous on both surfaces, scaberulous on the margins. Panicle loose and nodding, open or contracted, 8.5 – 20cm, the branches scabrid. Spikelets lanceolate to oblong, 7.5 – 12mm, 3- to 6(7)-flowered, the uppermost floret often rudimentary; lower glume narrowly lanceolate, (3)3.5 – 5(5.5)mm; upper glume oblong-lanceolate, (4)4.5 – 6.5mm; lemmas narrowly lanceolate in profile, 4.9 – 7(8.4)mm, glabrous, narrowed above into an awn (1.5)2.5 – 5mm; anthers (1.8)2.3 – 4.5mm. Caryopsis pubescent at the summit, adherent to the lemma and palea. $2n = 28, 42$. Flowering and fruiting early June to mid-July.

F. heterophylla is thinly scattered in mainland Britain from Dorset to the Moray Firth and occurs in one locality in Ireland (Grange, Co Limerick). Although generally rare it may be locally abundant in a few sites, especially in the south of England. Found in woods and woodland borders, it tends to occur on light, sandy, mainly calcareous soils. It is sometimes found growing with *Poa chaixii*, a grass which was also widely introduced in these habitats by Victorian gardeners. It is a lowland species. (AGB: 14).

Various-leaved Fescue was introduced partly as a fodder grass and partly for its ornamental value in woodland gardens, parks and woodland rides. The tall stems with nodding panicles and flat leaves arising from a dense basal tuft of very slender leaves is certainly very eye-catching, especially *en masse*. Individuals appear to be fairly long-lived and are polycarpic. Whilst the large anthers suggest that the species is cross-pollinating we have no information on its breeding system or the relative importance of seed production versus vegetative spread in maintaining populations. Viable seed can be found in the wild.

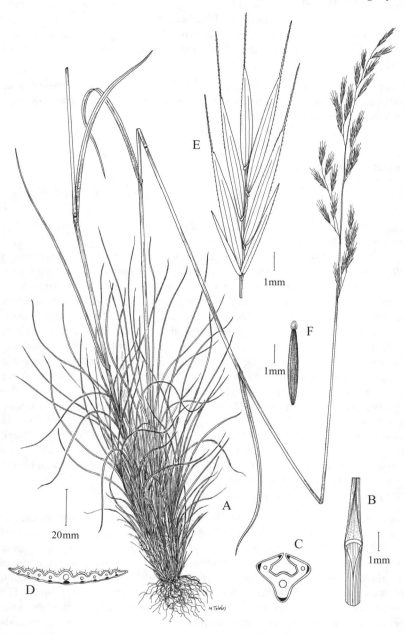

Festuca heterophylla: A, habit; B, ligule of tiller leaf; C, transverse section of tiller leaf; D, transverse section of culm leaf; E, spikelet; F, caryopsis.

F. heterophylla is a neophyte, introduced into Britain in 1812 and first recorded as naturalized in the wild in 1874. It has occurred in recent times as a contaminant of grass-seed mixtures. A European Temperate species, *F. heterophylla* occurs through central and southern Europe and in SW Asia. Apart from some new records from Scotland, its British distribution has not changed much since the 1962 Atlas.

It is the only fescue in the British Isles to have markedly dimorphic leaves (although *F. rubra* has them to a lesser degree); the hairy ovary is also unusual but is not exclusive to this species.

14. Festuca rubra L.

Red Fescue   New Atlas: 743-745

Loosely to densely tufted usually with rhizomes, sometimes without; culms erect or ascending, up to 100cm; tillers mostly extravaginal; leaves green or glaucous; sheath-margins fused almost to the top, smooth or scaberulous, glabrous to pilose; ligule a narrow membranous rim; blades tightly folded with conspicuous keel, sometimes junciform without keel, occasionally flat, 0.4 – 1mm from midrib to edge when folded, up to 5mm wide when flat, (3)5- to 9-nerved, upper surface sparsely puberulent to densely pubescent, lower surface usually smooth, sometimes scabrid or pilose; sclerenchyma above lower epidermis sometimes continuous and the blade rounded or oval in section without keel, but usually discontinuous with rounded keel or in 5 – 13 discrete islets and the blade polygonal in section, often with acute keel; sclerenchyma rarely present above the ribs below the upper epidermis. Panicle dense or loose, erect or nodding, 3.5 – 16(20)cm, the two lowest nodes (7)10 – 50mm apart; pedicels 0.7 – 3.1(3.6)mm. Spikelets 7 – 11.5(12.5)mm, 4- to 7(10)-flowered, the uppermost floret nearly always rudimentary; glumes oblong-lanceolate, the lower (2)2.6 – 6(7)mm, the upper (3)3.7 – 7(9)mm; lemmas narrowly oblong-lanceolate in profile, not overlapping at maturity, (4.3)4.7 – 8.5(10)mm, glabrous, scaberulous or pilose, with an awn (0.2)0.6 – 3.5(4.5)mm; anthers 2 – 4(4.5)mm. $2n = 28, 42, 56, 63, 70$. Flowering and fruiting mid-May to early August.

Red Fescue, in some form or other, is found throughout Britain and Ireland. It is common and often abundant in a great variety of managed and unmanaged grasslands and in an extremely wide range of habitat-types. A highly variable species comprising different chromosome races, its ubiquity is to some extent explained by the presence of several edaphic- and habitat-based ecotypes and the widespread use of cultivars in agricultural and amenity grasslands. The distributions of several subspecific taxa (see below) are mapped separately in the New Atlas. *F. rubra* sens. lat. can be found in a variety of semi-natural grasslands including those on chalk and limestone, in fen meadows, heaths, saltmarshes, sand-dunes, sea cliffs, hill and mountain pasture, scree slopes and rock ledges.

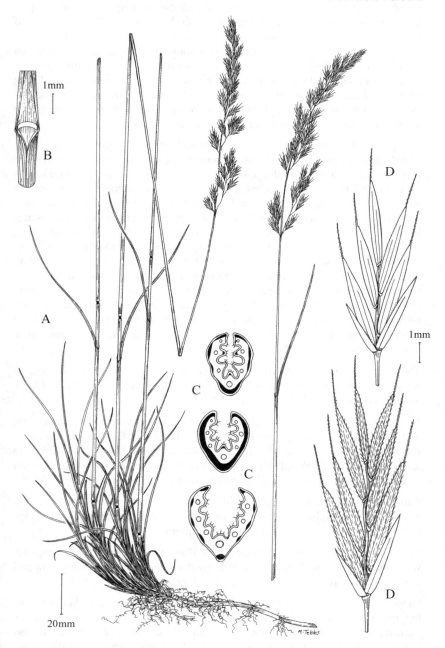

Festuca rubra: A, habit; B, ligule; C, transverse sections of tiller leaves; D, spikelets.

It occurs in lowland meadows, all types of sown grassland such as lawns, road verges and sports turf, and in waste ground including mining and industrial spoil (and sometimes in woodland, hedgerows or scrub). Mostly on base-rich soils of pH >5.0, it is absent only from the most acidic habitats. Across this wide range of habitats it has many associates and can be found in dense monospecific stands (on motorway verges), as a co-dominant (of hill pasture with *Agrostis capillaris* or upper saltmarsh with *Agrostis stolonifera*), as a common component (of fertile agricultural grassland), as an understory plant (in tall grassland communities) or as scattered individuals (in species-rich meadows or on metal contaminated mine waste). It occurs from sea-level to 1080m on Snowdon (Caerns).

The presence of cytological races, widespread ecotypic differentiation, many introduced and bred varieties and its occupancy of a wide range of habitats suggest that *F. rubra* is a highly variable species. However, most segregates are variations on the central theme of a long-lived, fairly slow-growing, winter-green, polycarpic perennial able to spread both vegetatively and by seed which are released each summer and germinate mainly in the autumn. Some individuals may be very long-lived as revealed by a study of genotype distribution in semi-natural grassland in the Pentland Hills which used morphology and cross-compatibility studies to demonstrate that many clones were widely distributed and that one was likely to be between 400 and 1000 years old (Harberd, 1961). The species is mainly self-incompatible. Particular subspecies and populations display tolerance of a wide range of extreme conditions including drought, salinity and lead-contaminated soils. This variation has been exploited by plant breeders to produce a range of specialized cultivars for environments such as spray-affected coastal grasslands and mine wastes. (CPE: 308).

The *F. rubra* complex contains both native and introduced elements most of which are widely distributed as natives in Europe and several of which are widely naturalized outside their native range.

F. rubra is similar to *F. ovina* in the sense that it is a complex comprising an uncertain number of morphologically poorly circumscribed cytological and ecological races. It is represented in the British Isles by two main ploidy levels, hexaploid ($2n = 42$) and octoploid ($2n = 56$) and although they overlap in many characters and cannot be reliably separated by morphology alone, some trends do exist:

Tufted plants with numerous intravaginal shoots and slender leaves and culms are likely to be hexaploid, while strongly rhizomatous, more robust plants with few or no intravaginal shoots are likely to be octoploid.

In leaf structure, plants with few vascular bundles and ribs are probably hexaploid, while those with more bundles and ribs, greater sclerenchyma development and stiff leaves with rounded section are probably octoploid.

Hairy lemmas are common in octoploids, except in subsp. *megastachys*; amongst the hexaploids, only subsp. *arctica* commonly has hairy lemmas. Lemmas exceeding 5.5mm suggest octoploids, while those less than 5.5mm suggest hexaploids, but there are many plants that straddle these limits (especially subsp. *litoralis*).

The following are taxa that are commonly encountered in modern European literature, all of them reported for the British Isles:

Subsp. *oraria* Dumort (*F. juncifolia* Chaub) is one of the more readily recognizable races with its stiff junciform leaves and extensive rhizomes without intravaginal shoots. The sclerenchyma is confluent into an uninterrupted ring and the blade is smoothly rounded in section and sharply pointed at the tip. The relatively large spikelets are borne in a rather dense panicle and have characteristically pilose lemmas; the panicle is not always fully exserted and is of a rather pale green colour. Octoploid. This and the following subspecies are plants of coastal sand-dunes, shingle, sandy places near the sea and cliff-tops in scattered localities northwards to NE Scotland but are generally rare on the west coast north of S Wales (SPB: 171). They are found most often on semi-mobile foredunes with *Ammophila arenaria* and *Leymus arenarius* where they spread by rhizomes and seed. On heavy shingle, subsp. *oraria* tends to be more clump-forming. Due to taxonomic uncertainties this and the following subspecies (subsp. *arenaria*) have been placed on the **Waiting List** by Cheffings & Farrell (2005).

Subsp. *arenaria* (Osbeck) F.Aresch (*F. arenaria* Osbeck) is similar to subsp. *oraria* and merges with it. Its leaves are marginally less junciform because the sclerenchyma is broken into separate islets although these are of low profile and often contiguous at their margins. In T/S the blade shows a distinct rounded keel; the upper surface is said by some authors to be densely pilose, but this is not diagnostic (cf. subsp. *megastachys*). The panicle is shorter, somewhat more spreading and has some degree of purple coloration to it. The two elements are similar in spikelet morphology and leaf and lemma pubescence, and they grow in similar habitats. They were amalgamated by Stace under the name *F. arenaria*.

Subsp. *litoralis* (G.Meyer) Auquier has shorter rhizomes and narrower, less junciform leaves that are at most sparsely pubescent on the upper surface; the sheaths are glabrous. The blade in T/S shows a definite keel because the sclerenchyma is broken into separate islets. The panicle is narrow with relatively few spikelets and is closed even at anthesis. The glabrous lemmas are probably the longest amongst the hexaploids. Although hexaploid, it is reluctant to cross with other hexaploids. Scattered around the British coast, mainly on the grazed saltmarshes of the west coast, subsp. *litoralis* is found in the middle and upper zones of saltmarshes where, with *Puccinellia maritima* and/or *Agrostis stolonifera* it can dominate large areas (and has been cut for 'sea-washed' turf of the highest quality for tennis courts and bowling greens). It is also found in brackish grazing marsh and occasionally in dune slacks.

Subsp. *pruinosa* (Hack.) Piper is usually a compact, often pruinose, tufted plant. The panicle is short, dense and ovate. It tends to have shorter spikelets, shorter, narrower lemmas and shorter awns than *litoralis*, but overlap is considerable. It is hexaploid and similarly reluctant to cross. It occurs on exposed sea cliffs mainly in western Britain from the Isle of Wight to southern Scotland including the Channel Islands and the Isles of Scilly (and also in Ireland). Typically found on well-drained soils and cliff ledges, including seabird colonies, it is often associated with *Armeria maritima*.

Subsp. *juncea* (Hack.) K.Richt. is distinguishable from *pruinosa* by its lack of glaucous coloration. It is, however, an inland plant, often tufted and turf-forming. It was amalgamated with *pruinosa* by Stace but it is hard to see how Hackel's original description of a plant from the gravelly shores of lakes and rivers could encompass *pruinosa*. Both hexaploid and octoploid counts are known for it, but Hackel's original plant may have been octoploid.

Subsp. *scotica* S.Cunn & Al-Bermani, a recently described variant unknown outside of the British Isles, is widespread in the north but is not particularly montane. It is said to have sclerenchyma beneath the upper epidermis but the illustration in Stace (1997) shows it without (see also the key to subspecies of *F. rubra* and the description of subsp. *scotica*). The panicle is narrow with erect branches, but other diagnostic characters such as spikelet, lemma and awn lengths are not convincing. The lemmas are often hairy, a feature not mentioned in the original description, and this can cause confusion with subsp. *arenaria*. Octoploids, nonaploids and decaploids are known and some specimens may even be hexaploid. The conservation status of this subspecies is uncertain (**data deficient**, Cheffings & Farrell, 2005).

Subsp. *arctica* (Hack.) Govor. (*F. richardsonii* Hook) is a mixture of hexaploids and nonaploids. The plants have a short, densely pilose lemma with short awn and the upper part of the panicle is often racemose. Glabrous plants occur in some populations and can be misleading. Occurs on mountains and on basic rocks in northern England, Wales and Scotland, mainly on wet slopes, ledges and flushes, but does seem to come down to sea-level (often on serpentine) where a similarity to subsp. *arenaria* becomes evident and has caused confusion in the past. It is almost certainly under-recorded, the first reports from England being as recently as 1995 (Halliday, 1995).

Subsp. *commutata* Gaudin (*F. nigrescens* Lam.) is an inland race popular as a lawn grass (as 'Chewing's Fescue') but which occurs as a native in grassland on well-drained soils. It has an almost complete lack of rhizomes, but rhizome production in the genus is known to be at least partly under environmental control (Skálová *et al.*, 1997) and the boundary between subsp. *commutata* and subsp. *rubra* can be hard to identify; in hot dry summers it can virtually disappear as subsp. *rubra* abandons its rhizomes and adopts a loose tufted habit. Plants with small glossy yellow-green and purple florets with long awns (2 – 3mm) resemble those continental plants that have been segregated as *F. nigrescens*. Normally hexaploid; tetraploid counts have also been reported but these are likely to have come from misidentified plants. Scattered throughout mainland Britain north to southern Scotland and apparently especially frequent in S Devon, subsp. *commutata* occurs in a range of open habitats such as road verges and railway embankments usually on well-drained chalky or sandy soils.

Subsp. *megastachys* Gaudin (*F. diffusa* Dumort., *F. heteromalla* Pourr., *F. rubra* subsp. *fallax* (Thuill.) Nyman) is a widespread form for which various chromosome numbers have been reported (2n=42, 56, 70). It is a little known and poorly defined taxon, but is usually described as a tall, loosely tufted plant with a more or less diffuse panicle. It has a tendency to produce flat basal leaves that often have pilose ribs; sclerenchyma beneath the upper epidermis is the rule, but is not diagnostic. It has probably been much introduced as an amenity grass and is classed as a neophyte in the New Atlas but native populations have been known since the late-eighteenth century.

Subsp. *rubra* is nowadays regarded as a hexaploid. It forms loose tufts or patches with numerous non-flowering fine-leaved shoots. In unimproved soils it generally has slender culms seldom exceeding 50cm. The panicle is usually laxer than in *arctica, litoralis* and *pruinosa* and ± opens out at anthesis. The lemmas are up to c.5.5mm (excluding awn) and usually glabrous or almost so. It is ecologically less specific than other subspecies and is widely distributed, including in the habitats of many other *F. rubra* subspecies. Agricultural strains are widespread, often atypical of the native plant, and can give rise to yet further confusion. There is little doubt that many plants allocated to this subspecies are a mixture of elements of uncertain affinity within the currently suggested classification.

From the above it is clear that the infra-specific taxonomy of *F. rubra* is too vague to be of much practical value in the field and attempts at determination of subspecies are to be discouraged without adequate laboratory and experimental growth facilities. The three most recent accounts of the group – Kerguélen & Plonka (1989), Stace (1997) and Portal (1999) – differ on number, circumscription and rank of taxa, and indeed their chromosome numbers. The value of chromosome number is doubtful as several taxa appear to show a considerable range, but how much of this variation can be attributed to uncertain or incorrect identification is unknown. On the other hand, some of this variation could well be the product of differing views on the circumscriptions of segregate taxa.

F. rubra hybridizes with various species of *Vulpia* and in all cases the hybrid is perennial with sparse or absent rhizomes and some leaf-sheaths have overlapping margins. They all seem to be male-sterile although Stace (1997) speculates that some fertility may exist. They can occur where the parents grow together but they are easily overlooked. They are very similar to one another but can be distinguished as follows:

F. rubra × *V. fasciculata* (×**Festulpia hubbardii** Stace & R.Cotton; incl. *F. arenaria* × *V. fasciculata* (×*Festulpia melderisii* Stace & R.Cotton)) generally has a distally expanded pedicel, an awned upper glume and a long-awned lemma. That version called ×*F. melderisii* has longer glumes and lemma, but a similar lemma-awn and anther; $2n = 42$. ×*F. hubbardii* is $2n = 35$.

F. rubra × *V. bromoides* lacks the swollen pedicel and has an awnless upper glume; the panicle is inclined to be open. It may have originated from more than one segregate of *F. rubra*.

F. rubra × *V. myuros* is very similar to the preceding but tends to have the narrow panicle of its *Vulpia* parent. Again, more than one segregate of *F. rubra* may have contributed to it.

15.   **Festuca longifolia** Thuill.

Blue Fescue

New Atlas: 748

Densely tufted plant without rhizomes; culms erect, up to 40(45)cm; tillers intravaginal; leaves usually strongly glaucous, stiff; sheaths open to the base, glabrous; ligule a narrow membranous rim; blades tightly folded with rounded keel, 0.5 – 0.85mm from midrib to edge, 7(9)-nerved, usually with 4 grooves on the upper surface defining 3 rounded ribs along the midline, upper surface glabrous to puberulent, lower surface usually smooth and glabrous, often pruinose; sclerenchyma continuous and the leaf ± oval in section, or subcontinuous in 3 main and several minor islets of low profile and with lateral tails often contiguous to their neighbours, the leaf in section ± oval or the epidermis contracted between the major islets. Panicle 2.5 – 6cm; pedicels 0.6 – 1mm. Spikelets 5.4 – 7.7mm, 4- to 7-flowered, the uppermost floret often rudimentary; glumes oblong-lanceolate, the lower (1.6)2 – 3(3.3)mm, the upper (2.5)3.2 – 3.8(4.5)mm; lemmas narrowly oblong-lanceolate in profile, not overlapping at maturity, 3.8 – 5.2mm, with awns 1.2 – 2.2mm; anthers 1.7 – 2.6mm. $2n = 14$. Flowering and fruiting late May to mid-July in the east, earlier in the southwest.

A rare grass in Britain, *F. longifolia* has a curiously disjunct distribution, being found in acid heathland-type habitats in eastern England and maritime cliff-tops in S Devon, Cornwall (one site) and the Channel Islands. In eastern England it occurs in the Breckland of W Suffolk where it was first discovered in 1804, in Lincolnshire and in Nottinghamshire (one site), almost all rather small populations on dry, often rabbit-grazed, acid heaths or sandy roadsides. In S Devon, Cornwall and the Channel Islands it is limited to thin, immature soils on rocky coastal cliffs, again mostly acidic but not exclusively so (most populations in S Devon are on soils between pH 4.7 and 6.1, but 2 sites are on limestone at pH 7.3 to 8.5 (Smith & Margetts, 2001)). The very different plant associates in the two contrasting types of habitat in England are listed in full by Gibson & Taylor (2005).

Blue Fescue is a slow-growing densely tufted perennial which spreads by seed. The plant requires a period of winter chilling in order to flower and individuals do not flower every year. Plants in the southwest appear to flower earlier (April/May) than those in Breckland (May/June). The seed, often dispersed in groups of florets, are capable of immediate germination but the main period of seedling establishment is not known. Young seedlings are susceptible to drought, although mature plants are very drought tolerant and almost all occur in xeric environments. In fact, its restriction to the drier more open parts of the habitat, often on the thinnest soils which cannot support more vigorous species, indicates that the species is a poor competitor and vulnerable to shading from taller plants. It is an outbreeder, being completely, or almost completely, self-sterile. (Biol. Flora: Gibson & Taylor, 2005; RDB: 157; also Smith & Margetts, 2001).

F. longifolia is native and endemic to Europe, being found only in England, the Channel Islands and France (and perhaps Belorussia; see Gibson & Taylor, 2005).

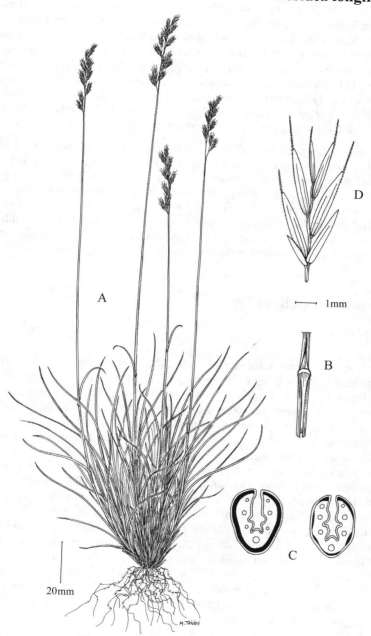

A

D

1mm

B

C

20mm

M.Tebbs

Festuca longifolia: A, habit; B, ligule; C, transverse sections of tiller leaves; D, spikelet.

It is thus an Oceanic Temperate species. Although probably confused in the past with other blue-grey fescues (see below) creating uncertainties about changes in distribution, it is clear that *F. longifolia* populations in eastern England are under threat from change in their habitat. Several have been lost in Breckland, where reduction in rabbit grazing may have allowed coarse grasses to overrun some colonies and the widespread planting of conifers has shaded out others (RDB: 157). Its coastal cliff habitats appear less threatened and the species could be more widely distributed in the southwest where most sites were discovered relatively recently (the early 1990s in Devon, although first recorded there in 1936), and where apparently suitable habitat is plentiful.

The species has been misunderstood in the past, and many names have been applied – or misapplied – to it, among them *F. caesia* Sm., *F. glauca* Vill. and *F. glauca* var. *caesia* (Sm.) Howarth. The true *F. glauca* is a related – but quite distinct – species available in garden centres under the name 'Blue Fescue'. *F. longifolia* is most likely to be confused with *F. brevipila* but this has (mostly) puberulent sheaths and conspicuously longer pedicels; it, too, has stiff blades but these are rather less glaucous than those of *F. longifolia;* it is also more widespread, being included in many seed-mixes for amenity grass.

16.   Festuca brevipila R.Tracey

Hard Fescue   New Atlas: 748

Densely tufted plant without rhizomes; culms erect, up to 50(70)cm; tillers intravaginal; leaves green or glaucous, stiff; sheaths open to the base, usually pubescent; ligule a narrow membranous rim; blades tightly folded with rounded, sometimes prominent, keel, 0.5 – 0.8(0.9)mm from midrib to edge, (5)7(9)-nerved, usually with 4 grooves on the upper surface defining 3 rounded ribs along the midline, upper surface sparsely puberulent, lower surface mostly pubescent below, scaberulous to scabrid above, sometimes pruinose; sclerenchyma rarely continuous and the leaf ± oval in section, mostly subcontinuous with 3 main and sometimes several minor islets of low profile with lateral tails often contiguous to their neighbours and the leaf in section less smoothly oval with the epidermis slightly contracted between the major islets, especially on either side of the keel. Panicle 3.5 – 9.5cm, usually somewhat nodding; pedicels 1.7 – 3(3.5)mm. Spikelets 6.5 – 8(8.5)mm, (4)5- to 7(8)-flowered, the uppermost floret usually rudimentary; glumes oblong-lanceolate, glabrous to scabrid or puberulous, the lower 2 – 3.5mm, the upper 3 – 4.7mm; lemmas narrowly oblong-lanceolate in profile, not overlapping at maturity, (4.2)4.4 – 5.3mm, glabrous to scabrid or puberulous, with awns 2 – 3.2mm; anthers 1.8 – 3mm. $2n = 42$. Flowering and fruiting early May to early July.

F. brevipila is widely scattered in man-made habitats throughout England as far north as Yorkshire, and is most common in the south and east. It has been

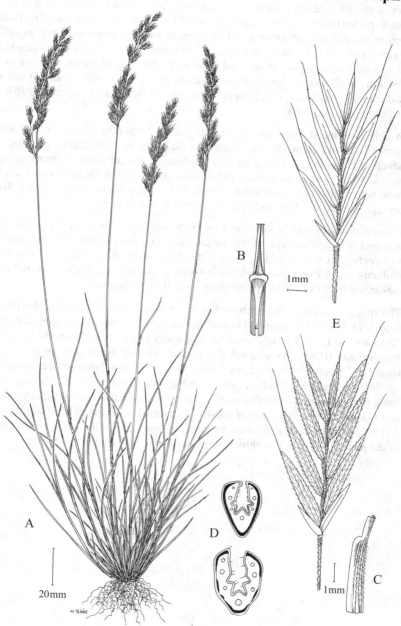

Festuca brevipila: A, habit; B, ligule; C, top of sheath; D, transverse sections of tiller leaves; E, spikelets.

recorded from one or two isolated sites in W Scotland, from Newport Docks in Wales and from Jersey (AGB: 13). It is absent from Ireland. Introduced as a turf grass species (also as *F. duriuscula*, see below), it is now well established on road verges and railway embankments, in a range of amenity grasslands such as golf courses and sports grounds, in lawns and on waste ground. It has been recorded in at least two locations from fixed dune turf. The soils in which it grows are generally well-drained sandy or stony substrates and are usually acidic. It has a wide range of associates and, although generally a lowland species, reaches 365m at Taddington (Derbys).

Widely introduced (here and in the USA) as a component of turf for amenity purposes, Hard Fescue (the name refers to the hardness of the mature panicle) is advertized as being hard-wearing, drought-tolerant and providing 'bottom' to the sward in the form of its densely tufted habit. Beyond that we have no detailed information on its reproductive or population biology in the areas where it has become naturalized. It is perennial and probably outbreeding.

Classed as a neophyte in the New Atlas, *F. brevipila* is a native of C Europe and was probably first introduced into Britain from Germany in the early part of the 19th century. It was recorded in the wild about 1830 (from Middlesex) and is probably much overlooked today. However, taxonomic confusion (see below) makes it difficult to assess current changes in its distribution.

The species has been misunderstood in the past and was often confused with *F. longifolia*. It has been imported in seed mixes, mostly under the misapplied name *F. duriuscula* L., and widely sown as an amenity grass. It also bears the name *F. trachyphylla* (Hack.) Krajina but this epithet properly belongs to an unrelated species (*F. trachyphylla* Hack. ex Druce; the epithet can, however, be correctly applied at subspecies level – *F. stricta* subsp. *trachyphylla* (Hack.) Patzke – as some European authors choose to do). The main differences between this species and *F. longifolia* are found in the usually pubescent (rather than glabrous) sheaths and the longer pedicels and awns. Awn lengths overlap to a small degree but those of the pedicels do not. The chromosome numbers, also, are very different.

17. Festuca vivipara (L.) Sm.

Viviparous Sheep's-fescue

Densely tufted plant without rhizomes; culms erect, up to 50cm; tillers intravaginal; leaves usually green, sometimes glaucous, slender (rarely filiform); sheaths open to the base, smooth; ligule a narrow membranous rim; blades tightly folded with rounded keel, (0.3)0.35 – 0.6(0.7)mm from midrib to edge, 5-nerved, usually with 2 grooves on the upper surface defining a single rounded rib along the midline, upper surface sparsely puberulent, lower surface smooth and glabrous; sclerenchyma continuous and the leaf ± oval in section, or subcontinuous in 3(5) main islets of low profile and the leaf less smoothly oval in section with the epidermis slightly contracted between the main islets. Panicle 3.5 – 6cm, the two lowest nodes (5)9 – 20mm apart; pedicels (0.5)1 – 2(2.4)mm. Spikelets with some or most (rarely all) florets proliferous, 4 – 6.3mm to the tip of the uppermost non-proliferous lemma (usually the second or third, sometimes the lowermost), 3- to 7-flowered, the basal 1 – 3 normal, the rest proliferous; glumes oblong-lanceolate, the lower 1.6 – 3.1mm, the upper 2.6 – 4.4mm; lemmas oblong-lanceolate in profile, often barren, without a palea and with their margins overlapping, rarely fertile, the lowermost (if not proliferous) 3 – 5.5mm, often pubescent, muticous or rarely with a mucro up to 0.3mm, proliferous lemmas with distinct sheath and blade up to several cm long; anthers rare, 1.6 – 2.6mm. $2n = 21, 28$. Flowering and fruiting mid-June to early September.

F. vivipara has a strongly northwestern distribution in Great Britain and Ireland, being found in NW Scotland, the Western Isles, Orkney and Shetland, the Scottish Southern Uplands, NW England, NW Wales and the west of Ireland. Outlier populations occur, e.g. in Co Waterford in Ireland, and those in the Brecon Beacons in Wales are at the species' southern limit. It is predominantly a grass of the uplands occurring on hill pasture, heathland, rock ledges and mountain slopes and plateaux at high altitudes. It is found in open woodland (mostly birch and oak), on the banks of streams and in bogs. Soils can be basic or acidic and sometimes very immature and thin. It has a range of associates. In the high plateaux in Scotland, where it grows in very harsh conditions, it may be found with *Deschampsia flexuosa, Juncus trifidus* and *Luzula spicata*, often surrounded by extensive beds of the moss *Racomitrium lanuginosum*. As well as these high altitudes (up to 1215m on Ben Macdui, S Aberdeen) *F. vivipara* also occurs down to sea-level in western Scotland and Ireland.

A key feature of the biology of *F. vivipara* is the replacement of most spikelets by small 'plantlets' capable of dispersal and independent establishment. This process, correctly termed 'proliferation' or 'pseudovivipary', is seen in several other British grasses, and is extensive in some such as *Poa alpina*, but in none is it the exclusive, or almost exclusive, method of reproduction as in *F. vivipara*. Vegetative proliferation is generally regarded as an adaptation to a short growing season and extremes of cold and/or rainfall. The plantlets have between 3 and 4 times as much carbohydrate reserve and a greater mineral nutrient content than the seeds of *Festuca ovina* (Harmer & Lee, 1978a, b), which may enable them to establish more easily at low temperatures (although they cannot, of course, remain dormant for long periods). The adaptive value of proliferation is indicated by its distribution in *Poa alpina*, the proliferous forms (which are polyploids) tending to occur at higher elevations and in harsher environments than the sexual and agamospermous forms (diploids and tetraploids). Conversely (or perhaps perversely) the frequently proliferous *Poa bulbosa* is a lowland grass of dry coastal sands and shingle in the southeast (see that account). It has been shown that seed from *F. vivipara*, rarely found in the field, produce plants which are mainly proliferous, and thus the condition is heritable. Presumably, it leads to large areas being covered by one or two genotypes but we have no confirmation of this.

F. vivipara is native in the British Isles where its range appears to be stable. It is part of the Circumpolar Boreo-arctic element in our flora.

Despite the, as mentioned above, the species is not strictly viviparous (with seeds germinating while still attached to the parent) but proliferous with the uppermost lemmas reverting to their ancestral role of foliage leaves by developing a significant blade at the summit of the body (this originally being a bladeless sheath). It is sometimes difficult to tell whether or not a lemma has begun to proliferate, the only indication being its unusual length compared with those below. Even when only the upper florets have proliferated the lower often lose their paleas. Only rarely are the lower florets complete and fertile.

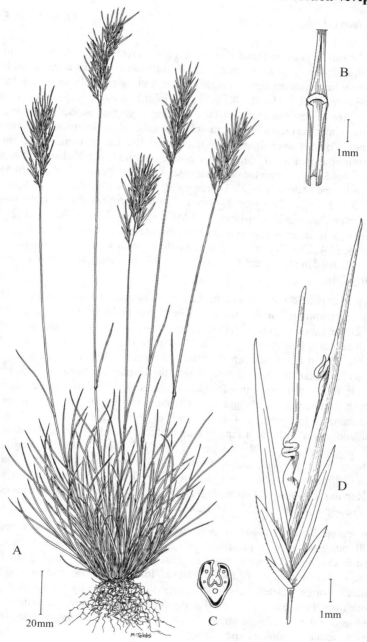

Festuca vivipara: A. habit; B. ligule; C, transverse section of tiller leaf; D, spikelet.

18. Festuca filiformis Pourr.

Fine-leaved Sheep's-fescue   New Atlas: 747

Densely tufted plant without rhizomes; culms erect, up to 45(60)cm; tillers intravaginal; leaves usually green, slender to filiform; sheaths open to the base, smooth or scaberulous; ligule a narrow membranous rim; blades tightly folded with rounded keel, 0.25 – 0.4(0.5)mm from midrib to edge, 5(7)-nerved, usually with 2 grooves on the upper surface defining a single rounded rib along the midline, upper surface glabrous to sparsely puberulent, lower surface smooth or scaberulous; sclerenchyma continuous and the leaf ± oval in section, or subcontinuous in 3 main islets of low profile and the leaf ± Y-shaped in section with the epidermis contracted on either side of the keel. Panicle (2)4 – 7.5(9.5)cm, the two lowest nodes (5)8 – 22(31)mm apart; pedicels 1 – 2.1(2.6)mm. Spikelets (3.8)4.3 – 5.6mm, (3)4- to 7(8)-flowered, the uppermost floret nearly always rudimentary; glumes oblong-lanceolate, the lower 1.4 – 2.3mm, the upper (2.1)2.3 – 3.1(3.4)mm; lemmas narrowly oblong-lanceolate in profile, not overlapping at maturity, (2.4)2.7 – 3.8mm, glabrous, muticous or with a mucro or short awn-point to 0.3(0.5)mm; anthers 1.3 – 2mm. $2n = 14$. Flowering and fruiting late May to early July.

Widely, but patchily, distributed in the British Isles, *F. filiformis* is frequent but much less common than *F. ovina* and is quite rare in the west where it can attain local conservation importance. Possible confusion with *F. ovina* makes its status and distribution somewhat uncertain but the most recent map in the New Atlas indicates that it has a number of centres of distribution in areas of acidic soils such as the Dorset heaths, the New Forest, the Tertiary sands and gravels around London, East Anglia including Breckland, the N Yorkshire Moors, Teesdale, the Scottish Southern Uplands and the extreme northwest of Scotland. It appears to be scattered in the north of Ireland and very rare in the south. Its habitats are heathland, moorland and a range of unproductive acidic grasslands, including open woodland and parkland where it may have been sown in amenity turf mixtures. Soils are acid, well-drained, sandy or peaty, and generally nutrient-poor. *F. filiformis* may also be found in the heathland-type communities which develop in the older decalcified stages of fixed sand-dunes and shingle. It occurs from sea-level to 1035m (Meall Ghaordie, M Perth).

Fine-leaved Sheep's-fescue is perennial and polycarpic and under suitable conditions may form a persistent compact turf able to withstand close and frequent cutting and grazing. It is fairly drought resistant and tends to be found in the higher, drier parts of lowland heath. In such habitats, and in woodland, it usually forms isolated tufts (distinguished in the south by their darker green colour from the equally fine-leaved *Agrostis curtisii*). It is reported to have short-lived seed and to be self-incompatible but we are unaware of any detailed studies of its reproductive biology and ecology.

F. filiformis is native in the British Isles and part of the Suboceanic Temperate

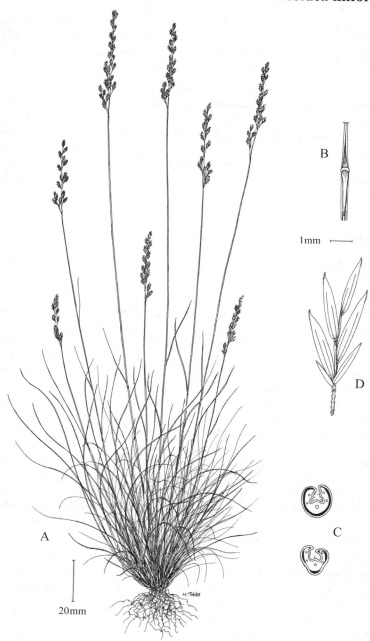

B

1mm

D

C

A

20mm

M.Tebbs

Festuca filiformis: A, habit; B, ligule; C, transverse sections of tiller leaves; D, spikelet.

element in the flora (P&H, 1997). It has been introduced as a lawn grass in N America. Its apparent increase here in the last 40 years is entirely due to increased recording and it may still be under-recorded in some areas. However, the ease with which it may be confused with *F. ovina* (see below and the account of that species) means that it could also be over-recorded elsewhere (see New Atlas and Perring & Sell, 1968).

This should be one of the easier members of the *F. ovina* complex to recognize but unfortunately it does intergrade somewhat with *F. ovina* itself. It characteristically has longer filiform leaves (these may, on occasion, be of similar length) and shorter lemmas, the latter bearing little more than a terminal mucro. A form with shortly hispid lemmas has been described, but this seems to be better regarded as a variant of *F. ovina*; its glumes and lemmas are too long for *F. filiformis* and the awn of the lemma rather too well developed; its leaves, however, are very similar.

19.   Festuca ovina L.

Sheep's-fescue   New Atlas: 746

Densely tufted plant without rhizomes; culms erect, up to 45(60)cm; tillers intravaginal; leaves usually green, sometimes glaucous, slender or rarely filiform; sheaths open to below the middle, smooth or scaberulous, glabrous to thinly pubescent; ligule a narrow membranous rim; blades tightly folded with rounded keel, (0.3)0.4 – 0.55mm from midrib to edge, 5- to 7-nerved, usually with 2 grooves (rarely 4) on the upper surface defining a single rounded rib (rarely 3) along the midline, upper surface sparsely puberulent, lower surface smooth or scaberulous, glabrous or pubescent towards the base; sclerenchyma continuous and the leaf ± oval in section, or subcontinuous in 3 main islets of low profile and the leaf ± Y-shaped in section with the epidermis contracted on either side of the keel. Panicle (2)2.5 – 8cm, the two lowest nodes (5)8 – 19(23)mm apart; pedicels 0.6 – 2.6mm. Spikelets (4.5)5.2 – 7mm, 4- to 7(8)-flowered, the uppermost floret nearly always rudimentary; glumes oblong-lanceolate, the lower 1.6 – 3.3mm, the upper 2.4 – 4.2mm; lemmas narrowly oblong-lanceolate in profile, not overlapping at maturity, 3.1 – 4.8(5)mm, glabrous, scaberulous or hairy, with an awn 0.1 – 1.8mm; anthers 1.4 – 2.6mm. $2n = 14, 28, 42$. Flowering and fruiting mid-May to mid-July or early August.

F. ovina is widely distributed throughout Great Britain and Ireland and is especially abundant in the uplands where it is often the major constituent of extensive areas of permanent pasture. Its habitats are wide-ranging and include upland heaths and moors, mountain slopes, screes and rocky habitats as well as lowland grassland and maritime heathland and cliffs. They may be highly acidic or strongly calcareous but are characteristically on well-drained infertile and often shallow soils. The species may dominate unproductive undisturbed grassland and

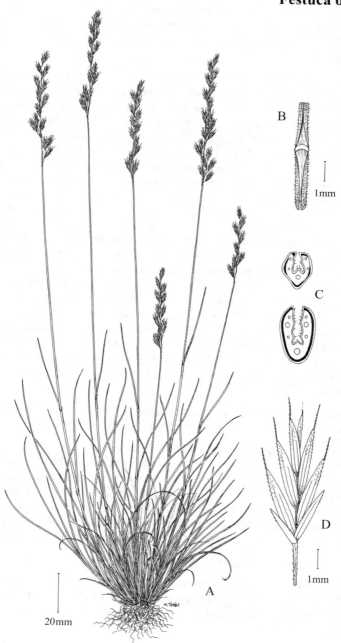

B

1mm

C

D

1mm

20mm

Festuca ovina: A, habit; B, ligule; C, transverse sections of tiller leaves; D, spikelet.

is usually absent or rare in fertile and/or frequently disturbed sites, although it will grow on quarry and mine spoil. It is occasionally included in seed mixtures for amenity or wildflower grassland. It has a wide range of associates, including calcicoles and calcifuges, and occurs from sea-level to 1305m (on Ben Macdui, S Aberdeen).

Sheep's-fescue is a highly variable, polycarpic, winter-green perennial able to thrive in thin, poor soils. Its hardiness, drought-resistance and ability to withstand heavy grazing make it an economically important grass for the hill farmer. It is essentially a species of permanent pasture where individuals may be very long-lived, clones more than 10m in diameter being estimated to be hundreds of years old (Harberd, 1962). Experiments suggest that the species' survival and abundance depends on its occupancy of infertile, seasonally-droughted sites or the suppression of more competitive species in less stressed environments. For example, protection from grazing by sheep in upland grassland on mineral soils in Wales led to the decline of *F. ovina* in favour of species such as *Calluna vulgaris* and *Agrostis capillaris*. By contrast, *F. ovina* attained dominance within rabbit-proof exclosures on the acidic, nutrient-poor soils of the English Breckland. *F. ovina* also responds poorly to added nitrogen compared to other species. Its drought tolerance is despite a fairly shallow fibrous root system, and is likely to be linked to the very narrow leaves and the early annual growth and flowering. The species is self-incompatible and produces seed which germinate in summer (apart from a few in spring in northern populations) and do not form a persistent seed bank. Its ability to occupy both acidic and calcareous soils is linked to the development of edaphic ecotypes which differ in their response to calcium, and other ecotypic differentiation (including the development of races that are tolerant of heavy metals) undoubtedly exists within the species complex (see below). (CPE: 304).

F. ovina is native in the British Isles and belongs to the Eurasian Boreo-temperate element in our flora. It is widely naturalized outside its native range.

F. ovina is rather hard to define. It has smaller spikelets and thinner blades than either *F. brevipila* or *F. longifolia*, but larger spikelets and thicker blades than *F. filiformis*. The latter is nearly always awnless and the blades and spikelets are generally taken to be glabrous. Specimens resembling *F. filiformis*, but with hairy blades and/or lemmas are accommodated in *F. ovina* but a compelling case could be made for allowing several of them into *F. filiformis* on virtually all other characters. The boundary between these two species needs to be clarified.

The variation of *F. ovina* can be summarized as follows:

Diploids. Specimens with $2n = 14$ are usually assigned to subsp. *ovina*. According to Wilkinson & Stace (1991) this has spikelets 5.3 – 6.3mm, scabrid lemmas 3.1 – 4.2mm, awns 0 – 1.2mm and glabrous blades with stomata <31.5μ. It is found on the more acid soils.

Tetraploids. Two taxa have chromosome numbers of $2n = 28$. Subsp. *ophioliticola* (Kerguélen) M.J.Wilk. has spikelets 5.5 – 7.5mm and lemmas 3.6 – 4.9mm. It is found on calcareous and serpentine soils. Subsp. *hirtula* (Hack. & Travis) M.J.Wilk. is similar to subsp. *ovina* but has shorter awns (0 – 0.8mm) and its blades and lemmas are usually pubescent; stomata are >31.5μ It is found in similar habitats but is said to be the more common.

Hexaploids. Specimens with $2n = 42$ are often separated as a distinct taxon, *F. lemanii* Bastard. This is hard to distinguish from the rest of the *ovina* complex but is usually said to have spikelets over 7.5mm. It is also said to be widespread but this is not apparent from available material. Spikelet size may give rise to confusion with *F. brevipila* but the two are otherwise quite different, especially in leaf characters. As a species *F. lemanii* is not convincing in Europe and has a very vague circumscription. In spikelet size and leaf characters it is closer to *F. huonii* and *F. armoricana* both of which are confined to coastal areas in the Channel Islands.

F. ovina is best regarded as a complex of intergrading cytological and ecological races for which suitable discriminating morphological characters are not readily available. Identification beyond species level should not be attempted without adequate laboratory facilities.

20. Festuca armoricana Kerguélen

Breton Fescue   New Atlas: 747

Densely tufted plant without rhizomes; culms erect, up to 40cm; tillers intravaginal; leaves usually green, slender; sheaths open from just above the middle, smooth and glabrous or rarely puberulous above; ligule a narrow membranous rim; blades tightly folded with rounded keel, 0.4 − 0.5mm from midrib to edge, 5- to 7-nerved, with 2 or 4 grooves on the upper surface defining 1 or 3 rounded ribs along the midline, upper surface puberulent, lower surface usually smooth and glabrous, rarely puberulous; sclerenchyma usually continuous, occasionally subcontinuous, the leaf ± oval in section. Panicle 2.5 − 4.5cm, the two lowest nodes 8 − 16mm apart; pedicels 0.6 − 1.5mm. Spikelets 6.8 − 7.4mm, 3- to 6-flowered, the uppermost floret usually rudimentary; glumes lanceolate, the lower 2.8 − 3.4mm, the upper 3.7 − 4.8mm; lemmas oblong-lanceolate in profile, not overlapping at maturity, 4.5 − 5.1mm, usually glabrous or scaberulous, with an awn 1.4 − 2.2mm; anthers 1.9 − 2.4mm. $2n = 28$. Flowering and fruiting late May to mid-June.

F. armoricana is a little-known species in the *F. ovina* group confined to Jersey in the Channel Islands where it occurs over large areas of fixed sand-dunes in St Ouen's Bay and St Bredale's Bay. It is regarded as a native species and has been recorded from similar habitats in Brittany. It was not mapped in the 1962 Atlas and may have been overlooked on other islands (and perhaps even in southern England). We have no specific information on the species' ecology but believe it to be a fairly long-lived perennial, polycarpic and probably outbreeding.

F. armoricana is similar in spikelet size and awn length to both *F. longifolia* and *F. brevipila* but usually has more slender leaves. It differs also from the former by its green foliage and allopatric distribution and from the latter by its shorter pedicels. Some material determined by Markgraf-Dannenberg as *F. armoricana* (including one sheet from Vc1) has smaller spikelets and shorter lemmas with shorter awns and the lemmas, furthermore, are pilose. It seems better to accommodate these plants in *F. ovina* otherwise any attempt to distinguish the two taxa on their morphology becomes an impossibility. *F. armoricana* can be distinguished from *F. ovina* only by its spikelet dimensions, and the relationship between them is clearly very close.

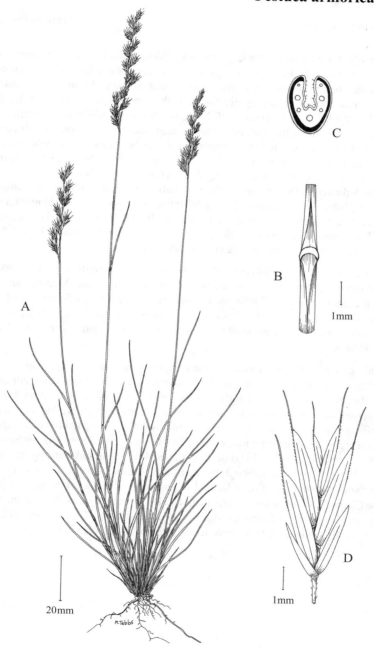

Festuca armoricana: A, habit; B, ligule; C, transverse section of tiller leaf; D, spikelet.

21. Festuca huonii Auquier

Huon's Fescue New Atlas: 747

Densely tufted plant without rhizomes; culms usually prostrate, sometimes erect, up to 25cm; tillers intravaginal; leaves green, sometimes faintly pruinose; sheaths open from just above the middle, smooth and glabrous; ligule a narrow membranous rim; blades tightly folded with rounded keel, 0.35 – 0.8mm from midrib to edge, 5- to 7-nerved, with 2(4) grooves on the upper surface defining 1(3) rounded ribs along the midline, upper surface weakly puberulous, lower surface usually smooth and glabrous, rarely weakly puberulous below; sclerenchyma continuous or subcontinuous, the leaf oval in section. Panicle 2.5 – 3.5(5.5)cm, the two lowest nodes 8 – 10mm apart; pedicels 0.8 – 1.6mm. Spikelets 6 – 7(8)mm, 3- to 5-flowered, the uppermost floret usually rudimentary; glumes lanceolate to oblong-lanceolate, the lower 2.2 – 2.5(3)mm, the upper 3.1 – 4(4.5)mm; lemmas lanceolate in profile, not overlapping at maturity, (3.7)4.3 – 4.8(5.3)mm, usually scabrid above, rarely hairy, with an awn 1.2 – 1.5(2.3)mm; anthers 1.5 – 2.6mm. $2n = 42$. Flowering and fruiting early to late May.

As with *F. armoricana* this is a little-known species limited to the Channel Islands and Brittany. It has been recorded from Guernsey, Jersey and Alderney and may be present on other smaller islands. It occurs on maritime cliff-tops, rock ledges and screes on acidic soils. *F. huonii* was not recognized in the 1962 Atlas but appears to be frequent and stable within its range. It is probably similar to *F. ovina* in its basic biology.

The species' morphological circumscription is rather vague and varies considerably from author to author but seems to rely mainly on the small stature of the plant, the stiff, strongly curved leaves, a panicle sometimes scarcely exserted from the uppermost sheath and a generally prostrate habit in turf on cliff-tops. Wilkinson & Stace (1991) emphasise the cliff-top habitat of the species but there is some material that was collected in dunes on Jersey. Its chromosome number is hexaploid but this is of little practical value. Its spikelets overlap in size with those of *F. ovina* although the awns are generally longer. It does not occur on the British mainland or in Ireland so problems of recognition are confined to the Channel Islands where its distinctive habit is probably still the best guide for distiguishing it from *F. ovina* and the much more similar *F. armoricana*. There is little to distinguish the latter beyond its habit and chromosome number.

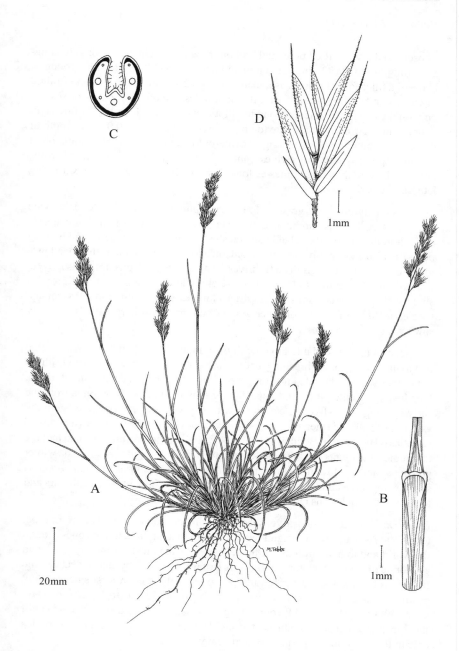

Festuca huonii: A, habit; B, ligule; C, transverse section of tiller leaf; D, spikelet.

22. **Lolium perenne** L.

Perennial Rye-grass

Loosely to densely tufted perennial without rhizomes; culms erect or spreading-ascending, up to 70(90)cm; ligule a membranous rim 0.7 – 1.5(2)mm; youngest blade of a tiller folded lengthwise; mature blades 2 – 6mm wide. Raceme straight or curved, stiff, (4)10 – 20(30)cm, the internodes smooth and glossy or scabrid only on the edges. Spikelets oblong to elliptic, 8 – 21mm, 4- to 11(13)-flowered; upper glume narrowly lanceolate to oblong-lanceolate, 0.45 – 0.9 × the length of the spikelet, blunt; lemmas oblong or ovate-oblong, (4.5)5.5 – 7.5(9.5)mm, blunt or bluntly pointed at the tip, awnless; anthers (2)2.5 – 4(5)mm.; caryopsis narrow, not turgid, more than three times as long as wide. $2n = 14$. Flowering & fruiting late May to early August.

This extremely common grass is found throughout the British Isles in a wide range of largely grass-dominated habitats. Abundant, and often dominant, in agriculturally improved lowland pasture, short-term grass leys, parks and playing fields, it also commonly occurs in old meadows, downland, water-meadows, road verges and waste ground. It thrives best, and populations are longer-lived, in fertile heavy neutral soils under moist climatic conditions, but will grow in slightly acidic or basic soils and in drier climates under cultivation. Associated species include a long list of other grasses and grassland herbs. It is frequently sown with clover species.

The species is very variable biologically, no doubt due in part to the wide range of habitat-types, its outbreeding nature and the ease with which it hybridizes with other species, but also resulting from plant breeding and selection during a long history of cultivation and importation. A major axis of variation is from the early heading, short-lived, erect types, with few vegetative tillers (the 'stemmy' varieties) to the late heading, longer-lived types with many tillers (the 'leafy' varieties) (Biol. Flora: Beddows, 1967; CPE: 406). Modern cultivars also include tetraploids and plants bred for a huge variety of specialist purposes such as winter greenness and hard wearing properties for amenity and sports turf. *L. perenne* is self-incompatible and there is some evidence for gene flow between cultivars and local 'wild' populations (Warren *et al.,* 1998).

L. perenne is our only native species in the genus. It is native in Europe, temperate Asia and N Africa and has been introduced to temperate zones around the world and to high altitudes in the tropics. It is the most commonly sown and economically important forage grass in Britain, and was by many decades the first grass to be sown for agricultural purposes. Cultivated at least since the 17th century (Graves (1822) says it was grown prior to 1577), Rye-grass, or Ray-grass, fell somewhat out of favour during Victorian times (Armstrong, 1943) until modern plant breeders produced the highly productive and palatable varieties able to tolerate trampling, mowing and heavy grazing.

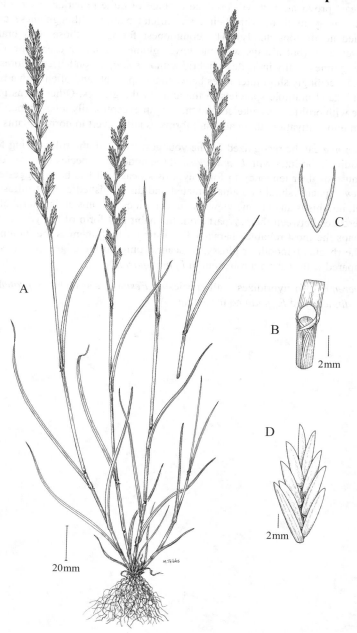

Lolium perenne: A, habit; B, ligule and auricles; C, outline of youngest leaf in section; D, spikelet.

Most of the inflorescence characters in this species are highly unstable and with the least provocation it will produce a range of quite remarkable teratological forms, many of them with their own varietal names (although these are not applied at all consistently). The commonest forms are those with branched inflorescence (but always with the lower glume missing; presence of a small lower glume usually indicates a hybrid with *Festuca*), a condensed inflorescence with exceedingly short internodes between the spikelets and often with a twisted rhachis, and multiple spikelets in the axils of the glumes. Other forms include those with proliferous spikelets and those with exceptionally long glumes. When taken into cultivation, these aberrant forms usually revert to normal plants.

L. perenne can be recognized by the youngest leaves in the tillers being folded. It readily hybridizes with *L. multiflorum*; see under that species for more details. Because of their tendency to form hybrids so easily it has been suggested that the two species should be amalgamated and distinguished only at infraspecific level, but this is an extreme view that undervalues the substantial morphological differences between them. Apart from the habit and form of the youngest leaf, perhaps the most reliable character for distinguishing them is the indumentum of the rhachis (smooth or glossy, or scabrid only on the edges, in this species compared with scabrid throughout in *L. multiflorum*).

L. perenne also hybridizes with species of *Festuca*; see under *F. pratensis*, *F. arundinacea* and *F. gigantea* for details.

23. Lolium multiflorum Lam.

Illustration, page 159

Italian Rye-grass

New Atlas: 749

Annual or sometimes biennial; culms erect or geniculately ascending, up to 100(120)cm; ligule a membranous rim 0.7 – 2.6mm; youngest blade convolute; mature blades flat, up to 11mm wide. Raceme straight or curved, stiff, 15 – 35cm, the internodes dull, scabrid on both the surface and the edges. Spikelets oblong, (13)16 – 25(37)mm, (8)10- to 18(23)-flowered; upper glume oblong-lanceolate, (0.3)0.35 – 0.6 × the length of the spikelet, blunt; lemmas oblong or ovate-oblong, 6 – 9mm, blunt or bluntly pointed at the tip, with an awn 2 – 10mm, sometimes awnless; anthers (2.5)3 – 4.5(5.5)mm; caryopsis narrow, not turgid, more than three times as long as wide. $2n = 14$. Flowering & fruiting early June to late August or even to early October.

Italian Rye-grass is very common in lowland Britain (reaching >400m), having escaped widely from cultivation since it was first introduced in the 1830s. Outside cultivation it is essentially a plant of periodically disturbed habitats such as field headlands, farm tracks, around farm buildings and gateways, roadsides, rubbish tips and waste ground. In these places it may be found growing with a variety of ruderal species.

As in the case of *L. perenne* plant breeding has produced a range of biological variation. Thus *L. multiflorum* includes very short-lived annuals (typified by the cultivar Westerwolths Rye-grass) which do not require cold temperatures or short days in order to flower, and obligate biennials which do require these conditions. In the wild, populations may persist for several years by self-sowing, especially in rich moist soils. Seed rapidly loses viability in storage. (Biol. Flora: Beddows, 1973).

L. multiflorum is a neophyte in Britain. Probably native to the Mediterranean area, the species was cultivated in the Lombardy region of Italy by the 14th century, and is now widespread in temperate zones around the world where it has been introduced for fodder. The first authenticated date of introduction to Britain is 1831 (Armstrong, 1943).

As with *L. perenne* certain inflorescence characters are unstable; in particular there is a strong tendency for the raceme to branch into a panicle, but always with the lower glume missing. The two species are clearly very closely related and hybridization is quite common wherever they grow together. The hybrid (**L. ×boucheanum** Kunth) is an annual or short-lived perennial with the youngest blade convolute. It is therefore readily distinguished from *L. perenne* but is not so easily separated from *L. multiflorum*. It is intermediate in nearly all respects between its parents, but since it can backcross to either there is a complete gradation of intermediate forms to be found and it is not always possible to be sure whether one is dealing with parent or hybrid. There is an intermediate number of florets in the spikelet, a poorly formed or absent awn and a lightly scabrid

157

raceme internode; it is about 70% fertile. Selected strains of the hybrid have been introduced for fodder under the name 'Short-rotation Rye-grass'. Hybrids with *L. rigidum* and *L. temulentum* have been reported, but are doubtful; they would be extremely difficult to recognise.

In general, *L. multiflorum* can be distinguished from *L. perenne* by its annual (rarely biennial) habit, youngest leaf-blade convolute, taller, more robust culms, broader leaf-blades and scabrid raceme internodes; number of florets in the spikelet is a guide, but is not wholly reliable, and while the majority of specimens of *L. multiflorum* have awned lemmas, a significant proportion are quite awnless. The upper glume is usually less than half as long as the spikelet, but this will depend to a certain extent on absolute number of florets.

L. multiflorum also hybridizes with species *Festuca*; see under *F. pratensis* and *F. arundinacea* for details.

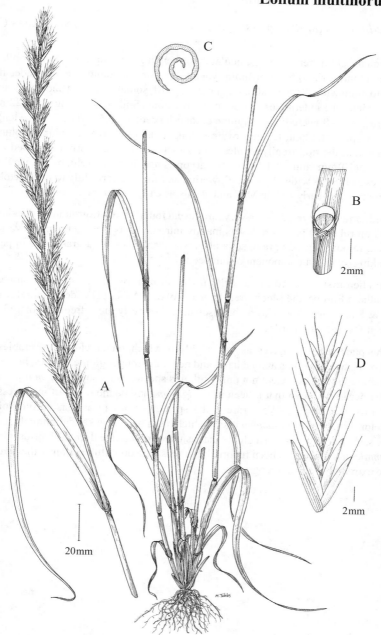

Lolium multiflorum: A, habit; B, ligule and auricles; C, outline of youngest leaf in section; D; spikelet.

24. Lolium rigidum Gaudin

Mediterranean Rye-grass   New Atlas CD

Annual; culms erect or geniculately ascending, up to 50(85)cm; ligule a membranous rim 0.5 – 1.5(2)mm; youngest blade convolute; mature blades flat, up to 8mm wide. Raceme straight or curved, stiff, sometimes stout and cylindrical, 4 – 23cm, the indernodes smooth or scaberulous. Spikelets oblong, 10 – 22mm, 4- to 11(12)-flowered; upper glume oblong-lanceolate, 0.5 – 1(1.25) × the length of the spikelet, blunt; lemmas ovate-oblong, (5)5.5 – 7.5(8)mm, blunt or bluntly pointed at the tip, usually awnless but sometimes with a poorly developed awn up to 5(10)mm; anthers 1.5 – 4mm; caryopsis narrow, not turgid, more than three times as long as wide. $2n = 14$. Flowering and fruiting early July to mid-October, sometimes as early as late May and as late as early December.

Mediterranean Rye-grass is a very rare casual found on waste ground, in docklands and on rubbish tips where it was mainly introduced as a contaminant of various plant imports such as grain, soya bean waste and esparto (a grass used in paper making) and as a component of birdseed.

An alien first recorded in the wild in Britain in 1864, *L. rigidum* is a native of southern Europe, the Mediterranean and SW & C Asia. It is widely naturalized in N & S America, Australasia and elsewhere. Formerly more frequent, there have been few recent records.

The plant usually arrives as var. **rigidum** which rather closely resembles *L. perenne* apart from its annual habit and generally longer glume. It does, however, intergrade to some extent not only with this species but also with *L. multiflorum*. The occasional awn that is seen in *L. rigidum* may be the result of introgression from *L. multiflorum*. Very rarely, the species comes in as var. **rottbollioides** Heldr. ex Boiss (*L. loliaceum* auct.) which has a much thicker cylindrical raceme axis, shorter lemmas and a glume that usually exceeds the florets. Hybrids with *L. temulentum* have also been reported, but these are doubtful; certainly they would be extremely hard to recognise.

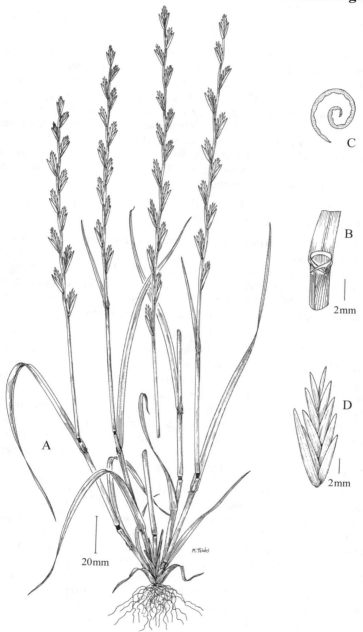

Lolium rigidum: A, habit; B, ligule and auricles; C, outline of youngest leaf in section; D, spikelet.

25. Lolium temulentum L.

Darnel   New Atlas: 750

Robust annual; culms erect, up to 85(120)cm; ligule a membranous rim 0.8 – 2mm; youngest blade convolute; mature blades up to 13mm wide. Raceme straight or curved, stiff, (7)10 – 25(30)cm, the internodes smooth or scaberulous. Spikelets oblong, 12 – 20(25)mm, (4)5- to 8(10)-flowered, the uppermost 2 or 3 florets rudimentary; upper glume narrowly oblong, (0.8)0.9 – 1.3(1.4) × the length of the spikelet, blunt; lemmas elliptic to ovate, 6.5 – 8.5mm, becoming hardened at maturity, blunt or somewhat erose at the tip, awnless or with an awn up to 15mm; anthers 2 – 3.5mm; caryopsis turgid, not more than three times as long as wide. $2n = 14$. Flowering and fruiting early June to mid-September, sometimes as late as early November.

Once a common arable weed, *L. temulentum* is now a fairly rare casual, more or less restricted to waste ground and rubbish tips.

Classed as an archaeophyte and certainly recorded in Britain by 1548, the species is likely to have been imported accidentally by early farmers. It remained a serious weed of cereal crops into the early part of last century but had largely disappeared from this habitat by the 1930s. There have been relatively few records since 1970. *L. temulentum* is probably native to the Mediterranean region and SW Asia and is naturalized in Japan, N & S America, Australasia and elsewhere.

Darnel has a reputation as our only 'poisonous' grass – Plues (1867) calling it "a noxious weed and the one evil species in the wholesome grass tribe" – and is thought to be the infamous 'tare' of Biblical reference. However, the symptoms of ingestion (variously described as intoxication, tremor, convulsions, and coldness of the extremities) and careful analysis of the caryopsis clearly point to infection of the seed by fungi, most notably Ergot (*Claviceps purpurea*). The alkaloids, including derivatives of lysergic acid, produced by this fungus are toxic to humans and animals and poisoning by ergot-infected rye bread was prevalent in the Middle Ages. Well-preserved fungal mycelia have been found in Darnel seed from an Egyptian tomb believed to date from 2000 BC (Arber 1934).

Darnel is the most instantly recognizable species of *Lolium* with its short turgid caryopsis, hardened lemmas and long glume. Production of awns is rather haphazard, with awn length and presence sometimes variable even within a single spikelet. The awn is conspicuously subterminal and often in those specimens that appear awnless a small rudiment can be found on the back of the lemma near the tip. The more robust specimens often have a lower glume, and this varies from a small vestige in the lower spikelets of the raceme to a scale half as long as the upper glume. The lower glume is usually absent from the upper part of the raceme and its presence below is not indicative of introgression from *Festuca*. In Darnel the infloresence-form is stable and branched or other teratological forms are not known.

Hybrids with *L. multiflorum* and *L. rigidum* have been reported, but are doubtful; they would be very hard to recognize.

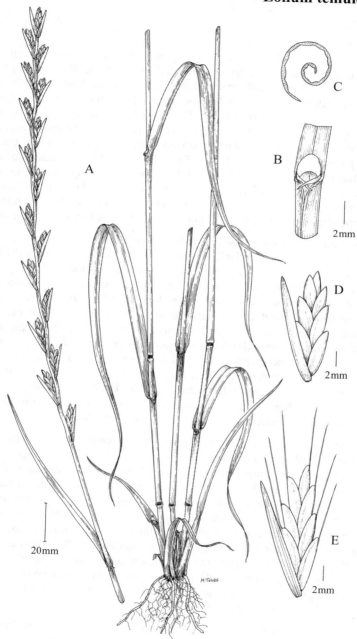

Lolium temulentum: A, habit; B, ligule and auricles; C, outline of youngest leaf in section; D, spikelet with awnless lemmas; E, spikelet with awned lemmas.

26.   Vulpia fasciculata (Forssk.) Fritsch

Dune Fescue   New Atlas: 750

Annual; culms up to 35(50)cm, erect or geniculate; ligule a narrow rim 0.2 – 0.7mm, bluntly auriculate. Panicle oblong, dense, 1-sided, often reduced to a raceme, erect, 3 – 9cm, usually exserted from the uppermost sheath, the spikelets articulated with the axis or branches and often falling entire with the pedicel. Spikelets narrowly oblong or cuneate, (9)11 – 16(18)mm (excluding the awns), 5- to 8(9)-flowered, the uppermost (2)3 – 5(6) florets sterile and much reduced; floret callus triangular and bluntly pointed, minutely scabrid; lower glume narrowly lanceolate, 1-nerved, 0.3 – 1.5mm, less than 0.1 × the length of the upper; upper glume lanceolate, 3-nerved, 12 – 26mm including the awn; lemma narrowly lanceolate in profile, 7.5 – 10.5mm, 5-nerved, scabrid, tapered above into an awn 13 – 25mm; anthers 1 – 3, (0.7)0.9 – 1.5mm; ovary with a minute hairy appendage at the tip. $2n = 28$. Flowering and fruiting late May to mid-July.

V. fasciculata is confined to coastal sand-dunes and sandy shingle in England, Wales and the east coast of Ireland, reaching as far north as Cumbria and the Isle of Man. It is sparsely distributed but is more frequent in dunes along the west and southwest coasts and in the Channel Islands. Populations can vary considerably in size and may be found on mobile dunes dominated by *Ammophila arenaria* through to the more disturbed parts of fixed dunes with *Carex arenaria* and *Festuca rubra* and even closed dune turf with lichens and mosses which is not green in winter and contains perennials such as *Ononis repens* and *Anthyllis vulneraria*. In these habitats it is sometimes found with other winter annual grasses such as *Aira praecox, Phleum arenarium* or, more rarely, *Mibora minima*. The soils in which Dune Fescue occurs are generally neutral or basic, infertile with little humus, free-draining and often dry during the summer. It appears to be absent or rare in wet dune slacks and transplants to such habitat-types have low survival.

Dune Fescue is a winter annual, germinating in the autumn (ranging from late August to December) and overwintering as a small plant before flowering the following year. Germination is favoured by the higher soil moisture at this time of year and the seed, which have short-lived dormancy, must be shallowly buried for the young plants to survive wind and moisture fluctuations. Occasional spring germination occurs and plants can be from 6 to 10 months old at flowering. By the time the ears emerge the basal and culm leaves are generally dead. The species is self-compatible and probably largely inbreeding. The inflorescences have a characteristically red appearance as the caryopses mature. Caryopses are typically dispersed over very short distances and there appears to be no permanent seed bank, despite which populations may persist in a given area for many years. (Biol. Flora: Watkinson, 1978; SPB: 439).

V. fasciculata is native in the British Isles, where it reaches its northern limit. It occurs around the Mediterranean, extending into western Europe and to inland localities in SW Asia. It has been introduced to Australia where it is a weed in

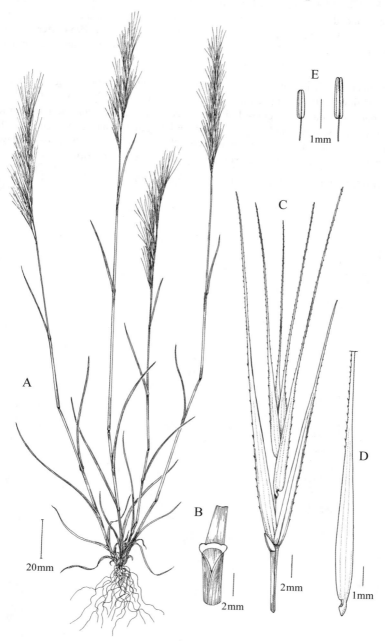

Vulpia fasciculata: A, habit; B, ligule; C, spikelet; D, floret showing callus; E, anthers.

some areas. The increase in Britain since the 1962 Atlas may be due to the plant being missed by earlier recorders, but it is thought to have prospered when rabbits were reduced by myxomatosis in the early 1950s. For example, at Braunton Burrows, N Devon, there were only about 100 plants prior to 1954 after which a huge increase occurred to "millions of plants over a substantial area of the dune system" (A.J.Willis in Watkinson, 1978).

The species is distinguished from others in the genus by the triangular, bluntly pointed floret callus. Supporting characters are the extremely small lower glume (so inconspicuous that 'One-glumed Fescue', *Festuca uniglumis*, is a former name for the species) and dense 1-sided panicle often reduced to a raceme. The spikelets are conspicuously articulated with the axis or primary branches and can be readily detached intact; they sometimes fall entire at maturity.

It hybridizes with *F. rubra*; see under that species for further details.

27.   Vulpia ciliata Dumort.

Illustration, page 169

Bearded Fescue

New Atlas: 751

Annual; culms up to 30(40)cm, erect or geniculate; ligule a membranous rim 0.2 – 0.5(0.6)mm, bluntly auriculate. Panicle linear or narrowly lanceolate, contracted, usually erect, 5 – 15cm, often not fully exserted from the uppermost sheath. Spikelets oblong or cuneate, (4.5)5.5 – 7.5(8.5)mm (excluding the awns), 4- to 7-flowered, only the lowermost 1(2) florets fertile, the rest sterile and progressively smaller; floret callus short and blunt, minutely scabrid; lower glume ovate or oblong, nerveless, 0.4 – 1mm, 0.2 – 0.4 × the length of the upper; upper glume oblong-lanceolate, 1-nerved, 1.3 – 2.8mm, awnless; lemma narrowly lanceolate in profile, (3.5)4.2 – 5.1mm, faintly 3(5)-nerved, scabrid, tapered above into an awn 7.5 – 11.5mm; anther 1, 0.3 – 0.9mm; ovary glabrous. $2n = 28$. Flowering and fruiting late May to early July.

Bearded Fescue is a scarce grass of open sandy places mainly inland in East Anglia and the east and south coasts of England. Outlier populations have been recorded in N Lincolnshire (a quarry entrance at Crosby Warren) and Wales (a coastal golf course at Aberdyfi) but the species is otherwise largely confined to SE England on sandy heaths, maritime, especially, fixed dunes and maritime and inland shingle. It typically occurs in disturbed places, especially along the edges of tracks and roads on nutrient-poor sandy soils which may range in pH from 3.4 to 7.9. In its Breckland stronghold the grass is commonly associated with *Arenaria serpyllifolia*, *Rumex acetosella* and *Sedum acre*, species which are found with it elsewhere, along with grasses such as *Aira praecox*, *Bromus hordeaceus*, *B. sterilis*, *Poa pratensis* and *Holcus mollis* (in one site in N Norfolk it was recorded with 3 other *Vulpia* species, *V. fasciculata*, *V. bromoides* and *V. myuros*, within a small area). Associated herbs include *Plantago lanceolata*, *P. coronopus*, *Erodium cicutarium* and, on coastal shingle, *Glaucium flavum* and *Rumex crispus*.

V. ciliata has a similar life history to *V. fasciculata*. It is a winter annual, germinating in the autumn, overwintering as small plants (rarely as seed), flowering the following year and producing seed which do not typically disperse very far and do not form a seed bank. Individual plants and populations can vary greatly in size and reproductive output from year to year but most populations appear to produce viable seed and seedlings every year, allowing them to persist for decades (an average half-life of just over 30 years was calculated for 46 populations studied by Watkinson *et al.*, (1998). Plants can vary from 2 to 10 months old at flowering, more northerly populations flowering later than those in the south. The species is cleistogamous and likely to be completely inbreeding. Unlike *V. fasciculata*, *V. ciliata* does not appear to be grazed by rabbits and in some areas burrowing activity provides open ground for plants to establish. Studies of the population ecology of *V. ciliata* have included competition and transplant experiments which suggest that it is favoured by warm, wet springs and hot, dry summers and, providing disturbed ground is available, could spread with climatic warming. (Biol. Flora: Watkinson *et al.,* 1998; SPB: 438).

Our native plant (described above) is subsp. **ambigua** (Le Gall) Stace & Auquier. Outside Britain it occurs only in northern France and Belgium and may have been under-recorded in all these locations in the past. However, the discovery of new populations since 1980 suggests it may be spreading in some areas such as the New Forest. Subsp. **ciliata**, widespread in Europe, has been introduced on occasion with grain and wool shoddy. It has slightly larger spikelet parts and the lemmas – both fertile and sterile – are conspicuously hairy on the dorsal midline and margins.

Bearded Fescue is distinguished from both *V. bromoides* and *V. myuros* by the nerveless lower glume, 1-nerved upper glume and mostly 3-nerved lemma. There is usually only a single fertile floret (sometimes 2) and the succeeding sterile florets differ by their progressive, rather than abrupt, reduction in size. The species differs from *V. bromoides*, and more closely resembles *V. myuros*, by virtue of the extreme size difference between the glumes.

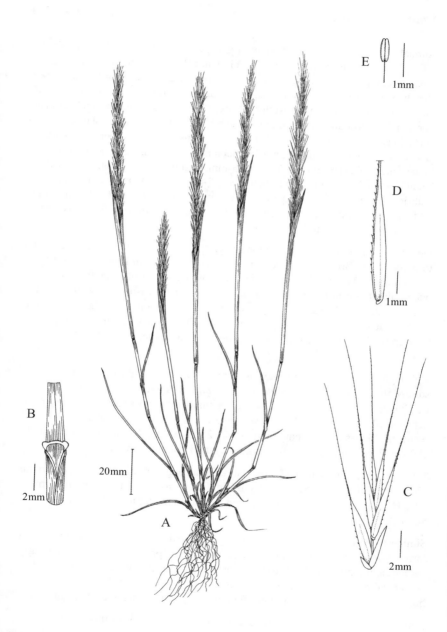

Vulpia ciliata subsp. *ambigua*: A, habit; B, ligule; C, spikelet; D, floret showing callus; E, anther.

28. Vulpia bromoides (L.) Gray

Squirreltail Fescue   New Atlas: 751

Annual; culms up to 45(75)cm, erect or geniculate; ligule a membranous rim 0.2
– 0.4(0.6)mm, bluntly auriculate. Panicle lanceolate to narrowly oblong, rather
loose to compact, erect or nodding, 2 – 9cm, well-exserted from the uppermost
sheath. Spikelets oblong or cuneate, 8 – 10.5(12)mm (excluding the awns), (4)5-
to 7(8)-flowered, the uppermost floret (rarely 2 florets) sterile and much reduced;
floret callus short and blunt, minutely scabrid; lower glume linear-lanceolate, 1-
nerved, 3.2 – 5.3mm, 0.45 – 0.7(0.75) × the length of the upper; upper glume
lanceolate or oblong-lanceolate, conspicuously 3-nerved, 5.5 – 8.4mm; lemma
linear-lanceolate in profile, (5)5.5 – 7(7.5)mm, >1 mm wide in dorsal view (without
being flattened; >1.3 mm when flattened), 5-nerved, sometimes only faintly so,
scabrid, tapered above into an awn 6 – 14mm; anther 1, 0.2 – 0.6(0.9)mm, rarely
up to 1.7mm; ovary glabrous. $2n = 14$. Flowering and fruiting late May to late
July, mostly mid- to late June.

Our most common and widespread species of *Vulpia*, *V. bromoides* is found
throughout the British Isles and is particularly common in England (apart from
the Pennines), Wales, SE Scotland and the south and east of Ireland. It occurs in
open habitats on grassland, heaths, sand-dunes and cliff-tops as well as walls,
waste ground, quarries, roadsides, railways, gravel paths and other man-made
habitats. It occurs from sea-level to almost 500m on soils that are typically
well-drained, are often stony and may be basic or acidic. It has a wide range of
associated species.

Although the population biology of *V. bromoides* in Britain has been less well
studied than that of *V. fasciculata* and *V. ciliata*, it is likely to have a very similar
life history. It appears to be a winter annual (although seedlings which have
germinated in the spring have been observed in several populations), the seed
requiring high summer temperatures (17-25°C) to break dormancy (Cheplick,
1998). It has cleistogamous florets and is largely or exclusively inbreeding.

V. bromoides is native in the British Isles and throughout much of Europe and the
Mediterranean region (part of the Submediterranean-Subatlantic floristic element
– P&H). It is widely naturalized around the world including N & S America and
South Africa.

Similar to *V. myuros* but with panicle well exserted from the uppermost sheath, a
lower glume rarely less than half the length of the upper, the latter very strongly
nerved, and a marginally narrower lemma with marginally stronger nerves. The
anther is mostly very small, but occasionally it may be two or three times as long,
but there is no evidence that plants with the longer anthers are chasmogamous.

It hybridizes with *Festuca rubra*; see under that species for further details.

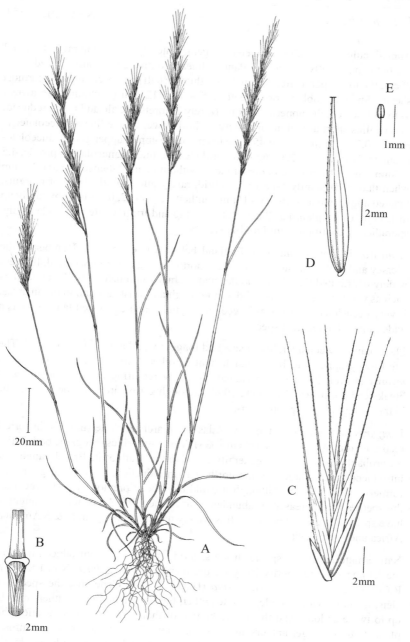

Vulpia bromoides: A, habit; B, ligule; C, spikelet; D, floret showing callus; E, anther.

29. *Vulpia myuros* (L.) C.C.Gmel.

Rat's-tail Fescue

New Atlas: 751

Annual; culms up to 65(85)cm, erect or geniculate; ligule a membranous rim 0.2 – 0.6(1)mm, bluntly auriculate. Panicle linear, contracted, usually curved, 10 – 30cm, the lower part (often as much as a third or half) enclosed in the uppermost sheath. Spikelets oblong or cuneate, 6.5 – 10.5(12)mm (excluding the awns), 4- to 7-flowered, the uppermost floret (rarely 2 florets) sterile and much reduced; floret callus short and blunt, minutely scabrid; lower glume linear-lanceolate, 1-nerved, 0.7 – 2.7mm, 0.2 – 0.45 × the length of the upper; upper glume lanceolate-subulate, 1(3)-nerved, 2.5 – 6.5mm; fertile lemma linear-lanceolate in profile, 4.5 – 7mm long, <1mm wide in dorsal view (without being flattened; up to c.1.3mm when flattened), faintly 5-nerved, scabrid, rarely pilose on the back or margins, tapered above into an awn 7.5 – 15mm; anthers 1, rarely 2, 0.3 – 0.7mm, rarely up to 1.5mm; ovary glabrous. $2n = 42$. Flowering and fruiting late May to late July, sporadically continuing until mid-November.

V. myuros is more common in England below a line from the Humber to the Mersey and in Wales, and is scattered in northern England and Scotland. It is less widely distributed than *V. bromoides* and is chiefly confined to artificial habitats such as walls, pavements, roadsides, and rough and waste ground in urban areas. It very occasionally occurs as a weed of hayfields and cultivated land and has a wide range of associated species.

Plants can vary considerably in size and longevity and are often very small. The life history appears to be similar to that of other *Vulpia* species in Britain. *V. myuros* is probably a winter annual, normally requiring high temperatures to break seed dormancy (Cheplick, 1998) although germination has been observed in the spring in some populations.

V. myuros is classified in the New Atlas as an archaeophyte (the first historical record is from Winchester, Hants in 1633). Most authorities recognize both native (or probably native) plants, generally found in the south of its British range, and introduced plants, largely in the north. The introductions occur with grain and, formerly, wool shoddy. Although it could have been previously under-recorded the species has increased in abundance since the 1962 Atlas and is thought to have spread via the rail network. It is widely naturalized (e.g. in N & S America, Africa and Australasia).

Native material of this species has a scabrid lemma, but in introduced material the lemma may be shortly hairy on the margins (f. *megalura* (Nutt.) Stace & R.Cotton, or on the back (f. *hirsuta* (Hack.) Blom). Generally, the species is cleistogamous with a single, minute anther, but occasionally the anthers may be up to twice as long, and there may be two of them. There is no indication that plants with the larger anthers are chasmogamous. The species may be confused with *V. bromoides*, but has a narrow, elongated panicle embraced below by the

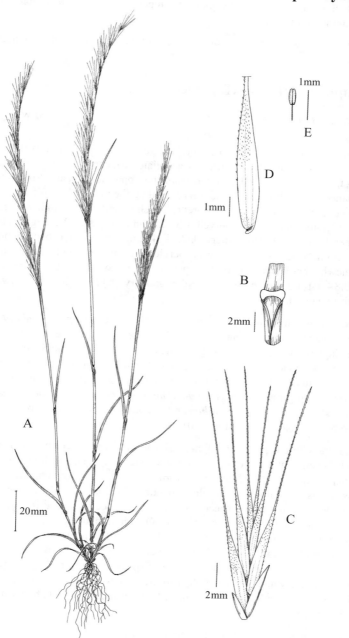

Vulpia myuros: A, habit; B, ligule; C, spikelet; D, floret showing callus; E, anther.

uppermost leaf-sheath, a relatively much shorter lower glume (less than half as long as the upper), a mostly 1-nerved upper glume and a marginally narrower lemma with fainter nerves.

It hybridizes with *Festuca rubra*; see under that species for further details.

30. Vulpia unilateralis (L.) Stace

Mat-grass Fescue   New Atlas: 752

Annual; culms up to 30(40)cm, erect; ligule a membranous rim 0.2 – 0.3mm, bluntly auriculate. Panicle usually a unilateral raceme, rarely branched below, erect, 3.5 – 7.5cm, well exserted from the uppermost sheath. Spikelets oblong to lanceolate-oblong, 4.5 – 7.5mm (excluding the awns), 3- to 6-flowered, rarely the uppermost floret vestigial; floret callus short and blunt, minutely scaberulous; lower glume lanceolate, 1-nerved, 1.3 – 2.5mm, 0.4 – 0.6 × the length of the upper; upper glume lanceolate, 3-nerved, 2.7 – 4.3mm; lemma lanceolate in profile, 3.3 – 4.3mm, 5-nerved, smooth or scaberulous to minutely and stiffly hairy above, somewhat hardened at maturity, tapered above into an awn 1.5 – 6.5mm; anthers 3, 0.8 – 1.1(1.3)mm, exserted at anthesis; ovary glabrous. $2n = 14$. Flowering and fruiting late May to early July.

The least common and most easily overlooked of our *Vulpia*s, *V. unilateralis* has been recorded from a relatively small number of widely-separated localities in SE England, almost all below a line from the Humber to the Severn. It is found in dry open places on base-rich stony soils and also in artificial habitats such as waste ground, railway tracks, walls and quarry spoil heaps. It may be found with other annual grasses such as *Catapodium rigidum* and *Vulpia bromoides* or with herbs such as *Cerastium pumilum* and *Minuartia hybrida*, but is often on its own in otherwise bare soils. (SPB: 440).

Mat-grass Fescue plants are often small and short-lived, germinating in the spring and flowering at the end of May or early June. The slender inflorescences (which superficially resemble Mat-grass, *Nardus stricta*, hence the common name) are easily missed or mistaken for depauperate individuals of *Vulpia bromoides* or *V. myuros*. Like these two species *V. unilateralis* occurs in 2 different categories of habitat, semi-natural and artificial. On the chalk and limestone it has the appearance of a native plant (see below), whilst habitats such as walls and quarry rubble provide it (and the 2 other species) with open, competition-free, topographically complex sites and early spring warmth and moisture to break seed dormancy and allow the plant to grow, flower and set seed before the arid high summer, conditions which mimic those in semi-natural habitats at the centre of its native range.

V. unilateralis is classified as a neophyte in the New Atlas, having been first recorded in the British Isles as recently as 1903 (S Lincs) and from only a few

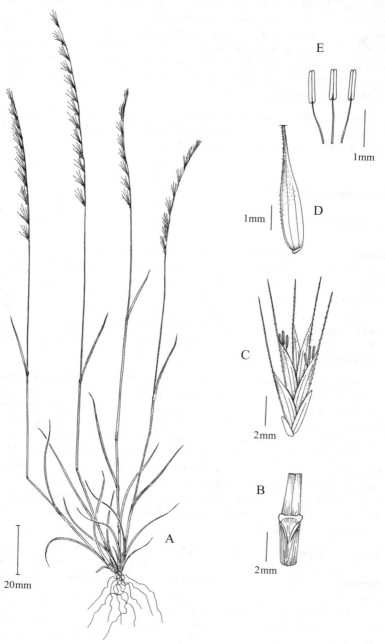

Vulpia unilateralis: A, habit; B, ligule; C, spikelet; D, floret showing callus; E, anthers.

localities before 1949. Stace (1961), Hubbard (who first described the species only in the 2nd edition of his book), and others argue that it is probably native in Britain. It is a Submediterranean-Subatlantic species (P&H) widespread throughout southern Europe and also recorded in C Asia. It is difficult to say whether the increase in records since the 1962 Atlas means that the species is spreading, since it was probably overlooked in the past and may continue to be under-recorded. Therefore Cheffings & Farrell (2005) have placed it on the conservation status **Waiting List**.

The small spikelets, racemose inflorescence and 3 exserted anthers distinguish this species. In general, there is a lack of obviously barren florets in the spikelet but occasionally the uppermost is markedly vestigial.

31. Cynosurus cristatus L.

Crested Dog's-tail   New Atlas: 752

Tufted perennial up to 80cm; ligule a membranous rim 0.5 – 2mm. Panicle narrowly oblong, 3 – 10cm, the primary branches usually bearing two pairs of spikelets, sometimes three. Sterile spikelets 3.5 – 5.5(6)mm including awns, comprising 7 – 14 narrowly lanceolate, finely pointed lemmas. Fertile spikelets 3.5 – 6mm, 2- to 6-flowered; glumes narrowly ovate, (2.5)3 – 4.2(5)mm, shorter than the lemmas; lemmas 3 – 4(5)mm, tipped with an awn up to 1mm; anthers 1.4 – 2.5mm. $2n = 14$. Flowering and fruiting early June to mid-August, rarely to September or even early October.

This very common grass occurs throughout the British Isles in a broad range of grassland environments. It is particularly abundant in short, grazed turf in well-established grassland, but can be found on a great range of soil types in temporary pastures, lawns, banks, verges and grassy paths and even more artificial habitats such as building rubble and walls. More common in lowland Britain, it extends to 600m above sea-level, and even 845m on Great Dun Fell, Westmorland. *C. cristatus* is not found on very acid (pH<4.0), waterlogged, highly disturbed or shaded soils, but is otherwise encountered in most grassland. It has a huge variety of associated species but was recorded most frequently in the Sheffield area with *Alopecurus pratensis, Bellis perennis, Lolium perenne, Phleum pratense* and *Trifolium pratense* (CPE: 238).

In heavily grazed (especially sheep-grazed) swards Crested Dog's-tail forms a low compact carpet of leaves which often remain green through the winter. The unmistakable inflorescences are borne above the sward on wiry stems which can also persist into the winter months, facilitating the collection of seed in former times for sowing into new pastures. Within the carpet individual plants are short-lived, although polycarpic, and do not expand very far laterally. The species is self-incompatible (Ennos, 1985) and there is no persistent seed bank. Populations are maintained by seedling establishment in vegetation gaps with germination

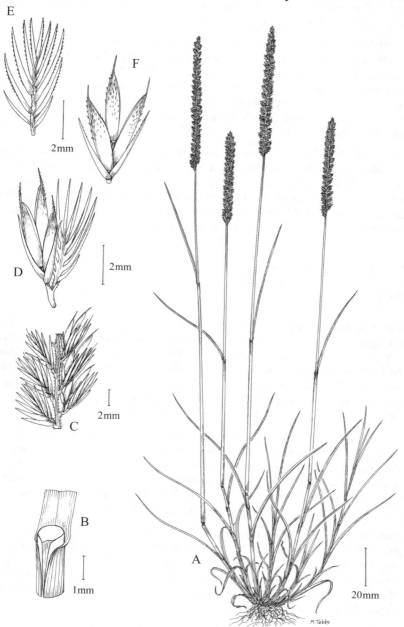

Cynosurus cristatus: A, habit; B, ligule; C, segment of inflorescence; D, spikelet pair; E, sterile spikelet; F, fertile spikelet.

mainly occurring in the autumn. *C. cristatus* has a growth habit better suited to pasture than hayfields and in these latter habitats it may be outcompeted by more robust species. (Biol. Flora: Lodge, 1959).

C. cristatus is native in the British Isles and throughout temperate Europe (part of the large European-Temperate element in our flora; P&H) and is widely naturalized elsewhere including N America and Australasia. It was formerly a common constituent of seed mixtures for pastures and lawns before these became dominated by a few species, but has more recently returned to favour in mixtures used to restore or create floristically diverse grassland. It may also be sown in upland leys on poor soil.

Crested Dog's-tail is the only native species of grass to have dimorphic spikelets. It is distinguished from the introduced Rough Dog's-tail by its perennial habit, longer and narrower panicle, shorter glumes and shorter awn at the tip of the lemma. On rare occasions the lowermost 2 or 3 lemmas of the fertile spikelet are barren and resemble those of the sterile spikelet, but this is very unusual. Proliferating spikelets are common late in the season.

32.   Cynosurus echinatus L.

Rough Dog's-tail   New Atlas: 752

Annual up to 70(100)cm; ligule a membranous rim 2 – 7(10)mm. Panicle ovoid or oblong, often lobed, 2 – 4.5(5.5)cm, the primary branches bearing two to several pairs of spikelets. Sterile spikelets 7.5 – 11.5(16)mm including awns, comprising 9 – 18 finely pointed lemmas, the upper relatively broader than the lower. Fertile spikelets (5.5)7 – 10.5mm, 2- to 3-flowered; glumes narrowly lanceolate, as long as the spikelet; lemmas (5)5.5 – 7mm, tipped with an awn (3.5)5 – 12(17)mm; anthers 1.5 – 3mm. $2n = 14$. Flowering and fruiting late May to early August.

This uncommon grass is now largely confined to the Channel Islands, the Isles of Scilly and a small number of scattered localities in the south of England, largely along the coast. Here it is found on bare dry sandy or rocky soils and occasionally on shingle or cultivated land, where it is said sometimes to be a pest of bulb fields. Elsewhere it is an increasingly rare casual in waste places, introduced with grain or, formerly, wool shoddy, or resulting from its occasional use as an ornamental grass.

Populations of *C. echinatus* may persist for some years, especially in open sandy places. The mostly stunted plants from such habitats rarely display the striking panicles produced by cultivation in fertile soil. Its value as an agricultural grass is summed up by Gordon (undated Manual) with "this species, which is fairly common on the Sandwich meadows, is most useful to the farmer when it dies to prepare the soil for a better grass".

C. echinatus is a neophyte, first recorded in the wild in Britain in 1778. It is a native of southern Europe and the Mediterranean region, probably native in SW Asia, and is widely naturalized outside its native range.

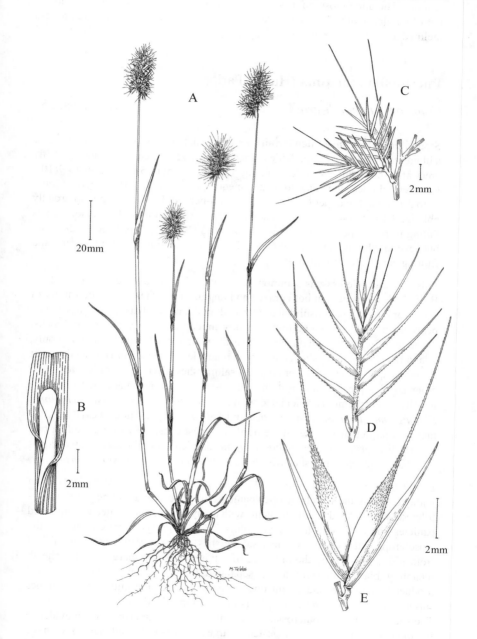

Cynosurus echinatus: A, habit; B, ligule; C, segment of inflorescence; D, sterile spikelet; E, fertile spikelet.

A very distinctive species with ovoid lobed panicle and very long awns on the lemmas. The uppermost lemmas of the sterile spikelet are shorter than the lower but of similar width; they therefore appear to be relatively broader and are less inclined to spread horizontally with age.

33. Puccinellia maritima (Huds.) Parl.

Common Saltmarsh-grass   New Atlas: 753

Stoloniferous perennial often forming extensive patches; culms up to 80cm; ligule a blunt membrane 1 – 3mm. Panicle linear to ovate, 5 – 20cm, the branches stiffly erect after flowering. Spikelets oblong, (5.5)7 – 12.5(15.5)mm, (3)4- to 9(10)-flowered; glumes lanceolate to ovate, unequal, the lower (1.3)1.6 – 3.1(3.5)mm, 1- to 3-nerved, the upper (2.1)2.5 – 4.3mm, 3-nerved; lemmas elliptic to broadly oblong, 3.1 – 5(5.4)mm, hairy below, weakly nerved, the midnerve sometimes failing to reach the broadly obtuse tip; anthers (1.1)1.5 – 2.6(2.8)mm. $2n = 56$, but several other numbers from 49 to 77 have also been reported. Flowering and fruiting early June to mid-July.

This very variable grass is common in saltmarshes around the entire coast of the British Isles. It occurs in both grazed and ungrazed marshes on a wide variety of soils from mobile unconsolidated intertidal mud and sandflats to well-developed peaty loams. It may also be found on firm muddy and sandy shingle and rocks, the edges of sea walls and ditches in coastal grazing marshes and, less commonly, inland in salt-affected habitats including roadsides. *P. maritima* is often the most abundant species on the lower zones of saltmarshes where, with only one or two other species present, it can dominate vast tracts of marshland. On ungrazed marshes it is commonly associated with *Atriplex portulacoides, Aster tripolium, Plantago maritima, Spartina anglica* and *Salicornia* spp., but on heavily grazed marshes, particularly those on the north and west coasts of Britain, the first two species disappear and *Puccinellia maritima* completely dominates the lower zones and shares the upper marshes with *Festuca rubra* and *Agrostis stolonifera*.

P. maritima biotypes vary from tall, erect, caespitose, stiff-leaved plants often without stolons and with large open panicles to, at the other extreme, short, many-tillered, small-leaved, prostrate plants with many stolons and reduced unbranched panicles borne on short horizontal culms. These latter types are common in the close-cropped turf of sheep-grazed saltmarshes, where they may be distinguished from *Festuca rubra* by the presence of a ligule, the free margins to the sheath (enabling blade and stem to be separated without tearing) and 'tramlines' produced by two secondary furrows on either side of the midrib on the upper surface of the leaf. *P. maritima* plants may be long-lived and flower every year. The species is mainly outcrossing but some selfing occurs (there is no evidence for apomixis as previously suggested). Large numbers of buried viable seed have been recovered from saltmarsh soils. The species is able to withstand frequent

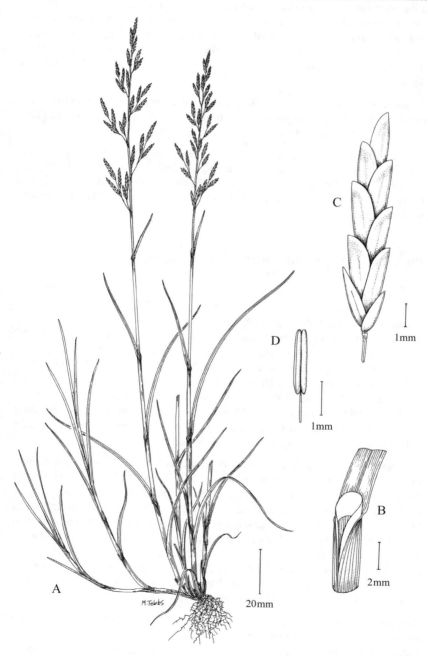

Puccinellia maritima: A, habit; B, ligule; C, spikelet, D, anther.

tidal submergences and unstable substrates and is highly salt tolerant, but is not a good competitor in non-saline conditions. These characteristics fix its position in the saltmarsh succession and enable it to occupy open areas in the higher zones and saline ground above the tidal limit. It has been ousted from many pioneer zones in the south since the beginning of the 20th century by *Spartina anglica* but replaces it on sandy soils from the R. Ribble northwards. (Biol. Flora: Gray & Scott, 1977).

P. maritima is a native species widespread along the shores of western Europe. It occurs north to Greenland where it was probably introduced by the Vikings (and rarely flowers) and in N America.

The main distinguishing features of *P. maritima* are the large anthers and the long lemmas. The species hybridizes with both *P. distans* (**P. ×hybrida** Holmb.) and *P. rupestris* (**P. ×krusemaniana** Jansen & Wacht.). Both hybrids are sterile and intermediate in morphology between their parents although that with *P. rupestris* is rare and little known.

34. Puccinellia rupestris (With.) Fernald & Weath.

Stiff Saltmarsh-grass   New Atlas: 754

Annual or biennial; culms up to 30(50)cm, sometimes erect but usually prostrate at first then curved- or geniculate-ascending; ligule a blunt membrane (1)1.3 – 2.7 (3.5)mm. Panicle ovate or oblong, (2)3 – 6(8)cm, rather dense and one-sided with short stiff branches and very short pedicels. Spikelets oblong, (4)5 – 7mm, 2- to 4-flowered; glumes ovate to elliptic, unequal, the lower (1.2)1.5 – 2.2(2.5)mm, 1- to 3-nerved, the upper (1.9)2.1 – 3(3.2)mm, 3-nerved; lemmas broadly elliptic, 3 – 3.8mm, minutely hairy below, strongly nerved, the midnerve usually reaching the broadly obtuse tip and sometimes slightly projecting; anthers 0.7 – 1mm. $2n$ = 42. Flowering and fruiting late May to late September.

P. rupestris is now largely confined to the south and east coasts of England south of a line from the Wash to the Severn Estuary. It occurs on bare ground in a range of habitats at and above the limit of the highest tides, mainly on the landward side of sea walls. These include trackways and edges of brackish ditches and pools and cattle-poached ground in grazing marshes. Here it can be found with two other *Puccinellia* species, *P. fasciculata* and *P. distans* (and even now and then *P. maritima*), *Hordeum marinum, Parapholis strigosa, Spergularia marina*, and in less saline areas, *Agrostis stolonifera* and *Sagina procumbens*. It also occurs on muddy shingle and in rock crevices such as the facing stones of sea walls, as well as, rarely, inland on salt-affected roadside verges.

This attractive grass is one of a number of short-lived species, some mentioned above, which occupy disturbed, usually saline and mostly ephemeral sites close to the sea. It is self-fertilizing, flowering once and being spread by seed. Single

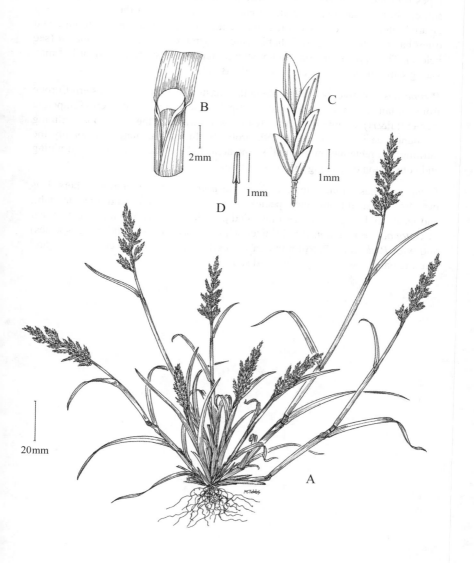

Puccinellia rupestris: A, habit; B, ligule; C, spikelet; D, anther.

individuals may found colonies on newly disturbed mud before other plants shade them out. *P. rupestris* is rarely found in closed vegetation, especially where it is dominated by *Elymus athericus*, the most common grass in these habitat types (despite its common name Stiff Saltmarsh-grass is very rarely found on saltmarshes). It can reappear after many years' absence on the edges of newly cleared ditches or fresh tyre tracks where it appears to withstand trampling and often has a distinctive growth habit which resembles *Catapodium rigidum* (see below). The populations on muddy shingle tend to be more persistent but may vary greatly in size from year to year. (SPB: 341).

P. rupestris is native, occurring along the coasts of northern and western Europe from Britain and the Netherlands to Spain (the Oceanic Southern-Temperate element; P&H). It appears to be retreating southwards in the UK and is declining in abundance in southern England, probably through habitat loss, notably the infilling and reclamation of small saline areas behind sea walls and the draining and conversion of grazing marshes to arable.

P. rupestris has a long lemma as in *P. maritima* but much shorter anthers. It is best distinguished from other species in the genus by its annual or biennial habit and its stiffly branched, rather one-sided panicle that is very reminiscent of that of *Catapodium rigidum*. It hybridizes with *P. maritima* (see under that species) and with *P. distans* (**P. ×pannonica** (Hack.) Holmb.). The latter is rather rare, intermediate between its parents and sterile.

35. Puccinellia fasciculata (Torr.) E.P. Bicknell

Illustration, page 187

Borrer's Saltmarsh-grass

New Atlas: 754

Loosely to densely tufted perennial; culms up to 75(90)cm; ligule a blunt membrane 1.3 – 2.7mm. Panicle lanceolate to narrowly ovate or oblong, 5 – 15(19)cm, the shorter branches bearing spikelets to the base, the longer often bare of spikelets below, pedicels very short, the branches erect at maturity. Spikelets oblong, (3)3.5 – 5(6)mm, 3- to 6(7)-flowered; glumes ovate to elliptic, unequal, the lower (0.7)0.9 – 1.3(1.5)mm, 1-nerved, the upper (1.3)1.4 – 1.9mm, 3-nerved; lemmas elliptic, 2.1 – 2.6mm, minutely hairy below, strongly nerved, the midnerve slightly projecting beyond the narrowly obtuse tip; anthers 0.5 – 0.9(1)mm. $2n = 28$. Flowering and fruiting early June to mid-September, rarely beginning in May or lasting until well into October.

This scarce, but probably overlooked, grass is confined to the coasts of southern and eastern England as far north as Norfolk and to scattered localities in SE Ireland. It occurs on open ground close to the sea on bare, free-draining saline soils. Typical places to find this species, and its associates such as *Puccinellia rupestris*, *P. distans* and *Hordeum marinum*, are the edges of recently dredged ditches and cattle-poached mud in grazing marshes and reclaimed land, and in vehicle tracks and bare places along the landward edges of sea walls, and indeed the best place to look for all the short-lived *Puccinellia*s is probably along the 'berm', the flat area between the sea wall and the parallel counter dyke which drains the agricultural land. The communities in these areas also include *Spergularia marina* and other plants from the higher levels of saltmarsh such as *Aster tripolium* and *Atriplex hastata* as well as, more rarely, *Parapholis strigosa* and *Polypogon monspeliensis*. *P. fasciculata* has also been recorded from salt-affected roadsides.

Although it is a short-lived perennial, *P. fasciculata* has a very similar ecology to *P. rupestris*, occupying ephemeral habitats which, at least initially, are usually too saline for the more competitive plant species. It is self-pollinating and, although it forms small patches, spreads entirely by seed. As with similar grasses it seems to produce seed from even the most depauperate plants. The seeds are probably distributed with soil during bank and ditch construction and new colonies appear when the ground is disturbed. Hence the species spread extensively in the Netherlands (and probably in England) following the 1953 floods and subsequent sea wall reconstruction. (SPB: 340).

P. fasciculata is native in Britain where it is close to its northern limit, and is native along the Atlantic coast of Europe, in N America and South Africa. It was introduced with other *Puccinellia* species to Western Australia to reclaim saline soils in sheep pasture. It appears to be decreasing in SE England, even in its stronghold areas on the sea walls and coastal grazing marshes of Essex and Kent , probably for the same reasons that *P. rupestris* and associates of this community are declining: the improvement and draining of coastal agricultural land. Consequently it is classified as **vulnerable** by Cheffings & Farrell (2005).

The small lemmas distinguish this species from both *P. maritima* and *P. rupestris* and the strongly nerved lemma with projecting midnerve distinguishes it from *P. distans*. It can, however, also be recognized by its panicle which is very like that of *Agrostis stolonifera* in that the branches are clustered, the larger ones are bare of spikelets below but with the naked portion concealed among the shorter branches which bear spikelets to the very base. It hybridizes with *P. distans* but the hybrid is rare. As with other hybrids in the genus it is sterile with intermediate morphology. At one time *P. pseudodistans* (Crép.) Jansen & Wacht. was segregated because of its intermediacy between *P. fasciculata* and *P. distans*, especially with regard to panicle shape, but there is little else to support it and it is best regarded as a variant of *P. fasciculata*. It has branches that bear spikelets to the base and the midnerve of the lemma reaches the tip. It has the same chromosome number as *P. distans* subsp. *borealis* but is not otherwise very much like it.

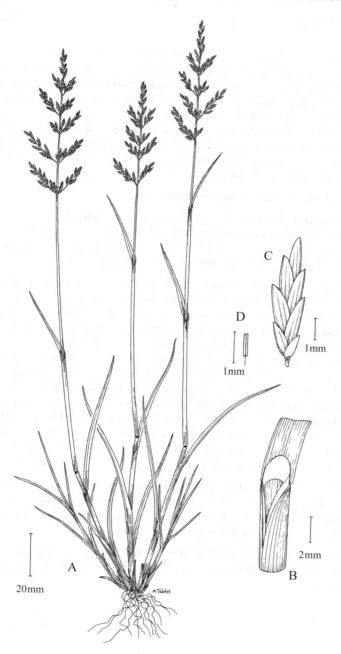

Puccinellia fasciculata: A, habit; B, ligule, C, spikelet; D, anther.

36.   **Puccinellia distans** (Jacq.) Parl.

Reflexed Saltmarsh-grass   New Atlas: 753

Tufted perennial; culms up to 60(100)cm; ligule a blunt membrane 0.8 – 2.8mm. Panicle narrowly to broadly ovate or pyramidal, 3 – 20cm, the branches usually all bare of spikelets below and often reflexed at maturity, sometimes only patent or erect. Spikelets narrowly oblong, 3.5 – 9mm, (2)4- to 9-flowered; glumes ovate to elliptic, unequal, the lower 0.8 – 1.6mm, 1-nerved, the upper (1.2)1.3 – 2.2(2.6)mm, 3-nerved; lemmas broadly oblong-ellptic, 2 – 3(3.2)mm, minutely hairy below, very weakly nerved, the midnerve failing to reach the broadly obtuse tip; anthers 0.5 – 1.1mm. Flowering and fruiting early June to early September, sometimes lasting until mid-October.

Two fairly readily distinguished subspecies occur:

36a.   subsp. **distans**. Culms (20)30 – 60(100)cm; blades mostly flat, 1 – 4mm wide, sometimes folded and occasionally inrolled and 0.5 – 1.2mm across; panicle mostly 8 – 16(20)cm with the branches reflexed at maturity; spikelets 3.5 – 6.5(8)mm; lemmas 2 – 2.7mm; anthers 0.7 – 1.1mm. $2n = 42$.

This is the most frequently encountered of the short-lived *Puccinellia* species in open muddy places near the sea in SE England, extending further north than *P. rupestris* and *P. fasciculata* (and into Wales and Northern Ireland). It is found in similar habitats around sea walls and disturbed land, and with the same associates such as *Hordeum marinum* and *Spergularia marina*. It is more likely than the other two species to be found on poorly drained heavy soils on the upper edge of saltmarshes and also occurs on waste land and spoil heaps near the sea and inland. Subsp. *distans* has been a spectacular invader on roadsides affected by de-icing salt. This invasion, which began in the mid-1970s in the northeast of England (and has been mapped by Scott & Davison (1982) and Scott (1985)), has extended along roads over most of the eastern half of England. On roadsides it is found with other coastal fugitives such as *Spergularia marina*, *Aster tripolium*, *Hordeum marinum* and, especially since the 1980s, *Cochlearia danica*.

Some biotypes of subsp. *distans* have extensive vegetative development and are probably long-lived, whilst others comprise a few flowering tillers and appear to be annual. Delicate specimens of this species, and *P. fasciculata*, can be overlooked as *Poa annua*. It is largely outbreeding.

A native in the British Isles and most parts of Europe, subsp. *distans* occurs in temperate Asia, NW Africa and N America, and is widely naturalized outside its native range.

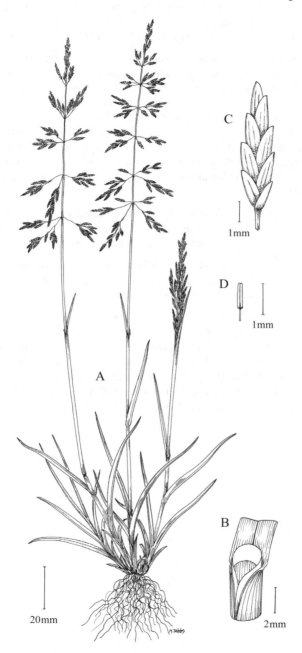

Puccinellia distans subsp. *distans*: A, habit; B, ligule; C, spikelet; D, anther.

36b.   subsp. **borealis** (Holmb.) W.E.Hughes. Culms 5 – 25(40)cm; blades mostly inrolled and 0.3 – 0.6(0.9)mm across, rarely flat or folded and 0.8 – 2.7mm wide; panicle 3 – 7(11)cm, with the branches usually erect, rarely patent; spikelets 3.5 – 9mm; lemmas (2.1)2.4 – 3.2mm; anthers 0.5 – 0.8(1)mm. $2n = 28$.

This subspecies occurs along the coast of Scotland from the Firth of Forth (including Bass Rock) northwards to the Shetland Islands. As the common name 'Northern Saltmarsh-grass' implies, its distribution is centred on northeastern Caithness and the Orkney and Shetland Islands. Its natural habitat is rocky seashore platforms within the reach of the highest tides, especially cracks in the Old Red Sandstone paving, where it occurs with *Armeria maritima, Plantago maritima* and *Sagina maritima*. It occurs less frequently on rocky or pebble beaches or even saltmarsh. It is locally common on the tops of quays, slipways and other man-made structures which provide an ideal habitat at the same elevation (Trist & Butler, 1995).

Plants vary in growth habit although they are frequently procumbent and appear to vary in longevity and flowering time but comparatively little is known about the reproductive biology and ecology of this subspecies.

P. distans subsp. *borealis* is native and is found elsewhere on the coasts of northern Europe from Norway to the Netherlands. It is known from the Faeroes, Iceland, Greenland and northeastern N America.

In most characters the two subspecies show considerable overlap but apart from their almost completely allopatric ranges they are best distinguished by the form of the panicle (branches reflexed in *distans*, patent or erect in *borealis*) and the nature of the leaf-blades (flat or folded in *distans*, inrolled in *borealis*) although the latter is less reliable. Subsp. *borealis* was at one time recognized as a species in its own right (*P. capillaris* (Lilj.) Jansen) and it is a moot point whether or not this might still be appropriate; see Trist & Butler (1995) for more detailed discussion.

20mm

Puccinellia distans subsp. *borealis*: habit.

37. Briza media L.

Quaking-grass   New Atlas: 754

Loosely tufted, shortly rhizomatous perennial up to 80cm; ligule a blunt membrane 0.6 – 1.8(2.1)mm. Panicle very loose, more or less pyramidal, (5)7.5 – 13(19)cm long and almost as wide, bearing numerous small spikelets. Spikelets drooping, elliptic to broadly ovate, (3.5)4.5 – 6.5(7.5)mm long and almost as wide, 5- to 10(14)- flowered; glumes subequal (the upper slightly the longer), horizontally spreading, 2.5 – 3.5mm, hooded at the tip; lemmas 2.8 – 4.2mm, cordate at the base, smooth and glabrous on the back, hooded at the tip; palea a little shorter than the lemma; anthers (1)1.3 – 2.4mm. $2n = 14$. Flowering and fruiting early June to mid-August.

B. media is widely distributed throughout the British Isles except for the far north and west of Scotland and the north and southwest of Ireland. It is a common constituent of calcareous grassland, particularly grazed, unimproved, often species-rich grassland on dry, infertile, well-drained soils. It also occurs on a range of basic to neutral soils (in habitats such as old meadows and pastures, waste ground, quarry spoil, scree slopes, road verges and even stabilized sand-dunes) as well as in moist and acid grassland and even the drier parts of fens and in soligenous mires. As a consequence of this broad spectrum of habitat and soil types, *B. media* occurs in a range of plant communities and with a huge number of associated species (it also occurs from sea-level to >700m). An analysis of communities containing *B. media* is given in Dixon (2002).

In what can be regarded as its most characteristic habitat, semi-natural well-grazed calcareous grassland, *B. media* is ecologically very similar to *Cynosurus cristatus*. It is slow growing (investing mostly in root growth in the spring), retains a few green leaves through the winter, does not expand very far laterally (despite having rhizomes) and establishes new plants from fresh seed dispersed into gaps in the autumn. Seed is shed from July to September and germinates in the autumn, there being no germinable seed in the soil during spring and early summer. Plants flower in the first summer after germination and are self-incompatible. Since edaphic ecotypes have been identified, it is suspected that ecotypic differentiation has been the major mechanism enabling the species to occupy its wide range of habitat types. However, it is not generally very competitive, eventually disappearing from the sward when grazing is removed or nutrients are added, when it typically loses out to taller grasses such as *Brachypodium pinnatum* or *Dactylis glomerata*. Thus it is generally absent from highly productive and heavily disturbed environments. (Biol. Flora: Dixon, 2002; CPE: 158).

B. media is a native species first recorded in 1570 and part of the large European Temperate floristic element in the British and Irish flora (P&H). Outside Europe it has been recorded from northern and western Asia, South Africa and, as an introduction, from N America, Australia and New Zealand. Although there has been little change in its British range since the 1962 Atlas it is believed to be declining on a local scale through ploughing and improvement of grasslands.

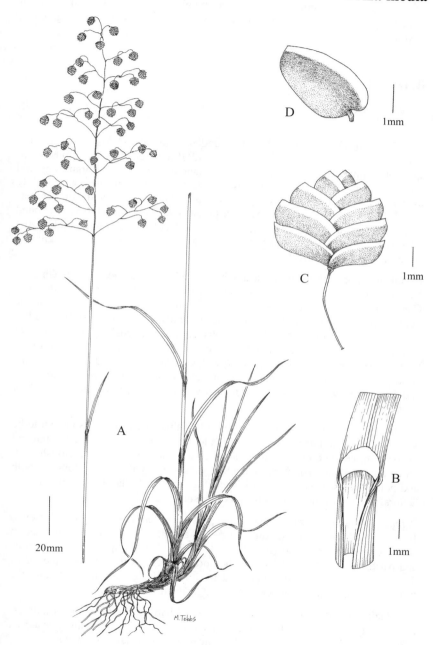

Briza media: A habit; B, ligule; C, spikelet; D, lemma in profile.

This distinctive and beautiful grass has attracted people's attention for many years, its trembling panicle and attractive spikelets giving rise to a host of local names. The spikelets are commonly tinged with purple but may also be greenish or yellowish.

38.   Briza minor L.

Lesser Quaking-grass   New Atlas: 755

Annual up to 60cm; ligule a bluntly rounded membrane (1.5)4 – 6.5(7.5)mm. Panicle loose and open, obovoid, 4.5 – 13(19)cm, bearing numerous small spikelets. Spikelets nodding, orbicular to triangular-ovate, 3 – 5.5mm long and often wider than this, (3)5- 9(11)-flowered; glumes subequal (the upper slightly the longer), horizontally spreading, (1.6)2 – 3(3.3)mm, hooded at the tip; lemmas (1.5)1.8 – 2.8(3)mm, cordate at the base, smooth and glabrous on the back, hooded at the tip, this often inrolled; palea a little shorter than the lemma; anthers 0.3 – 0.6mm. $2n = 10$. Flowering and fruiting mid-June to mid-September, beginning earlier in the far southwest.

Established populations of this scarce grass are largely restricted to the Channel Islands, the Isles of Scilly and the southern counties of England, particularly Cornwall and Hampshire. It is mainly found on light, base-poor soils in arable fields often near the coast, but can occur as a ruderal by roadsides, on sandy verges, waste places and rubbish tips. Its associated species are generally other weeds of non-intensive 'scruffy' cultivation: in one Cornish weedy field it was recorded with *Sisymbrium officinale, Silene gallica, Spergula arvensis* and *Holcus lanatus*. Associates may also include uncommon annuals such as *Chrysanthemum segetum* and *Misopates orontium*, and even formerly in one Hampshire site, *Gastridium ventricosum*.

Relatively little is known about the biology of this species but it is known to be self-compatible and normally inbreeding, to germinate mainly in the autumn and to be a poor competitor requiring regular disturbance for seedling establishment. It flowers from March onwards in the Scilly Isles, where it is mostly found in bulb and potato fields. It is probably restricted in its British distribution by climatic factors, requiring mild winters for seedling survival. (SPB: 62).

B. minor is classified as an archaeophyte, first recorded in the wild from Jersey in 1696. It is a Mediterranean-Atlantic species and has been widely naturalized in warm temperate regions around the world (South Africa, Japan, N & S America and Australia). In Britain it is near the northern edge of its range but the major threat to its survival is the increased use of herbicides and nutrients and the 'tidying-up' of fields under agricultural intensification.

It is distinguished from *B. media* by its annual habit and much smaller anthers. On maturity, the tip of the lemma is often inrolled giving a very distinctive aspect to the spikelet but making the length of the lemma very hard to ascertain.

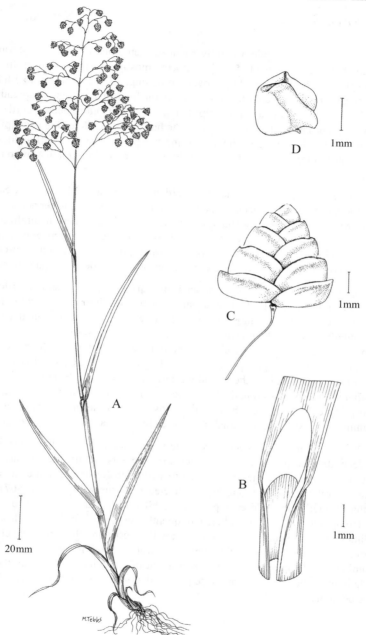

Briza minor: A, habit; B, ligule; C, spikelet; D, lemma in profile.

39. Briza maxima L.

Annual up to 60cm; ligule a bluntly rounded membrane (1.5)3 – 3.5(4.5)mm. Panicle loose and open(1)2.5 – 5.5(6.5)cm, mostly bearing no more than 7 large spikelets. Spikelets nodding, ovate to oblong, 13 – 20mm, 10- to 14(17)-flowered; glumes subequal (the upper slightly the longer), horizontally spreading, (5)5.5 – 6.5(7)mm, hooded at the tip; lemmas 7 – 8.5(9)mm, deeply cordate at the base, glabrous or glandular-hairy on the hardened middle of the back, pilose on the membranous margins, hooded at the tip; palea little over half as long as the lemma; anthers 1.2 – 2mm. $2n = 14$. Flowering and fruiting late May to mid-June.

B. maxima has been most frequently recorded in the Channel Islands, the Scilly Isles and SW England, especially Cornwall, but it is scattered further north to the Isle of Man and southern Scotland eastwards to Norfolk. Where naturalized, in the south, it occurs in dry open places such as banks, field margins or cultivated ground in similar habitats to *B. minor*. Elsewhere, it may appear on sand-dunes and cliffs or as a casual in waste ground, rubbish tips, gardens and pavements.

A neophyte, *B. maxima* was introduced into Britain by 1633 and recorded in the wild in Jersey by 1860. It is a native of the Mediterranean region and is now well established in most warm temperate countries. Although it can be accidentally introduced with wool shoddy and esparto, most records are probably from garden escapes. The species can be quite persistent as a garden weed. It appears to be increasing, especially in SW England and the Channel Islands. In view of its origins and southerly and westerly distribution in Britain (which like *B. minor* suggests it is climatically limited to areas with milder winters) and its widespread cultivation for ornamental purposes, the species may provide us with an unintended experiment in tracking future climate change.

All three Quaking-grass species are quite unmistakable and all have been used for decorative purposes in dried flower arrangements. Whilst the spectacularly beautiful *B. maxima* is the only one cultivated, both for drying and as a border plant, the other two have long been collected from the wild. Plues (1867) tells us that "eagerly do children repair to the hill-side pastures in June to gather the Trembling-grass ... the cottager frequently suspends it in bunches from the ceiling whilst the Squire's lady mingles it with Everlasting flowers in the elegant Cornucopia" and "young ladies would do well to exercise their ingenuity in grouping minute sprays ... for the adornment of valentines which may thus be made in much better taste than those procured at great cost in the shops". Times have certainly changed!

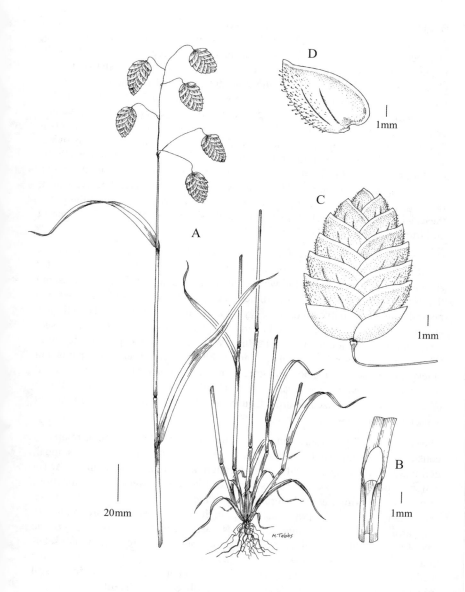

Briza maxima: A, habit; B, ligule; C, spikelet; D, lemma in profile.

40. Poa annua L.

Annual Meadow-grass

Bright or dark green annual or short-lived perennial, the latter the result of procumbent culms rooting at the nodes; culms up to 35(45)cm, erect, ascending or procumbent, slightly compressed; sheaths compressed and keeled, smooth; ligule of uppermost leaf blunt, (0.5)1 – 3(3.5)mm; blades thin, flat or folded, glabrous, often wrinkled when young, abruptly pointed or hooded at the tip. Panicle ovate or triangular, loose and open or rarely lightly contracted, 1 – 8.5(13)cm, the branches solitary or paired, rarely 3 together, smooth, spreading or reflexed at maturity. Spikelets ovate or oblong, 3.5 – 7(8)mm, (2)3- to 6(8)-flowered; glumes unequal, acute at the tip, the lower lanceolate to narrowly ovate, 1.5 – 2.8(3.5)mm, 1-nerved (rarely with faint lateral nerves), the upper elliptic or oblong, 1.7 – 3.5(4.7)mm, 3-nerved; lemmas semi-elliptic to ovate in profile, 2.5 – 3.8(4.5)mm, sparsely to densely hairy on the keel and lateral nerves below, rarely glabrous, blunt at the tip; palea with curled or crispate hairs on the keels, these dense or sparse, rarely absent; anthers 0.6 – 1.1(1.4)mm. $2n = 28$. Flowering and fruiting throughout the year.

Occurring throughout the British Isles, *P. annua* is one of the most abundant weeds of cultivation in both arable fields and gardens, is widespread in open sites such as waste ground, paths and walls, and is a common constituent of grassland that is heavily grazed, mown or trampled. It can occur on a wide range of basic to neutral soils from coarse sands to heavy clay, avoiding only very acid conditions, and in damp or dry places as well as in the open or in shade. It is found at sea-level and on high mountains (to >1200m). We can therefore expect to encounter this ubiquitous grass in most man-made habitats (e.g. garden beds, pavement cracks, driveways, lawns, bowling greens and golf courses) and on pathways and in disturbed or overgrazed areas in all types of grassland, though not usually in taller, less heavily grazed swards. Consequently, *P. annua* has a huge range of associated, mainly weedy, species.

The species' ability to flourish in many different types of habitat can be related to considerable variation in life history and other traits. It is mostly a summer annual, germinating in the spring, but can go through several generations in a year (in extreme conditions flowering and setting seed within six weeks of germination) or behave as a winter annual, germinating in the autumn and overwintering as a small plant. Perennial biotypes first flower in their second year and are frequently polycarpic. Famously, *P. annua* can be observed in flower in every month of the year. In favourable conditions individuals may produce more than 20,000 seeds in a year; at the same time small plants may produce as few as 10 seeds. Some seed can germinate immediately whilst large numbers remain viable in the soil for long periods. Thus the species is able to rapidly colonize disturbed soil. Plants in grazed areas can withstand severe defoliation and trampling and can set seed in very heavily grazed swards and when cut regularly as low as 6.5mm. This enables

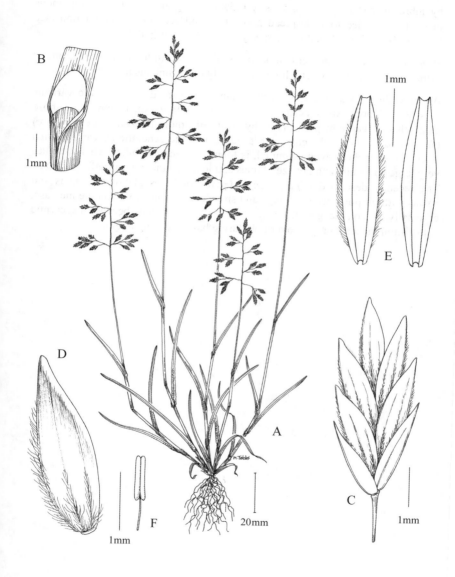

Poa annua: A, habit; B, ligule; C, spikelet; D, lemma in profile;
E, palea, with keels hairy (left) and glabrous (right); F, anther.

P. annua populations to persist in and dominate close-cropped, fertilized and well-watered swards even though individual plants may be short-lived. Much of this variation is known to be genetic and correlated with habitat, and, reinforced by inbreeding (the species is mostly (85%) selfing and can be cleistogamous in winter), has led to widespread population and ecotypic differentiation (see below). (Biol. Flora: Hutchinson & Seymour, 1982; CPE: 474).

P. annua is native, with a circumpolar distribution in all temperate zones and is naturalized around the world. It occurs mainly on mountains in the tropics.

An exceedingly variable species with numerous named infra-specific variants mostly of minor taxonomic interest. Var. *reptans* Hausskn. is applied to those plants that appear to be perennating by means of stolons (rhizomes are very rare) but it is not known if the character is stable over the generations. Var. *aquatica* Asch., another short-lived perennial, is found in aquatic habitats. This often has very large spikelets with outsize glumes and lemmas, the latter usually glabrous. The recently described f. *purpurea* M.Grant combines glabrous lemmas and paleas with purplish-brown foliage and spikelets. It seems to be on the increase, especially in botanic gardens where it was first noticed, because its cryptic colouration makes it easy to overlook during hand-weeding operations.

41. **Poa infirma** Kunth

Early Meadow-grass

Illustration, page 203

New Atlas: 755

Yellowish green annual; culms up to 10(25)cm, slender, erect or procumbent; sheaths compressed and keeled, smooth; ligule of uppermost leaf obtuse or truncate, 0.8 – 1.8(2.7)mm; blades thin, flat or folded, blunt or abruptly pointed at the tip. Panicle lanceolate to ovate, loose and open, 0.5 – 4(6.5)cm, the branches solitary or paired, smooth, erecto-patent at maturity. Spikelets ovate or oblong, 2.5 – 3.5(5.5)mm, 2- to 3(5)-flowered; glumes unequal, blunt at the tip, the lower ovate, (0.8)0.9 – 1.4(1.6)mm, 1-nerved, the upper elliptic or oblong, (1)1.1 – 1.8(2.3)mm, 3-nerved; lemmas oblong in profile, 1.8 – 2.3(2.6)mm, densely hairy on the keel and lateral nerves below (up to or beyond the middle), blunt at the tip; palea with dense curled or crispate hairs on the keels; anthers broadly oblong or oval, 0.15 – 0.4mm, often scarcely longer than wide. $2n = 14$. Flowering and fruiting early March to mid-April, sometimes lasting until mid-June.

This rare, and possibly overlooked, little grass is restricted in the British Isles to the Channel Islands, the Isles of Scilly and southern coastal counties of England from Cornwall to E Sussex, including the Isle of Wight. It was recently recorded in the wild in Ireland (W Cork). It occurs mostly near the sea in open or short turf habitats such as cliff-top paths, lawns and car parks, and in sandy places such as dune grassland and semi-fixed dunes. Typical associates include *Bellis perennis, Cerastium diffusum, Leontodon saxatilis, Plantago coronopus, P. lanceolata, Poa annua, Trifolium ornithopodioides* and *T. scabrum*.

P. infirma is a short-lived annual, flowering very early in most habitats and has sometimes set seed and virtually disappeared by early March. It can be later flowering in sand-dunes. Relatively little is known about its biology but the seeds are clearly long-lived and populations may reappear after an absence of one or two years. Populations of this species are often remarkably local, appearing in the same circumscribed area each year even when there is a great deal of apparently suitable habitat nearby (e.g. along well-trodden paths). Like *P. annua*, it seems to withstand trampling, although it has often completed the vegetative part of its life-cycle before coastal paths are heavily used. (RDB: 287).

A native species, *P. infirma* was first collected in W Cornwall in 1876 and at one time was thought to be restricted to that county, the Isles of Scilly and the Channel Islands. Its present distribution, which suggests that there has been a considerable eastward extension of its range since the 1962 Atlas, presents us with an intriguing problem. Has this often tiny plant been overlooked, perhaps mistaken for *P. annua*, until botanists began to look out for it? (The rather paler yellowish green colour is a useful characteristic to look out for, but is not reliably diagnostic; see below). Or has the species expanded its range, especially in the milder winters of the 80s and 90s? (It is reported to have spread rapidly in the Isles of Scilly since the early 1980s). Aspects of its biology, listed above, suggest it could have been overlooked, and continuing to search suitable habitats early in

201

the year might well bring rewards. *P. infirma* is part of the Mediterranean-Atlantic element in the British flora (P&H), occurring from the Canary Islands eastwards along both shores of the Mediterranean to Greece and Turkey. It also occurs in SW Asia and has been introduced to S America.

The extended ranges of the measurements given in parentheses above apply to European plants; the species is considerably more variable in Europe than it is in the British Isles (including the Channel Islands), with a flowering period extending from January to July. *P. infirma* is distinguished from *P. annua* on several counts including its paler colour, smaller spikelets, shorter anthers and distinctive erecto-patent panicle-branches.

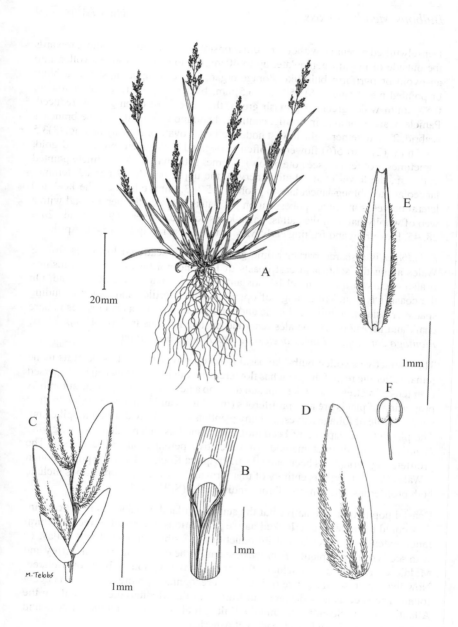

Poa infirma: A, habit; B, ligule; C, spikelet; D, lemma in profile; E, palea; F, anther.

42.   Poa bulbosa L.

Bulbous Meadow-grass

New Atlas: 760

Densely tufted perennial without rhizomes or stolons; culms erect, or those towards the outside of the tuft geniculate, up to 40cm, the lowest internode swollen into an ovoid or pyriform bulb-like storage-organ; ligule of uppermost leaf a blunt or pointed membrane (0.5)1.5 – 3.5(6.5)mm; blades very narrow, flat or folded, 0.5 – 2mm wide, green or greyish green, the uppermost often greatly reduced. Panicle ovate or oblong in profile, contracted and moderately dense, the branches scabrid, 2 – 3 together at the lowest node. Spikelets ovate or broadly oblong, (3)3.5 – 4.5mm, (2)3- to 5(6)-flowered, often variegated with green, purple and gold, sometimes proliferous (see note below). Glumes subequal, 2 – 3mm, finely pointed at the tip, the lower ovate, 1- to 3-nerved, the upper broader, 3-nerved; lemmas lanceolate to oblong-lanceolate in profile, 2.5 – 3.5mm, ciliate on the keel and lateral nerves, sometimes pubescent on the flanks between the nerves, and with a web of woolly hairs on the callus; palea-keels scabrid; anthers 0.9 – 1.6mm. $2n =$ 28, 45. Flowering and fruiting early May to mid-June, rarely as early as April.

P. bulbosa is a scarce paramaritime grass found in scattered localities from S Wales along the south and east coasts of England northwards to Lincolnshire. It also occurs in the Channel Islands and in a few inland sites in England. On the coast it is found in a range of open, usually infertile sandy soils including sparse grassland, stabilized shingle and sand-dunes, as well as in crevices in bare chalk and limestone. Associates recorded in such habitats include *Aira praecox, Plantago coronopus, Rumex acetosella* and *Trifolium striatum*.

The distinctive swollen bulb-like basal internodes which give this plant its name remain after the rest of the plant has flowered and died back. They can be dispersed over tens of metres. They take root and develop a new tuft, usually in the autumn. A proportion of plants are also proliferous (the glumes and lemmas reverting to their ancestral role of foliage leaves, and tiny plantlets being formed from the spikelets). The plantlets are capable of becoming established as independent plants, giving *P. bulbosa* two distinct methods of vegetative perennation and dispersal. The proliferating variant has been named var. **vivipara** Koel. At least one population in S Wales (Vc 41) consists entirely of this form and a few other populations include both proliferous and non-proliferous individuals. (SPB: 315).

Coastal populations are native but the status of inland populations is not certain: they could be hitherto-overlooked native populations, the result of recent natural range extension, or accidental introductions, possibly with sand and ballast or with seeds of forage plants. *P. bulbosa* seems to be on the increase in Surrey and Middlesex but the plants seldom flower and have obviously been overlooked. Now that botanists are aware of it and can recognize it, more and more is being found. The species is widespread in Europe in the Mediterranean and along the Atlantic coast to Scandinavia and the Baltic. It also grows in temperate Asia and N Africa and has been introduced to N America.

This grass is often grown in gardens, but the proliferating variant is preferred.

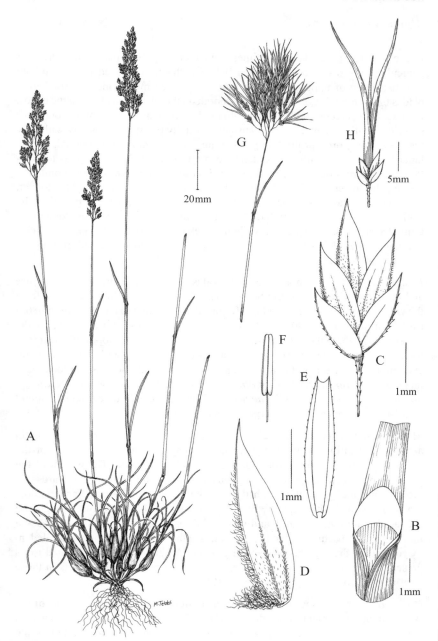

Poa bulbosa var. *bulbosa*: A, habit; B, ligule; C, spikelet; D, lemma in profile; E, palea; F, anther.
Poa bulbosa var. *vivipara*: G, panicle; H, spikelet.

43.　Poa alpina L.

Alpine Meadow-grass　　　　　　　　　　　　New Atlas: 760

Loosely tufted perennial, sometimes with creeping rhizomes; culms erect or geniculate, up to 40(45)cm, clothed below with the thickened remains of old sheaths; ligule of uppermost leaf a blunt or pointed membrane 1 – 3(4.5)mm; blades flat or folded, 1.5 – 4mm wide, smooth on the surface, scabrid on the edges. Panicle ovate, erect or nodding, open to moderately dense, 2 – 6cm, the branches scabrid, usually in pairs. Spikelets usually partially proliferous, mostly with only the uppermost florets proliferating, the glumes and lower floret(s) normal, but the latter barren; non-proliferous spikelets ovate to oblong, 3.5 – 7mm, 3- to 4(7)-flowered; glumes ovate to elliptic, scabrid on the keel above, sharply pointed at the tip, the lower (2.2)2.7 – 3.6mm, 1- to 3-nerved, the upper slightly longer, 3-nerved; lemmas elliptic-oblong in profile, 3.4 – 4.3mm, densely pilose on the keel and outer nerves, shortly ciliate or glabrous on the inner nerves, sometimes thinly hairy between the nerves, without a web of wool on the callus; palea-keels ciliolate; anthers 1.3 – 2.3mm. $2n = $ c.32, 35, 39, c.84. Flowering and fruiting late June to mid-August.

P. alpina occurs in the mountains of N Wales, northern England (NW Yorkshire and the Lake District) and the Scottish Highlands, and has been recorded from the west of Ireland (S Kerry and Co. Sligo). It is restricted to altitudes from 580m (in Westmorland) to 1190m (in Westerness). (Wilson (1949) gives 300m as the lower limit), where it occurs on steep open faces, ledges and slopes of calcareous rock. It usually grows in scattered small tufts and most populations are small, even in the Scottish Highlands. Other species found with the grass on rock faces include *Carex atrata, Cerastium alpinum, Draba incana, Poa glauca, Saxifraga oppositifolia, S. nivalis* and *Silene acaulis*. The grass can also be found in alpine/dwarf-herb swards and moss carpets on base-rich soils.

Most British populations of *P. alpina* are proliferous (var. **vivipara** L.) or contain a few seed-bearing plants, but there is no clear pattern of distribution of the two forms. The non-proliferous form is probably apomictic. The weight of the panicles produced on proliferous plants bends the inflorescence towards the ground and once in contact with the soil the plantlets take root. Early authors praise the high nutritive quality of this 'broad leaved hill grass of the Highland shepherd' (Gordon, undated), and it is said to have been either planted or sown into mountain pastures after burning the heather, the seed being trampled in by repeatedly driving sheep over the ground. Certainly it may be limited to its present distribution by grazing. For example, it is not confined to cliffs in those parts of Norway where grazing is light. (SPB: 314).

P. alpina is a native species with a disjunct circumpolar distribution, part of the Arctic-montane element in our flora (P&H). It is widely naturalized in mountains outside its range. The species is believed to have suffered from collecting in some outlying British sites and several populations have been lost. However, it is likely to be present in remote rarely visited sites from where it was recorded before 1970.

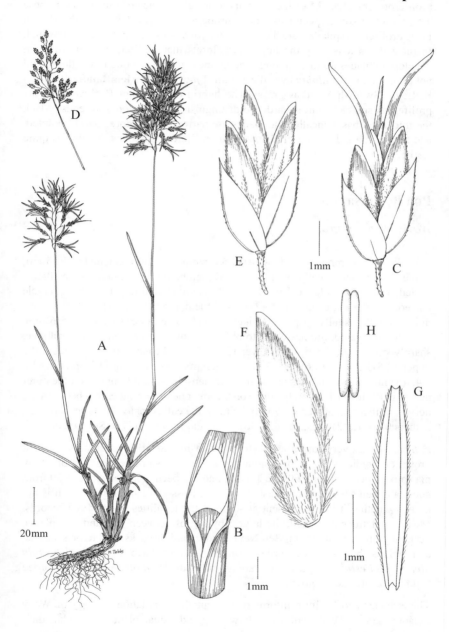

Poa alpina: A, habit, B, ligule, C, proliferous spikelet; D, panicle from non-proliferous plant; E, non-proliferous spikelet; F, lemma from E; G, palea from E; H, anther from E.

This is a very distinctive species forming tufts of broad leaves and panicles of proliferous spikelets. Most literature indicates an absence of rhizomes but these are present in some specimens from Europe as well as a few from the British Isles. Proliferous spikelets are the rule with normal spikelets being rather unusual. In most cases it is only the uppermost florets that proliferate, some of them developing blades up to 2cm long. The glumes and at least one lower floret tend not to proliferate. *P. alpina* hybridizes with *P. flexuosa* (**P.** ×**jemtlandica** (Almq.) K.Richt., Swedish Meadow-grass). The hybrid differs from *P. flexuosa* by its proliferous spikelets, but is harder to distinguish from *P. alpina*. It tends to lack the thickened basal sheaths, the blades are narrower and more sharply pointed, and the lemma is less densely hairy. Non-proliferous spikelets are always quite sterile.

44. Poa flexuosa Sm.

Wavy Meadow-grass   New Atlas: 758

Loosely tufted perennial, rarely with short rhizomes; culms erect, up to 17(25)cm; ligule of uppermost leaf a bluntly pointed membrane 1.5 – 3mm; blades flat or folded, 1 – 2mm wide, scaberulous on the margins and upper surface. Panicle lanceolate to ovate, erect, loose, (2)3 – 4(5.5)cm, the branches slender, flexuous, quite smooth, usually in pairs. Spikelets ovate to elliptic, (3.5)4 – 5.5(6)mm, 2- to 4(5)-flowered; glumes ovate to oblong-elliptic, scabrid on the keels above, sharply pointed at the tip, the lower (2.2)2.7 – 4(4.5)mm, 1- to 3-nerved, the upper (2.5)3.2 – 4.2(4.6)mm, 3-nerved; lemmas oblong-elliptic in profile, 3.2 – 4.4(5)mm, pilose on the keel, sometimes densely so, thinly pilose on the outer nerves in the lower 1/4, rarely ciliate on the inner nerves or pubescent between the nerves, with a sparse web of woolly hairs on the callus; palea-keels scaberulous; anthers 0.6 – 1.6(2)mm. $2n = 42$. Flowering and fruiting July to September.

P. flexuosa is a very rare grass restricted to a few Scottish mountains where it grows on acidic rocks among stones in screes, on stone ledges and on stony plateaux. It occurs from 760m to 1100m, and has been recorded since 1970 from about a dozen sites in Aberdeenshire, Moray, Ross-shire and Inverness. It is not known whether it is still present at some of the localities of pre-1987 records. Most populations are small, the largest by far, of between 200 and 300 plants, occurring on scree slopes on Ben Nevis. Individual tussocks tend to be scattered and isolated but species recorded from the vicinity have included *Alchemilla alpina* and *Festuca vivipara*. The rare hybrid with *Poa alpina* has been recorded from some sites (see below).

There appears to be little information about the population biology of Wavy Meadow-grass. We do not know how long individual plants live, what their breeding system is – although probably apomictic – or how frequently they set seed (RDB: 286).

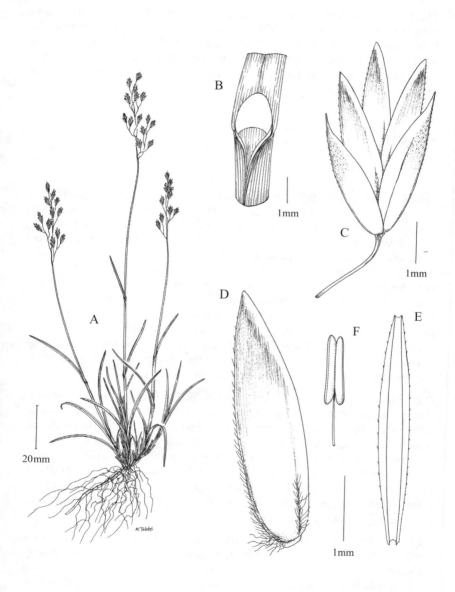

Poa flexuosa: A, habit; B, ligule; C, spikelet with pedicel; D, lemma in profile; E, palea; F, anther.

P. flexuosa is a native grass, endemic to Scotland, Norway, Sweden and Iceland. In some areas of Scotland it may be threatened by human activities such as climbing and is classified as **vulnerable** by Cheffings & Farrell (2005).

This very rare but fairly distinctive species is recognized by its perfectly smooth panicle-branches. It hybridizes with *P. alpina*; see under that species for details. It is scarcely different from the Central European **P. laxa** Haenke; the main distinguishing feature being the hairs on the outer lemma-nerves being sharply pointed and confined to the lower 1/4 in *flexuosa* compared with blunt and present to at least half-way in *laxa*.

45.   Poa trivialis L.

Rough Meadow-grass   New Atlas: 756

Tufted perennial up to 75(90)cm; outer culms often ascending from a procumbent base, rooting at the nodes to produce slender, shortly creeping stolons; sheaths mostly faintly scabrid but sometimes quite smooth; ligule a narrowly triangular, pointed membrane 3 – 9mm; blades flat or folded, 2 – 4.5(6)mm wide. Panicle ovate to oblong, erect or nodding, open and very loose to contracted and rather dense, 6 – 20cm, the branches scabrid, in a cluster of 3 – 6(9) at the lowest node. Spikelets ovate to elliptic, 3 – 4.5(6)mm, 2- to 4-flowered; glumes unequal, scabrid on the keel, sharply pointed at the tip, the lower lanceolate, (1.7)2 – 3mm, 1-nerved, the upper ovate, 2.2 – 3.5mm, 3-nerved; lemmas narrowly oblong in profile, (2.5)2.7 – 3.5(3.7)mm, ciliate on the keel below, mostly glabrous on the lateral nerves and flanks (rarely the outer nerves ciliolate) and with a tuft of long woolly hairs on the callus; palea-keels scaberulous; anthers 1.2 – 2.1mm. $2n = 14$, 28. Flowering and fruiting late May to late July or mid-August.

P. trivialis is widely distributed throughout the British Isles in a range of habitats. It is very common in meadows and pastures, especially in the lowlands on moist fertile soils, and in marshland, mires and around the edges of ponds and streams where it can appear semi-aquatic but is usually rooted in the banks. It is also a frequent colonist of waste and cultivated land and a weed of herbage seed crops, winter cereals and cultivated grassland. Finally, it occurs in open woodland, hedgerows and scrubland. In this wide range of habitats it grows on all but extremely acid, dry or infertile soils and with a huge number of plant associates. It is found from sea-level to 1065m in Easterness.

Strikingly, although Rough Meadow-grass occurs on a wide range of habitats it rarely dominates in any. It is the ultimate 'companion' grass which was formerly included in seed mixtures for permanent pastures (and is still sown in amenity grassland) for its understorey of low vigorous growth combined with palatability and the ability to colonize bare patches. Sensitive only to drought (it is shallow rooting), continuous low mowing and heavy trampling, the species seems able to co-exist in tall swards with a wide range of dominant species. Grime *et al.,* (2007)

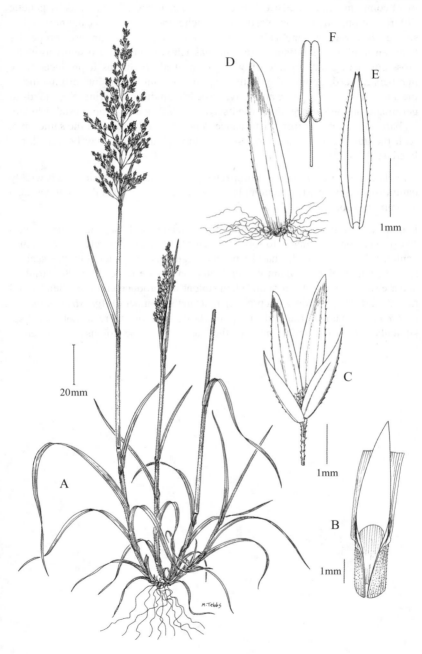

Poa trivialis: A, habit; B, ligule; C, spikelet; D, lemma in profile; E, palea; F, anther.

describe *P. trivialis* as "arguably the most successful subordinate constituent of plant communities in the British Isles". Whether it has achieved this by genetic differentiation, phenotypic plasticity or niche specialization is unknown. The species is certainly genetically variable (e.g. in seed germination properties between arable and grassland plants) and has a flexible breeding system (normally cross-pollinating but capable of selfing). In ideal conditions it produces huge numbers of seed, germinating both in spring and autumn, plants originating in the autumn producing more and heavier seeds than those in spring. Seed tends to germinate on the surface and buried seeds persist, enabling rapid establishment on bare soils resulting from disturbance, a good 'weedy' trait. At the same time, with the ability to produce short stolons, individual plants may be very long-lived. (CPE: 478).

P. trivialis is native throughout Europe, temperate Asia and N Africa and is widely naturalized elsewhere (a Circumpolar Wide-temperate species; P&H). It was also a common wool alien.

It is a very variable species, ranging from slender, reddish-tinged plants with sparse, very open panicles, to robust, green plants with contracted, rather dense panicles. The elongated, sharply pointed ligule is characteristic; the scabrid sheaths, which give the plant its vernacular name, are rather prone to variation and are sometimes quite smooth. When stolons are produced they are slender and rather short; the plant does not produce mats in the manner of *Agrostis stolonifera* or *A. canina*. Our material is all subsp. **trivialis**; in Europe there is another, subsp. **silvicola** (Guss.) H. Lindb., in which the internodes of the stolons are swollen.

46. Poa nemoralis L.

Illustration, page 215

Wood Meadow-grass   New Atlas: 759

Loosely tufted perennial without rhizomes; culms erect or geniculate, up to 80(100)cm, the uppermost node above the middle; leaves usually green, rarely glaucous, the uppermost above the middle of the culm; ligule a truncate or shallowly convex rim 0.15 – 1.3(2.1)mm; blades 1 – 2.5(3)mm wide, flat or folded, smooth or scaberulous. Panicle usually nodding, sometimes stiffly erect with suberect branches, lanceolate to ovate or oblong, 3 – 15(20)cm, the branches scabrid, (1)2 – 5(7) together at the lowest node. Spikelets lanceolate or ovate to oblong, 2.5 – 6.5mm, (1)2- to 5-flowered; glumes slightly unequal, 3-nerved, usually sharply pointed, the lower lanceolate, 2 – 3.5(4)mm, the upper often broader, 2.5 – 4.5mm; lemmas narrowly oblong to lanceolate-oblong in profile, 2.5 – 4.5mm, pilose on the keel and marginal nerves below, sometimes pubescent between the nerves, with or without a tuft of few to many long woolly hairs on the callus; palea-keels scaberulous; anthers 1 – 2mm, but often aborted. $2n = 42, 56$. Flowering and fruiting late May to mid-August, sometimes to mid-September.

This common grass is widely distributed in Britain, occurring in two quite different types of habitat. It is best known as a rather delicate grass of woodland and other shaded habitats where it can be locally abundant along woodland rides and clearings as well as in hedgerows. It also occurs in open dry places, particularly walls and on rock ledges on mountains; in these latter habitats it has a more erect growth habit (see below). In woodland habitats it can be found on a range of soil types from sand to heavy clay. It is mainly a lowland species but occurs at 915m in Easterness.

The shade tolerance, winter greenness, rich leaf colour and attractive panicle have led to *P. nemoralis* being sown in parks and woodlands for both cover and ormanent. It is a very variable species, even within woodland habitats, but it is not known how much of the variation is genetic and how much is due to environmental factors such as degree of shading; for example, individuals from more deeply shaded woods tend to have fewer florets in each spikelet. Both sexual (probably mostly selfing) and facultatively apomictic plants occur (see below).

The status of *P. nemoralis* in the Britsh Isles is complicated by its widespread introduction, both deliberate and accidental. It is usually regarded as native in most of Britain but probably introduced in parts of NW Britain and Ireland. The species occurs throughout temperate Europe and Asia and in N Africa, Japan and N America. It may be spreading in NW Britain and Ireland.

P. nemoralis is a facultative agamospermous species that produces a mixture of sexual and apomictic races with the inevitable consequences for its taxonomy. Numerous segregate taxa have been described, of which only one, *P. glauca* (q.v.), seems worth maintaining, albeit with some difficulty. The two species have traditionally been distinguished by the length of the ligule and most texts

213

quote a maximum length of 0.5mm for *P. nemoralis* and a minimum of 1mm for *P. glauca*. On closer inspection the value of 0.5mm is found to be nearer to the mean for *P. nemoralis* (0.4mm) than the maximum; fully one-third of specimens studied had a ligule between 0.5 and 1mm, and one in twenty had a ligule above 1mm (to a maximum of 2.1mm). The ligule is therefore rather less useful than hitherto supposed. Montane and wall-top forms of *P. nemoralis* adopt a stiffer, more tightly tufted habit similar to shade forms of *P. glauca* ('*P. balfouri*'), and it is these that often have the longer ligules. Trist (1986a) has attempted to clarify matters, but the table of discriminating characters given in his paper is so full of typographical errors that it is quite unhelpful. Olonova (1990) has drawn attention to two further characters. One concerns the development of wool on the callus of the floret, poorly developed in *P. nemoralis*, well developed in *P. glauca*, but both species seem to have a similar proportion of specimens with no wool, scanty wool and ample wool. The other character Olonova mentioned is more promising and would well repay closer examination; it certainly seems to work on our material. In *P. nemoralis* the uppermost node of the culm is above the middle of the plant, certainly in the upper two-thirds, and the uppermost leaf is consequently towards the upper end of the culm. In *P. glauca* the uppermost node is confined to the base of the culm, within the lower third, and the uppermost leaf, while on a relatively long sheath, is below the middle of the culm.

P. nemoralis is usually green but some collectors have remarked on the intense blueness of some strains. The species also tends to have a fuller panicle of smaller spikelets than *P. glauca*, but these characters are both too vague to be of any diagnostic value.

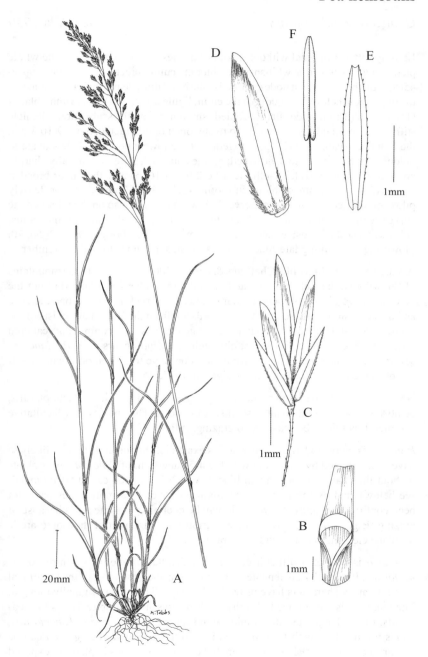

Poa nemoralis: A, habit; B, ligule; C, spikelet; D, lemma in profile; E, palea; F, anther.

47. Poa glauca Vahl

Glaucous Meadow-grass   New Atlas: 759

Loosely tufted perennial without rhizomes or these rarely developing, the whole plant often coated in a whitish waxy bloom; culms erect or geniculate, up to 45(55)cm, the uppermost node confined to the basal third; leaves green or glaucous, the uppermost below the middle of the culm; ligule blunt, (0.5)1 – 2(3)mm; blades (1)1.5 – 2.2(3)mm wide, flat or folded, smooth or faintly scaberulous. Panicle stiffly erect or nodding, lanceolate to ovate, open or contracted, 3.5 – 9(10.5)cm, the branches scabrid, (1)2 – 3(4) together at the lowest node. Spikelets ovate to oblong, 4 – 6.5mm, 2- to 4-flowered; glumes unequal, 3-nerved, usually sharply pointed, the lower ovate or elliptic, (2.6)2.9 – 4.1(4.5)mm, the upper broader, 3 – 4.7(5.5)mm; lemmas oblong in profile, (3.1)3.4 – 4.7mm, thinly or densely pilose on the keel and marginal nerves below, sometimes also on the intermediate nerves, with or without a tuft of few to many long woolly hairs on the callus; palea-keels scaberulous; anthers 1.2 – 1.9mm, but often aborted. $2n = 42, 56, 70$. Flowering and fruiting late June to mid-August, sometimes to mid-September.

A scarce grass (**vulnerable**, Cheffings & Farrell, 2005) restricted to the mountains of Snowdonia, the Lake District and central and northern Scotland (but not the outer isles), *P. glauca* is found on damp calcareous rock faces and open ledges, and on stony slopes and screes. Most records are from the Dalradian schists of the central Scottish Highlands. Populations are generally small, comprising scattered tufts with few associated species, although *P. alpina* occurs with *P. glauca* in several sites. The species occurs from 305m on Skye to 1110m on Lochnagar. It has been recorded as a casual in Cardiganshire (Vc 46).

Nothing seems to be known about the longevity of individual plants or tufts, or how frequently new plants establish from seed. The species is a facultative apomict. It is said to be sensitive to grazing. (SPB: 316).

P. glauca is native to Britain. Charting its exact distribution and status is likely to have been affected by confusion with the montane form of *P. nemoralis* or plants without the characteristic whitish bloom (which have been called '*P. balfouri*'; see below), and by the fact that records in many of its remotist sites have not been confirmed recently. However, it may be declining in some areas because of grazing. *P. glauca* has a circumpolar distribution and is part of the Boreo-arctic Montane element in our mountain flora (P&H).

P. glauca is part of a difficult complex of facultative apomicts centred on *P. nemoralis*. It is just barely tenable as a separate species, but most of the traditional discriminatory characters have proved to be less reliable than originally thought. The complex is still in need of a thorough reassessment despite Trist's (1986a) efforts. Ligule length, usually employed to separate *P. glauca* from *P. nemoralis*, varies too much in both taxa to be entirely reliable. Much of *P. glauca* can be recognized by its whitish waxy bloom, but this only develops in plants in exposed

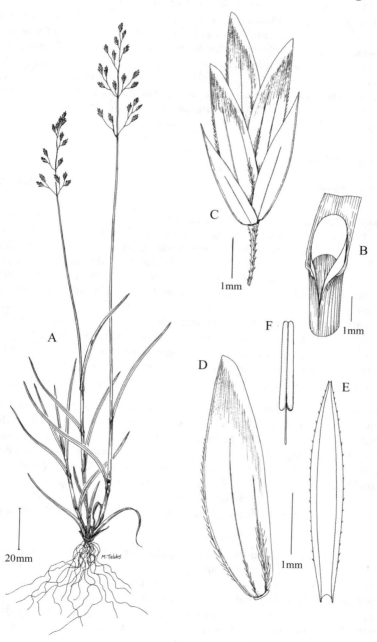

Poa glauca: A, habit; B, ligule; C, spikelet; D, lemma in profile; E, palea; F, anther.

situations. Plants from sheltered places ('*P. balfouri*'), but still at high altitude, lose this bloom and can resemble montane forms of *P. nemoralis* (the latter tending to have longer ligules than is normal for the species). The position of the uppermost node of the culm seems to offer an alternative means of separating the taxa (see under *P. nemoralis* for further details), but its implications have not yet been thoroughly explored. The node appears to retain its basal position in cultivated material and may therefore be stable and probably reliable. The position of the uppermost leaf, as a consequence of the basal position of the node, also contributes to the characteristic appearance of the species.

48. Poa palustris L.

Swamp Meadow-grass   New Atlas: 759

Loosely tufted short-lived perennial without rhizomes; culms erect or procumbent and often rooting from the lower nodes, up to 120(140)cm, the uppermost node usually in the upper two-thirds; leaves green; ligule a blunt membrane (2)2.5 – 4.5(6)mm; blades 2 – 4mm wide, usually flat, scaberulous. Panicle usually nodding, sometimes erect, ovate to oblong, loose and very open, 10 – 30cm, the branches scabrid, subverticillate, with up to 8 together at the lowest node. Spikelets ovate to oblong, 3 – 5.5mm, 2- to 5-flowered; glumes subequal or unequal, sharply pointed, the lower lanceolate, 2.1 – 3.2mm, 1- to 3-nerved, the upper broader, 2.4 – 3.4mm, 3-nerved; lemmas narrowly oblong in profile, 2.5 – 3.6mm, pilose on the keel and marginal nerves below, with a tuft of long woolly hairs on the callus; palea-keels scaberulous; anthers 0.9 – 1.4mm, but often aborted. $2n = 14, 28, 42$. Flowering and fruiting mid-June to mid-August.

P. palustris is a scarce but probably overlooked grass which has been recorded from a series of widely scattered wetland localities in the British Isles. These include marshes, fens, ditches and willow carr, as well as the margins of ponds, lakes, rivers and canals. It also occurs occasionally on waste ground around docks and railways and on urban rubbish dumps. In aquatic habitats it has a wide range of associates which may include *Filipendula ulmaria, Galium uliginosum, Holcus lanatus, Juncus effusus, Lythrum salicaria, Phalaris arundinacea, Phragmites australis, Persicaria amphibia, Ranunculus aquatilis* and *Senecio aquaticus*. (SPB: 317).

We are not aware of any studies of the population biology of this species in the wild. It is said to be a facultative apomict and new populations clearly establish from seed when introduced as a grain alien into docks. The wetland populations, which can form fairly large patches, may represent the escape of the grass from the more competitive terrestrial environments in which it was at one time grown as a fodder plant. Many populations may have been transient, giving the impression that the species is declining in distribution.

Poa palustris: A, habit; B, ligule; C, spikelet; D, lemma in profile; E, palea; F, anther.

P. palustris is considered to be a neophyte, introduced initially into Britain in the early part of the 19th century for fodder (probably from N America), and being first recorded from the wild in 1879. Suggestions that it may be native in East Anglia are thus far unsubstantiated but could well be correct. It occurs from Scandinavia and W & C Europe through parts of temperate Asia to Japan and China. It is widespread in N America. It is naturalized in many parts of Great Britain and Ireland, but does not appear to be spreading – indeed it appears to be declining – although it is still occasionally introduced as a grain alien.

Poa palustris is a close relative of *P. nemoralis* and differs mainly by the length of the ligule. Other supporting characters are the large open panicle with subverticillate branches, weak procumbent culms and habitat.

49.   Poa compressa L.

Flattened Meadow-grass   New Atlas: 758

Extensively rhizomatous perennial with solitary or loosely tufted culms; culms wiry, erect or ascending, up to 60cm, conspicuously flattened, the sheaths mostly shorter than the internodes and exposing the brown- or purple-tinged nodes; sheaths keeled, smooth and glabrous; ligule of uppermost leaf a blunt membrane 0.6 – 2.2mm; blades bluish or greyish green, flat or folded, 1 – 4mm wide, smooth or faintly scaberulous. Panicle narrowly oblong to ovate-elliptic, contracted and dense, sometimes loose and more open, (2)3 – 9cm, the branches scabrid, 1 – 5 (usually 2) together at the lowest node. Spikelets ovate to elliptic or oblong, 3.5 – 6mm, 3- to 7-flowered; glumes subequal, ovate to elliptic or oblong, 3-nerved, bluntly pointed, the lower 1.8 – 2.8mm, the upper very slightly longer; lemmas narrowly oblong in profile, 2.3 – 3.1mm, thinly pilose on the keel and marginal nerves below, often with a scanty web of wool on the callus, but often quite glabrous, becoming firm with inrolled margins; anthers 1 – 1.5mm but often aborted. $2n = 42$. Flowering and fruiting mid-June to mid-September.

P. compressa is fairly widespread in most of England where it has an odd patchy distribution, being common in some counties but absent from large areas of others. It becomes scattered in northern England and Scotland, largely coastal in Wales and quite scarce in Ireland. It is largely a grass of man-made habitats, notably old walls, cinder tracks and dry banks, and can be found in poor thin grassland, waysides and waste and stony ground on or beside paths and railways. The soils where it grows are mostly shallow and well-drained and carry a range of dry grassland species such as *Leontodon autumnalis* and *Sagina procumbens*. The species is found mainly in the lowlands but reaches 365m in Westmorland.

Flattened Meadow-grass spreads both by its creeping rhizomes and by seed, although the longevity of individual plants and the relative role of plants and seed in maintaining populations is not known. It appears to withstand long periods of drought, and in grassland the plant is noticeably absent from more

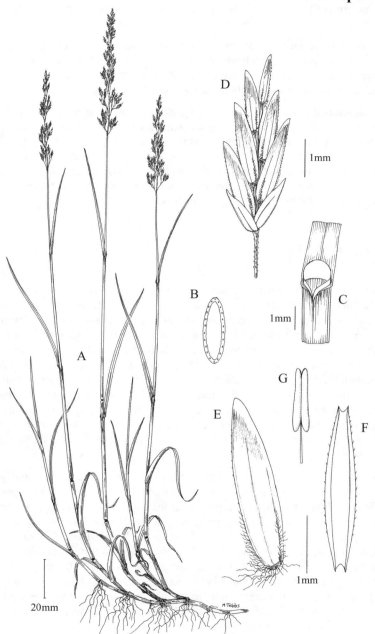

Poa compressa: A, habit; B, transverse section of culm; C, ligule; D, spikelet;
E, lemma in profile; F, palea; G, anther.

nutrient-rich areas such as the latrines of grazing animals. This indicates that it is characteristically a stress tolerant species unable to compete in more fertile moist conditions. It is said to be apomictic.

P. compressa is native in Britain but some populations are probably introduced and it is not possible to clearly delineate native and introduced populations, especially in Scotland. It is classed as an alien in Ireland. A European temperate species, *P. compressa* is widely naturalized outside its range.

An unmistakable species recognized by its remarkably flattened culms (when growing on walls *P. pratensis* subsp. *irrigata* may also have strongly compressed stems), tight narrow panicle and conspicuous nodes. There is some variation in habit, the culms being solitary or loosely (and rarely even densely) tufted, but the rhizomes, however long or short, are always present. The hardened, inrolled lemmas are also characteristic. Despite its fairly obvious facies, there is a suggestion that the species may be under-recorded.

50.   **Poa pratensis** L.

Loosely to densely tufted perennial with well developed rhizomes; culms erect, up to 70(100)cm; ligule a blunt membrane 0.5 – 2(3)mm, glabrous or hairy on the back, usually decurrent on the sheath margins; blades smooth, up to 30cm but often much shorter, flat or tightly folded-setaceous and 0.5 – 4(6)mm wide. Panicle open, pyramidal to ovate or oblong, 2.5 – 12(20)cm, with (1)2 – 5(6) branches at the lowest node. Spikelets ovate to oblong or elliptic, 3.5 – 6(8.5)mm, 2- to 5(7)-flowered; glumes unequal, acute or shortly acuminate, the lower narrowly ovate, 2 – 3.6mm, 1- or 3-nerved, the upper broader, 2.3 – 4.1mm, 3-nerved; lemmas narrowly ovate to oblong in profile, 2.6 – 4(4.5)mm, thinly to densely pilose on the keel and marginal nerves below, with a copious web of wool on the callus; anthers 1.2 – 2.3mm, often aborted. $2n = 42 – 119$. Flowering and fruiting mid-May to mid-July.

P. pratensis comprises a mixed swarm of apomictic and sexual races (mostly the former) and, not surprisingly, it also has a host of chromosome numbers, many of them aneuploid. The range of chromosome numbers alone would suggest that the taxonomy of the complex is not going to be straightforward. In *Flora Europaea* four species are recognized, three of them in the British Isles (*P. pratensis, P. angustifolia* and *P. subcaerulea* (= *P. humilis* of modern texts)). Tzvelev (1976) treated a single species with ten subspecies. Olonova (1990) recognized one segregate taxon (*P. angustifolia*) but treated the rest as a single variable taxon (*P. pratensis*). As with other apomictic complexes it is difficult to steer a middle course between over-lumping and over-splitting. On the surface, the three British and Irish taxa are reasonably distinct, but on closer inspection it is actually very difficult to decide where to draw the boundaries. The key and notes below are a compromise.

1. Culms often solitary at the nodes of the rhizome; panicle-branches 1 – 3 at the lowest node; both glumes 3-nerved .... **50c.** subsp. **irrigata**
+   Culms usually in dense tufts at the nodes of the rhizome; panicle-branches 3 – 6 at the lowest node; lower glume usually 1-nerved, the upper 3-nerved

    2

2. All blades broad and flat; ligule of lower leaves decurrent on the sheath-margins .... **50a.** subsp. **pratensis**
+   Basal and tiller blades folded-setaceous, those on the culm often flat; ligule of lower leaves usually not decurrent on the sheath-margins .... **50b.** subsp. **angustifolia**

The characters only irregularly occur in the above combinations and all of them are variable within the segregates. In ideal conditions the segregates can be recognized with reasonable confidence but in more marginal or intermediate habitats they merge imperceptibly until they are impossible to identify with any certainty. Lawn grasses are generally taken to be subsp. *pratensis*, but are more likely to be selected forms intermediate between subsp. *pratensis* and subsp. *irrigata*, neither of which, in a pure form, is suitable as a lawn grass. These, along with amenity and grazing forms, may well have escaped into the wild and thus exacerbated the difficulties. Because of apomixis there is a tendency for local races to become more or less stabilized whether they be one or other of the segregates or intermediates between them, but the occurrence of sexual races serves only to confuse the issue still further by constantly shifting the boundaries through hybridization. In light of these difficulties it is impossible to recommend the recognition of more than one species and any segregates of it should, for now, be treated as no higher than subspecies.

50a. Poa pratensis subsp. pratensis

Smooth Meadow-grass   New Atlas: 757

Culms in dense tufts at the nodes of the short rhizome; ligule often glabrous on the back, decurrent on the sheath-margins; blades flat, glabrous at the junction with the sheath; branches several (3 – 6) together at the lowest node of a rich panicle; lower glume 1-nerved, upper glume 3-nerved.

P. pratensis subsp. *pratensis* is widespread in the British Isles in a variety of mainly grass-dominated habitats, most commonly in old meadows and pastures, grassy road verges and amenity grassland. It also grows on waste ground, on walls and occasionally in shaded places. The distribution of subsp. *pratensis* is inexactly known but it is generally the most frequently encountered of the three subspecies in grassland over most of lowland Britain, although the map in the New Atlas suggests it may be unevenly recorded. It occurs on a range of mostly neutral to basic soil types from sands to loams but does not grow well in heavy clays. In old grassland it has a range of associates and in unmanaged tall grassland on road verges it often occurs with *Arrhenatherum elatius, Dactylis glomerata* and *Elymus repens*.

Smooth Meadow-grass has been widely sown in the past in permanent and semi-permanent pasture (often using seed imported from N America as 'Kentucky Blue-grass'), and is still a component of seed mixtures for amenity and wild-flower grasslands. It is both drought and cold tolerant and recovers well from grazing and heavy trampling, traits which enable the grass to make a contribution to the grazed sward early in the year (spring 'bite') and under dry conditions. The wear resistance (Armstrong (1943) declares that "no British grass withstands constant treading better") is undoubtedly related to the often extensive rhizome system which can bind the soil surface, making it an ideal species for sowing on slopes and embankments, and may also penetrate deep into soils allowing the species to survive drought. The rhizome system also contributes to the persistence of *P. pratensis* subsp. *pratensis* in old grassland, even as a minor component (e.g. in most plots in the Park Grass experiment at Rothamsted where grassland, although variously treated, has not been ploughed since 1856). Casual observation suggests that there is considerable variation in the regeneration strategy of different populations, some in tall vegetation only rarely flowering, but the extent to which this and other variation in the species complex is due to genetic or environmental factors is not known. (CPE: 476).

P. pratensis subsp. *pratensis* is native, occurring throughout Europe and temperate Asia, and has been widely naturalized outside its native range. Changes in its status in the British Isles are difficult to determine due to a lack of reliable historical data.

Often very leafy and ideal for grazing, it is extremely variable but is usually recognized by the lush foliage and densely tufted habit. Nervation of the glumes is variable and the lower is often 3-nerved.

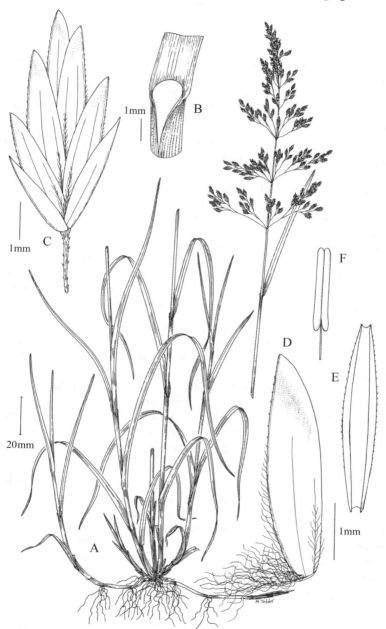

Poa pratensis subsp. *pratensis*: A, habit; B, ligule; C, spikelet; D, lemma in profile;
E, palea; F, anther.

50b. Poa pratensis subsp. angustifolia (L.) Lej.

Narrow-leaved Meadow-grass   New Atlas: 757 (as *Poa angustifolia*)
(also Crit. Suppl.: 150)

Culms in dense tufts at the nodes of the short rhizome; ligule glabrous on the back, not decurrent on the sheath-margins (usually decurrent on the culm-leaves); basal and tiller blades folded-setaceous, those on the culm often flat, glabrous at the junction with the sheath; branches several (3 – 6) together at the lowest node of a rich panicle; lower glume 1-nerved, upper glume 3-nerved.

P. pratensis subsp. *angustifolia* is common in suitable habitats in SE England south of a line from Flamborough Head to the Severn Estuary, becoming rarer to the north and west where it has been recorded chiefly along railways. It is not recorded from Ireland. In the southeast its semi-natural habitats are dry grassland, mostly on chalk, but also beech-woods, sand-dunes and occasionally heathland. It occurs in a range of man-made habitats, usually on infertile sandy or gravelly substrates including roadsides, walls, waste ground and railway verges. Its associates in dry grassland include *Brachypodium pinnatum, Bromus erectus* and *Helictotrichon pubescens* and on railway banks it was recorded most frequently by Sargent *et al.,* (1986) with *Arrhenatherum elatius, Brachypodium pinnatum, Dactylis glomerata, Plantago lanceolata, Festuca rubra* (which it can superficially resemble) and *Achillea millefolium.*

This is the most xerophytic of the three subspecies, its growth habit allowing survival in extremely dry conditions. It has a shorter period of spring growth than subsp. *pratensis* and tends to flower and set seed three to four weeks earlier. The successful spread of subsp. *angustifolia* along railways since first recorded from this habitat in 1897 can be related to the fact that the ground alongside railway tracks often produces a warm, free-draining, infertile, largely ungrazed and untrampled environment which mimics that of semi-natural dry grassland. Sargent *et al.,* (1986) point out that the management of railway land, especially in former times when burning was commonly used to control vegetation, will also have favoured the spread of this grass.

P. pratensis subsp. *angustifolia* is native and part of the Circumpolar Southern-temperate flora (P&H). Distributional trends in Britain are difficult to assess because of confusion with other *P. pratensis* segregates and probable under-recording, and hence a lack of historical data. It is likely that the pre-railway populations on chalk downs and beech woodland in the southeast are native but it is not known if others are derived from that source or introduced and spread by the road and rail network.

Although merging with the other two segregates (subsp. *pratensis* more than subsp. *irrigata*), it causes perhaps the fewest problems since many field botanists are familiar with it. The tall slender habit and setaceous basal leaves are characteristic, as are the slightly smaller spikelets, but boundaries can often be hard to find. A 3-nerved lower glume is not unusual.

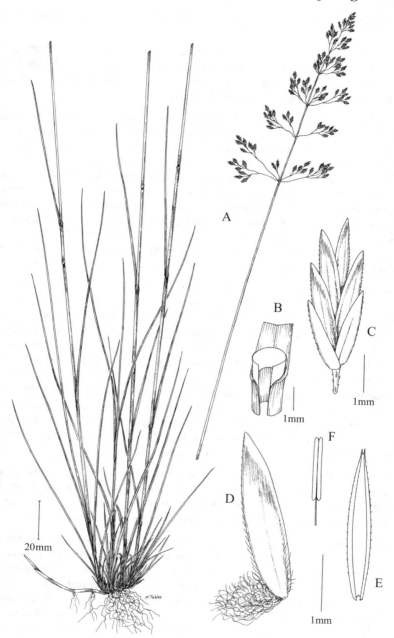

Poa pratensis subsp. *angustifolia*: A, habit; B, ligule; C, spikelet; D, lemma in profile;
E, palea; F, anther.

50c. **Poa pratensis** subsp. **irrigata** (Lindm.) H.Lindb.

Spreading Meadow-grass   New Atlas: 757 (as *Poa humilis*)

Culms often solitary from the nodes of the long rhizomes, but sometimes in loose tufts; ligule pubescent on the back, decurrent on the sheath-margins; blades flat, hairy at the junction with the sheath; branches few (1 – 3) at the lowest node of the rather sparse panicle; both glumes 3-nerved.

This subspecies is common on hill pastures in the west of England, Wales and Scotland and is widespread in moist environments elsewhere, including Ireland. Its favoured habitats include permanent damp grassland, marshland, stream and river banks, road verges and waste places, including walls and spoil tips. It also occurs in sand-dunes and coastal grassland around the British coast. It has almost certainly been under-recorded and is not always distinguished from other subspecies, especially *pratensis*. The range of habitat types means it can be found with many associates but in hill pastures it is often recorded with *Agrostis capillaris, Festuca rubra, F. ovina, Molinia caerulea, Juncus effusus* and, in sheep shelters, with *Poa annua* and *Stellaria media* (Barling, 1962). It occurs to 670m in Westmorland and is probably to be found at even higher altitudes.

P. pratensis subsp. *irrigata* is morphologically and cytologically variable; for example, plants with very different chromosome numbers have been recorded from the same population ($2n = 82$ to 119 within a 10m circle in one study). Sexual and apomictic individuals can also occur together and transplant experiments have revealed much phenotypic plasticity. However, subsp. *irrigata* shares a life style with other segregates of *P. pratensis*, namely the ability, conveyed by an extensive rhizome system, to 'forage' in patchy, sometimes nutrient-poor, environments to find space and nutrients in which to produce culms (in the case of subsp. *irrigata* this is often a single culm, making the plant easy to overlook in dense vegetation) and perhaps to flower. This strategy, combined with homogamy and apomixis, has enabled *P. pratensis* sens. lat. to successfully occupy an array of widely different, often extreme environments.

P. pratensis subsp. *irrigata* is native in the British Isles where it is probably at its southern limit. It has been recorded from Fennoscandia, Denmark, northern Europe and Iceland, but its world distribution is uncertain. A lack of reliable historical data makes assessment of recent distributional changes uncertain.

Previously known as *P. humilis,* and before that *P. subcaerulea*. Little-known to many field botanists and greatly under-recorded until recently, but as people become more aware of it so it is increasingly reported. The habit is fairly obvious – often very short with stiff, somewhat curved glaucous leaves and solitary culms and the spikelets large in relation to the panicle – but fine details can be variable. The ligule is not always hairy on the back and the lower glume is not always 3-nerved (even when it is, it is not necessarily diagnostic). It intergrades with subsp. *pratensis* more than with subsp. *angustifolia* and is often only vaguely distinct.

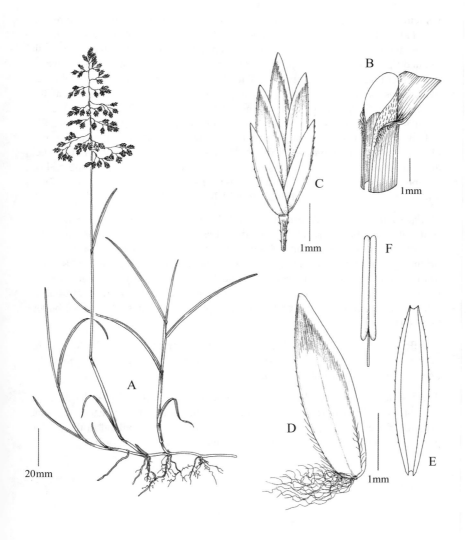

Poa pratensis subsp. *irrigata*: A, habit; B, ligule; C, spikelet; D, lemma in profile;
E, palea; F, anther.

51. Poa chaixii Vill.

Broad-leaved Meadow-grass   New Atlas: 758

Densely tufted perennial without rhizomes or stolons; culms up to 135cm, erect or geniculate at the base, stout, somewhat compressed; tillers strongly compressed and flattened; sheaths compressed and sharply keeled; ligule of uppermost leaf a membranous rim (0.5)0.9 – 1.9mm; blades bluntly pointed, initially folded with hooded tip, eventually flat and 5 – 10(14)mm wide, scaberulous on the margins and sometimes also on the midrib. Panicle erect or nodding, ovate to oblong-ovate, loose and open, 10 – 22(30)cm, the branches in groups of 2 – 8 at the lowest node. Spikelets ovate to oblong, (3.5)4.5 – 7.5mm, 2- to 4(5)-flowered; glumes unequal, firm, sharply acute, scabrid on the keel, the lower lanceolate, 2.2 – 3.2mm, 1(3)-nerved, the upper narrowly ovate, 2.7 – 4mm, 3-nerved; lemmas oblong-lanceolate in profile, firm, (2.8)3.2 – 4.3(5)mm, scabrid on the keel and lateral nerves, sometimes also between the nerves, glabrous on the callus, abruptly pointed at the tip; palea scabrid on the keels; anthers 1.6 – 2.7mm. $2n =$ 14. Flowering and fruiting late May to mid-July or early August.

P. chaixii occurs in widely scattered localities in the British Isles; it is more frequent in Scotland, largely absent from the eastern half of England and the southwest, and rare in Ireland. A grass of open woodlands and copses, it was originally introduced for ornament or cover, especially into large estates. It tends to occur on the margins of woodland and in clearings and may sometimes be found with *Festuca heterophylla*, another ornamental grass widely introduced into Victorian gardens. It is mainly a lowland plant but reaches 395m in N Ebudes (Vc 104).

The flattened culms radiating from the tufted base and the broad flat leaves are very eye-catching. The species appears to thrive best in light shade on well-drained infertile soils and in cooler, moist environemnts.

A neophyte, *P. chaixii* has been grown in gardens or in managed woodlands since 1802 and was first recorded in the wild in 1852. Its distribution appears to be little changed since the 1962 Atlas. It is a native of montane woodland in the cooler parts of Europe and SW Asia and is widely naturalized further north.

Poa chaixii: A, habit; B, ligule; C, spikelet; D, lemma in profile; E, palea; F, anther.

52. Poa flabellata (Lam.) Raspail

Tussac-grass   New Atlas CD

Large, tussock-forming perennial with a basal stool up to 1m high and 1m across; culms erect, rising to 2.5m; ligule a blunt or pointed, often lacerate, membrane 5 – 12mm; blades 5 – 15mm wide, flat or inrolled, smooth. Panicle contracted, spike-like or interrupted, 5 – 20(40)cm. Spikelets 7 – 9mm, 3- to 5-flowered; glumes unequal, ovate-lanceolate, faintly ciliolate on the keel, sharply pointed or briefly awned at the tip, the lower 1-nerved, 4.5 – 7.5mm, the upper 3-nerved, a little longer than the lower; lemmas ovate-lanceolate, 5 – 6.5mm, scabrid on the back and on the nerves, obtuse to acuminate and tipped with an awn 0.5 – 3mm; palea-keels coarsely scabrid; anthers 2 – 2.5(4)mm. $2n = 42$. Flowering and fruiting late February to late June.

Tussac-grass (the name appears to be no more than a corruption of the word 'tussock') occurs in Shetland, where it was introduced in 1845 and has been used for making baskets, and in Mull where it was more recently introduced for experimental purposes. It is persistent on walls and within enclosures in Shetland (e.g. Dunrossness, Exnavoe), but does not appear to have established in the wild. (AGB: 22).

A neophyte, *P. flabellata* is a native of Tierra del Fuego, South Georgia and the Falkland Islands.

The species is an oddment in *Poa* because of its awned lemmas and was transferred to a separate genus, *Parodiochloa* C.E.Hubb., for this reason. However, in S America there is a gradation from awnless to awned species and the segregate genus is difficult to justify.

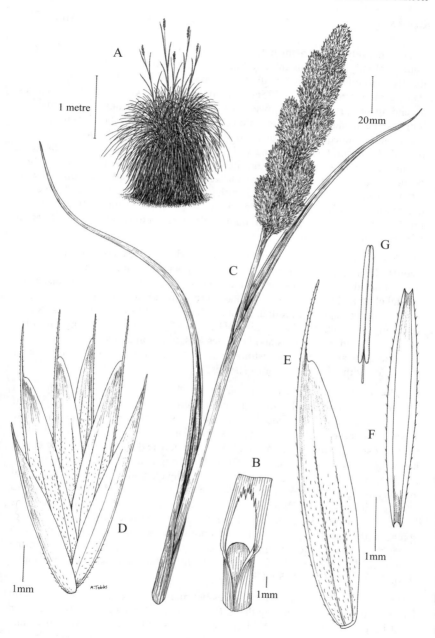

Poa flabellata: A, habit; B, ligule; C, panicle; D, spikelet; E, lemma in profile; F, palea; G, anther.

53. Dactylis glomerata L.

Cock's-foot

New Atlas: 760

Coarse, densely tufted plant with erect or ascending culms up to 120(145)cm; ligule a bluntly pointed membrane (2.5)4 – 9(11)mm; blades green or glaucous, mostly glabrous but occasionally hairy, smooth or faintly to coarsely scabrid. Panicle oblong to ovate, 3 – 25cm, green, purplish or yellowish, the branches ascending or spreading, the lowermost often remote and mostly about half as long as the panicle. Spikelets oblong or cuneate, 4.5 – 7.5(9.5)mm; glumes membranous, unequal, lanceolate to ovate, finely pointed, the lower 1- to 3-nerved, 3 – 6mm, the upper 3-nerved, 3.5 – 7mm, scabrid or hairy on the keel; lemmas lanceolate to oblong in profile, 4 – 7mm, ciliolate, scaberulous, scabrid or more usually pectinate-ciliate on the keel, blunt or pointed at the tip and with a mucro or awn-point 0.2 – 1.6mm; anthers (1.7)2 – 3.7mm. $2n = 28$. Flowering and fruiting mid-May to late September or beyond; plants attempting to flower much after about mid-August commonly fail and resort to vegetative proliferation of the spikelets ('vivipary').

D. glomerata occurs throughout the British Isles and, except for parts of the Scottish Highlands, is common and often abundant in a range of habitats. These include meadows, pastures, downland, rough grassland, woodland, river banks, coastal cliffs and fixed dunes, as well as more artificial habitats such as roadsides, paths, hedgerows, waste ground, manure heaps, spoil tips and quarries. It occurs on a range of neutral to basic soils (pH 5.0 – 8.0) of moderate to high fertility, but is not found in wetlands and becomes less common above 550m (occurring exceptionally at 845m in Westmorland). Across these various habitats it is associated with a large number of species.

Cock's-foot is an extremely variable grass, the variation having been much affected by a long history of cultivation, introduction and selection by plant breeders, often from indigenous populations. As with Rye-grass, one can draw a general contrast between biotypes selected for grazing which are generally more prostrate, later flowering, high tillering and leafy and those selected for hay which are coarser, more erect, earlier flowering and stemmy. But all types of intermediates exist, there are different ploidy levels and known morphological and physiological ecotypes; gene flow from cultivars to wild populations (both as seed and via cross-pollination in this predominantly outbreeding species) is likely to be widespread. Individual plants have a restricted capacity for lateral spread, although the species can form huge tussocks in unmanaged sites, and regeneration appears to be almost exclusively by seeds which germinate in the spring. Seeds may persist for 2 or 3 years but there is not a large buried seed bank. (Biol. Flora: Beddows, 1959; CPE: 242).

The species is native in the British Isles but many wild populations will contain introductions or be affected by them. (C.E.Hubbard thought that those on south coast headlands, in old oak and hazel woodlands and in the woods of the Lake District are most likely to be native). Early introductions, in 1764, were from N America but more recently seed and breeding material has come from around the

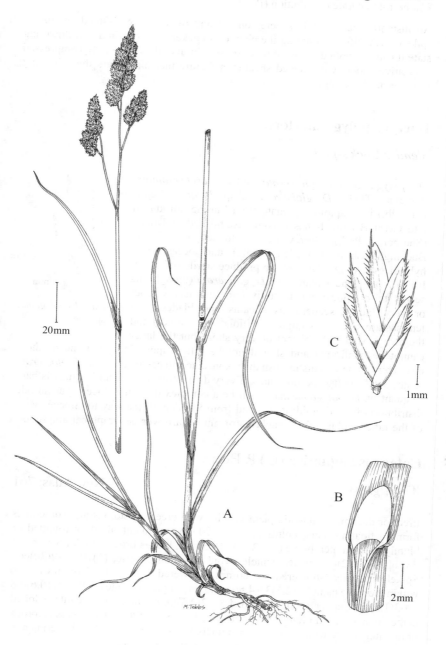

Dactylis glomerata: A, habit; B, ligule; C, spikelet.

world especially Scandinavia and New Zealand. *D. glomerata* has a Circumpolar Southern-temperate distribution (P&H).

An instantly recognizable species on account of its dense, 1-sided clumps of spikelets (fancifully imitating the claw of a cockerel's foot); in a non-flowering state it can be spotted amongst other grasses by its tufts of strongly compressed vegetative shoots with keeled sheaths, a feature that disappears the following summer on flowering.

54.   Dactylis polygama Horv.

Slender Cock's-foot

D. polygama (*D. glomerata* subsp. *aschersoniana* (Graebn.) Thell., *D. glomerata* subsp. *lobata* (Drejer) H.Lindb.) is a diploid segregate from Europe introduced into Great Britain. It has become established in Dorset (Sherborne Park), Surrey (West Horsley Place) and Buckinghamshire (Cliveden Estate) and occasionally hybridizes with *D. glomerata* to produce sterile offspring. It is a more slender plant than *D. glomerata* (though this seems to disappear when cultivated) and has smooth or very faintly scaberulous sheaths and blades. The lemmas are smooth or minutely ciliolate on the keel and the awn is said to be absent or very short, but the latter

1mm

Dactylis polygama: spikelet.

cannot be confirmed and should not be relied upon. In fact, none of these characters alone will distinguish the taxon, since all can be found in *D. glomerata* s. str., but *D. polygama* does have a very distinctive look about it which is hard to quantify. *D. polygama* may itself be a complex of forms since it has an odd distribution for a diploid: it is found from Sweden all the way to Greece. Most of the other diploids form enclaves of much narrower geographical amplitude.

55.   Catabrosa aquatica (L.) P. Beauv.

Whorl-grass   New Atlas: 761

Erect or decumbent aquatic plant usually with creeping stolons and sometimes forming floating mats; culms up to 45(90)cm, succulent; ligule a rounded or bluntly pointed membrane (1.5)2 – 4.5(6.5)mm; blades broad and flat with blunt tip, up to 8(12)mm wide. Panicle ovoid or oblong, loose, (7)10 – 22(30)cm. Spikelets usually 2-flowered, sometimes 3-flowered or 1-flowered, often variable within the same panicle, (2.5)3 – 4.5(6)mm; lower glume ovate to elliptic, (0.6)0.8 – 1.3(1.5)mm; upper glume broader, 1.3 – 2(2.5)mm, rounded or irregularly lobed at the tip; lemma elliptic-oblong or oblong, 2.3 – 3.2(3.5)mm, the nerves glabrous or minutely hairy, truncate at the tip; anthers 1.2 – 1.8mm. $2n = 20$. Flowering and fruiting late May to mid-August or rarely to late September.

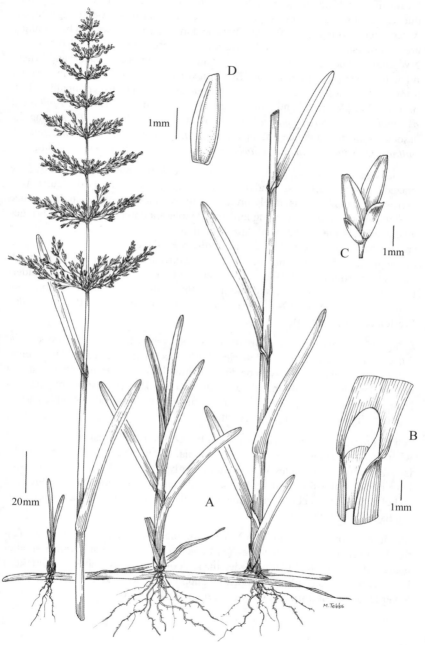

Catabrosa aquatica: A, habit; B, ligule; C, spikelet; D, lemma.

Whorl-grass is widely but very patchily distributed in the British Isles. It occurs locally in central and southern England and in Ireland on the muddy edges of ponds, ditches, canals and streams, especially those with still or slow-running shallow water where it often forms floating mats, and in water-meadows and bare muddy areas in marshland. It seems to be declining in these habitats. It is also found in NW England and Scotland on freshwater flushes in wet open coastal sand, where it has long been recognized as a different taxon (see below). It is predominantly a lowland species but reaches 380m at Malham Tarn and, exceptionally, 710m on Little Fell, Westmorland where it grows in montane flushes with *Epilobium alsinifolium* and *Saxifraga stellaris* (Roberts & Halliday, 1979). Among its associates in its waterside habitats are *Caltha palustris, Glyceria maxima, G. fluitans, Lythrum salicaria, Phalaris arundinacea* and *Mentha ×verticillata*.

The leaves, stems and even rhizomes of this succulent perennial grass are eagerly grazed by cattle and, unless ponds and streams are fenced, it may be difficult to find in heavily trampled areas, rarely producing the distinctive purplish inflorescence with its whorled branches (being fairly shade tolerant it may flower under bridges where cattle have no access). Although it may therefore be overlooked, the species has undoubtedly declined in southern England, along with at least two of the grasses of similar habitat, *Glyceria notata* and *Poa palustris*. By contrast, the variant from coastal sands in northern and western Britain may be under-recorded, particularly in Ireland and in Scotland where it is said to be abundant in the Western Isles (see New Atlas and map in Perring & Sell (1968); see also Preston & Croft (1997)).

C. aquatica is native in the British Isles and occurs throughout Europe, NW Africa, temperate Asia and N America. It also occurs in S America. The decline in southern England is likely to be due to habitat loss as ponds have been infilled and wetland has been drained in agricultural land. However, some populations have apparently disappeared from areas such as water-meadows which have, superficially at least, changed very little.

Whorl-grass resembles a species of *Poa* but can be readily distinguished by the whorled panicle branches and 3-nerved lemma. The number of florets per spikelet is rather variable; panicles with predominantly 2-flowered spikelets will often have occasional 3-flowered spikelets, and those with predominantly 1-flowered spikelets will have occasional 2-flowered spikelets; only rarely is the number of florets consistent throughout the panicle.

Specimens from coastal sands in NW Britain mentioned above fall into the 1(2)-flowered category rather than the 2(3)-flowered and are generally rather smaller plants. Although sometimes accorded the rank of subspecies (subsp. *minor* (Bab.) F.H.Perring & P.D.Sell) it might be more appropriate to make the distinction at a lower level, as var. **uniflora** Gray (var. *littoralis* Parnell).

56. Catapodium marinum (L.) C.E.Hubb.

Illustration, page 241

Sea Fern-grass

New Atlas: 761

Culms tufted or solitary, erect or ascending, rather stout and stiff, up to 15(20)cm; ligule membranous, obtuse to truncate, 0.5 – 2(3)mm, the margin lacerate. Panicle (1.5)2 – 5.5(6)cm, narrow, racemose above, sparingly branched, if at all, below, the axis stiff, flat on the back, angular in front. Spikelets 6- to 12(15)-flowered, (4.5)5.5 – 9.5(11)mm; upper glume 2 – 3(3.4)mm; lemma 2.4 – 3.6mm; anthers (0.4)0.5 – 0.7(0.9)mm. $2n = 14, 28$. Flowering and fruiting late May to early August.

C. marinum occurs on bare, generally infertile, substrates around the coasts of the British Isles, being frequent in most of southern and western England, Wales and Ireland, but absent from long stretches of the coast in England north of the Wash and in Scotland. Typical habitats include rocks and cliff-tops, sand-dunes, stable shingle and the walls and pavements of seaside towns and villages. It is also one of a handful of coastal grasses which have successfully established populations inland along the edges of roads treated with de-icing salt (others include species of *Puccinellia* and *Hordeum marinum*). It has a range of associates in its coastal habitats which include other short-lived annuals such as *Aira praecox, Cerastium diffusum, Phleum arenarium* and *Vulpia bromoides* (and in artificial habitats many of the species listed for *C. rigidum*). It is quite often found with *Catapodium rigidum*.

Sea Fern-grass is a small winter annual typically found in little colonies a few metres apart, a distribution pattern which probably reflects poor seed dispersal; caryopses are usually found between 5 and 10cm from the parent plant. It has a very similar life history to *C. rigidum*, seed germinating in the autumn and small plants surviving the winter. Leaves produced during the winter are longer-lived than those produced during spring and summer prior to flowering. *C. marinum* produces on average fewer, larger seeds per plant than *C. rigidum* and experiments have indicated that it may be more tolerant of acid soils. The number of seeds produced by each plant is strongly affected by soil depth and nutrient conditions but viable seed are found on even very tiny isolated plants indicating, as one might expect in an annual grass, that the species is self-compatible and probably largely inbreeding.

C. marinum is a native species which is widespread in the Mediterranean region and extends northwards along the Atlantic coast of Europe to the Netherlands (the Mediterranean-Atlantic element; P&H). Its distribution in the British Isles has changed little since the 1962 Atlas. The spread along inland roads is mainly in the south of England and S Wales (along the M4 motorway) and is relatively recent.

The species is well described by two former epithets 'Stiff Sand-grass' and 'Darnel Poa', having a characteristic stiff habit and an inflorescence which somewhat resembles that of a miniature Rye-grass. It is difficult to be too precise about measurements to discriminate between the two species of *Catapodium*; their spikelets are almost identical and the most useful distinction can be found in the length of the glumes. However, the two species do not look at all alike and it is the thickness of the inflorescence axis and degree of branching which are really the most informative. The inflorescence of *C. marinum* is almost always a simple raceme; any branches that may occur towards the base bear only 2 or 3 spikelets.

Hybrids between this species and *C. rigidum* are known; see under the latter for more details.

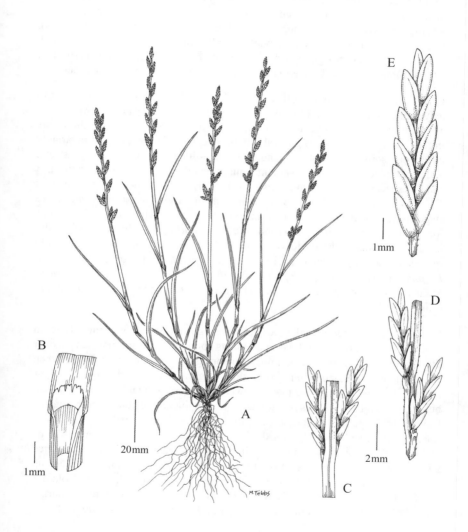

Catapodium marinum: A, habit; B, ligule; C, segment of inflorescence from the back;
D, segment of inflorescence from the front; E, spikelet.

57. **Catapodium rigidum** (L.) C.E.Hubb.

Fern-grass   New Atlas: 761

Culms tufted or solitary, erect or ascending, rather stiff, up to 25(30)cm; ligule membranous, obtuse to truncate, 0.5 – 3.5mm, the margin lacerate. Panicle 2 – 8cm, narrowly ovate to ovate, branched below (usually in only 2 dimensions), often racemose above, the axis slender, 3-angled. Spikelets 6- to 9(12)-flowered, (4.5)5 – 8(9)mm; upper glume 1.4 – 2(2.3)mm; lemma 2 – 3mm; anthers (0.3)0.4 – 0.5(0.6)mm. $2n = 14$. Flowering and fruiting late May to early September.

C. rigidum is scattered but locally common in suitable habitats in the southeastern halves of both England and Ireland, extending westwards and northwards largely as a coastal plant, reaching as far north as the Firth of Tay, its most northerly site in the world. It is a grass of generally thin, bare, well-drained, almost invariably calcareous soils in habitats ranging from sand-dunes, shingle, chalk grassland and rocky places to walls, pavements, quarry spoil heaps and railway ballast. It can be especially common in towns near the coast in the same sort of habitats as *Catapodium marinum*. Young plants can be distinguished in the early vegetative stage from *C. marinum*, and other annual grasses with which it occurs such as *Aira praecox, Phleum arenarium* and *Vulpia bromoides*, by their characteristically incurved and sickle-shaped leaves. Among the other associates most commonly recorded in a range of habitats are *Arenaria serpyllifolia, Cerastium atrovirens, Erophila verna, Medicago lupulina, Saxifraga tridactylites* and *Sedum acre*. Mainly a lowland species, *C. rigidum* reaches 320m in Derbyshire and 355m near Llangollen.

Fern-grass is a winter annual, seeds germinating from July to November (later in sand-dune populations), and the small plants continuing to form new leaves over the winter. Some seed may germinate in spring. Individual plants flower when 3 to 8 months old, depending on the time of germination, and live for 5 to 11 months. In most populations plants flower freely and set viable seed every year but, even though the species is extremely drought tolerant, whole colonies may be lost during dry periods in spring. *C. rigidum* requires low temperatures for flower tiller initiation and long days for the inflorescences to develop. It appears to be mainly self-fertilizing and cultivation in common garden conditions has revealed a wide range of heritable variation. In cultivation, single plants may produce up to 15,000 caryopses but usually range between 1 and 400 in the field. Colonies can form dense mats, especially when grazed by rabbits or hares, the manuring impact of which enhances tiller number. (Biol. Flora: Clark, 1974; CPE: 200).

C. rigidum is a native species with a broadly circum-Mediterranean and western Asian distribution, which extends along the European coast to Scotland. It has been introduced to N & S America and Australia. Var. *majus* (see below) occurs in the Mediterranean and SW Europe.

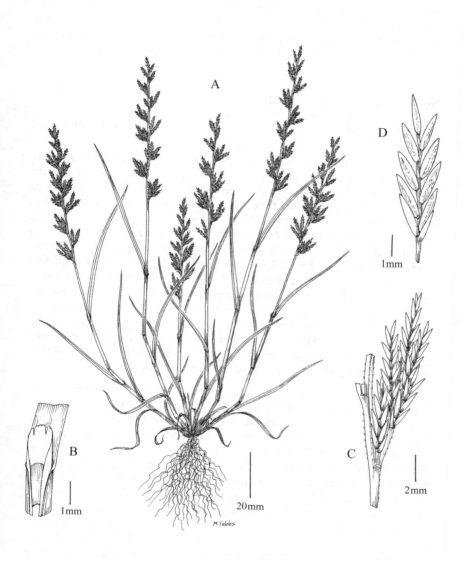

A

D

1mm

B

1mm

C

2mm

20mm

M·Tebbs

Catapodium rigidum: A, habit; B, ligule; C, segment of inflorescence; D, spikelet.

Quite different in appearance from *C. marinum*, with marginally smaller spikelet parts, but the main difference lies in the degree of branching of the panicle and stiffness of the axis. Plants from nearer the coast in SW England, southern Ireland and the Channel Islands have a more profusely branched panicle, branching in 3 dimensions, and have a slightly different aspect as a result. They are probably best accommodated at varietal level, as var. **majus** (C.Presl) Laínz. The two species of *Catapodium* have been known to produce a sterile hybrid; this is intermediate in morphology and has indehiscent anthers that contain imperfect pollen.

58. Sesleria caerulea (L.) Ard.

Blue Moor-grass   New Atlas: 762

Densely tufted with short slender rhizomes; culms erect, up to 55cm; leaves bluish green, glabrous, mostly basal, those on the culm much shorter than the basal; sheaths open; ligule a very short membranous rim with minutely fimbriate margin, 0.3 – 0.7(1)mm; blades flat or folded, 2.5 – 5(6)mm wide, smooth except for the scabrid margins and midrib below towards the tip, blunt and hooded at the tip. Panicle ovoid or cylindrical with very short pedicels, 1.5 – 2.5(3.5)cm including the terminal spikelet, bluish or tinged with purple, the subtending scales broad and often lobed. Spikelets oblong, (4.5)5 – 6(6.5)mm, including awns, 2- to 3-flowered; glumes equal or the upper a little longer than the lower, ovate, 1-nerved, (3.5)4 – 6mm, finely pointed or awned at the tip; lemmas broadly oblong or elliptic, 3- to 5-nerved, 4 – 5.5(6)mm, firm except for the membranous tip and margins, scaberulous or pubescent especially on the margins and nerves, 3- to 5-lobed at the tip with the nerves running into awn-points; palea sometimes exceeding the lemma, shortly awned at the tip of the keels; anthers 2 – 3.3(3.8)mm. $2n = 28$. Flowering and fruiting mid-April to early August.

S. caerulea has a rather disjunct distribution in the British Isles with four centres. One is northern England where it is common on the Carboniferous Limestone of the southern Lake District, Lancashire and Yorkshire and occurs in Durham and Northumberland on Magnesian limestone. An additional small population was discovered in the Peak District of Derbyshire in 1989. A second is in Scotland where it occurs in a few localities in the Breadalbane range on strongly calcareous mica schists. The other two areas are in Ireland where it occurs in the northwest and in central and western districts, especially on the Burren. *S. caerulea* is typically found in open communities in limestone grassland and heath, on limestone scree, on limestone pavement in grikes and in hollows on the clints, in open woodland and on coastal sands in Ireland. A variety of soil types overlie these rocks but are usually shallow, free draining, and with a pH >6.0, although peat over limestone may be as low as 4.7. The variety of plant communities in which the grass occurs means that it has a range of both montane and lowland associates; these are listed by Dixon (1982). It occurs from sea-level to 1005m on Ben Lawers in M Perth.

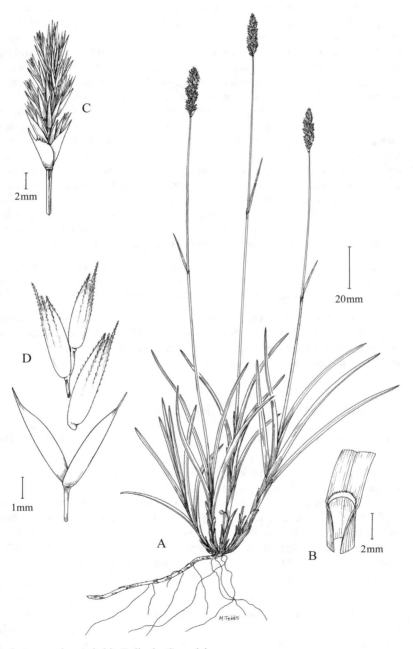

Sesleria caerulea: A, habit; B, ligule; C, panicle;
D, spikelet with florets separated from glumes.

This very distinctive grass, with its stiff rush-like culms, green or greyish leaves with a waxy bloom on one side and its ovoid or cylindrical panicle subtended by scarious bracts and typically blue or bluish purple at the base, can become the dominant species in sheep-grazed limestone grassland. It has a number of features which adapt it well to summer drought and enable it to occupy limestone screes and pavements as well as the thinnest of soils where its competitors would struggle to survive. These include a deep wiry and persistent root system, tissues which tolerate desiccation, sunken stomata, heavy wax deposits on the adaxial surface of the leaves and tough rhizomes which, though short and slender in grazed swards, can be long and creeping in screes and limestone pavement (new plants are sometimes produced at the ends of long rhizomes hanging down rock faces). The relative importance of vegetative spread and seed dispersal varies between habitats but seeds, the production of which is reduced by grazers, are important in colonizing new sites in screes and grikes. Seed are produced every year, plants mostly flowering for the first time in their second season. The species appears to be normally outbreeding; isolated plants set few seed and some populations produce albino seedlings, a sure sign of inbreeding effects in a habitually outbreeding species. (Biol. Flora: Dixon, 1982; SPB: 378).

S. caerulea is native and was first recorded from Ingleborough in 1670. It occurs in the mountains of C Europe from the Pyrenees to the Carpathians and in Iceland, Spain and Albania. (European Boreo-temperate element; P&H).

Differences in the field between English plants (generally shorter inflorescence and lemma lengths) and those from Scotland and Ireland are retained in cultivation. Occasionally there are forms with a white panicle (var. *luteo-alba* Opiz) which are sometimes grown as an ornamental.

59. Parapholis incurva (L.) C.E.Hubb.

Curved Hard-grass   New Atlas: 762

Annual; culms stout, strongly curved, rarely straight, usually decumbent below and ascending to 15(25)cm; ligule 0.3 – 0.6mm; blades flat and 1 – 2mm wide, or inrolled and 0.4 – 0.6mm across, smooth beneath, scabrid above and on the margins. Inflorescence (1)3 – 8(10)cm, usually not fully exserted from the uppermost leaf-sheath. Spikelets (3.5)4 – 5(6)mm, a little longer than the internodes (1.2 – 1.3 times as long); glumes wingless on the keel; lemma 3 – 4.5mm; anthers 0.5 – 0.8(1.1)mm. Cleistogamous. $2n = 36, 38, 42$. Flowering and fruiting early June to mid-July.

Almost entirely confined to the coast in southern and eastern England below the Humber and in Wales, this scarce and rather curious little grass is found in a range of habitat types including cliff-tops, sea walls, bare mud and shingle. It is most commonly found on open gravelly mud and muddy shingle on well-drained saline soils above the high tide level. Unlike *P. strigosa*, it rarely occurs

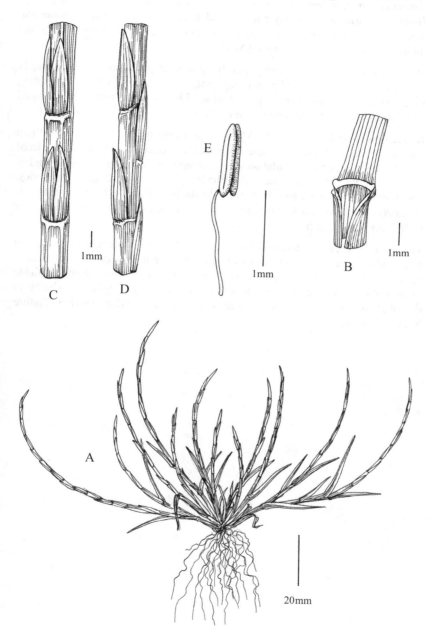

Parapholis incurva: A, habit; B, ligule; C, segment of raceme from the back;
D, segment of raceme from the side; E, anther.

in saltmarshes, preferring drier habitats on open ground or very sparse grassland. Associates include *Spergularia marina, Puccinellia distans, P. fasciculata* and *Hordeum marinum* in muddy habitats and *Beta maritima, Rumex crispus* and *Silene uniflora* on shingle. It is very occasionally recorded around docks and inland as a wool and ballast alien. (AGB: 27).

P. incurva is annual, reproducing entirely by seed. Populations may vary greatly in size from year to year and plants may appear in isolated situations, suggesting long distance seed dispersal or persistent seed banks. On the other hand, small individuals are easily overlooked. (SPB: 303).

Native to western Europe and the Mediterranean, the species reaches its northern limit in Britain and Ireland (where it was first discovered in 1979). Its scattered distribution, fluctuating population size, and the fact that it was probably under-recorded in the 1962 Atlas, make it difficult to assess any change in frequency. Together with other grasses in these habitats (e.g. *Puccinellia fasciculata, P. rupestris, Hordeum marinum*) it may have disappeared from areas where sea walls have been rebuilt.

The species is generally distinguished from *P. strigosa* by its stout, strongly curved culm and inflorescence, the latter partially enclosed in the subtending leaf-sheath, but the characters are not wholly reliable. Specimens that grow inland – in fields or on rubbish tips – are likely to adopt a slender, perfectly upright habit similar to that of *P. strigosa*; in these circumstances the only reliable distinguishing feature is anther length.

60. **Parapholis strigosa** (Dumort.) C.E.Hubb. Illustration, page 251

Hard-grass   New Atlas: 762

Annual; culms slender, mostly straight, rarely stout and strongly curved, up to 35(55)cm; ligule 0.3 – 0.8mm; blades flat and 1.5 – 2.5mm wide, or inrolled and 0.4 – 0.6mm across, smooth beneath, scabrid above and on the margins. Inflorescence (2)4 – 9(13)cm, usually fully exserted from the uppermost leaf-sheath. Spikelets 4 – 6(7)mm, a little longer than the internodes (1.2 – 1.3 times as long); glumes wingless on the keel; lemma 3.5 – 5(6)mm; anthers (1.7)2.2 – 3.1(3.5)mm. Cleistogamous. $2n = 28$. Flowering and fruiting mid-June to mid-August.

P. strigosa is widely distributed around the coasts of England and Wales, Ireland and southern Scotland as far north as the Firth of Forth on the east coast and the island of Mull on the west. It occurs in the upper zones of saltmarshes and is particularly common in the grazed saltmarshes of NW England. It may also be found on stable muddy shingle, banks and sea walls and in other brackish areas above the high tide level. This species prefers damper situations to the rarer *P. incurva* but is seldom found in waterlogged soils. On grazed saltmarsh it occurs with the perennials *Agrostis stolonifera, Armeria maritima, Festuca rubra, Juncus gerardii* and *Plantago maritima* and in some areas descends into the zone dominated by *Puccinellia maritima*. On muddy shingle and sea walls it has a range of associates. It is also found very occasionally inland on salt-affected road verges.

A slender annual grass, spreading entirely by seed, Hard-grass varies considerably in size and habit. It is often difficult to find among the perennial grasses of grazed *Festuca rubra/Agrostis stolonifera* saltmarsh, except when the pale yellow anthers are visible extruding from the curious narrow raceme. Furthermore, when flowering is finished the brittle racemes break up at the joint below each spikelet, dispersing the segments separately and the plant 'disappears'. However, isolated plants on deep soils may become large and spreading.

P. strigosa is a native grass which occurs along the Atlantic coast of Europe from Scandinavia to Portugal and extends into, but is rare in, the Mediterranean region (a Suboceanic Southern-temperate distribution; P&H). It is most probably under-recorded, especially as a component of saltmarsh and brackish pasture. The fact that it can easily be overlooked may be the reason for apparent gains in some areas, especially Ireland, since the 1962 Atlas.

The species is distinguished from *P. incurva* by its slender, ± straight culms and inflorescence, the latter fully exserted from the subtending sheath, but the characters are not wholly reliable. In all cases it is worth checking anther length if possible since there is no overlap in the ranges (not less than 1.7mm in *P. strigosa*; not more than 1.1mm in *P. incurva*). The species has often been referred to as **P. filiformis** (Roth) C.E.Hubb., but this name properly belongs to a Mediterranean species, distinguished by its narrowly winged glume-keels, that has rarely been found as an alien in Britain. *P. strigosa* tends to grade into **P. pycnantha** (Hack.) C.E.Hubb. which is poorly distinguished by the spikelets being at least 1.5 times as long as the internodes and by the much longer anthers (generally 3.2 – 4mm); it, too, has only rarely been recorded from Britain.

61. Hainardia cylindrica (Willd.) Greuter

One-glumed Hard-grass

A frequent, mostly birdseed alien scattered on waste ground in southern England. It is distinguished from species of *Parapholis* by the absence of the lower glume in all spikelets but the terminal. The single glume covers the floret which is orientated with the back of the lemma (rather than the side) towards the rhachis.

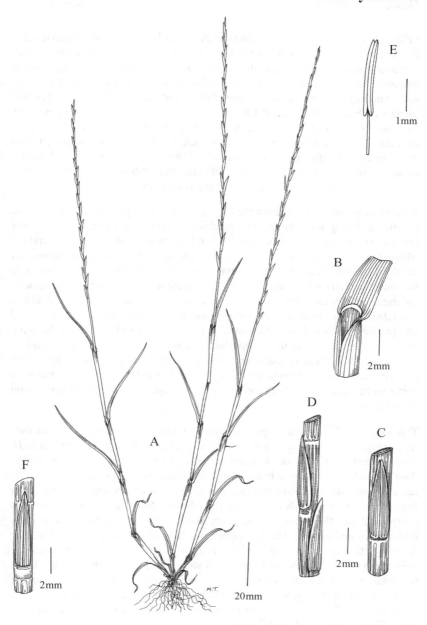

Parapholis strigosa: A, habit; B, ligule; C, spikelet from the back;
D, segment of raceme from the side; E, anther. *Hainardia cylindrica*: F, spikelet.

62.   **Helictotrichon pubescens** (Huds.) Pilg.

Downy Oat-grass   New Atlas: 765

Loosely tufted plant up to 90cm; sheaths pilose with spreading or deflexed hairs; ligule a triangular membrane 3.5 – 8mm (shorter in basal leaves); blades soft, folded at first, 2 – 6mm wide, softly hairy but becoming glabrous with age. Panicle oblong or lanceolate, 10 – 18cm, the branches clustered, bearing up to 3 spikelets each. Spikelets 3-flowered, or 2-flowered plus a rudiment, 11.5 – 17mm; rhachilla joints with hairs at the summit 3.5 – 5(7)mm; glumes lanceolate, finely pointed, the lower 1-nerved, (7)8 – 11(12.5)mm, the upper 3-nerved, 10.5 – 15(17)mm; lemmas (9)10 – 13.5mm, rounded on the back, 2-toothed at the tip, awned from just above the middle; awn geniculate, 13 – 21mm, the column flattened, tightly twisted, smoothly parallel-sided in silhouette, the limb straight; anthers 4.5 – 6.5mm. $2n = 14$. Flowering and fruiting late May to early July.

H. pubescens occurs throughout the British Isles in a range of mainly calcareous grasslands, being most abundant on rendzinas and calcareous brown earths over chalk and limestone in England, Scotland and Wales and over limestone in Ireland where it is a characteristic species of the central plain. It is common in the west of Scotland but less frequent in the central highlands. It also occurs less commonly on non-calcareous substrates. Habitats include meadows and pastures (especially old meadows), open woodland and woodland clearings, hedgerows, fixed dunes, coastal cliffs, limestone outcrops, grassy roadsides, railway banks, gravel pits and old quarries, walls and even heathland. It prefers moist soils with a pH between 5.0 and 7.9 but can occur in dry grassland and at a pH of 4.1. It occurs from sea-level to 550m at Moor House, Cumberland and in the central part of its British range it is more common on north-facing slopes. Dixon (1991) describes the plant communities in a range of calcareous and mesotrophic grasslands which contain *H. pubescens*.

This loosely tufted perennial grass occurs in a wider range of habitat types than *H. pratense*. It is relatively shallow rooted and less drought resistant than *H. pratense* and where they occur together the latter species tends to occupy higher drier ground. *H. pubescens* is also more deciduous than *H. pratense*, the softer leaves dying back over the winter months before new shoots appear in the spring from the perennating buds protected within the tuft. Seed appears to be produced every year and the species is probably outbreeding; the flowers are slightly protandrous and experimentally isolated plants have not set seed. Seed is shed from July to August, germination occurs from August to October, and there is only a transient seed bank with few seeds surviving for more than a year. There is a great deal of habitat-correlated variation in plant size and spikelet number and in the extent of vegetative spread by the short rhizomes. An average tussock produces more than 50 inflorescences and can produce about 4000 seeds per year. (Biol. Flora: Dixon, 1991; CPE: 346).

Helictotrichon pubescens: A, habit; B, ligule; C, spikelet;
D, glumes and detached lowermost floret.

H. pubescens is native, occurring in NC & E Europe, N Africa and C Asia and is widely naturalized outside its range. It is cultivated for forage in NW Germany. Although losses have occurred throughout its range in the British Isles, the species appears to have a stable distribution here.

The two Oat-grass species have very distinctive, attractive inflorescences. The traditional character for separating them – hairy versus glabrous sheaths – is reliable for most of the time, but there are occasions on which a glabrous form of *H. pubescens* may be encountered. Other helpful features of *H. pubescens* include the softer leaves, fuller panicle less inclined to be racemose, the 2 or 3 florets in the spikelet, the longer, more conspicuous hairs at the summit of the rhachilla joint, and the smooth cylindrical column of the awn. The column of the awn in *H. pratense* is generally more loosely twisted and in silhouette resembles a string of beads.

63.   Helictotrichon pratense (L.) Pilg.

Meadow Oat-grass   New Atlas: 765

Densely tufted plant up to 85 cm; sheaths quite glabrous; ligule a triangular membrane 2 – 4.5(6)mm (shorter in basal leaves); blades rather stiff, folded at first, 1 – 5mm wide. Panicle narrow, ± racemose, 7.5 – 18cm, the branches paired or solitary, bearing 1 or 2 spikelets each. Spikelets 3- to 5(rarely 8)-flowered, (13.5)16 – 23.5(28.5)mm; rhachilla joints with hairs at the summit 1 – 2mm; glumes lanceolate, finely pointed, 3-nerved, the lower 9.5 – 16mm, the upper (11)13 – 20mm; lemmas 10.5 – 17.5(20)mm, rounded on the back, 2-toothed at the tip, awned from just above the middle; awn geniculate, 12 – 27mm, the column flattened, loosely twisted, often moniliform in silhouette, the limb straight; anthers 4 – 7mm. $2n = 126$. Flowering and fruiting early June to mid-July, occasionally lasting to mid-August.

Meadow Oat-grass is largely restricted to shallow calcareous soils, its distribution closely following the chalk in southern and central England, the limestone in northern England and Wales, and a range of basic rocks in southern and central Scotland. It is absent from Ireland. A common component of old grazed chalk and limestone grassland, it also occurs in derelict grassland, on scree slopes, rock outcrops and limestone pavement, and, less commonly, in open Ash woods, shell-rich sand-dunes and montane rock ledges (where it is a component of the *Dryas octopetala-Silene acaulis* ledge community). The soils it occupies are typically shallow with a surface pH between 5.0 and 8.0 for rendzinas and calcareous brown earths but it occurs exceptionally in soil of pH 4.0. The range of plant communities in which *H. pratense* occurs are described by Dixon (1991) who lists many of the associated species. It occurs to 835m in M Perth.

A relatively poor competitor, *H. pratense* seems to fare better in grassland which is lightly grazed or mown where more competitive grasses such as *Arrhenatherum*

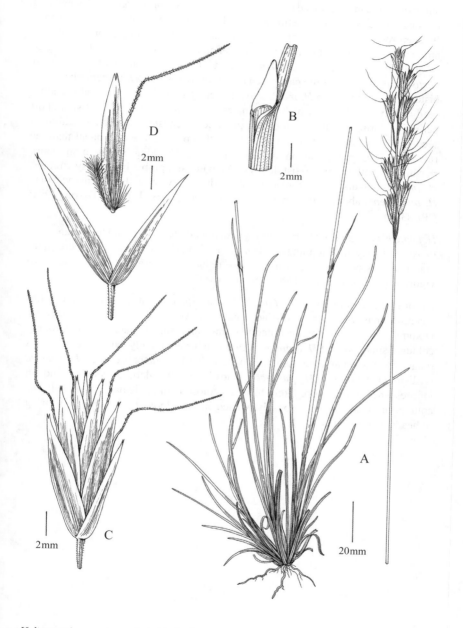

Helictotrichon pratense: A, habit; B, ligule; C, spikelet;
D, glumes and detached lowermost floret.

elatius, Brachypodium pinnatum or *Bromus erectus* are held in check, or on nutrient-poor soils and bare scree or rock where such species are absent. In these latter sites, and in abandoned pasture, *H. pratense* may form large tough spreading tussocks, whereas it is sometimes difficult to find the plant in grazed swards. Its deep root system (up to 50cm), waxy leaves which can be strongly folding, and ability to recover from high water deficits give this species a high degree of drought resistence. In woodland, like other glaucous grasses (e.g. *Agrostis curtisii*), its leaves become pale green and it rarely flowers. *H. pratense* has a life history not dissimilar to *H. pubescens*, flowering in early summer and shedding seed in July and August which germinates in the autumn following a very short period of dormancy. It also does not produce a persistent seed bank (although seed may survive from three to twelve months) but is more dependent than the rhizomatous *H. pubescens* on spreading by seed. The long bent awn and hairy rhachilla in both species assist dispersal by wind and probably by furry animals. *H. pratense* is also an outbreeder but produces fewer seeds per tussock than *H. pubescens*: about a 1000 per season on average. (Biol. Flora: Dixon, 1991; CPE: 344).

H. pratense is native, occurring throughout temperate Europe and temperate parts of Asia. It may be declining in Britain, particularly in the south, where older grassland has been ploughed and where reduction in grazing allows the more vigorous grasses mentioned above to take over.

According to Holub (in Tutin *et al.,* 1980) the alpine variant, *H. alpinum* (Smith) Henrard, may represent a distinct taxon. However, an exhaustive study by Dixon (1988) clearly demonstrated that this is not so. The larger, more strongly coloured spikelets that *H. alpinum* is said to have are merely part of a continuous range of variation and not associated with either latitude or altitude. *H. pratense* is distinguished from *H. pubescens* mostly by the glabrous sheaths and an inflorescence that is more likely to be racemose than paniculate. Above all, the column of the awn is more loosely twisted and in silhouette is more like a string of beads than parallel-sided.

64. **Arrhenatherum elatius** (L.) P.Beauv. ex J. & C.Presl

False Oat-grass

Illustration, page 259

New Atlas: 766

Loosely tufted perennial up to 150(180)cm; culms glabrous or hairy at the nodes, the basal internodes sometimes swollen and corm-like; ligule a blunt membrane 0.5 – 2mm; blades flat, scabrid, loosely hairy or not. Panicle loose to moderately dense, lanceolate to oblong, (10)15 – 30cm, the branches in clusters. Spikelets 7 – 10.5mm; glumes persistent, unequal, the lower lanceolate, 1-nerved, (3)4 – 6(7)mm, acute, the upper ovate, 3-nerved, as long as the spikelet; lower (or lowest) lemma oblong-lanceolate, 7.5 – 9.5mm, subacute or shortly 2-toothed, glabrous or sparsely hairy, awned from the back in the lower third; awn geniculate, twisted below, 11 – 16mm; upper lemma (or lemmas) similar to the lower but awnless or awned from the back in the upper third, the awn straight and up to 2.5(4.5)mm or geniculate and up to 10.5mm; anthers 3, 3.7 – 5.2(5.5)mm. $2n = 28$. Flowering and fruiting from late May or early June onwards, often persisting well into October.

A. elatius is widespread throughout the British Isles and is often abundant in rough grassland, road verges, hedgerows, riverbanks and waste ground. It is common as a colonizer of calcareous slopes and screes, and of maritime shingle, and occurs as a weed of arable land (var. *bulbosum*, see below). It is not found in mature woodland and only rarely in well-grazed pasture (except that grazed solely by horses who seem to avoid it). The species thrives best on well-drained, fairly deep neutral to base-rich soils (pH range 5.0 – 8.0) of moderate to high fertility. It avoids acid substrates. In this wide range of habitats *A. elatius* is associated with numerous species; a list of associates from various habitats is given by Pfitzenmeyer (1962). They include, from rough grassland and managed road verges, other grasses such as *Dactylis glomerata, Festuca pratensis, F. rubra, Helictotrichon pratense, Holcus lanatus, H. mollis* and *Lolium perenne*. On limestone screes in C England *A. elatius* grows with species such as *Geranium robertianum, Senecio jacobaea* and *Teucrium scorodonia* (CPE: 132). It occurs from sea-level to 550m (E Perth).

This very familiar, often tall and tussocky grass, which in full flower can seem to dominate large areas of ungrazed verge and hedgerow in lowland Britain, was once valued as a constituent of pastures (especially in France and other parts of continental Europe). However, it can largely be regarded as one of the 'sprinters' of the grass world, being quick to establish, rapid growing, deep rooted and 'leafy', but tending to die out in pasture after 3 or 4 years (although more prostrate grazing-tolerant ecotypes are known from chalk areas). It will produce a good hay crop for 2 or 3 years but is susceptible to repeated defoliation having relatively few tillers per plant. It is more persistent in unmanaged, lightly grazed or mown and periodically disturbed areas where it can flower freely. It produces non-dormant seed which chiefly germinate in the autumn but can remain viable for some years. These large 'seed' (the caryopsis with attached lemma, palea and awn), which are said to be frequently despersed by ants, enable the species to colonize new areas, even on coarse dry substrates such as scree talus, shingle and railway ballast. Survival in these habitats is enhanced by the extensive deep root system. *A. elatius* is polycarpic and predominantly outbreeding, although self-fertile genotypes are known. Variation in growth habit, winter greenness and other traits, including the occasional production of short rhizomes, has been reported but the genetic basis is unknown. (Biol. Flora: Pfitzenmeyer, 1962; CPE: 132).

A. elatius is native, part of the European Temperate element in our flora (P&H, 1997) and was first recorded in 1597 from Chelsea. It has been widely introduced and naturalized outside its native range (e.g. N & S America, Australasia). It may be spreading in the British Isles as roadsides are less frequently mown and sheep grazing is relaxed or withdrawn from some areas.

The fully-opened inflorescences of this handsome grass, with their violet paleas and greenish yellow glumes were regarded by Plues (1867) as "an object of admiration to all grass lovers". Generally, the lower floret is male and the upper bisexual, but occasionally there may be up to four florets present only the lowermost of which is male. Rarely both, or all, florets are bisexual. Modern accounts recognize two varieties: var. **elatius** without swollen internodes; and var. **bulbosum** (Willd.) Spenner (*Onion Couch*) in which the lowest internodes are swollen into a string of (1)2 – 6(8) globose or pear-shaped corms 6 – 10mm in diameter. The two varieties interbreed and produce plants of intermediate 'bulbousness'. Var. *bulbosum* (which tends to be more erect, with stiffer, more blue-green leaves than var. *elatius*) in semi-natural habitats is largely confined to the west of Britain, whereas on arable land it occurs in southern and central England (Cussans & Morton, 1990). We are unaware whether it continues to be a troublesome weed in light soils in Britain as reported in many Floras.

Late-flowering plants often have their inflorescences blackened and distorted by an infection of Loose Smut, *Ustilago segetum* var. *avenae* (Pers.) Brun.

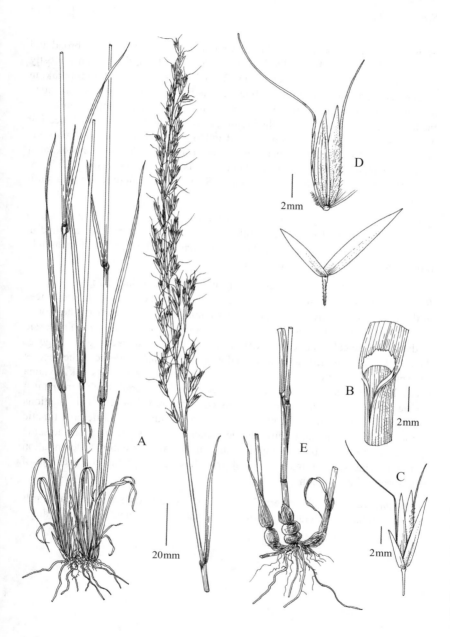

Arrhenatherum elatius var. *elatius*: A, habit; B, ligule; C, spikelet; D, glumes and detached florets. *Arrhenatherum elatius* var. *bulbosum*: E, base of culm.

65.   **Avena barbata** Pott ex Link

Slender Oat

Stout annual up to 100cm; ligule a blunt membrane 2 – 5mm; blades broad and flat, thinly hairy or glabrous. Panicle erect, 15 – 30(50)cm, the branches mostly turned to one side. Spikelets pendulous, 2- to 3-flowered, 14 – 30mm, breaking up above the persistent glumes and between the florets; glumes papery, subequal, as long as the spikelet, 5- to 9-nerved; lemmas narrowly lanceolate, rounded on the back, 12 – 20mm excluding the bristles, 2-toothed at the tip, the teeth bearing a fine bristle 3 – 5(12)mm, becoming hard and tough, stiffly hairy below, glabrous above, bearded around the callus-scar, awned from the middle of the back; awn stout, geniculate, twisted below, 3 – 6cm; anthers 3, (1.6)2.1 – 2.8mm. $2n = 28$. Flowering and fruiting late July to early September, sometimes lasting until October.

Slender Oat is a wool and grain casual which appears sporadically on waste and cultivated ground mainly in southern England and has been established in Guernsey since 1970. Easily mistaken for *A. strigosa*, the florets fall separately (probably enhancing its survival in the wild).

A. barbata, along with other grasses from the Mediterranean region such as *Bromus tectorum*, which are mainly casual or naturalized in one or two places in the British Isles, have been spectacular colonists in other parts of the world. The *A. barbata* populations in California, USA have been the subject of a classic study in ecological genetics by R.W.Allard and his co-workers (e.g. Clegg & Allard, 1972). Introduced to California during the Spanish settlement, the species has spread to become a major component of grassland and grass oak savanna over a large geographical area. Although less variable overall than their Spanish counterparts, the Californian populations comprise novel genetic combinations which, in less than 150 years, have become closely adapted to different climatic regions of California and to different ecological niches, sometimes on the same hillside. Such remarkable geographical and small-scale population differentiation in a colonizing self-pollinating annual grass has become a famous example of natural selection in action.

A. barbata is a native of southern Europe and the Mediterranean region eastwards to C Asia. It has been widely introduced and naturalized outside its native range.

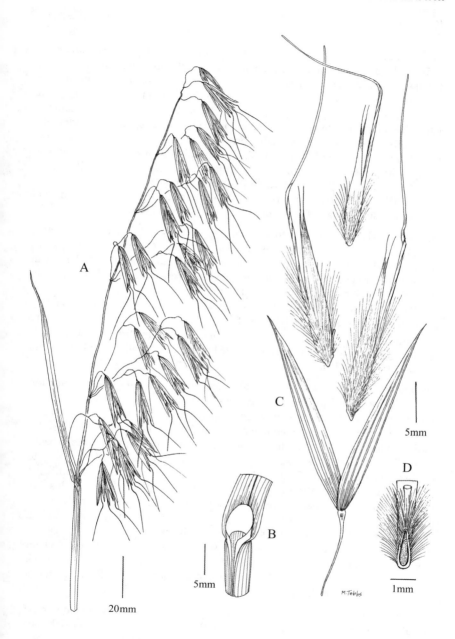

Avena barbata: A, panicle; B, ligule; C, glmues and detached florets;
D, callus of lowermost floret.

66.   Avena strigosa Schreb.

Bristle Oat   New Atlas: 766

Stout annual up to 120cm (mostly 60 – 90cm); ligule a blunt membrane 1.5 – 5mm; blades broad and flat, scaberulous. Panicle nodding, narrowly ovate, (6)10 – 19(30)cm, the branches spreading, often to one side. Spikelets pendulous, 2-flowered (very rarely a third floret present), 16 – 26mm, not breaking up at maturity; glumes papery, subequal, as long as the spikelet, 7- to 9-nerved; lemmas lanceolate or lanceolate-oblong, rounded on the back, 12 – 19mm excluding the bristles, 2-toothed at the tip, the teeth bearing a fine bristle (2.5)4 – 8mm, becoming hard and tough, scaberulous below, stiffly hairy above (or either scaberulous or stiffly hairy all over), without a beard at the base (there being no callus scar), awned from the middle of the back; awn slender to moderately stout, geniculate, twisted below, 2.5 – 4cm; anthers 3, 2 – 3.7(4.6)mm. $2n = 14, 28$. Flowering and fruiting late June to early September.

Bristle-oat (also known as 'Brown Oat', 'Sand Oat', 'Welsh Grey Oat' and, names it shares with some varieties of *A. sativa*, 'Black Oat' or 'Small Oat') was formerly widely cultivated in the north and west of Britain and in Ireland, and can be found as a relic of cultivation in arable, usually cereal, fields and occasionally on waste ground in western Wales, the Hebrides, the Orkney and Shetland Islands and the west of Ireland. It is still cultivated on at least one farm in Wales and by many crofters in the Western Isles and Shetland (see below). It occurs elsewhere on waste ground as a wool and grain casual and is cultivated from birdseed, but is becoming generally rare (although recorded relatively recently from Ireland and Wales (AGB: 31; Chater, 1993)).

The major value of *A. strigosa* as a cultivated oat was its ability to grow in poor, often acid, soils and to flourish in extreme conditions where Common Oat, *A. sativa*, could fail. It was grown in Celtic cultures for feed and fodder (when it was cut before fully ripe and fed like hay), mainly for working horses but also for cattle and has a very durable straw which was used in the Orkneys to make backs for traditional chairs. It was actually the main cereal grown in the Orkneys up to the beginning of the 20th Century. New varieties of Bristle Oat were still being produced (at the Welsh Plant Breeding Station in Aberystwyth) in the 1930s, but since the 1940s it has been largely replaced by cultivars of Common Oat (until recently a farm in Cardiganshire grew Bristle Oat, known in Wales as 'Ceirch Llwyd', continuously since 1942 saving seed each year). It is still grown, usually in a mixture with Rye, *Secale cereale*, on several islands in the Inner and Outer Hebrides, on mainland Argyll, on the Shetland Islands and on Fair Isle. Although it occurs as a crop contaminant with Common Oat, its ability to establish populations in the wild is undoubtedly hindered by the non-shattering spikelets.

The origins of *A. strigosa* are uncertain. It probably arose in cultivation in Europe and although it is still cultivated in parts of NW and C Europe, the Outer Hebrides may be the largest remaining area of *A. strigosa* cultivation. It was first recorded in the wild in Britain in 1790.

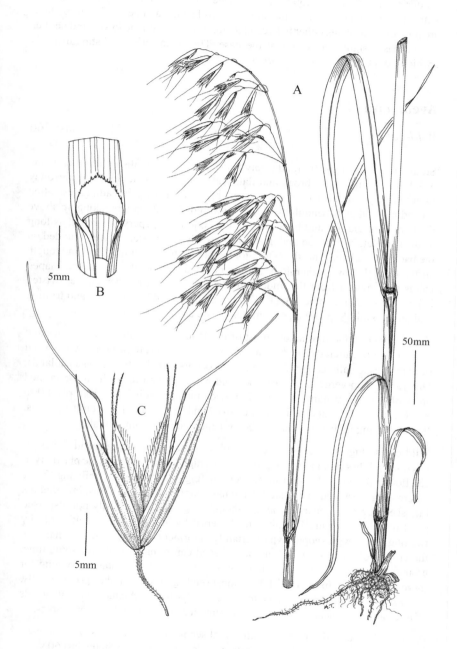

5mm

B

50mm

A

C

5mm

Avena strigosa: A, habit; B, ligule; C, spikelet.

In common with other grasses bred for use as cereals, Bristle Oat has non-shattering spikelets. The florets can easily be removed from between the glumes with a sharp tug, but the rhachilla simply snaps leaving an uneven fracture. There are no abscission rings either between the florets or beneath the lower, and neither lemma has a significant callus at the base. The apical bristles distinguish this species from Common Oat, *A. sativa*.

67. Avena fatua L.

Wild-oat   New Atlas: 766

Stout annual up to 150cm (and rarely less than 30cm); ligule a blunt membrane 3 – 4.5(6.5)mm; blades broad and flat, scaberulous. Panicle nodding, narrowly to broadly pyramidal, 10 – 35(40)cm, the branches usually spreading, less often ascending. Spikelets pendulous, 2- to 3-flowered, 19 – 28mm, breaking up above the persistent glumes and between the florets; glumes papery, subequal, as long as the spikelet, 7- to 11-nerved; lemmas narrowly oblong-lanceolate, rounded on the back, 14 – 21mm, shortly 2- to 4-toothed at the tip, becoming hard and tough, stiffly hairy below, scaberulous above, bearded around the horseshoe-shaped callus scar, awned from the middle of the back; awn stout, geniculate, twisted below, 2.5 – 4.5cm; anthers 3, (1.9)2.6 – 3.2mm. $2n = 42$. Flowering and fruiting mid-June to mid-September, sometimes as late as mid-October.

A. fatua is common throughout most of England, frequent in parts of Wales and Scotland, and scattered elsewhere including Ireland. It is often abundant as a weed of arable, especially cereal, fields and also occurs in habitats such as headlands, farmyards, road verges, and disturbed and waste ground throughout the farmed areas of lowland Britain. It occurs in a wide range of soil types from pH 4.0 to 8.5. It can also be found as a casual of wool and birdseed in more built-up areas. It is increasing in distribution (see below) and reaches 300m in Wales.

Wild-oat is a highly successful weed, displaying many key biological attributes for weediness. It has rapid seedling growth and a high level of phenotypic plasticity, it can flower from 6 to 12 weeks after germinating, is largely self-fertilizing (2-3% outcrossing measured in one study) and has a high seed output. Most importantly, the 'seed' are shed separately and, although large and thus mostly not dispersed great distances, are ideally suited to dispersal by animals and to self-burial by twisting of the hygroscopic awns. Certainly in former times the seed, which mimic the crop, were dispersed with it. Buried seed can remain viable for some time, around 20% remaining viable after a year and a small percentage surviving for more than 4 years. In the British Isles most seeds germinate in the spring. Finally, *A. fatua* has developed resistance to some widely-used herbicides and high levels of infestation in wheat and barley crops remain a common sight in some areas.

Probably introduced originally with cereal seeds, *A. fatua* is classed in the New Atlas as an archaeophyte. It has hugely increased in frequency in the last 60 years

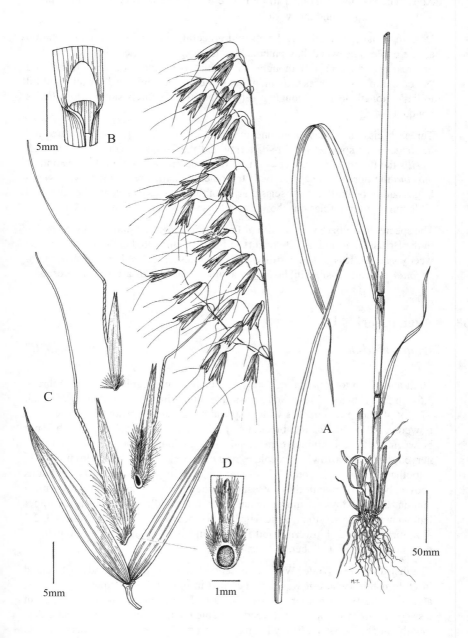

Avena fatua: A, habit; B, ligule; C, glumes and detached florets;
D, callus at base of lowermost floret.

and has expanded its British range northwards and westwards since the 1962 Atlas. The species is thought to be native to the Mediterranean but has spread with cultivation around the world.

Despite its large attractive spikelets and graceful panicle, Wild-oat's reputation as a troublesome weed has entered our language as a metaphor for careless procreation. Plues (1867) thought the plant "so destitute of any utility" and "so deleterious in its presence" that "its name has become used for all youthful follies". Nonetheless she thought it very beautiful and entirely suitable for a ladies bouquet.

Three abscission modes are found in the spikelets of *Avena*. In *A. sativa* and *A. strigosa* the spikelet is non-shattering and the florets remain attached; in *A. sterilis* the florets fall together as a unit from the glumes; and in *A. fatua* and *A. barbata* the florets fall separately. If the rhachilla hairs are scraped away with a finger nail or penknife, the abscission ring in this species can clearly be seen, and all lemmas, after abscission, show a neat horseshoe-shaped scar at the base.

The species hybridizes with *A. sativa*. The hybrid (**A.** ×**marquandii** Druce) is rare in the British Isles and usually occurs in fields of cultivated oat infested with the weedy species. It is of low fertility and resembles *A. sativa*, but the influence of *A. fatua* is clearly visible in the longer awn and (tardily) disarticulating florets.

68.　Avena sterilis L.

Winter Wild-oat　　　　　　　　　　　　　　　　　New Atlas: 767

Stout annual up to 160cm (and rarely less than 60cm); ligule a blunt membrane 2.5 – 6.5mm; blades broad and flat, scaberulous. Panicle nodding, pyramidal, 17 – 35(45)cm, the branches widely spreading. Spikelets pendulous, 2- to 3(4)-flowered, 20 – 30(32)mm, breaking up above the persistent glumes but not between the florets; glumes papery, subequal, as long as the spikelet, 9- to 11-nerved; lemmas narrowly lanceolate, rounded on the back, 16 – 24mm, shortly 2-toothed at the tip, becoming hard and tough, stiffly hairy below, scaberulous above, bearded around the horseshoe-shaped callus scar of the lowermost lemma, the two lower lemmas awned from the middle of the back, the upper lemma awnless; awn stout, geniculate, twisted below, 2.5 – 5.5cm; anthers 3, 2.7 – 4.3mm. $2n = 42$. Flowering and fruiting mid-June to late August, sometimes persisting well into October.

The distribution of Winter Wild-oat is centred on the south midlands of England in Oxfordshire (where it was first recorded in the wild) and adjacent counties, across to the Welsh border and eastwards to Essex. Here it is widespread but less common than *A. fatua* as a weed of arable land, notably winter wheat crops, mainly on clay soils and heavy loams. It is scattered elsewhere on waste ground as a wool or grain alien.

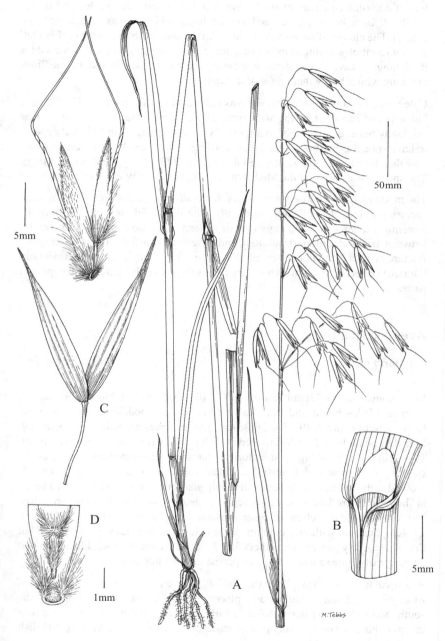

Avena sterilis subsp. *ludoviciana*: A, habit; B, ligule;
C, glumes and detached cluster of florets; D, callus of lowermost floret.

A. sterilis has most of the weedy attributes of *A. fatua* (see that account) and was at one time an equally troublesome weed of wheat, oats, barley and beans. Unlike *A. fatua*, however, the 'seed' are not dispersed initially as a single unit (see below). The cluster of florets may have given the species its old name of 'Fly Oat' since it resembles a winged insect and, aided by the twisting awns, it was used for fly fishing. *A. sterilis* seed germinate during the winter months and the seedlings are more winter hardy than those of *A. fatua*.

Categorized as a neophyte, this oat was cultivated in Britain in the 17th Century but was not recorded in the wild until 1910, at Port Meadow, Oxon (it was originally believed to have been imported via the south coast in 1914). It appears to have spread from this source but, according to the New Atlas, is less frequent now than twenty years ago (although Ryves *et al.,* (1996) suggest it is increasing). The species is a native of the Mediterranean region and SW & C Asia.

The mode of spikelet abscission makes *A. sterilis* easy to distinguish from other species provided the spikelets are mature. The florets fall as a cluster, only the lowermost lemma showing any signs of a clean abscission scar. The internodes between the florets are short and stout, and if the florets are forced apart an irregular fracture will occur without any obvious scar. Our plant is subsp. **ludoviciana** (Durieu) Gillet & Magne which differs from subsp. **sterilis** by its smaller spikelet parts.

69. Avena sativa L.

Common Oat   New Atlas: 767

Stout annual up to 130cm (mostly 60 – 100cm); ligule a blunt membrane 2 – 5mm; blades broad and flat, scaberulous. Panicle nodding, narrowly ovate to broadly pyramidal, (9)15 – 26(36)cm, the branches ascending or spreading. Spikelets pendulous, 2- to 3-flowered though the third floret is usually a rudiment, 19 – 27mm, not breaking up at maturity; glumes papery, subequal, as long as the spikelet, 9- to 11-nerved; lemmas lanceolate, rounded on the back, 12 – 18mm, 2-toothed at the tip, becoming hard and tough, glabrous throughout, without a beard at the base (there being no callus scar), awned or awnless, the two sorts often mixed within the panicle; awn, when present, dorsal, slender to moderately stout, 2 – 4cm, flexuous without a column, or the column sometimes well developed but the awn scarcely geniculate; anthers 3, 2.3 – 3.1(3.5)mm. $2n = 42$. Flowering and fruiting early June to mid-August or persisting well into autumn.

A. sativa is found throughout the British Isles as a non-persistent casual of roadsides, field margins and waste places, tending to be more common in the south. Most plants are derived from nearby oat crops but it can also occur as a casual of birdseed on rubbish tips and waste land. Common Oat does not establish populations in the wild.

Avena sativa: A, habit; B, spikelet; C, florets removed from glumes.

The origins of *A. sativa* are obscure but it is believed to have been selected from *A. fatua* and first cultivated in C Europe in the Bronze Age. It provided a cereal which thrived where the soil was too poor or the climate too wet to grow wheat or barley. It was extensively grown for fodder when horses were the main form of transport, but has also provided food for people since first cultivated. Dr Johnson, unaware of the extensive consumption of oatmeal in the north of England once remarked sarcastically that "in England oats are food for horses and in Scotland food for man". Records of Common Oat as a casual only began in the early part of the 20th Century.

The species' non-shattering spikelets, glabrous lemmas without apical bristles and poorly developed awn are distinctive and there should be little difficulty distinguishing the cultivated oat from its wild relatives. It hybridzes with *A. fatua*; see under that species for details.

70.   Gaudinia fragilis (L.) P.Beauv.

French Oat-grass   New Atlas: 767

Softly hairy annual, biennial or perhaps short-lived perennial up to 85cm; ligule a membranous rim up to 0.5mm; blades flat, up to 2.5mm wide. Raceme (8.5)10 – 16cm. Spikelets 12 – 19mm, 4- to 7-flowered, usually with an additional sterile rudiment; lower glume oblong-lanceolate, 2.5 – 5(6)mm, acute or subacute; upper glume oblong, 5 – 9.5(11)mm, subacute or obtuse, sometimes asymmetrically toothed; lemmas lanceolate, 6.5 – 10.5mm, with a dorsal geniculate awn 7.5 – 14mm; anthers 3, (3.2)3.6 – 5mm. $2n = 14$. Flowering and fruiting early May to mid-July.

G. fragilis is largely confined to central southern and southwestern England, with outlier populations in S Wales and Sussex, and to the Channel Islands and the west of Ireland. Initially regarded as a casual, especially as a contaminant of grass-seed, it has been infrequently recorded from tips, roadsides, waste ground, docks and disturbed habitats, although seemingly long-established populations were known from meadows in Guernsey and the Isle of Wight. In the last 20 years it has increasingly been recorded from apparently unimproved or semi-improved haymeadows and pastures. These are mostly on neutral to calcareous clay soils which are dry in summer and wet in winter, and within such areas *G. fragilis* tends to occur in the more open, shorter or patchy swards. Associated species in such habitats include the grasses *Anthoxanthum odoratum, Cynosurus cristatus, Festuca rubra, Holcus lanatus* and *Lolium perenne* and the forbs *Lotus corniculatus, Ranunculus acris, Trifolium pratense* and *T. repens*. A detailed analysis of the habitats of *G. fragilis* in the British Isles is given by Leach & Pearman (2003) who review the history of its discovery and attempt to assess whether it may be a native species (see below).

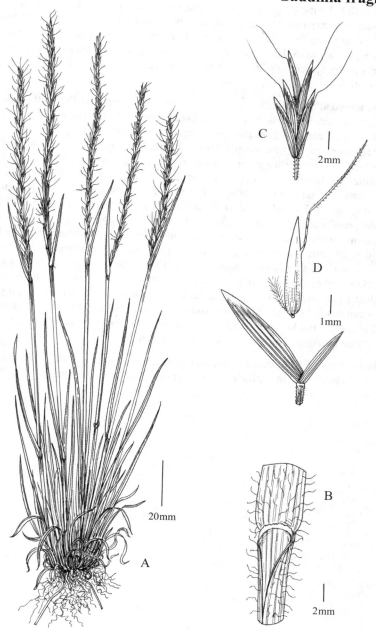

Gaudinia fragilis: A, habit; B, ligule; C, spikelet and raceme internode;
D, glumes and detached lowest floret.

Little seems to be known about the population biology of *G. fragilis* in its British and Irish habitats. Its preference for thin, open areas of sward may indicate that populations are maintained principally by regeneration from seed. Although individual plants flower freely, and the inflorescences rapidly break up at maturity (perhaps leading to the species being overlooked) we are unaware whether any plants are polycarpic or how long they live. The species is believed to be self-compatible.

First recorded as a casual in 1903, the status of *G. fragilis* in the British Isles is uncertain. Leach & Pearman's intriguing analysis balances the case for it being introduced, probably from the Mediterranean or southern Europe (suggested by the relatively recent first records both as a casual and in semi-natural vegetation, the fact that the earlier records were from artificial habitats, there have been a large number of new records in the 1990s, there are suspected sources of introduction, and it is classed as an introduced species in other parts of northern Europe and in Ireland), against the case for it being native (suggested by its widespread occurrence in a definable species-rich semi-natural habitat, which contains almost entirely native plants, some of which has not been ploughed for at least 80 years, and it has a geographically familiar distribution shared by other natives such as *Oenanthe pimpinelloides*). They conclude that for now it cannot be classified as alien or native. The recent number of new records could certainly reflect a genuine increase (under climatic warming?) or the fact that it is a grass that can easily be overlooked until you have once seen it. The species is native in S Europe and the Mediterranean (the Submediterranean-Subatlantic element) and has been introduced elsewhere (S America and Australia).

The racemose inflorescence is unusual in Aveneae. It disarticulates at the base of each internode and the spikelets fall entire attached to this internode.

71. Trisetum flavescens (L.) P.Beauv.

Yellow Oat-grass

New Atlas: 768

Glabrous or softly hairy, loosely tufted perennial up to 80(100)cm; ligule a blunt membrane 0.3 – 1.1mm; blades flat, up to 4mm wide. Panicle erect or nodding, loose or rather dense, lanceolate to narrowly ovate, 7 – 15cm. Spikelets 2- to 4-flowered, 5 – 7(8)mm; lower glume 1-nerved, narrowly lanceolate, 2.5 – 4.7mm, acute; upper glume 3-nerved, elliptic, 4.3 – 6.5mm, acute; lemmas 5-nerved, narrowly lanceolate to narrowly oblong in profile, 4.4 – 6.3mm, tipped with 2 short narrow teeth or fine bristles, awned from or near the middle of the back; awn 4.5 – 7.5(9)mm, with twisted column and straight limb; anthers 3, 1.3 – 2.5(2.8)mm. $2n = 28$. Flowering and fruiting mid-June to late July, sometimes persisting until mid-August.

T. flavescens is common in suitable habitats over most of England (except the southwest peninsula), N Wales, SE Scotland north to the central valley and the central limestone plains of Ireland, but is rare or absent from southwest central and northern Scotland. It is frequent or locally abundant in a range of neutral and calcareous grassland types, including lush lowland meadows and pastures, as well as dry downland. It is also found in grassy road verges and hedgerows and artificial habitats such as railway embankments, old quarries and waste ground. It occurs less commonly on walls, cliff faces, consolidated scree and shingle, fixed dunes, open oak/ash woodland and hawthorn scrub, and even acid heath (in Nottinghamshire). It is found on a range of soil types, mainly over chalk or limestone and with a pH >6.0, but occurs over non-calcareous substrata (and in soils down to pH 4.1). *T. flavescens* tends to be a relatively scattered minor component of most grasslands, although it may dominate moderately tall hay meadows, and is absent from severely droughted habitats and those with densely productive vegetation. An analysis of the full range of plant communities containing *T. flavescens* is given by Dixon (1995). It occurs from sea-level to 550m at Moor House, Westmorland.

Yellow Oat-grass was at one time included in seed mixtures for hay or pastures (it is still grown for fodder in northern Europe), mainly because it is highly palatable to sheep and cattle who will eat the young stems as well as the leaves. Unfortunately, it is poorly adapted to repeated defoliation being shallow rooted, having a relatively low tillering capacity and investing most of its growth in flowery culms (in one experiment less than 10% of the dry weight of single plants was made up of root growth, compared to almost 60% in *Helictotrichon pratense*, a grass from similar habitats). Therefore, although it will flower again after early grazing or a June hay cut, the species is intolerant of heavy grazing and, for the same reason, intolerant of trampling and extreme drought. It is better suited to hay meadows and lightly grazed or unmanaged grassland where more dominant species such as *Arrhenatherum elatius* and *Brachypodium pinnatum* are held in check. Considerable variation in size and seed output has been observed between habitats but seed are set throughout the plant's range, the first inflorescences being produced in the year following germination. Seed are shed in July and August and germinate in the field from August to October, most seed requiring only a slight period of after-ripening, and like those of similar grasses the seed are probably dispersed on animal fur as well as by wind. No persistent seed bank has been reported. *T. flavescens* is self-incompatible. Overwintering leaves produced in late summer have usually died back before new growth starts in March and April. (Biol. Flora: Dixon, 1995; CPE: 606).

A native of temperate Europe and Asia, *T. flavescens* is widely naturalized outside its native range, including the north of Europe. It is alien in Shetland and possibly elsewhere in the northern and western parts of its British range.

Unlikely to be confused with any other grass from the British Isles on account of its panicles of glossy yellow or golden spikelets. Its nearest relatives are *Koeleria*, with a compact panicle of silvery, awnless spikelets, and *Helictotrichon*, with fewer much larger spikelets. A robust form of this species, usually taller (more often reaching 100cm or more) with broader blades (5 – 10mm wide) and richer, denser panicle has occasionally been sown in grass mixes. It has been separated as subsp. *purpurascens* (DC.) Arcang., but its true relationship to the type still needs to be examined.

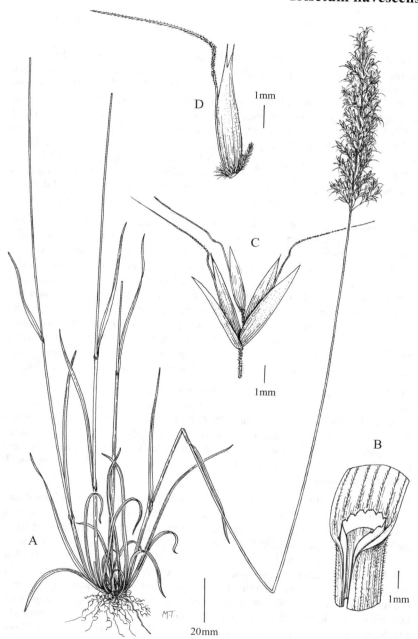

Trisetum flavescens: A, habit; B, ligule; C, spikelet; D, floret.

72.   **Koeleria vallesiana** (Honck.) Gaudin

Somerset Hair-grass   New Atlas: 768

Densely tufted plant up to 40(50)cm, the stems thickened and somewhat woody at the base; lower sheaths tightly imbricate, disintegrating into a persistent mass of reticulate fibres; ligule a blunt membrane 0.3 – 0.7mm; leaves of non-flowering shoots greyish green, straight or curved, inrolled and setaceous or flat and up to 3mm wide, stiff. Panicle spike-like, dense, oblong to ovate-oblong, 2 – 5.5(7.5)cm, silvery or tinged with purple or brown. Spikelets 4.5 – 6.5mm, 2- to 3-flowered (mostly 2); glumes persistent, acuminate to very shortly awn-pointed, the lower narrowly elliptic, (3.2)3.6 – 5(5.7)mm, the upper elliptic, (3.7)4.1 – 5.2(6.3)mm; lemmas elliptic, 4 – 5.3(5.7)mm, keeled above, acute or with a short awn-point 0.1 – 0.4mm; anthers 3, (1.7)2 – 2.5(2.7)mm. $2n =$ mostly 42, but some 14, 28, 49, 63. Flowering and fruiting early June to mid- or late August.

K. vallesiana is known only from a small number of sites at the western end of the Mendip Hills in NW Somerset where it occurs in short turf and rocky ledges and outcrops generally along south-facing slopes of the Carboniferous Limestone. All the populations of this distinctive grass occur within a 15km-sided triangle, and vary in size from many thousands (at least 10,000 at Brean Down) to around 100 plants (in the only small population, at Worle Hill). Typical associates are *Pilosella officinarum, Sanguisorba minor, Festuca ovina, Thymus polytrichus* and *Helianthemum nummularium* (the rare species *Helianthemum apenninum* and *Trinia glauca* also occur at one or two sites with *K. vallesiana* in this area). Annual or short-lived plants in these dry swards include *Blackstonia perfoliata, Carlina vulgaris, Centaurium erythraea* and *Euphrasia nemorosa* (RDB: 205).

Individuals are perennial, polycarpic and probably long-lived, but with little lateral vegetative spread. The very thin soils and rocky ledges in which they grow can become extremely hot and dry during the summer months. The species is clearly very drought tolerant (or drought avoiding). *K. vallesiana* is self-incompatible and only about 5% of florets appear to set seed (Callow & Parker, 1979). Despite this, sterile hybrids ($2n = 35$) with *K. macrantha* have been found in most populations.

K. vallesiana is native and has always been restricted to the Mendip Hills (it has been introduced to one site, Goblin Combe). The British populations are outliers of the species' main range in central and western Europe and N Africa, and have almost certainly been isolated from them since late Glacial times (*c.*12,000 BP), an isolation reflected in heritable morphological differences between British and French populations. The species has an extremely interesting history in Britain, having been first recorded (from Uphill and Brean Down) in 1726 but not rediscovered until 1904 (by G.C.Druce who was working on the papers of Dillenius who originally discovered the plant) and was found at its most northerly site, Sandpoint, as recently as 1974. Although classified as **vulnerable** (Cheffings & Farrell, 2005), the future of this Red List species seems assured as most of its locations are protected by SSSI status.

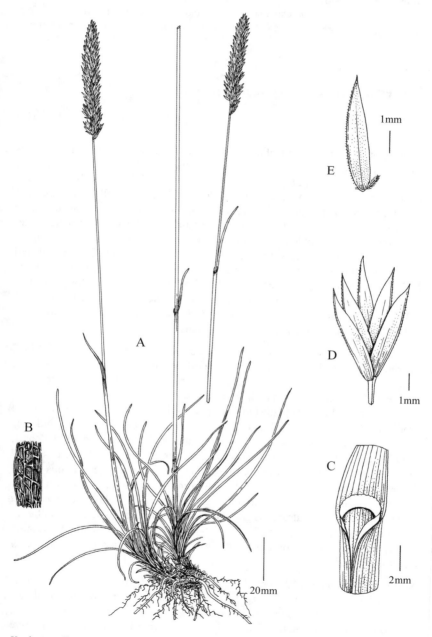

Koeleria vallesiana: A, habit; B, fibrous remains of leaf sheath; C, ligule; D, spikelet; E, floret.

K. vallesiana is distinguished from *K. macrantha* by the thickened stem bases clothed in a mass of reticulate fibres derived from the interconnecting veins of the sheaths. *K. macrantha* can also have a thickened base, but the sheaths are less likely to disintegrate; if they do, they do so into parallel filaments, not a reticulate mass.

73.   **Koeleria macrantha** (Ledeb.) Schult.

Crested Hair-grass   New Atlas: 768

Loosely or densely tufted plant up to 45(60)cm, sometimes developing rhizomes and rarely thickened and somewhat woody at the base; lower sheaths remaining intact or eventually disintegrating into discrete parallel filaments; ligule a blunt membrane 0.2 – 0.7mm; leaves of non-flowering shoots inrolled, flexuous and bristle-like, hairy or glabrous, green or glaucous, rarely flat and up to 2.5mm wide, sometimes short and stiff and very glaucous and scabrid. Panicle spike-like, dense, narrowly oblong, sometimes lobed and interrupted, (2)3 – 7.5(10)cm, silvery green, often tinged with purple. Spikelets (3.5)4 – 6mm, 2- to 3-flowered (mostly 2); glumes persistent, subobtuse to acuminate, the lower narrowly oblong, (2)3 – 4.5mm, the upper broader, (3)4 – 5(5.6)mm; lemmas oblong, (3.2)3.7 – 5.2(5.8)mm, keeled above, subobtuse to acuminate or with an awn-point 0.1 – 0.4(0.7)mm; anthers 3, 1.4 – 2.4mm. $2n = 28$. Flowering and fruiting early June to late July, sometimes persisting to mid-August.

Widely found on well-drained, mostly calcareous soils, *K. macrantha*'s British distribution traces the chalk and limestone ridges and downland of southern and central England, is scattered on limestone in the north and west, and becomes increasingly limited to coastal sites in Scotland. It occurs on off-shore islands from the Channel Islands to the Orkneys but not the Shetland Isles. It is scattered around the Irish coast and is found inland in the west. Typical habitats include dry pasture, rock outcrops and screes, derelict mines and quarries and, on the coast, sand-dunes, cliff-tops and even consolidated shingle banks, all characteristically open habitats on generally infertile soils. Soil types range from calcareous brown earths and rendzinas over chalk and limestone to almost pure sand and even sandy peat, but are mostly base-rich (the full range is from pH 3.0 to 8.4). *K. macrantha* is mainly a species of calcareous grassland and the range of these communities in which it occurs is described by Dixon (2000) who also lists associates from other largely maritime vegetation types containing the grass. It occurs from sea-level to 680m in S Kerry.

Not found in heavily disturbed habitats or those where there is extreme competition from more vigorous grasses, *K. macrantha* has a similar, subordinate role in calcareous pasture to that of *Trisetum flavescens* in meadows (CPE: 380). Individuals are perennial, free-flowering and polycarpic and, with little vegetative extension, populations increase by autumn germination of newly-released seed. A

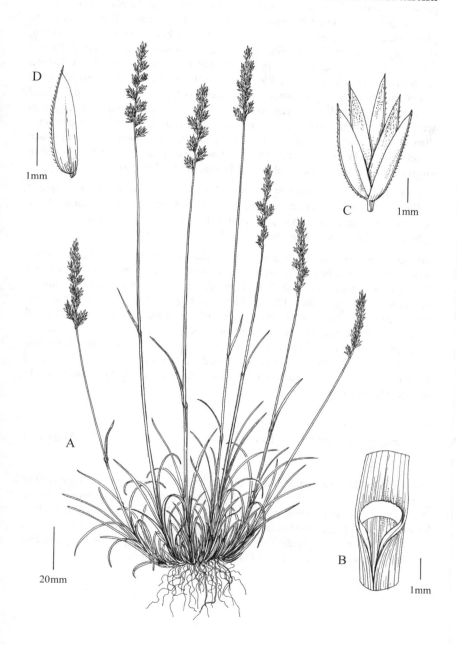

Koeleria macrantha: A, habit; B, ligule; C, spikelet; D, floret.

short after-ripening period is necessary for most, but not all, seed and there is no persistent seed bank. Seed are not dispersed very far from the plant, most (almost two-thirds) remaining on the panicle (hence the plant's patchy distribution). The plant remains green over winter and new growth begins very early in spring (February onwards). The species invests heavily in root growth (almost 40% of its dry weight in one experiment in Dixon (2000) compared with 25% in *Sesleria caerulea* and 18% in *Helictotrichon pratense*) and its survival in dry soils may be largely due to its ability to produce rapid new root growth following periods of drought (it is generally less drought tolerant than the two aforementioned species with which it often grows). *K. macrantha* is outbreeding and British populations display much morphological variation, especially in growth habit, some of which is habitat-correlated (e.g. sand-dune ecotypes) and is at least partly retained in cultivation (Dixon, 2001). (Biol. Flora: Dixon, 2000; CPE: 380).

K. macrantha is native in the British Isles. It is a circumpolar species widespread in Europe and the temperate zones of Asia and N America and it is known to be declining in places due to habitat loss and changes in grassland management. It hybridizes with the rare *K. vallesiana* in the latter's UK sites.

An extremely variable species in which relationships between the numerous entities have not yet been fully explored. One such entity, given the rank of species (Humphries in Tutin *et al.*, 1980), is *K. glauca* (Schrad.) DC.; it is distinguished by a combination of blunt glumes and lemmas, short stiff very glaucous and very scabrid leaves on the non-flowering shoots and a thickened woody base. While all of these characteristics can be found in populations in the British Isles they do not occur in combination. Comparison with European material indicates that while there is little doubt that *K. glauca* is as good a species as one is likely to get in *Koeleria*, it does not occur in the British Isles as Dixon's (2001) extensive study has recently affirmed.

74. Rostraria cristata (L.) Tzvelev   New Atlas CD

An annual with a subterminal awn on the lemma. It is otherwise very similar to species of *Koeleria*. The glumes and lemmas are usually glabrous or thinly hairy but occasionally there are specimens with densely woolly lemmas. It is an introduction from the Mediterranean region, usually in birdseed but also as a weed of hops and bulb fields; formerly widely scattered in parts of England and Scotland but seldom persisting and now much less common.

75. Deschampsia cespitosa (L.) P.Beauv.

Illustration, page 283

Tufted Hair-grass

Densely tufted, up to 150(200)cm, often forming large tussocks; sheaths smooth or scaberulous above; ligule a narrow, sharply pointed membrane 4.5 – 14mm; blades flat or loosely inrolled, 2 – 4(5)mm wide, coarsely scabrid on the margins and upper surface, smooth below. Panicle very loose and open, 15 – 35(50)cm, with capillary branches. Spikelets 2-flowered (rarely 3-flowered; proliferating spikelets sometimes with up to 5 florets) with long rhachilla-extension (1 – 2(2.5)mm), green, often variegated with silver, gold or purple, sometimes proliferating; glumes unequal or subequal, lanceolate, the lower (2)2.5 – 4(4.5)mm, the upper (2.5)2.8 – 4.8mm; lemmas oblong, (1.9)2.6 – 3.9mm, unevenly toothed at the tip, awned from near the base (rarely from the middle or above); awn weakly geniculate, 2 – 4mm, scarcely projecting from the glumes, often absent in a proliferating spikelet even on the occasional sexual floret; rhachilla-internode 0.8 – 1.4mm; anthers 3, 1.1 – 2mm. $2n = 14 – 56$. Flowering and fruiting mid-June to mid-August.

D. cespitosa is widespread throughout the British Isles in rough grassland, marshes, water-meadows, woodland and moorland. It also occurs on riverbanks, fen, carr, montane grassland and ledges, and on derelict land and a range of artificial habitats such as spoil heaps. It is found on a great variety of soil types but these usually have impeded drainage, are seasonally flooded and/or are nutrient-poor. Most abundant on soils in the pH range 4.5 to 6.5, it has been found to tolerate extremely acid colliery spoil (pH 2.8) and extremely basic brick and mortar spoil (pH 12.2). *D. cespitosa* has been recorded from a diverse range of grassland, wetland and woodland plant communities and in several it is a distinctive and dominant component. Davy (1980) provides an analysis of these, noting that the grass has been found in association with more than 1000 other species in Britain alone. It occurs from sea-level (as a component of the saltmarsh to brackish marsh transition) to more than 1200m (Ben Macdui, S Aberdeen).

A familiar tussock-forming grass with extremely coarse leaves and beautiful silvery panicles, *D. cespitosa* seems able to persist in a range of environments. In wet pasture and marshy fields in the lowlands it is highly unpalatable to stock and can be a serious weed which is difficult to eradicate even by improving the drainage. In woodland the tussocks can persist for many years, probably >30, often without flowering in the mature woodland phase, and when the trees are felled or thinned new populations are established from the long-lived seed bank. In the uplands, where the leaves are grazed by cattle, sheep and deer, it is a persistent component of grazed swards, and in the high mountains vegetative reproduction occurs by means of proliferating spikelets (notably in subsp. *alpina*; see below). Whilst populations are maintained for many years by clonal growth, except in deep shade or when heavily grazed, most tussocks flower and set seed every year. The florets are protandrous and plants are self-incompatible. Seed production can be huge, with up to 2000 caryopses per panicle being normal, and a mature tussock may produce at least 500,000 caryopses in one season. The seed are relatively light and may be dispersed over long distances by wind, a feature of the plant's ecology which enables it to rapidly colonize bare and disturbed ground. The species' tolerance of poor soil aeration, seasonal waterlogging, infertile soils, shading and a wide range of edaphic extremes (including heavy metals) may be due to a combination of physiological, phenotypic and genetic adaptations and is reflected in the high level of intraspecific variation. (Biol. Flora: Davy, 1980; CPE: 248).

D. cespitosa is native in the British Isles. It is part of the Circumpolar Wide-boreal element in our flora (P&H 1997) and is widely naturalized outside its native range. Grassland improvement may be leading to a decline of lowland populations in the British Isles although it may be increasing in managed woodland and artificial habitats.

It is distinguished from the other species of *Deschampsia* by its broader, usually flat blades. It is, however, exceedingly variable and is represented by three ploidy levels (diploid, triploid and tetraploid). Clarke (in Tutin *et al.*, 1980) divided it into eight ill-defined subspecies; two of these are accepted by Stace (1997) for the British Isles, along with a third not recognized by Clarke. The three are exceedingly difficult to distinguish and both morpholgy and ecology play a part in their recognition. Characters used to separate them include the extent to which the leaf-tip is hooded; the presence or absence of scabridities on the panicle branches and pedicels (they vary from absent through sparse to quite dense); whether the primary branches are ascending or reflexed (the latter seems rarely to be expressed and is often exceedingly difficult to see in herbarium specimens); and the position of the awn (this unfortunately varies even within a spikelet; the awn moves to a higher position in the upper lemmas and a vestigial awn on the lemma of a proliferating floret is of little help; often, however, the lowermost floret of a proliferating spikelet is sexual and may have a perfect awn).

75a. subsp. **cespitosa** is the most variable of the subspecies. Forms with short, stiff, tightly inrolled blades (but clearly not the filiform blades of the other two species) have been separated as var. *brevifolia* (Parnell) Druce, but variation between the extremes is continuous. Variants with proliferating spikelets have been called either var. *vivipara* Gray or var. *pseudo-alpina* (Syme) Druce. This variant is a problem because proliferating spikelets are also characteristic of subsp. *alpina*. Subsp. *cespitosa* is represented at three ploidy levels, diploid ($2n = 26$), triploid ($2n = 39$) and tetraploid ($2n = 52$); all three are found in upland areas, the last also in the lowlands.

The most widespread subspecies, the distribution and ecology of which is described above, subsp. *cespitosa* is found throughout the species' range, including woodland and montane habitats.

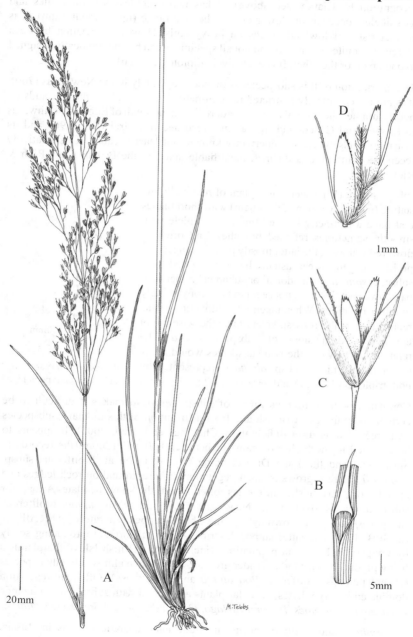

Deschampsia cespitosa subsp. *cespitosa*: A, habit; B, ligule; C, spikelet; D, florets.

75b.   subsp. **parviflora** (Thuill.) Cosson & Germ., is the variant not given formal recognition by Clarke (see above). It has narrower, less scabrid blades and its spikelets occur at the lower end of the size range (up to about 3mm); it is characteristic of lowland woods on heavy soils. However, variation between extremes is quite continuous and not all specimens can be unequivocally assigned to one taxon or the other. It is exclusively diploid ($2n = 26$).

The distribution of this subspecies is mapped separately in the New Atlas (769). It is almost completely restricted to semi-natural woodlands in the lowlands on poorly-drained, heavy soils, and is scattered from the south of England northwards to Kintyre and C Scotland. It was first recorded from Ireland in 1969 and its distribution elsewhere is imperfectly known, not least because of its relatively recent recognition as a distinct, identifiable taxon in the British Isles (Rich & Rich, 1988).

75c.   subsp. **alpina** (L.) Tzvelev is a plant of relatively low stature (generally around 20 – 40cm) with short blades that have a distinctly hooded tip, small panicle with smooth, sometimes reflexed branches, and often 3-flowered spikelets, the latter mostly proliferating. Non-proliferating forms can usually be distinguished from subsp. *cespitosa* by the dorsal or subapical rather than basal awn, but this does not seem to hold convincingly for all populations. When taken into cultivation plants retain their proliferous spikelets but otherwise adopt the overall dimensions of subsp. *cespitosa*. The relationship between the two subspecies would repay closer examination. Subsp. *alpina* is represented by both triploids ($2n = 39$) and tetraploids ($2n = 52 – 56$).

10mm

Deschampsia cespitosa subsp. *alpina*: panicle.

Confusion with proliferous forms of subsp. *cespitosa* makes it difficult to be certain about the exact British and Irish distribution of this montane subspecies (it is regarded as **data deficient** by Cheffings & Farrell, 2005). It appears to be confined to the high mountains of between 800 and 1200m (the records in Snowdonia and the Lake District being thought to be all proliferous subsp. *cespitosa* where it grows in open vegetation or bare ground on rock ledges and gravelly or peaty flushes in corries, often where the snow lies late. A map for subsp. *alpina* is given in the New Atlas (769) and subsp. *alpina*, proliferous subsp. *cespitosa* and known hybrids have been mapped separately by McAllister (in SPB: 132). The latter author describes subsp. *alpina* as reproducing solely by vivipary in European populations (including the British Isles), the plantlets being produced in a shorter, colder growing season than almost any other species (except perhaps proliferous *Poa alpina* and *P. flexuosa*). Often in vegetation dominated by bryophytes, vascular plants associated with subsp. *alpina* include *Cerastium cerastoides, Huperzia selago, Oxyria digyna* and *Saxifraga stellaris*.

D. cespitosa subsp. *alpina* occurs in arctic and subarctic regions in Russia, Scandinavia, Iceland, Greenland, eastern Canada and E Asia. It is absent from the mountains of C Europe.

The subspecies outlined above indicate the main lines of variation within the British Isles. They are not at all easy to distinguish and those that produce non-proliferating spikelets have both chasmogamous and cleistogamous forms. It is probable that rank of subspecies over-emphasises the differences and reduction to varietal level may be more appropriate. Subsp. *parviflora* is the least convincing and Clarke was probably right not to recognize it.

76. Deschampsia flexuosa (L.) Trin.

Illustration, page 287

Wavy Hair-grass

New Atlas: 770

Loosely to densely tufted, up to 80cm, occasionally producing slender rhizomes; sheaths often minutely scaberulous above; ligule a blunt membrane (1)1.5 – 3.5mm; blades tightly inrolled, bristle-like, 0.3 – 0.5(0.6)mm across. Panicle very loose and open, 6 – 13(15)cm, with flexuous capillary branches. Spikelets 2-flowered with short rhachilla extension (c.0.5mm), silvery, tinged with purple or brown; glumes ovate to elliptic-ovate, the lower 3.5 – 5mm, the upper 4.5 – 5.5(7)mm; lemmas elliptic-oblong, 3.9 – 5.1mm, blunt and minutely toothed at the tip, the teeth ± equal, awned from near the base; awn geniculate, 4.5 – 6.5mm, projecting well beyond the glumes; rhachilla internode 0.4 – 0.6(0.7)mm (c.1/4 the length of the lower lemma); anthers 3, 1.9 – 2.8(3.1)mm. $2n = 14, 28$. Flowering and fruiting late May to mid-August.

Wavy Hair-grass is widely distributed in suitable base-poor habitats throughout the British Isles. It is largely absent from the predominantly calcareous soils of southern C England and C Ireland. It is a common, and often dominant, grass, of moorland and hill pasture, lowland heathland and open woodland (usually dominated by birch, oak, rowan or conifers). In these habitats it is found on a range of well-drained acid soils (pH generally <4.5) including sands, coarse gravels, sandy shales, brown earths, peats and other soils derived from acid rocks, and occasionally on well-leached soils over limestone. It also occurs as a colonist of screes, railway cuttings, shale heaps and quarries as well as eroded or cut areas of heath and moorland. In its range of habitats it is associated with other common grasses of drier acidic soils such as *Agrostis capillaris, Anthoxanthum odoratum, Festuca ovina, Holcus mollis* and *Nardus stricta*, as well as the frequent dominants of those habitats such as *Pteridium aquilinum, Calluna vulgaris* and species of *Erica, Vaccinium* and *Ulex*. It occurs from sea-level to 1220m (Ben Macdui, S Aberdeen).

Tolerant of nutrient-poor acid soils, of shade and of grazing (by sheep and rabbits), *D. flexuosa* forms evergreen tufts or continuous carpets in a variety of habitats, and is arguably "the most successful calcifuge grass in Britain" (CPE: 250). (It is certainly among the most attractive, swards in full flower in a woodland glade with their graceful spreading panicles of shining spikelets being among the finest displays in nature). Although tolerant of shade, growth is generally reduced in denser woodland under tree litter and under bracken or heather. Thus the grass performs best and flowers more freely when its habitats are opened up, as by felling or coppicing in woodland, burning of heather moor or grazing of young heather by sheep. On these occasions new plants may be established from tiny long-lived seedlings which persist for some years among the humus layers until conditions are suitable, a method of regeneration it shares with *Agrostis curtisii*, the grass which largely replaces it in heathland habitats in SW Britain. Plants also flower more freely in open habitats along the edges of paths and on south-facing slopes. The species is mostly cross-pollinating, although a few viable seed have been produced by selfed plants. Seed, averaging >100 in each panicle, are dispersed from August onwards (later in woodland) but there is no persistent seed bank. (Biol. Flora: Scurfield, 1954; CPE: 250).

Native in the British Isles, *D. flexuosa* occurs throughout Europe and is also found in northern Asia and N & S America. In the British Isles it is declining locally in the lowlands due to loss of heathland and acid grassland, but has a stable distribution in the uplands.

It is distinguished from the similar looking *D. setacea* by a combination of rather minor characters, including the scaberulous sheaths, shorter, blunter ligule, shorter internode between the florets and the minute, subequal teeth at the tip of the lemma. The only other common species is *D. cespitosa* which has broader, generally flat blades. An alpine variant (*D. flexuosa* var. *montana* (L.) G.Don ex Loud.) has a smaller contracted panicle with fewer, slightly larger spikelets but it is scarcely worth formal recognition.

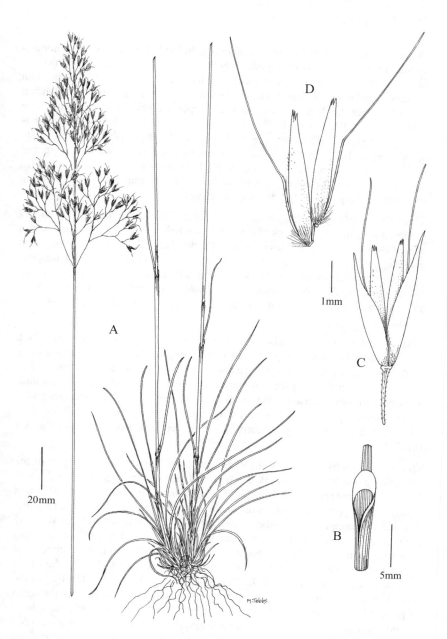

Deschampsia flexuosa: A, habit; B, ligule; C, spikelet; D, florets.

77.   **Deschampsia setacea** (Huds.) Hack.

Bog Hair-grass   New Atlas: 770

Densely tufted, up to 65(80)cm; sheaths smooth; ligule a narrow, sharply pointed membrane (2)3.5 – 8(9)mm; blades tightly inrolled, very slender and bristle-like, 0.2 – 0.4(0.6)mm across. Panicle very loose and open, 8 – 15(18)cm, with flexuous capillary branches. Spikelets 2-flowered with long rhachilla extension (1 – 1.7(2.6)mm), silvery, variegated with purple and yellow; glumes oblong or elliptic-oblong, the lower (3)3.5 – 4.5mm, the upper 3.5 – 5(5.5)mm; lemmas oblong, (2.6)2.8 – 3.4(3.6)mm, unequally 4-toothed at the tip, the outer teeth up to 0.4mm longer than the inner, awned from near the base; awn geniculate, 3 – 6mm, projecting well beyond the glumes; rhachilla internode 0.8 – 1.2(1.4)mm (1/3 – 1/2 the length of the lower lemma); anthers 3, 1 – 1.7mm. $2n = 14$. Flowering and fruiting early or mid-July to early September.

This scarce grass is now largely confined to N & NW Scotland and a few widely scattered localities southwards to Cornwall (see below). It occurs on the margins of shallow pools and loch sides in seasonally-flooded hollows in heathland and in acid bogs. It is found on open bare stony or peaty soils over a range of base-poor substrates. Associates include *Molinia caerulea* (present with most populations), *Carex panicea, Eleocharis multicaulis, Hydrocotyle vulgaris* and species of algae. It is mostly coastal and lowland but occurs to 320m at Loch Morlich (Easterness).

Little seems to be known about the population biology of *D. setacea* which occurs in small numbers at most of its sites. It appears to be very exacting in its ecological requirements, occupying a narrow niche at the margins of water bodies which are drawn down in the summer or in other areas which are wet in winter and dry in summer. It also favours open sites and ones where the water is not still. It is probably a poor competitor and thrives best where it is not overwhelmed by other species. Proliferating spikelets have been recorded from some populations (SPB: 134).

D. setacea is native, occurring in W Europe from Norway to Spain (part of the Oceanic Temperate element; P&H 1997), and also occurs in S America. In N & NW Scotland the species has been recorded in more areas since the 1962 Atlas and it may still be present in many sites on the Outer Hebrides not checked recently. Outside this core area it has been lost, through habitat destruction or possibly undergrazing of heathland, from sites in Scotland and England and appears now to be confined to five scattered areas: W Cornwall (Vc1); the Purbeck and New Forest Heaths (Vc9 & 11); the Bagshot Heaths, Surrey (Vc17); the Lleyn Peninsula, Caerns (Vc49); and the Connemara Bogs, W Galway (H16). On the other hand, it is easily overlooked, especially when not in flower and in the south of England can be passed over as *Agrostis curtisii* which is similarly tufty, fine-leaved and glaucous (but grows in drier areas). For example, it was not recorded from the Lizard Downs, a botanically well studied area, until 1982, when from nine separate pools the population was estimated at 500 plants (Hughes, 1984).

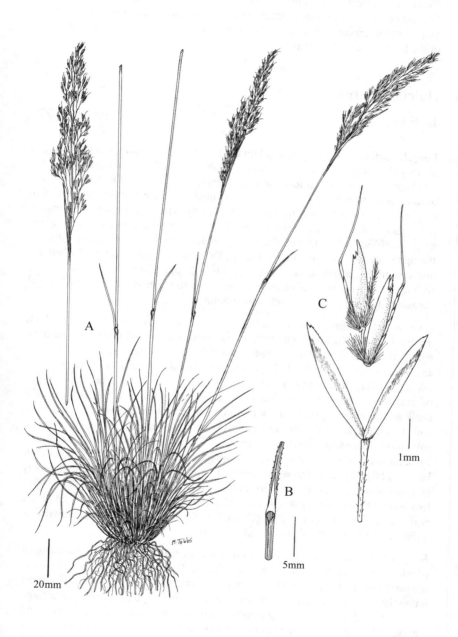

Deschampsia setacea: A, habit; B, ligule; C, spikelet with florets detached from glumes.

It is similar in many respects to *D. flexuosa*, but apart from being much less common, it differs by a combination of characters: the sheaths are smooth rather than scaberulous; the ligule is much narrower, sharply pointed and considerably longer; the internode between the florets is much longer; and the teeth at the tip of the lemma are quite different.

78. Holcus lanatus L.

Yorkshire-fog New Atlas: 770

Loosely to densely tufted perennial up to 80(120)cm, the culms and leaves green or greyish, softly hairy or rarely almost glabrous; ligule a blunt membrane 1 – 2.5(4)mm; blades flat, up to 10mm wide. Panicle dense to rather loose, oblong to lanceolate or ovate, (3)7 – 14(17)cm, whitish, pale green or tinged with pink or purple. Spikelets 4 – 5(6)mm; glumes stiffly hairy on the keel, scabrid or pubescent on the flanks; lemmas subequal, 2 – 2.6mm, firm and glossy, separated by an internode 0.5 – 0.6mm, the lower awnless (rarely awned like the upper), the upper awned from just below the tip, the awn becoming recurved when dry and resembling a fish-hook; anthers 3, 1.6 – 2.5mm. $2n = 14$. Flowering and fruiting early June to mid- or late August, sometimes as early as mid-May and occasionally persisting until well into autumn.

An extremely common and familiar grass, Yorkshire-fog is widespread throughout the British Isles. In fact it qualifies as our most widespread grass, having been recorded in the New Atlas in more than 97% of all 10Km squares in Britain and Ireland (and in 98%, 2767 of 2823, in Great Britain alone). It probably occurs in every square in which it could possibly grow. It is found in all types of grassland, especially hay meadows, pastures and rough grassland, but also chalk and limestone grassland, moorland, open woodland and scrub, hedgerows and stream sides, arable land as well as lawns, waste ground and other artificial habitats such as paths, spoil heaps and walls. The species tolerates a wide range of soils, although it is most abundant on relatively fertile soils of pH 5.0 – 6.0 which have slightly impeded drainage. There are few records from highly acidic soils or those which are either severely droughted or waterlogged. Beddows (1961) lists some of the other grasses and dicots with which it occurs most frequently. It is found from sea-level to 650m (Cross Fell, Cumberland) and exceptionally at 845m (Great Dun Fell, Westmorland).

H. lanatus has many of the attributes of a successful weedy species, not the least of which is its prolific seed output, despite the fact that caryopsis production is frequently limited to the lower floret in each spikelet. Seed may germinate almost immediately and buried seed remain viable for many years, producing a large persistent seed bank. The species readily colonizes bare soil and disturbed ground and can persist in a wide range of both managed and unmanaged environments. It tolerates both grazing and mowing, although it has little value as an agricultural

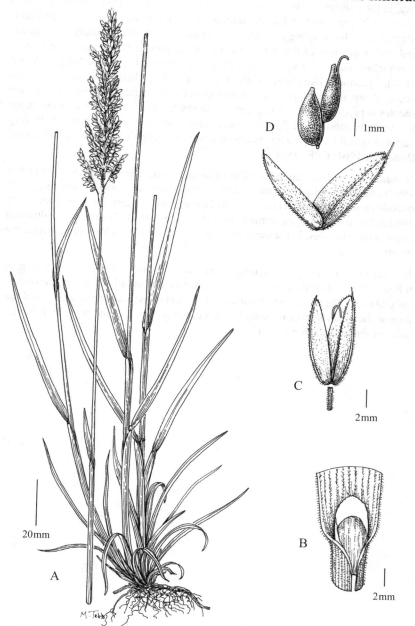

Holcus lanatus: A, habit; B, ligule; C, intact spikelet;
D, spikelet with florets detached from glumes.

grass except in poor soils or swards where the other species are less palatable (e.g. in the Falkland Islands) and is an unwelcome constituent of well-kept lawns and amenity grassland. It does not tolerate heavy trampling. In optimal conditions plants form a loose spongy carpet of stems and shoots, often rooting at the nodes and with a network of fine white roots over the ground surface (surface rooting may make it vulnerable to drought). They may commonly produce 'mops' (Arber, 1934), a pompom-like cluster of shoots, at the end of a long stem bearing several nodes. Plants in British populations flower in the year after establishment and the species is predominantly outcrossing (anthesis has been observed to occur twice a day; early morning at 5.00 a.m. and early afternoon at 1.00 p.m.). It is very variable in habit and contains morphological and edaphic ecotypes. (Biol. Flora: Beddows, 1961; CPE: 352).

H. lanatus is native, a member of the European Southern-temperate flora (P&H 1997) and has been widely naturalized in the temperate zones around the globe outside its native range. Its range in the British Isles appears unchanged since the 1962 Atlas. It was also a common wool alien here (AGB: 34) and was cultivated and threshed for seed in the early 18th Century, especially in Yorkshire, hence the common name.

H. lanatus can readily be distinguished from *H. mollis* in several ways: it is tufted without rhizomes; the culms and leaves are usually softly hairy (rarely subglabrous); the nodes, while pubescent, are not conspicuously bearded; and the awn of the upper lemma is strongly curved, not geniculate, and projects from the sides of the glumes, not from the tips.

79. Holcus mollis L.

Illustration, page 295

Creeping Soft-grass

New Atlas: 771

Loosely tufted or mat-forming rhizomatous perennial up to 110cm, the culms bearded at the nodes, otherwise glabrous; ligule a blunt membrane 1 – 4.5mm; blades flat, up to 12mm wide, green or greyish green, glabrous or pubescent. Panicle dense or rather loose, narrowly oblong to ovate, (4)5.5 – 12(13.5, rarely even to 22)cm, whitish, greyish or tinged with purple. Spikelets (3.5)5 – 7mm; glumes stiffly hairy on the keel, scaberulous or pubescent on the flanks; lemmas subequal, (2.2)2.5 – 3mm, firm and glossy, separated by an internode 0.6 – 0.7mm, the lower awnless, the upper awned from below the tip, the awn geniculate, (3)3.5 – 5(5.5)mm; anthers 3, 1.6 – 2.7mm. $2n = 28, 35, 49$. Flowering and fruiting late June to late August.

H. mollis is widespread in the British Isles, although scattered or absent in central and western Ireland and in an area of eastern England centred around Cambridgeshire. It is predominantly a grass of woodlands on acidic or neutral soils, especially oak and birch woods but also mixed deciduous woodland including sycamore and ash and the open rides in conifer woods. It also occurs in hedgerows, scrubland and heathland where it favours areas shaded by gorse or bracken. It is a less frequent component of open acid grassland and grass verges, the banks of drainage ditches, reclaimed coastal grassland, stable scree, sands and quarry waste and sandy arable land where it is said to be sometimes a troublesome weed. It is found on a range of moist but usually well-drained, light friable loams, sands and sandy clays and is essentially a calcifuge becoming scarce in soils above a pH of 5.0. Its associates include a wide range of woodland and acid grassland species (including the grasses *Deschampsia flexuosa, Agrostis capillaris* and *Anthoxanthum odoratum*). It occurs from sea-level to 580m on Greygarth Fell, W Lancs.

The ecology of *H. mollis* contrasts very markedly with that of *H. lanatus*. Apart from its tolerance of shade and restriction to acid soils, *H. mollis* appears to regenerate mainly vegetatively, individuals expanding by means of extensive spreading rhizomes. Some populations may comprise a fairly small number of large, ancient clones, like those studied by Harberd (1967) which, using a combination of cytological and morphological evidence, he concluded may have contained at least one clone as large as 1km in diameter. Again in contrast to *H. lanatus*, many populations either flower very sparingly (especially in shade) or appear to produce little viable seed (germination was less than 5% in one experiment). This may be related to an effective self-incompatibility system and the presence of large clones in which most adjacent flower heads will be from the same individual. However, the species is made up of a polyploid series, the chromosome races of which cannot be separated on morphological criteria and there are also individuals derived from hybridization with *H. lanatus* (e.g. the common $2n = 35$ genotype could be a cross between a 28 chromosome *H. mollis* and an unreduced gamete of a 21 chromosome race originally derived from a hybrid between a 28 chromosome *H. mollis* and the 14 chromosome *H. lanatus* (Jones, 1958)). Many of these cytotypes may be sterile. Some populations do produce seed annually, which is shed in September and probably germinates in the spring, and self-fertile plants occur. In disturbed areas such as tree nurseries or arable land, plants can regenerate from rhizome and shoot fragments and there is often a rapid expansion and flowering of populations when woodland is felled or coppiced. Although frequent in grassland, *H. mollis* is not tolerant of persistent grazing. It is a fairly polymorphic species, displaying variation in leaf colour and hairiness. (Biol. Flora: Ovington & Scurfield, 1956; CPE: 354).

H. mollis is a native species in temperate Europe and in Africa. It has been introduced in N America and Australia (possibly as a wool alien). Its range in the British Isles appears unchanged since the 1962 Atlas.

A plant of quite different appearance to *H. lanatus*, often being less pubescent with brighter green culms and leaves, and with a conspicuously contrasting white beard at the nodes, hence the schoolboy mnemonic to distinguish it from Yorkshire-fog "Molly has hairy knees". The creeping habit, forming mats rather than dense tufts, is also diagnostic. The two species occasionally hybridize and the hybrid (**H. ×hybridus** Wein) is sterile. It resembles *H. mollis* more than it does *H. lanatus* but has blunter glumes, a shorter, less exserted awn and more pubescent culms. It is scattered over much of Britain and Ireland but is easily overlooked.

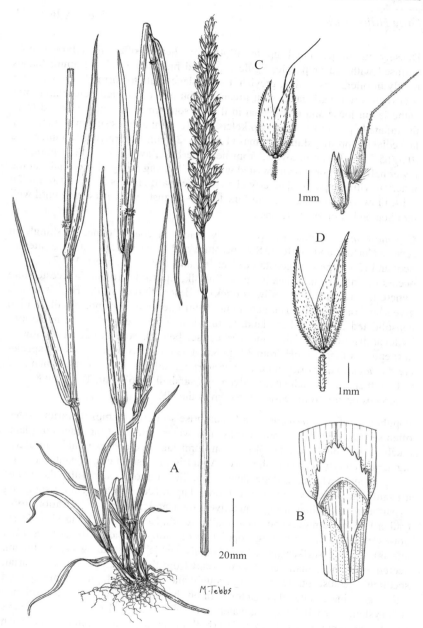

Holcus mollis: A, habit; B, ligule; C, intact spikelet;
D, spikelet with florets detached from glumes.

80.   Corynephorus canescens (L.) P.Beauv.

Grey Hair-grass   New Atlas: 771

Densely tufted perennial up to 30(45)cm; sheaths often tinged or deeply
suffused with red or purple; ligule a pointed membrane 1.5 – 3.5mm; blades
tightly inrolled, bristle-like, greyish. Panicle lanceolate to narrowly oblong, (2)3
– 6(8)cm, often variegated with green and purple, contracted before and after
anthesis but loose and open when in flower, sometimes not fully exserted from
the inflated uppermost sheath. Spikelets 3 – 4(5)mm; glumes subequal, narrowly
lanceolate in profile, shiny; lemmas (1.6)1.8 – 2.2mm, separated by an internode
(0.3)0.5 – 0.6(0.8)mm, awned from near the base; awn 2.5 – 2.8(3.1)mm, the
lower half orange or brown, twisted when dry, bearing a ring of short hairs at the
junction with the pallid slenderly clavate upper half; anthers 3, 1.2 – 1.6mm. $2n$
= 14. Flowering and fruiting late June to mid-August, rarely persisting until well
into September or even October.

C. canescens is a grass of open sandy places in coastal dunes or shingle in
Jersey, Norfolk and Suffolk, S Lancashire and three widely scattered sites in
Scotland (2 on the east coast, Vc82 & 95, and one on the west, Vc97). It also
occurs on inland sandy heaths in W Suffolk, Staffordshire and Worcestershire
(where it extends along a railway track). A description of all the British sites is
given by Trist (1998b). Habitats range from open mobile sand, usually within
consolidated dunes, or heathland, to firm sandy shingle, and are characterized
by local disturbance of the sand surface (see below). Soils are generally low in
nutrients but range in pH from 3.7 to 8.5. The most frequent associated species
are *Ammophila arenaria* and *Carex arenaria*; a full list of associates, which tend
to be rather few at each site, is given by Marshall (1967) and Trist (1998b). *C.
canescens* occurs from sea-level to 60m in the UK.

Populations of *C. canescens* usually comprise scattered clumps of various sizes,
often separated by open sand, and the few which consist of thousands of plants
(such as at Winterton, Norfolk) are an unmistakeable and extremely attractive
sight, particularly when in full flower. An intriguing aspect of the plant's ecology
is the extent to which it is dependent on mobile sand for its survival. Adult plants
are said to grow best where sand accretion of up to 10cm a year occurs, responding
to partial burial by increasing vegetative growth and producing adventitious roots
(rather like marram grass but on a smaller scale). However, such burial is clearly
not essential (as a flourishing population on shingly sand at Benacre, Suffolk
attests) and the surface must be relatively stable for seedling establishment,
accreting no more than 2cm a year. Apart from the danger of complete burial,
seedlings are susceptible to spring drought and those developing from any seed
which germinates later than October rarely have a sufficiently well-developed
root system to reach the spring water table. Mobile sand also prevents or delays
succession to more closed vegetation (both in coastal dune and inland sites such
as Kinver Edge (Blunt & Blunt, 2000) in which the grass eventually becomes
moribund and dies). It seems therefore that disturbance of the surface is a key

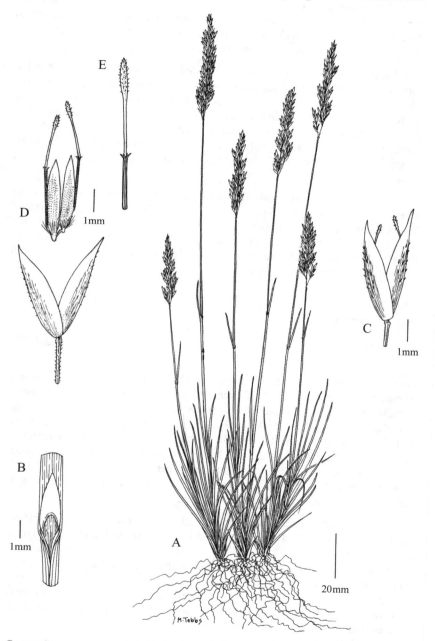

Corynephorus canescens: A, habit; B, ligule; C, intact spikelet;
D, spikelet with florets detached from glumes; E, awn.

factor in the species' survival. New plants are established from seed shed from early August onwards, individuals first flowering in their second year and living for at least 6 years in favourable conditions. Seeds remain viable for more than 5 years. The species is probably self-compatible. (Biol. Flora: Marshall, 1967; RDP: 104 & SPB: 122 (same account)).

The Jersey and East Anglian plants are regarded as native by most authorities but there is disagreement about the status of other UK populations (see New Atlas, above references, and AGB: 35). Classified as **near threatened** (Cheffings & Farrell, 2005), measures are in place to protect the species at most sites, including disturbing the sand surface. *C. canescens* occurs from the southern Baltic to Portugal and Spain, in northern Italy and central Ukraine (European Southern-temperate element; P&H 1997). It occurs in N Africa and as an introduction in N America.

The awn structure in *Corynephorus* (the generic name being derived from the Greek word for 'club') is unique in grasses, but its function remains a mystery. The brightly coloured lower half fits into a groove along the back of the lemma, the ring of hairs and the club-shaped terminal part protruding. The closest relatives of the genus are *Aira*, which is annual, and *Deschampsia*, which is perennial; both have an awn of conventional structure.

81. Aira praecox L.

Early Hair-grass   New Atlas: 772

Delicate annual up to 25cm; sheaths smooth or faintly scaberulous; ligule a bluntly pointed membrane 1.5 – 3.5mm; blades inrolled, smooth or scaberulous. Panicle contracted and spike-like, narrowly oblong, (0.5)1.5 – 3(4.5)cm, the branches erect, very short. Spikelets 3 – 3.5mm; glumes persistent, as long as the spikelet, obliquely lanceolate in profile, scabrid on the keels; lemmas narrowly lanceolate, firm at maturity, 2.7 – 3.1mm, 2-toothed at the tip, scabrid above, awned from the back in the lower third; awn geniculate, twisted below, 3.4 – 4.3mm; anthers 3, 0.25 – 0.3mm. $2n = 14$. Flowering and fruiting mid-May to early July, occasionally lasting to the end of July.

A. praecox is widely distributed in the British Isles, being common everywhere but the southeast midlands in England and in central Ireland. It is found in open dry places, most frequently on acidic sandy or rocky soils in lowland heath, dry fields and commons, sand-dunes, cliff-tops, walls, quarries, paths and in eroded and bare soils in the uplands. It often occurs in very thin soils at the edges of rock outcops or in the angle between walls and pavements. *A. praecox* occurs mostly on bare soils (in the range pH 3.5 – 6.0) but may have a range of associates in different habitats, often other winter annuals and mosses. It is most common in the lowlands but reaches 685m in S Kerry.

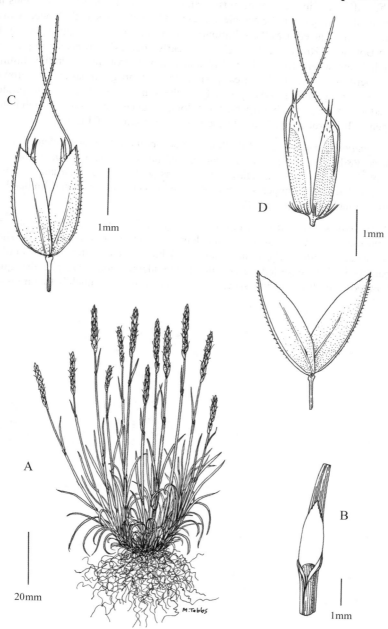

Aira praecox: A, habit; B, ligule; C, intact spikelet;
D, spikelet with florets detached from glumes.

This often very tiny winter annual grass can easily be overlooked, especially where it occurs in a carpet of mosses and lichens, and is most conspicuous just before flowering when the panicle is enclosed by a silvery sheath. Indeed, Graves (1822) pronounced it as "too diminutive to be an object of attention to any but the Botanist". However, *A. praecox* is clearly successful in occupying a range of habitats where low soil fertility and summer drought generally eliminate competitors. It avoids the driest periods by autumn germination and growing and flowering during early spring. Even the smallest plants appear to produce seed which are probably dispersed over long distances, including through human agency. It is probably self-fertile and largely inbreeding. (CPE: 94).

A. praecox is native, part of the Suboceanic Southern-temperate element of our flora (P&H 1997) and is widely naturalized outside its native range (including N & S America and Australia). It was occasionally found in Britain as a wool casual. The species appears to have declined in central Ireland and England, but not as much as *A. caryophyllea*.

A. praecox is distinguished from *A. caryophyllea* by the combination of compact inflorescence, smaller spikelets and lemmas, and smooth sheaths. The sheath character, unfortunately, is not wholly reliable, so it is better to wait until the panicle is fully exserted before attempting identification. Despite the epithet (*praecox* = early), very few specimens are seen flowering much before mid-May.

82. Aira caryophyllea L.

Illustration, page 303

Silver Hair-grass

New Atlas: 771

Delicate annual up to 35(55)cm; sheaths faintly scaberulous to scabrid; ligule a bluntly pointed membrane 2 – 5mm; blades inrolled, faintly scaberulous. Panicle loose and open, ovate to broadly ovate, (2)3.5 – 10(14)cm, the branches widely spreading and bare of spikelets below; pedicels not more than twice as long as the spikelets. Spikelets 2.4 – 3.1mm; glumes persistent, as long as the spikelet, obliquely lanceolate in profile, faintly scabrid on the keels; lemmas narrowly lanceolate, firm at maturity, (1.8)2 – 2.4(2.6)mm, minutely 2-toothed at the tip, scabrid above, awned from the back in the lower third; awn geniculate, twisted below, 2.6 – 3.6mm; anthers 3, 0.25 – 0.6mm. $2n = ?14, 28$. Flowering and fruiting mid-May to mid-August, but mainly June and July.

A. caryophyllea is distributed throughout the British Isles, but is scattered or absent from parts of SE England, the north of England, the central Highlands of Scotland and central Ireland. Elsewhere it occurs in a range of generally dry sandy, gravelly or rocky habitats including dry grassland, heaths, consolidated sand-dunes, cliff-tops, walls and railway ballast. It can also be found in open woodland on sandy soils, and in waste places formerly as a wool casual. *A. caryophyllea* occurs on a range of soils and in several types of plant community, often containing other winter annuals including *A. praecox*. It is found from sea-level to 560m (Mourne Mts, Co Down).

This species has a similar life history to *A. praecox*, being a winter annual germinating in the autumn and flowering and setting seed in the spring and early summer. It often occurs in similar situations to *A. praecox* but is more frequently found in short turf and over a wider range of soil types. When found at the same site, *A. caryophyllea* tends to be taller and to flower 3 to 4 weeks later than *A. praecox*. In closed grassland *A. caryophyllea* can be found in temporarily disturbed or open sites such as anthills. It is thought to be largely inbreeding and isolated plants in cultivation set viable seed.

A. caryophyllea is native, a member of the European Southern-temperate flora, and is widely introduced and established outside its native range (e.g. N & S America). It appears to have declined throughout its British and Irish range, particularly in SE England and the New Atlas notes that most losses have occurred since 1950. In speculating why this may have happened, it is interesting to note that both *Aira* species are short, have low nutrient requirements and grow in open dry habitats, a suite of characteristics shared by other plants which have suffered a relative decline in the British Isles in the latter part of the 20th Century.

Some accounts have divided the species into two subspecies. Subsp. *caryophyllea* is said to be 5 – 25cm in height with spikelets 2.5 – 3mm; subsp. *multiculmis* (Dumort.) Bonnier & Layens, is 20 – 50cm in height with spikelets 2 – 2.5mm. Both are supposed to occur in the British Isles, but the characters separating them are not at all convincing and seldom correlated in the manner described (differences in anther and caryopsis size overlap so much as to be worthless). It is doubtful whether subsp. *multiculmis* occurs in the British Isles and it is equally doubtful that it is worth attempting to recognize it in Europe; indeed, the tendency now is to abandon it. Subsp. *armoricana* (F. Albers) Kerguélen was distinguished as a separate taxon on account of its spikelets being over 3mm and its caryopsis being larger than in either of the other subspecies, but these characters are no more convincing than any others and none of the subspecies seems to be worth maintaining.

83. Aira elegantissima Schur

A European species occasionally introduced as a birdseed alien. It closely resembles *A. caryophyllea* but has a more diffuse panicle with pedicels 2 – 5 times as long as the spikelets, and the spikelets themselves are marginally smaller (1.5 – 2.5mm).

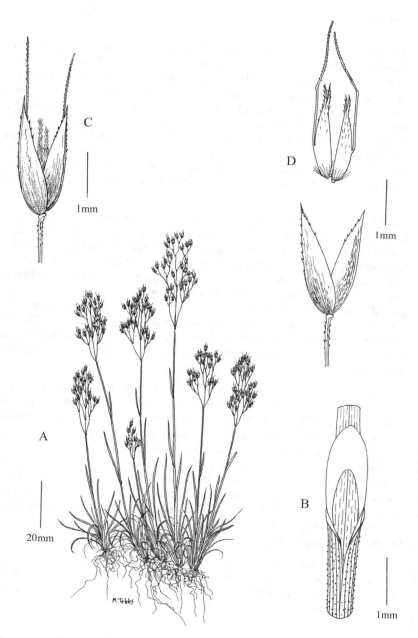

Aira caryophyllea: A, habit; B, ligule; C, intact spikelet;
D, spikelet with florets detached from glumes.

84.   Anthoxanthum aristatum Boiss.

Annual Vernal-grass   New Atlas: 773

Glabrous or sparsely hairy annual up to 40cm, often freely branched above; ligule a pointed membrane 1.5 – 3mm; blades flat, up to 5mm wide. Panicle moderately dense, spike-like, ovate or oblong, (1)2 – 4cm, often lobed or interrupted especially below. Spikelets 5 – 7.5(8)mm; lower glume ovate, 3.6 – 5.2mm, finely pointed; upper glume ovate or elliptic, as long as the spikelet, finely pointed; sterile lemmas ± equal, narrowly oblong, 2.8 – 3.9mm, hairy, the lower with a ± straight awn from the back, projecting 2.3 – 3.6(4.4)mm beyond the tip, the upper with a geniculate awn from near the base, projecting 4.8 – 7mm; fertile lemma rotund, (1.4)1.6 – 2.1mm, smooth and glossy; anthers 2, 2.8 – 4.1mm. $2n = 10$. Flowering and fruiting late May to mid-August, sometimes persisting until mid-October.

Annual Vernal-grass is a very rare casual which has been found mainly in England and once or twice in Wales and Scotland. It is absent from Ireland. It was at one time a weed of cereal crops on light soils in East Anglia and SE England but disappeared from this habitat more than 30 years ago. The scattered sites from which it has been recorded in the past are often described as having 'sandy' substrates – 'sandy fallow', 'in arable field on sandy soil', 'sandy waste ground', 'old nursery site on sandy soil', 'sandy path' etc. – and it has been found in roadside refuse tips, docks and the waste tip of a wallpaper factory. The last remaining population in an arable field, on the coast of E Suffolk, with abundant plants in the early 1960s, had disappeared by 1971 (apparently aided by cliff falls due to coastal erosion!).

A. aristatum is classified as a neophyte in the British flora, having been first recorded in the wild in 1872. It is thought to have been introduced with seed of fodder plants from France and briefly flourished as a persistent annual weed in the early part of the 20th Century. Its decline, along with several other arable weeds in England, has been fairly spectacular. In the New Atlas it has a relative decrease exceeded by only four other grasses, *Lolium temulentum, Bromus lepidus, B. arvensis* and *Avena strigosa*, all of which are also introduced in the British Isles, annual, and weeds or contaminants of cultivation. The decline of these species has undoubtedly been aided by agricultural intensification, the use of herbicides and improvement in seed-cleaning techniques. *A. aristatum* is a native of SW Europe and is widespread as a casual further north.

A. aristatum is almost identical to *A. odoratum*, differing by its smaller, annual habit and significantly longer awns; the tendency towards occasional branching of the culms is also a feature. The species itself is a complex of which our plant is subsp. **puelii** (Lecoq & Lamotte) P.Silva.

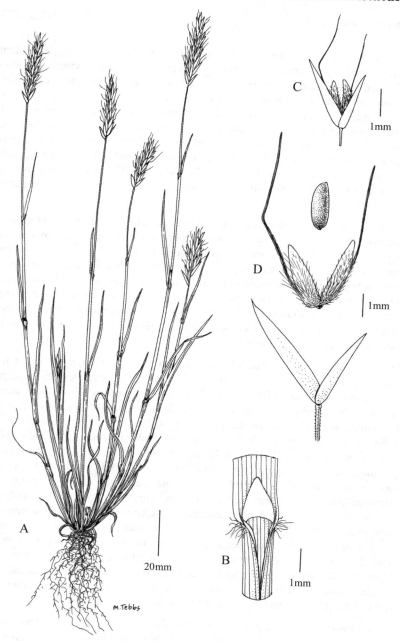

Anthoxanthum aristatum subsp. *puelii*: A, habit; B, ligule; C, intact spikelet;
D, spikelet with glumes, lower florets and fertile floret detached.

85. Anthoxanthum odoratum L.

Sweet Vernal-grass   New Atlas: 772

Glabrous or loosely hairy tufted perennial up to 75(100)cm; ligule a blunt
membrane 1 – 5.5(7)mm; blades flat, up to 9mm wide. Panicle contracted, spike-
like, narrowly ovate to oblong, (1)2 – 9(12)cm, often interrupted, especially
below. Spikelets 7 – 9.5mm; lower glume ovate, 3.7 – 5.2mm, acute; upper
glume ovate to elliptic, as long as the spikelet, acute; sterile lemmas ± equal,
narrowly oblong, 2.8 – 3.6mm, hairy, the lower with a straight awn from the back,
projecting 1.2 – 2.6mm beyond the tip, the upper with a geniculate awn from near
the base, projecting 4 – 5.5(7)mm; fertile lemma rotund, 1.7 – 2.4mm, smooth
and glossy; anthers 2, (2.9)3.5 – 4.8(5.5)mm. $2n = 20$. Flowering and fruiting
early May to late August, sometimes as early as April and rarely persisting until
early October.

A. odoratum is found throughout the British Isles in a huge variety of mainly
grassland habitats and is often abundant in hill pastures, heaths and moors, old
pasture and meadows and waste grassy places. It also occurs in woodland and
scrub, in sand-dunes, on marshy ground, riverbanks, stabilized scree, road verges
and waste tips (including those from metal mining). It appears to tolerate a very
wide range of soil types but is most frequent on damp soils of low to moderate
fertility within a pH range of 4.5 – 6.0. It is found growing with a large number
of associated species across its broad habitat range and occurs from sea-level to
more than 1000m (in the Cairngorms).

One of the earliest flowering of our common grasses, the appearance of the
familiar yellowish-green inflorescences of Sweet Vernal-grass heralds for many
the beginning of summer (and for some the hay-fever season!). Individual plants
are short-lived and polycarpic. They have distinct spurts of vegetative growth
in spring and autumn and remain green over winter. Population regeneration is
mainly by seed which are shed from June onwards and form a persistent seed
bank. *A. odoratum* is self-incompatible and strongly outbreeding. It is also a very
polymorphic grass, varying in growth habit, size, leafiness, hairiness and other
morphological and physiological traits. In fact the key to its broad ecological
tolerance (Arber (1934) described the grass as 'remarkably catholic in its tastes')
may lie in the ability to evolve ecotypes by selection from a diverse genetic
background. Snaydon & Davies (1976) demonstrated remarkable rapid and
small-scale genetic differentiation in populations from adjacent plots of the Park
Grass Experiment at Rothamsted in response to different fertilizers and liming
treatments. Populations of the species growing on zinc and lead contaminated
soils have been the subject of classic studies in gene flow and the evolution of
heavy metal tolerance and reproductive isolation. (CPE: 116).

A. odoratum is native in the British Isles and throughout the European and Asian
temperate zones. It is widely naturalized elsewhere, including N America. It was
formerly included in grass mixtures for hay and pasture because of its fragrance

Anthoxanthum odoratum: A, habit; B, ligule; C, intact spikelet;
D, spikelet with glumes, lower florets and fertile floret detached.

and early 'bite' but is not particularly productive or palatable, tending to be 'stemmy' and patchy, and is no longer sown except in wild flower conservation mixtures. It is almost certainly under-recorded as an alien (AGB: 36).

The tissues of Sweet Vernal-grass contain coumarin, a substance that imparts the smell of 'new-mown hay' to freshly cut grass. The flowers are strongly protogynous and the long white thread-like stigmas protruding from the spikelet tips are very much a feature of the plant in the early part of the season.

86. Anthoxanthum nitens (Weber) Y.Schouten & Veldk.

Holy-grass

Illustration, page 311

New Atlas: 772 (as *Hierochloe odorata*)

Glabrous or loosely hairy tufted plant up to 40(55)cm, with slender creeping rhizomes; ligule a blunt membrane 1.5 – 5(6.5)mm; blades flat, up to 10mm wide, the lower linear, the upper much shorter and often ± triangular. Panicle loose and open, ovate, 4 – 11cm, the branches spreading and naked below. Spikelets plump, 4 – 6mm; glumes subequal (the upper slightly the longer), broadly ovate, almost as long as the spikelet, blunt; male lemmas subequal (the upper slightly the longer), broadly and bluntly elliptic, minutely hairy on the back, shortly ciliate on the margins, with 3 anthers 2 – 3mm; fertile lemma ovate, a little shorter than the males, smooth and glossy, shortly hairy near the tip, with 2 anthers 1 – 2mm. $2n = 28, 42$. Flowering and fruiting late March to late May, sporadically in mid- to late August.

A. nitens is a rare grass of wetland habitats limited to a few sites in Scotland (mainly in the south but also at isolated locations northwards to Benbecula and the Orkney Islands), Lough Neagh in N Ireland and a recently discovered site in Northumberland. Apart from being wetlands, these sites are curiously disjunct and remarkably different. They include base-rich fen, raised bog, maritime grassland adjacent to saltmarsh, lakeside willow carr and sedge communities, riverbanks and the base of coastal cliffs in mires and thin peaty saltmarsh over shingle and boulders. They have in common a generally base-rich environment and a high water table, especially in winter. At some sites the plant may be fully submerged for much of the winter. The long list of species found with Holy-grass ranges from *Deschampsia cespitosa*, *Festuca rubra* and *Juncus maritimus* through *Filipendula ulmaria*, *Phalaris arundinacea* and *Phragmites australis* to *Molinia caerulea*, *Myrica gale* and *Schoenus nigricans*. In SW Scotland the sites are all coastal and are at or just above the level of the highest tides, but inland in Selkirks the species reaches 300m.

The British populations of Holy-grass vary considerably in size but all appear to be maintained vegetatively, spreading by means of long whitish rhizomes (most sites have been mapped and seem to be well established). Flowering is somewhat sporadic, may not occur every year and in some populations varies from year to year depending on the lowering of winter water levels. When not in flower the characteristic bright green leaves help to locate the grass which could otherwise be overlooked, but the flowering parts are very distinctive, almost *Briza*-like, pyramidal panicles of glistening spikelets. Seed set is very low (around 2% in samples from 6 populations), and a study by Ferris *et al.*, (1992), indicates that this is due to low pollen fertility and possibly low clonal diversity (a limited number of compatible genotypes in each population). Despite this Ferris *et al.*, (1992) suggest that most British populations reproduce sexually, with a number of populations containing several genetically different individuals. However, at least one population displays irregular patterns of chromosome and cell division during development of the pollen grains, a process which could presage apomixis (RDB: 191) as found in the octoploid races from Sweden and N America.

Holy-grass is native and has a Circumpolar Boreal-montane distribution, extending in continental Europe southwards to the Alps and the Black Sea. The scattered British populations are regarded as rare outliers and the first was only discovered in 1812 (by George Don of 'Don's Twitch' fame). It is interesting to speculate whether they are relics of a once more widespread distribution and are rare because they have exacting ecological requirements, (or indeed whether others remain to be discovered) and whether some are introductions (albeit ancient ones). Intriguingly, the Orkney populations occur exclusively near to the sites of Norse churches; the grass was named 'Holy Grass' or 'Mary's Grass' because it was dedicated to the Virgin Mary. In Prussia it was spread in and around churches for religious festivals and in Sweden was hung over beds to induce blessed sleep. These practices were probably stimulated by the aromatic nature of the coumarin-containing plant, a property which has also led to its sometime inclusion in eastern Europe in bottles of strong alcoholic drink!

Formerly known as *Hierochloe odorata* (L.) P.Beauv., but unfortunately the genus *Hierochloe* cannot be sustained and the epithet *odorata* has already been claimed for *Anthoxanthum*. The species is represented in our area by subsp. **nitens** (see Weimarck, 1971). This is usually tetraploid, but occasionally hexaploid, and mostly amphimictic. Its European counterpart, subsp. **baltica** (G.Weim.) G.C.Tucker, is an apomictic hexaploid. Sporadic late flowering, in this otherwise early flowering species, has been noted particularly in cultivated material.

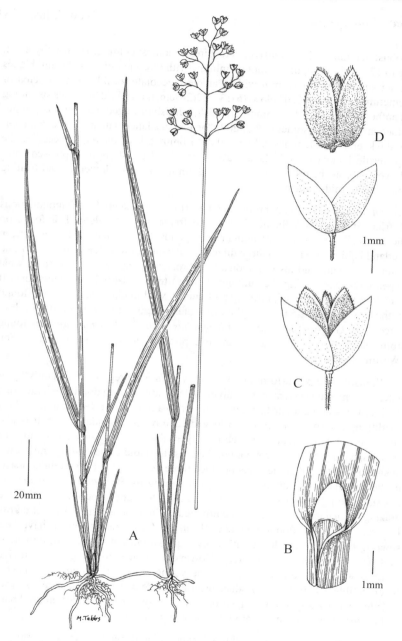

Anthoxanthum nitens: A, habit; B, ligule; C, intact spikelet;
D, spikelet with florets detached from glumes.

87.   Phalaris arundinacea L.

Reed Canary-grass   New Atlas: 773

Robust perennial with extensively creeping rhizomes; culms stout, usually erect, up to 175(225)cm; ligule a blunt membrane with erose margin, 3 – 11mm; blades broad and flat, up to 18 mm wide. Panicle lanceolate to oblong, contracted or sometimes loose or lobed below, (5)13 – 22(28)cm, the scabrid branches spreading at anthesis. Spikelets 4 – 5.5mm, greenish, whitish or tinged with purple; glumes subequal (the upper sometimes slightly the longer), lanceolate in profile, wingless on the keel; sterile lemmas 2, linear, 0.8 – 1.6mm, pilose, the hairs exceeding the tip; fertile lemma broadly lanceolate in profile, 3.1 – 4.3mm, appressed-hairy above, glabrous below; anthers 3, 2.2 – 3.4mm. $2n = 28$. Flowering and fruiting mid-June to mid-August.

P. arundinacea is common throughout the British Isles except for the mountainous districts of NC & NW Scotland and the extreme west of Ireland. It is found on the edges of water bodies including rivers, ponds, lakes, canals and reservoirs, in wetland habitats such as shallow ditches, water-meadows, alder/willow carr and damp woodland, and also periodically on roadsides and waste ground in what appears (at least during the summer months) to be relatively dry situations. It occurs in a range of soils, thriving particularly well in clays, and is rarely found in those with a pH <5.0. As a plant of water margins it usually occurs in drier places than *Glyceria maxima* and *Phragmites australis*. *P. arundinacea* is found from sea-level to 475m (Cards.) and exceptionally to 845m on Great Dun Fell (Westmorland).

A tall, distinctive patch-forming grass, *P. arundinacea* regenerates mainly by its extensive rhizome system, and in favourable conditions can dominate large areas of riverbanks and similar habitats to the exclusion of other vegetation. In these conditions it forms a dense broad-leaved canopy and abundant litter. It is also very deep rooted, a feature which clearly enables it to occupy apparently dry areas especially on open ground, but the grass also tolerates flooding and growth in shallow water when the roots produce more aerenchyma (intercellular spaces in the root tissue). It appears to be outcompeted by *Phragmites australis*, but tolerates the lighter shade of willow carr. Also tolerant of periodic cutting and grazing, *P. arundinacea* has been cultivated in the past as a hay or pasture grass for areas subject to flooding (especially in the USA) and is said to have been sown in marshland to 'dry it out', converting swampy waste to fertile meadow in 4 or 5 years (Gordon, undated). However, it is heavily suppressed on river margins where cattle have access to the young leaves. *P. arundinacea* is self-incompatible but appears to produce prolific numbers of seed which are dispersed over the water and germinate in spring. There is probably a persistent seed bank and dispersal by water may help found new populations. (CPE: 460).

Reed Canary-grass is native, with a Circumpolar Boreo-temperate distribution (P&H 1997) and is widely naturalized outside its native range.

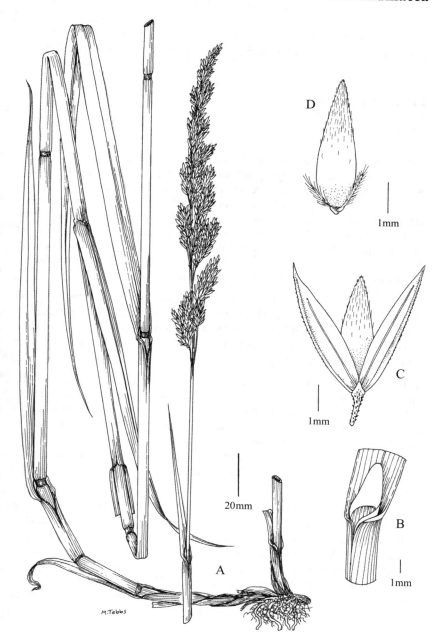

Phalaris arundinacea: A, habit; B, ligule; C, spikelet; D, florets.

This is the only native perennial species of *Phalaris* in the British Isles, and indeed the only native species of the genus. A variety with leaves striped green and cream (*P. arundinacea* var. *picta* L.) is often grown in gardens under the name 'Gardener's Garters' or 'Ribbon Grass'. It sometimes escapes, or is thrown out because of its invasive tendencies, but is otherwise unknown as a wild plant.

88. Phalaris aquatica L.

Bulbous Canary-grass   New Atlas: 773

Tufted, shortly rhizomatous perennial up to 150cm; culms often bulbous at the base; uppermost sheaths slightly inflated; ligule a blunt membrane 3 – 10mm. Panicle cylindrical and spike-like, occasionally lobed at the base, 1.5 – 11cm. Spikelets 4.4 – 7.5mm, whitish except for the green nerves; glumes equal, oblong-elliptic in profile, broadly winged on the keel, the wing entire; sterile lemma solitary, subulate 0.2 – 2.2mm, pubescent (sometimes with a short second floret up to 0.5mm); fertile lemma broadly lanceolate in profile, 3.1 – 4.6mm, densely pubescent; anthers 3, 3 – 4.3mm. $2n = 28$. Flowering and fruiting mid-July to mid-October, sometimes beginning as early as mid-June.

P. aquatica occurs in the Channel Islands and southern and eastern England mostly below a line from the Humber to the Severn Estuary. It is occasionally established and persistent in fields and field margins, open woodland, roadsides and rough ground, and occurs on tips and waste places as a casual introduced with grain, grass, clover seed or esparto.

With much shorter rhizomes than *P. arundinacea, P. aquatica* forms smaller clumps of tall dense grass often with grey to bluish green leaves. It is said to be slow-growing from seed but has become an invasive plant in Mediterranean-type climates, such as in California where it is known as Harding grass. Like *P. arundinacea*, it is deep rooted and can tolerate both wetland and dry conditions. It also produces copious seed and establishes a persistent seed bank. Little seems to be known about its ecology in Britain but it appears to be increasing in some areas, notably in East Anglia and SE England.

A neophyte, *P. aquatica* was first cultivated in Britain in 1778 and recorded in the wild by 1912. It was sown both for cover and food for game birds and also, at least experimentally, for grazing or forage. A native of the Mediterranean region and SW Asia, the species has been widely dispersed around the world as a forage crop because of its tolerance of a wide range of conditions, particularly drought (although it can be a cause of 'staggers' in sheep). It has been extensively cultivated, and improved, in Australia (as *P. tuberosa*), N America and South Africa. It is probably under-recorded in Britain.

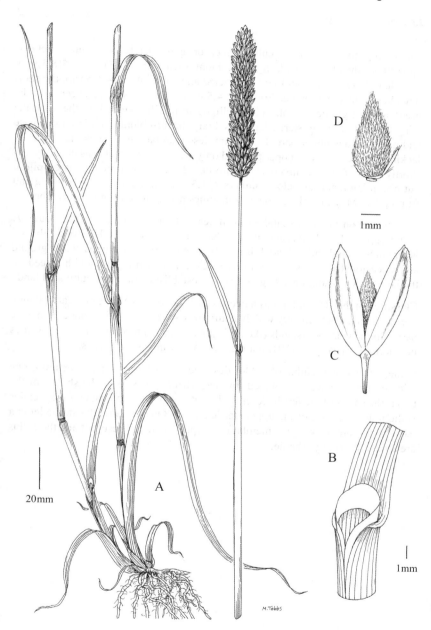

Phalaris aquatica: A, habit; B, ligule; C, spikelet; D, florets.

89. **Phalaris minor** Retz.

Lesser Canary-grass New Atlas: 774

Annual up to 70(100)cm; culms erect or geniculately ascending, slender; uppermost sheaths inflated; ligule a blunt membrane (1.5)3 – 6.5(8.5)mm. Panicle oblong or ovate-oblong, contracted and spike-like, 1 – 6(8)cm, the short branches tightly appressed. Spikelets 4.5 – 6(6.5)mm, whitish except for the green nerves; glumes equal, oblong-elliptic in profile, winged on the keel, the wing toothed or erose; sterile lemma solitary, linear-oblong with indurated base and membranous upper part, 1 – 1.4mm, less than half as long as the fertile, or lacking the membranous upper part and only 0.2 – 0.3mm, glabrous or thinly and shortly hairy; fertile lemma ovate in profile, (2.6)2.8 – 3.4mm, appressed-pilose but becoming glabrous below; anthers 3, 1.3 – 2.1mm. $2n = 28$. Flowering and fruiting late May to early October, sometimes persisting until mid-November.

An uncommon grass of scattered localities in England, mainly in the south, *P. minor* appears locally frequent in the Channel Islands and the Isles of Scilly and is rare in Scotland and Ireland. It is mostly found on rubbish dumps, waste ground and, occasionally, docks where it originates from esparto, grain and birdseed. In the Isles of Scilly and East Anglia it is well established in sandy cultivated land.

Classified in the British Isles as a neophyte, *P. minor* is a Mediterranean-Atlantic species which has been very widely naturalized outside its native range. It may be native in the Channel Islands (AGB: 38), having been recorded from sandy sites in Guernsey as early as 1791, but the New Atlas suggests otherwise.

Some authors (e.g. Hubbard, 1984) describe it as having 2 sterile lemmas, one minute, the other well developed. In fact, what appears to be the shorter of the two is the callus of the fertile floret, and what was presumably taken for the callus is the indurated base of the upper sterile lemma. On occasion, the sterile lemma itself is obscure, lacking the membranous upper part; as a result, it and the callus are almost indistinguishable.

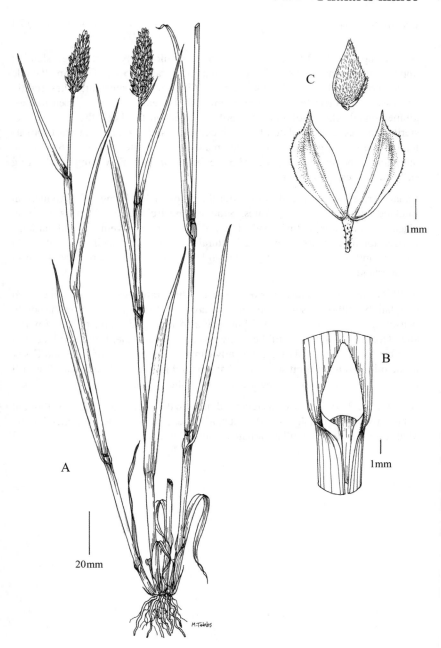

Phalaris minor: A, habit; B, ligule; C, spikelet with florets detached from glumes.

90.   **Phalaris canariensis** L.

Canary-grass   New Atlas: 774

Annual up to 85(120)cm; culms erect or geniculately ascending, slender; uppermost sheaths inflated; ligule a blunt membrane 2.5 – 7(8.5)mm. Panicle ovoid, contracted and spike-like, 1.5 – 5(7.5)cm, the short branches tightly appressed. Spikelets (6)7.5 – 9(10.5)mm, whitish except for the green nerves; glumes equal, oblong-elliptic in profile, winged on the keel, the wing entire; sterile lemmas 2, lanceolate-oblong, membranous, 3 – 4.3mm, at least half as long as the fertile, glabrous; fertile lemma ovate in profile, (4.7)5.2 – 6.4(7)mm, puberulous above; anthers 3, (2.8)3.3 – 3.7mm. $2n = 12$. Flowering and fruiting early June to early October.

Canary-grass is widespread throughout the British Isles, being quite frequent in England and much rarer in Wales, Scotland and Ireland. It is a grass of waste places such as rubbish tips, roadsides, walls and urban pavements and gardens. It occasionally occurs in peri-agricultural environments such as arable field margins and tracks. It is mostly found in lowland habitats but reaches 430m in Cumberland.

In all its habitats *P. canariensis* occurs as a casual, rarely establishing long-lived populations, although some populations may persist for a few years in the south. It usually derives from birdseed but may also be a grain (and formerly wool) alien (AGB: 37) and may still be cultivated on a small scale. It was cultivated as a speciality crop for bird (and especially canary) seed in parts of Kent and Essex in the mid 1800s, when it was reaped and bound in sheaves like wheat. It is still cultivated in some warm temperate regions of the world.

A neophyte, *P. canariensis* was recorded in the wild as early as 1632. It is thought to be native in the Canary Islands and NW Africa and is widely naturalized in the Mediterranean and in similar climates around the world.

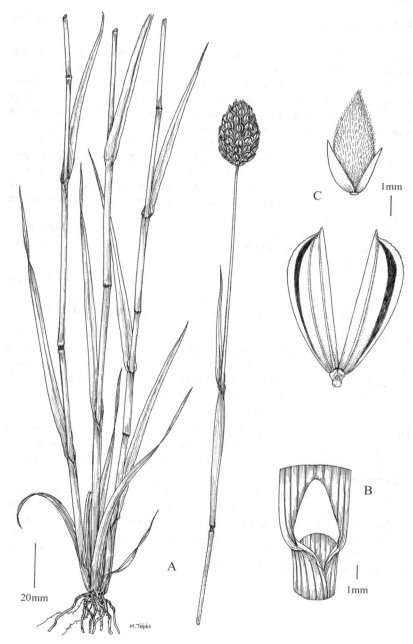

Phalaris canariensis: A, habit; B, ligule; C, spikelet with florets detached from glumes.

91. Phalaris paradoxa L.

Awned Canary-grass

Annual up to 60(100)cm; culms erect or geniculately ascending, usually slender; uppermost sheath very inflated and usually embracing at least the base of the panicle; ligule a blunt membrane 2 – 5(6.5)mm. Panicle oblong or obovate-oblong, contracted and spike-like, 2.5 – 6(8)cm, the short branches tightly appressed. Spikelets in deciduous clusters of 6 or 7, all but one sterile and forming an involucre around the fertile. Sterile spikelets: glumes equal, 2.5 – 5.5(7)mm, elliptic in profile, winged on the keel above the middle, acute to acuminate at the tip, resembling those of the fertile spikelet in the upper part of the panicle, those in the lower part sometimes reduced to clavate knobs. Fertile spikelet: glumes equal, 5 – 8.5mm, narrowly ovate in profile, winged on the keel above, the wing with a prominent tooth-like projection near the middle, acuminate to subulate at the tip; sterile lemma solitary, obsolete, 0.2 – 0.3mm; fertile lemma ovate-elliptic in profile, 2.5 – 3.7mm, glabrous or thinly hairy only at the tip; anthers 3, 0.7 – 1.5mm. $2n = 14$. Flowering and fruiting early June to late September, sometimes persisting until November.

Recent records of *P. paradoxa* have been confined to England where it is scattered in the south and east as a weed of mainly arable cultivation. It also occurs on waste ground and tips as a casual of birdseed, grain and esparto (AGB: 38).

A neophyte, which was cultivated in the latter half of the 17th Century (mostly for gamebird seed), *P. paradoxa* was recorded in the wild by 1959. It appears to be increasing as an arable weed in southern Britain and has probably been under-recorded. The species is a native of the Mediterranean region and SW Asia and, like the 3 previous species of *Phalaris* introduced to the British Isles, is widely naturalized or casual in many parts of the world.

The annual habit, glabrous fertile lemma, obsolete sterile lemma and the spikelets in deciduous clusters make this species unique in the genus. Specimens with the glumes of all the sterile spikelets reduced to clavate knobs have been separated as var. **praemorsa** (Lam.) Coss. & Durieu but in many specimens there is a gradation from well developed sterile spikelets in the upper part of the panicle to knob-like ones towards the base and the variety is probably not worth maintaining. Evidence is emerging that some plants with reduced sterile spikelets may in fact be referable to a distinct species (**P. appendiculata** Schult.; see Baldini, 1995) which is otherwise distinguished by its sterile lemmas being 0.5 – 0.7mm; it has not been found in the British Isles to date.

320

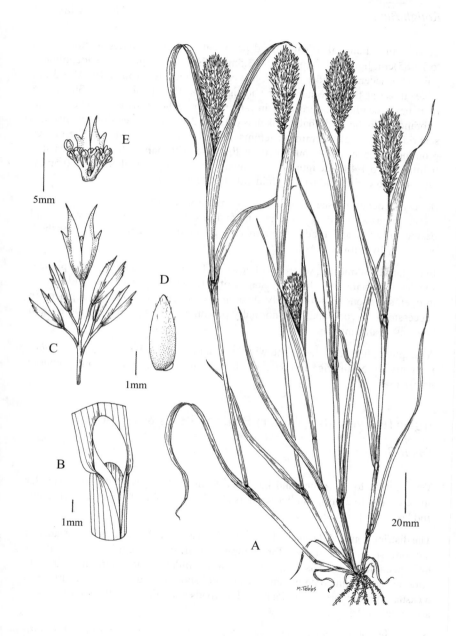

Phalaris paradoxa var. *paradoxa*: A, habit; B, ligule; C, spikelet cluster; D, florets.
Phalaris paradoxa var. *praemorsa*: E, spikelet cluster.

92.   **Agrostis scabra** Willd.

Loosely tufted annual or short-lived perennial without rhizomes or stolons, up to 70(85)cm; ligule of culm-leaf 2 – 3.5mm, distinctly longer than wide, bluntly pointed or lacerate; blades of culm-leaves flat or loosely inrolled, (0.5)1 – 3mm wide, those at the base narrower and tightly inrolled. Panicle 15 – 30cm, the branches ascending or spreading in rather remote whorls, bare of spikelets and unbranched in the lower half. Spikelets (2)2.3 – 2.9mm; glumes slightly unequal, scabrid on the keel, acuminate; lemma 1.4 – 1.8mm, 5-nerved with the nerves prominent above, thinly pubescent at the base with hairs c.0.2mm; palea 0 – 0.4mm, up to 1/4 the length of the lemma; awn usually 0; anthers 0.4 – 0.6mm. $2n = 42$. Flowering and fruiting mid-July to late September.

A. scabra occurs in scattered locations around Great Britain and appears to be increasing as a casual on waste ground and tips, in docks and timber yards, and beside railways and roads. A number of populations seem to be established, especially by railways (AGB: 40).

In its native N America, where it is known as Tickle Grass, *A. scabra* is a pioneer species which invades the early stages of a range of habitat types and thrives in open situations. It is relatively shade intolerant and is eventually replaced in successions to woodland. It is normally perennial in N America but more often behaves as an annual here.

A neophyte, first recorded in the wild in Britain in 1896 (Westerness), *A. scabra* is a native of N America and NE Asia. It was introduced as a grain (and probably wool) alien.

93.   **Agrostis hyemalis** (Walter) Britton, Sterns & Poggenb.

Very similar to *A. scabra* and has often been confused with it. It has smaller spikelets (up to 2mm), smaller lemmas (1 – 1.2mm) and all leaves are setaceous and less than 1mm across.

The distribution of *A. hyemalis* in Great Britain is difficult to determine because of the confusion with *A. scabra* (for example all *A. hyemalis* records from Middlesex have been determined as *A. scabra*). It has a similar history (introduced from N America as a grain contaminant or with wool shoddy) and ecology (occurring as a casual of rough ground in docks and by roads and railways). It also behaves as an annual in Britain.

A neophyte, *A. hyemalis* is a native of N America. It is much rarer than *A. scabra* and the New Atlas (CD) was unable to confirm any recent records.

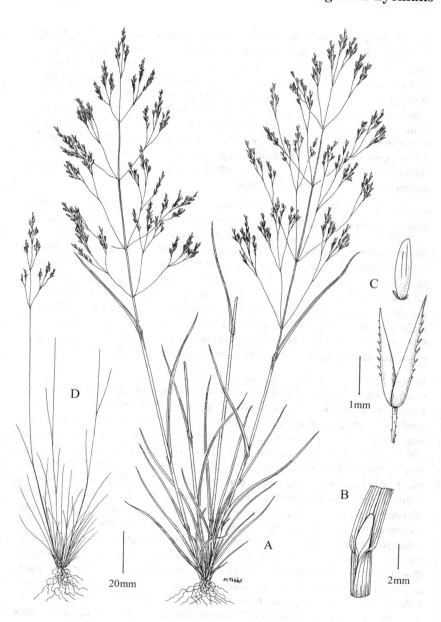

Agrostis scabra: A, habit; B, ligule; C, spikelet with floret detached from glumes.
Agrostis hyemalis: D, habit.

94.   **Agrostis curtisii** Kerguélen

Bristle Bent New Atlas: 776

Densely tufted perennial without rhizomes or stolons, up to 60(75)cm; ligule 2 – 4mm, distinctly longer than wide, acute; basal blades tightly inrolled and setaceous, 0.2 – 0.4mm across, those of the culms up to 0.6mm. Panicle (3)4 – 9(11)cm, contracted and spike-like before and after flowering. Spikelets (3)3.4 – 4mm; glumes slightly unequal, scabrid on the keel, acuminate; lemma 2 – 2.6mm, 5-nerved with the outer nerves excurrent, glabrous on the back, thinly pubescent at the base with hairs up to 0.4mm; palea 0.4 – 0.9mm, 1/5 – 1/3 the length of the lemma; awn arising from near the base of the lemma, well developed, 3 – 5mm, geniculate with twisted column, projecting beyond the tips of the glumes; anthers 1.3 – 1.8mm. $2n = 14$. Flowering and fruiting mid-June to mid-August, sometimes lasting until mid-September.

A. curtisii is confined to southern and southwestern England with outlier populations on the Bagshot sands in Surrey (and formerly E Sussex) and in S Wales as far west as the Gower Peninsula. It is locally abundant, and in some places dominant, on dry, sandy and peaty heathland from the New Forest and Dorset heathlands westwards. It may also be found in open woodland (frequently pine or birch woods), acid grassland and on leached acid soils over limestone (in S Wales). The soils in which it grows are generally nutrient-poor with low pH values (range 4.0 – 6.0). Common associates in the plant's typical habitats include *Calluna vulgaris, Erica cinerea, E. tetralix, Pteridium aquilinum* and *Ulex gallii* (and *U. minor* in the east of its range) but it may be found with a range of species in other habitats. It grows from sea-level to >600m on Dartmoor.

Bristle Bent is principally a gap-colonizing species. It is one of the first plants to re-invade burned heathland and areas of woodland opened up by felling. As succession proceeds to mature heathland, gorse scrub or woodland, *A. curtisii* is confined to the gaps in the vegetation such as paths and rides. Scattered flower heads may be seen protruding from dense *Calluna* or *Erica* heathland but the grass rarely flowers when shaded and in dense woodland takes on a floppy long-leaved, frequently non-glaucous, habit. By contrast, on moorland traditionally managed for sheep-grazing, such as parts of Exmoor especially along the N Devon coast, frequent burning produces a dense tufted, more or less continuous (and strikingly attractive, especially when in flower) sward of *A. curtisii* (which despite its appearance is freely grazed by sheep in these areas). A study of one post-fire colonizing population showed that seedlings produced by autumn germination were the most successful, those from spring germination rarely surviving. Moreover those plants recruited in the first year grew best, survived longest (>8 years at least) and eventually produced the most seed. One plant which appeared in the autumn following the fire having over twice the number of inflorescences produced by the entire population of more than 350 individuals recruited over the next 7 years (Gray, 1988). In suitable conditions *A. curtisii* flowers freely and produces large

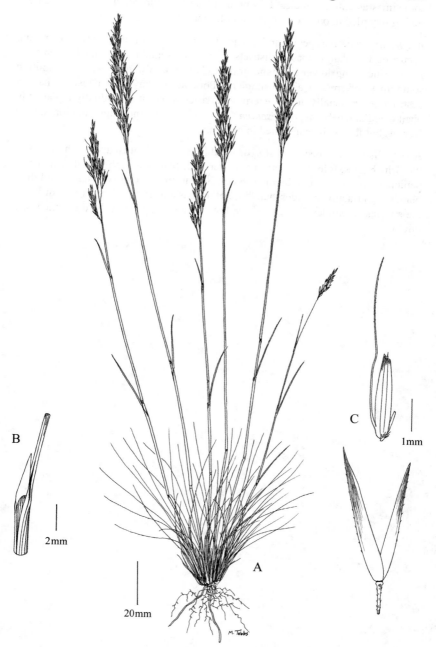

Agrostis curtisii: A, habit; B, ligule; C, spikelet with floret detached from glumes.

numbers of viable seed (around 250 – 300 per panicle) dispersed by wind and ants, sometimes as entire panicles. It is predominantly outbreeding with less than 1% selfing recorded in one experiment. (Biol. Flora: Ivimey-Cook, 1959).

A. curtisii is a native species and has an Oceanic Southern-temperate distribution, occurring in Atlantic coastal districts of France, Spain and Portugal down to N Africa (including lower montane grasslands in the W Pyrenees), a distribution sometimes referred to as 'Lusitanian'. Populations have been lost by habitat destruction, especially at its eastern boundaries where it is gradually replaced in open woodland habitats by *Deschampsia*, and by heathland fragmentation (e.g. in Dorset) but it is well established in many areas.

A very distinctive species of *Agrostis* unlikely to be confused with any other in the British Isles. It forms dense tufts of very fine blades with the tightly congested panicle rising well above them. The culms bear only one or two leaves and their blades are a fraction broader than those of the basal tuft and tillers. From a distance the species resembles *Festuca ovina*, but on close inspection the differences are obvious.

95. **Agrostis vinealis** Schreb.

Illustration, page 329

Brown Bent

New Atlas: 777

Densely tufted perennial with rhizomes but without stolons, up to 60(85)cm; ligules of culm-leaves 1 – 4(5)mm, rounded or bluntly pointed but often lacerate or shredded with age, those of the tillers longer than wide; blades of culm-leaves inrolled, setaceous and 0.3 – 0.8mm across, or flat and 1 – 3mm wide, firm, scabrid on both sides or at least above, sometimes glaucous. Panicle (4)6 – 12(16)cm, contracted and rather dense before and after flowering, the branches bare of spikelets in the lower half. Spikelets 2 – 3mm; glumes subequal or unequal, acute, the lower 1-nerved, scabrid on the keel, the upper shorter, 1- to 3-nerved, smooth or almost so; lemma 1.4 – 2.2mm, 5-nerved, the nerves neither prominent nor excurrent, glabrous on the back, minutely pubescent at the base with hairs c.0.2 mm; palea vestigial, 0.2 – 0.3(0.4)mm, up to 1/5 the length of the lemma; awn geniculate, arising from near the base of the lemma, 1.5 – 3.5(4)mm, or quite absent; anthers 0.8 – 1.3(1.5)mm. $2n = 28$, c.56. Flowering and fruiting mid-June to late August or late September.

A. vinealis occurs throughout the British Isles and is particularly frequent in the north and west. However, its exact distribution is unclear because of taxonomic confusion with *A. canina* (see below), and the existing map in the New Atlas is described as 'incomplete'. It is a grass of dry acidic grasslands and heaths, occurring in well-drained sandy or peaty soils on hills and moorland, and in the open parts of woodland. It may be found on acidic soils over limestone and is most abundant on soils in the pH range 3.5 – 5.0, but is sometimes found in less acidic conditions. It occurs from sea-level to 845m (Lttle Dun Fell, Westmorland) and probably higher in Scotland, and is more frequent in the uplands (above 200m) where there is more of its habitat. It is often found with *A. capillaris*, to which it is ecologically similar.

Although it has a narrower ecological range, occupying mainly the drier habitats, *A. vinealis* is biologically very like the more common *A. capillaris* and Grime *et al.,* (2007) remark that "the overlap in their ecological and geographical distributions [is] so complete that ecological reasons for the separation of the two species are hard to find" (CPE: 92). They note that Brown Bent flowers earlier and for a shorter period and may have greater ability to persist on acidic, relatively unproductive soils. It remains green over winter with some winter growth but little leaf expansion until late spring. *A. vinealis* tolerates grazing and mowing. Plants are polycarpic and seed is produced from September onwards and added to a persistent seed bank. Populations mainly regenerate by seed, there being relatively little lateral spread of individuals, certainly compared to other Bent grasses.

A. vinealis is native and is a European Temperate species which also occurs in N America (and temperate Asia).

It is extremely difficult to distinguish from *A. canina* and has been variously treated as a variety (var. *arida* Schltdl. or var. *montana* Hartm.) or subspecies (subsp. *montana* (Hartm.) Hartm.) of it, but the different chromosome number and lack of any evidence of hybridization indicate that species is the most appropriate rank. It has a marked preference for drier habitats than *A. canina* and can make a reasonable drought-resistant lawn-grass; its rhizomatous habit enables it to form a fine compact turf in contrast to the loose mats of *A. canina*. In addition, its blades are a little firmer than those of *A. canina*, the panicle has a tendency to contract after flowering and the plant does not produce stolons. The ligules, especially those on the flowering culms, are generally described as being shorter and blunter than those of *A. canina* but the correlation is not all that good and is best not relied upon to make a distinction.

The species hybridizes with *A. stolonifera*. The hybrid is intermediate between the parents, having the inflorescence of *stolonifera* but lacking a palea, and highly sterile. It is known for certain only from Cornwall. *A. capillaris* is also reported to hybridize with *A. vinealis* (**A. ×sanionis** Asch. & Graebn. is probably the name) but many of the specimens available are equivocal. Those that are more certain are intermediate in palea length and highly sterile.

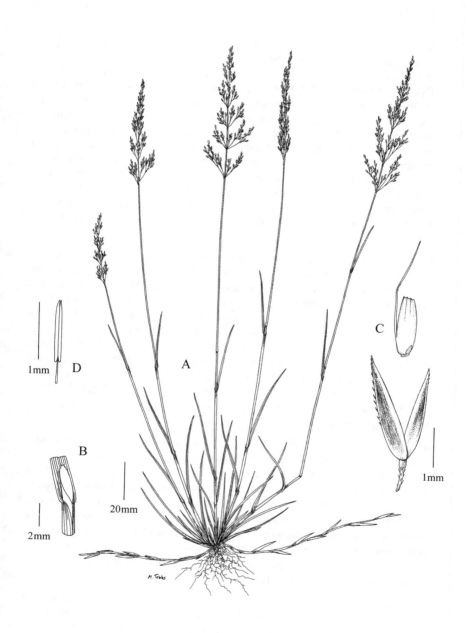

Agrostis vinealis: A, habit; B, ligule; C, spikelet with floret detached from glumes; D, anther.

96. Agrostis canina L.

Velvet Bent   New Atlas: 776

Tufted perennial with stolons but without rhizomes, up to 70(90)cm; ligules of culm-leaves 1.5 – 4.5mm, bluntly to sharply pointed, sometimes rounded, often lacerate or shredded with age, those of the tillers longer than wide; blades of culm-leaves usually flat, 0.8 – 2.5(3)mm wide, sometimes inrolled and 0.3 – 0.5(0.9)mm across, soft, scaberulous on both sides or at least above, usually bright green. Panicle 4.5 – 12(18)cm, usually open with spreading branches or loosely contracted after flowering, the branches bare of spikelets in the lower half. Spikelets 1.9 – 2.7mm; glumes subequal or unequal, 1-nerved, scabrid on the keel (the upper only towards the tip), acute; lemma 1.3 – 2mm, 5-nerved, the nerves neither prominent nor excurrent, glabrous on the back, minutely pubescent at the base with hairs c.0.2mm; palea vestigial, 0.2 – 0.3mm, up to 1/5 the length of the lemma; awn geniculate, arising from near the base of the lemma, 1.5 – 3(3.5)mm, or quite absent; anthers 0.8 – 1.3mm. $2n = 14$. Flowering and fruiting late June to late August or late September.

A. canina is a grass of wetland habitats occurring throughout most of the British Isles (the inclusion in the distribution map of the species in the 1962 Atlas of records for *A. vinealis* (then *A. canina* subsp. *montana*) could mean that *A. canina* sens. str. is under-recorded in those areas for which only records of the aggregate are available). Its habitats include wet meadows, mires, marshes, ditches, the margins of ponds, gravel pits and reservoirs, wet heathland, fens and fen-meadows, and open woodland, and are characteristically on infertile acidic peaty soils in the pH range 3.5 – 6.0. It occurs from sea-level to 1035m (S Kerry) and is generally more abundant above 400m. Although Velvet Bent may have a wide variety of associates it is often found in wetlands dominated by *Juncus* or *Carex* species or where mosses such as *Sphagnum* species or *Polytrichum commune* are among the ground vegetation.

Velvet Bent has surface creeping, leafy stolons and tends to form loose mats close to the ground (the presence of which distinguish it from *A. vinealis*). This, along with its soft green foliage, can make it a useful lawn grass especially on heavier soils. In semi-natural habitats it may form mats over *Sphagnum* bogs or floating in peaty pools, and in taller vegetation extend aerial stems into canopy gaps or exploit gaps in the vegetation by the 'foraging' of longer stolons. New populations are probably not only founded by seed but also by stolon fragments, since detached pieces of stolon are capable of rooting to form new plants. Individual plants are polycarpic and free-flowering except in deep shade. The species is normally outcrossing (CPE: 86).

A. canina is native and is a Boreo-temperate species with a disjunct circumpolar distribution. Along with other wetland grasses it may be decreasing in the British Isles, especially in lowland areas, by drainage of wetland habitats and the effects of habitat eutrophication.

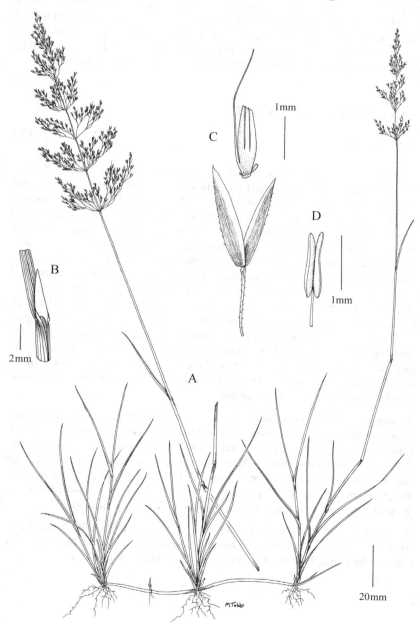

Agrostis canina: A, habit; B, ligule; C, spikelet with floret detached from glumes; D, anther.

Its habit and habitat are the only reliable means of distinguishing it – apart from chromosome number – from *A. vinealis*. It is supposed to have a longer and more sharply pointed ligule than *A. vinealis*, but the trend is only slight and is of limited practical value. The two taxa are more or less identical in spikelet structure, but whereas in *A. vinealis* the panicle contracts after flowering, in *A. canina* it usually does not, but again this cannot be relied upon as a distinguishing feature.

97. Agrostis avenacea J.F.Gmel.

Blown-grass   New Atlas CD

Annual or (very rarely in Britain) tufted perennial up to 85cm; ligules of culm-leaves (1.5)2.5 – 5.5mm, rounded to sharply pointed but often lacerate or shredded with age, those of the tillers longer than wide; blades of culm-leaves usually flat, 1 – 3.5mm wide, smooth or scaberulous. Panicle 10 – 35cm, wide open with spreading or drooping branches after flowering, the branches and branchlets bare of branchlets or spikelets, respectively, in the lower half to two-thirds, the spikelets gathered into clusters at the tips. Spikelets 2.3 – 4.2mm; glumes subequal or unequal, 1-nerved, scabrid on the keel, sharply acuminate; lemma 1.4 – 2(2.2)mm, 5-nerved, the lateral nerves running into 4 apical teeth, the nerves otherwise neither prominent nor excurrent, pilose on the back with long shaggy hairs up to 1mm, pubescent at the base with hairs c.0.3mm; palea well developed, 1 – 1.8mm, 3/4 – 4/5 the length of the lemma; awn geniculate, arising from the middle of the lemma, 3 – 6.5mm; rhachilla-extension 0.1 – 0.3mm but pilose with long hairs reaching to about the middle of the lemma; anthers 0.15 – 0.45mm. $2n$ = 56. Flowering and fruiting late August to early October, occasionally beginning in July or lasting until early November.

A. avenacea occurs in scattered localities in Great Britain along roads and railways and on waste and rough ground. First recorded in the wild in Britain in 1908 (Selkirks), it has been introduced with wool shoddy, and probably esparto, from the southern hemisphere, where it is a native in Australia and New Zealand and has become naturalized in S America and South Africa. There is some disagreement as to whether it is naturalized (Stace, 1997) or a casual (AGB: 38) in Great Britain. It is thought to have declined in frequency since 1970.

Blown-grass is remarkable for its hairy lemma and short rhachilla-extension. In Australia and New Zealand it commonly occurs in a perennial form, but this seems to be rare in Britain, probably because it cannot survive the winter.

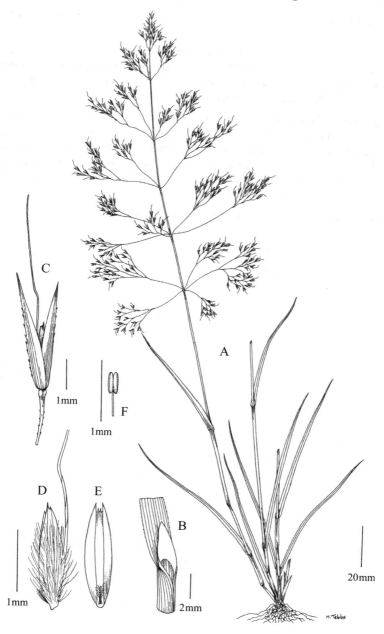

Agrostis avenacea: A, habit; B, ligule; C, spikelet; D, floret in profile;
E, floret in ventral view (hairs removed); F, anther.

98. **Agrostis lachnantha** Nees

African Bent

New Atlas CD

A. lachnantha shares the hairy lemma and well-developed palea of *A. avenacea*, but has longer anthers (0.4 – 0.7mm), a slender contracted panicle, a lemma almost as long as the glumes, the lemma awnless or with a short apical bristle up to 0.5mm and the rhachilla not extended.

First recorded from the wild in Britain in 1909 (Selkirks) it has subsequently been recorded rather infrequently and almost always from well known English wool alien sites, on rough ground and waste places and railway sidings. It is also mostly annual in this country and may be easily overlooked (nursery centres and water gardens may be likely habitats to look for it as the grass occurs in wet places in its native sites).

It is a native of Africa from Sudan and Ethiopia to South Africa.

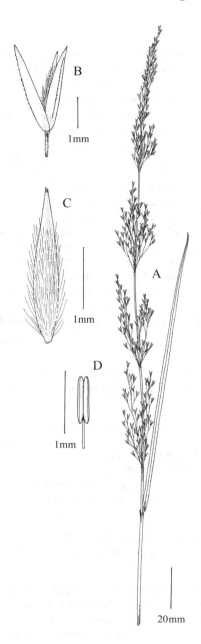

Agrostis lachnantha: A, panicle; B, spikelet; C, floret in profile; D, anther.

99.   *Agrostis castellana* Boiss. & Reuter

Highland Bent   New Atlas: 775

Loosely to densely tufted perennial with short stout rhizomes (usually with not more than 3 or 4 internodes) and culms up to 100cm; ligule of culm-leaves 1.5 – 3(4)mm, bluntly rounded but often lacerate or shredded with age, those of the tillers similar but often shorter, wider than long to longer than wide; blades of culm-leaves usually flat, 1.5 – 3mm wide, sometimes loosely inrolled, rarely tightly inrolled and setaceous, somewhat glaucous, scaberulous. Panicle (7)10 – 20cm, lanceolate to narrowly oblong, contracted after flowering but not dense, the branches bare of branchlets in the lower half, the branchlets also bare below with the spikelets densely clustered in the upper part; branches, branchlets and pedicels scabrid, the swollen pedicel-tips smooth. Spikelets 2 – 3.2mm; glumes subequal or unequal, 1-nerved, scabrid on the keel (especially the lower), sharply acute; lemma 1.5 – 2.2mm, the terminal on each branchlet 5-nerved, the nerves raised and prominently rib-like above and excurrent for up to 0.4mm, thinly pilose on the body especially towards the margins, pubescent at the base with hairs up to 0.5mm, otherwise 3-nerved without raised or prominent nerves, and glabrous; palea well-developed, 0.8 – 1.3mm, (1/2)2/3 – 3/4 the length of the lemma; awn geniculate, arising from or near the base of the lemma, 2.5 – 4mm, usually projecting beyond the glumes, or quite absent; anthers 1.1 – 1.7mm. $2n = 28, 42$. Flowering and fruiting mid-June to late July or into August.

Although it has been recorded from widely scattered localities in Britain, it is difficult to be certain about the distribution of *A. castellana* because of confusion with *A. capillaris* (see below). Most records are from lawns and amenity grassland including sports turf, but it has also been found on roadsides and in temporary leys on cultivated land.

Little seems to be known about the ecology of *A. castellana*, either as a casual of grass-seed (and wool) or a deliberately sown component of amenity or wild flower seed mixtures. Some Floras (e.g. Sell & Murrell, 1996, Stace, 1997) suggest that the species is likely to be under-recorded (or even 'much under-recorded') and is probably becoming more common, as do the records in the New Atlas. However, this suggestion is not supported by detailed examination of British and European material.

A. castellana is a neophyte, first recorded in Britain as a casual in 1924. It is a native of the Mediterranean region which has been introduced to northern Europe and elsewhere in grass-seed mixtures.

In Britain *A. castellana* is a rare introduction and probably over-recorded; a survey of continental material has indicated that most specimens from the British Isles ascribed to it are in fact one form or another of *A. capillaris* (which itself once bore the name Highland Bent). The only certain characters for distinguishing *A. castellana* from *A. capillaris* are the hairy terminal lemma and form of the

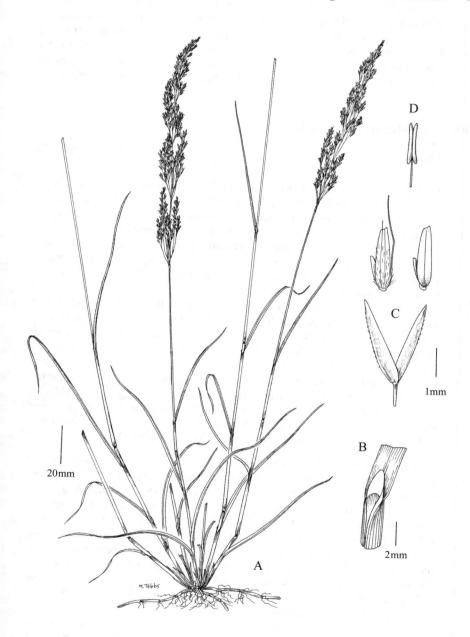

Agrostis castellana: A, habit; B, ligule; C, spikelet with two types of floret detached from the glumes; D, anther.

panicle; other characters, such as the length of the basal beard of the lemma, are of little significance. Some of the available British material is difficult to determine with confidence and it is possible that much of what has appeared in sowings of amenity grass is the hybrid between these two species (**A. ×fouilladei** P.Fourn.). Bolòs *et al.*, (1988) have reduced *A. castellana* to a subsp. of *A. capillaris* but this seems an extreme step that may be the result of a misunderstanding of the circumscription of *A. castellana*. Typically, the two species are very different.

100. Agrostis stolonifera L.

Creeping Bent   New Atlas: 776

Loosely to densely tufted, long- or shortly stoloniferous perennial without rhizomes, up to 65(120)cm; ligules of culm-leaves 2 – 6.5mm, rounded to truncate (and often lacerate), those of the tillers a little shorter and distinctly longer than wide; blades of culm-leaves usually flat, sometimes folded, 1 – 8mm wide, scaberulous, usually green but sometimes glaucous. Panicle 2 – 20(32)cm, branches, branchlets and pedicles contracted after flowering (rarely the lowermost branches slightly divergent), the branches and branchlets floriferous to the base (often the lower branches naked in the lower 1/4 – 1/3 but the naked portion concealed by the shorter, densely floriferous branches that arise in a cluster from the same node); branches, branchlets, pedicels and swollen pedicel-tips scabrid, very rarely smooth. Spikelets 1.8 – 3mm; glumes subequal or unequal, 1-nerved, scabrid on the keel (especially the lower; the upper often smooth), acute; lemma 1.3 – 2.1mm, 5-nerved (very rarely 3-nerved) with the nerves usually not prominent but occasionally the outer excurrent, glabrous on the back, rarely pubescent at the base with hairs 0.1 – 0.2mm; palea well-developed, 0.8 – 1.3(1.6)mm, (1/2)3/5 – 3/4 the length of the lemma; awn variable, 0.5 – 3mm, but in most cases quite absent; anthers 0.9 – 1.6mm. $2n = 28$ (30, 32, 35, 42, 44, 46). Flowering and fruiting late June to late August, occasionally as late as early October.

Widespread and abundant throughout the British Isles, *A. stolonifera* may be encountered in an exceptionally wide range of habitat types. It is probably most common in damp or wetland habitats on fertile heavy soils, including moist grassland and marshes, ditches, the margins of water bodies, pools and springs and open ground in areas of high rainfall. But it is also extremely common as a colonist of disturbed ground such as road verges and spoil heaps, as a weed of arable land and pasture, and as a component of more closed, permanent communities on a range of soil types including chalk grassland, saltmarshes, dune slacks and shingle, coastal cliffs, open woodland and amenity grasslands including lawns and bowling greens. In these habitats soils range from sand to clay, pH 3.5 to 8.0, nutrient-poor to -rich, and freshwater to saline. Consequently, *A. stolonifera* occurs with an extremely large number of associated species, although it rarely occurs in tall vegetation, growing best where taller species are absent or restricted by disturbance. It occurs from sea-level to 945m (Ben Lawers, M Perth).

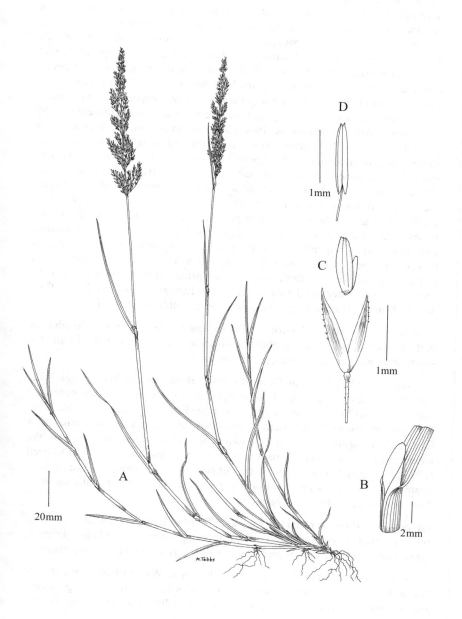

Agrostis stolonifera: A, habit; B, ligule; C, spikelet with floret detached from glumes;
D, anther.

The key to this species' successful occupation of so many different habitats has undoubtedly been its ability to evolve individuals and populations closely adapted to both large- and small-scale variation in its environment. Adaptation has occurred both by genetic differentiation and phenotypic plasticity and has been facilitated by high levels of background genetic variation (including polyploidy) and a variable regeneration strategy. It has resulted in widespread habitat-correlated variation which has been the basis for distinguishing intraspecific taxa (see below). Experimental studies have demonstrated that evolution in *A. stolonifera* can be rapid (over a few generations as in ecotypes tolerant to heavy metals) and maintained over very short distances (as in closely adjacent sea cliff populations (Aston & Bradshaw, 1966)) and can involve morphological and/or physiological traits. Thus plants from grazed saltmarsh have numerous short thin stolons forming a compact persistent tuft; turves of *A. stolonifera* and *Festuca rubra* from the upper levels of sandy saltmarshes of NW Britain (e.g. Morecambe Bay, the Solway) were formerly cut and sold as sea-washed turves to construct the highest quality lawns. Those from meadows tend to have few long, thick stolons and have high growth rates and rapid response to nutrients, whilst those from sand-dunes have a few, long, thin stolons and grow well under relatively poor nutrient conditions. Meadow plants regenerate mainly by vegetative extension whereas dune plants also produce mainly flowering tillers (Kik, 1987). It is protandrous and mainly outbreeding. Both autumn and spring germination occur and the species has a persistent seed bank in many of its habitats. It also regenerates from detached shoots, contributing to its success as an arable weed. (CPE: 90).

A. stolonifera is native in the British Isles and has a wide circumpolar distribution in the temperate zone of the northern hemisphere. It has been introduced into the southern hemisphere and is widely naturalized.

A. stolonifera is by a long way the most variable British species in the genus. It has a number of reasonably well-defined morphological races (ecads) each generated and maintained by – and more or less confined to – a particular habitat-type. Philipson recognized two varieties (*stolonifera* and *palustris*), the former with four ecads; Hubbard also recognized two varieties (*stolonifera* and *palustris*, the latter called Marsh Bent), but paid little attention to the ecads; Sell and Murrell (1996), recognize five infraspecific taxa of equal rank (variety). The last of these treatments, outlined below, is probably the most practicable but the varieties described are of doubtful taxonomic value.

var. *calcicola* (Philipson) P.D.Sell (ecad *calcicola* Philipson): stolons numerous and very short, sometimes quite absent, forming a dense turf; blades glaucous, flat or folded; panicle narrow and rather meagre; growing on chalk downland.

var. *marina* (Gray) P.D.Sell (ecad *salina* (Jansen & Wacht.) Philipson): stolons few and very short forming a dense turf; blades narrow, flat, often glaucous; panicle rather lax, usually not lobed; growing in saltmarshes and areas affected by salt spray.

var. *maritima* (Lam.) Koch (ecad *arenaria* (Jansen & Wacht.) Philipson): stolons widely creeping from a central tuft; culms prostrate at first, then ascending; blades folded and sheaths tinged with purple; panicle dense and lobed; growing in loose sand, usually on the coast.

var. *stolonifera*: stolons widely creeping from a central tuft; culms erect; blades flat and sheaths often tinged with purple; panicle dense and lobed; growing in grassland and waste places.

var. *palustris* (Huds.) Farw.: stolons far-creeping but tending to branch at random and not traceable to a central tuft; flowering culms usually rather few in number, tall and erect; blades broad, long and rather widely spaced; panicle much longer than in the other varieties, narrow or pyramidal rather than lanceolate or oblong, and with the lowermost branches often spreading and bare of branchlets in the lower 1/3 – 1/2; growing in damp soils in the lowlands.

The species hybridizes with *A. capillaris* (see under that species), *A. gigantea* and *A. vinealis*. Records of the first two are widely scattered, those of the last confined to Cornwall. All are probably under-recorded.

101. Agrostis capillaris L.

Common Bent

Loosely to densely tufted perennial with short rhizomes and rarely with stolons, up to 75(90)cm; ligules of culm-leaves 0.5 – 1.5mm, rounded to truncate, those of the tillers shorter, truncate and distinctly shorter than wide; blades of culm-leaves usually flat, 1.5 – 4mm wide, sometimes inrolled and 0.3 – 0.8mm across, soft to firm, smooth to scabrid, usually green but sometimes glaucous. Panicle 8 – 18cm, usually open with spreading branches, branchlets and pedicels after flowering, the branches and branchlets bare in the lower half, sometimes the branchlets contracting about the branches after flowering and rarely the branches contracting about the main axis; branches, branchlets and pedicels smooth or scabrid, the swollen pedicel-tip smooth. Spikelets 1.8 – 2.7mm; glumes subequal or unequal, 1-nerved, scabrid on the keel (especially the lower; the upper often smooth), acute; lemma 1.4 – 2.2mm, 5-nerved with the nerves sometimes prominent and occasionally excurrent, or 3-nerved with the nerves neither prominent nor excurrent, glabrous on the back, sometimes pubescent at the base with hairs 0.1 – 0.35mm (mostly when 5-nerved; usually glabrous when 3-nerved); palea well-developed, 0.6 – 1.3mm, (2/5)1/2 – 3/4 the length of the lemma; awn variable and usually only on the 5-nerved lemmas, 0.5 – 3mm, or commonly quite absent; anthers 0.8 – 1.4mm. $2n = 28$. Flowering and fruiting late June to early September.

A. capillaris is a very common grass widely distributed in the British Isles in a broad range of habitats. It is especially abundant on permanent pastures in the uplands where it can be the dominant species over extensive areas of poor, usually mildly acidic soils. But it is also common in lowland pasture, on heaths, in hay meadows, in open areas of plantations, woodland and scrub and in lawns and amenity grassland (where the species has been extensively sown to create dense fine turf). Additionally it occurs on waste ground and a variety of other man-made habitats such as spoil heaps, quarries, road verges and hedgerows, paths, railway ballast, walls, and mine waste, famously including soils contaminated with lead and other heavy metals. The soils in which Common Bent grows range from sands to clays but it is particularly prevalent on moderately acid brown earth (in the pH range 4.0 – 6.0) and can occasionally be found on both very acid and also base-rich substrates. It occurs from sea-level to 1210m (Ben Lawers, M Perth) and has a wide range of associates (it frequently coexists with *Festuca rubra* in short turf habitats).

Like *A. stolonifera*, *A. capillaris* comprises a set of genetically and ecologically distinct populations, although this has not been recognized taxonomically by habitat-based intraspecific categories as with the former species. In its typical upland and montane pasture habitat *A. capillaris* individuals form a short turf, often with a high density of small tillers. (This type of reponse to repeated defoliation makes the species a highly suitable grass for lawns and golf greens). It

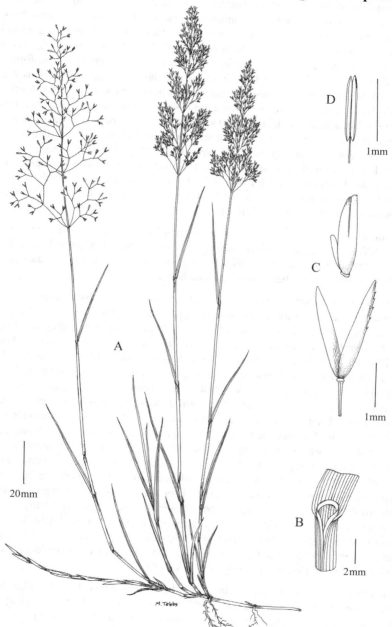

Agrostis capillaris: A, habit; B, ligule; C, spikelet with floret detached from glumes; D, anther.

is highly resistent to grazing and trampling and is also cold and drought tolerant, a prerequisite for its colonization of extremely dry habitats such as spoil heaps. Some growth occurs in the winter, and upland plants, which are mainly rhizomatous, display rapid spring and summer growth. *A. capillaris* is largely outbreeding and seed set, which can be irregular in upland populations (Bradshaw, 1959), occurs from August onwards, seeds germinating both in autumn and spring, to form a persistent seed bank. Plants from lowland grassland may develop stolons and some with slower growth rates are found in unproductive conditions such as mine spoil. Those from lead contaminated areas have been extensively investigated by A.D.Bradshaw and his colleagues and with *Anthoxanthum odoratum* have become iconic examples of rapid evolution in action (e.g. Bradshaw & McNeilly, 1981). The high genetic diversity in the species (which has not, unlike *A. stolonifera*, included the evolution of salt tolerance) is likely to have been augmented in Britain by hybridization with non-indigenous turf varieties imported from N America, Europe and New Zealand (and possibly those accidentally introduced as wool aliens (AGB: 39)). (CPE: 88).

A. capillaris is native, part of the Eurosiberian Boreo-temperate element in our flora (P&H 1997), and is widely naturalized outside its native range. It is said to have declined in the lowlands with the loss of permanent pasture but has been able to colonize a number of new artificial habitats.

A. capillaris is closely related to, and sometimes difficult to distinguish from, *A. gigantea*. Apart from its smaller size (except luxuriant shaded forms) it has, on the tillers, relatively shorter ligules that are distinctly shorter than they are wide; in *A. gigantea* they are at least as long as they are wide, usually longer. There is little in the form of the panicle that is helpful, although in *A. gigantea* the spikelets are never on spreading pedicels after flowering as they often are in *A. capillaris*, and in *A. gigantea* the swollen pedicel-tips are nearly always scabrid, at least in the lower part. Plants that form a dense turf and have a contracted panicle have been separated as *A. tenuis* var. *humilis* (Asch. & Graebn.) Druce, but the variant does not seem to be very significant. It should not be confused with a dwarf form once distinguished as *A. pumila* L., and which seems to be fairly common throughout the British Isles. It scarely ever exceeds 10cm, has a panicle 1 – 3.5(5.5)cm and spikelets 1.1 – 1.9mm. In every instance the fruits are distorted by the fungus *Tilletia decipiens* (Pers.) Körn., which is also presumably reponsible for the dwarfism. Specimens of Common Bent are occasionally found that are described as viviparous (*A. vulgaris* With. var. *vivipara* Reichb.); these have elongated glumes and lemmas, the latter often multi-nerved, and the ovary develops into an elongated purple gall, but the effect has been produced by a nematode, *Anguillina agrostis* (Steinbuch) Goodey.

The species hybridzes with *A. gigantea* (**A. ×bjoerkmannii** Widén), *A. stolonifera* (**A. ×murbeckii** Fouill. ex P.Fourn.) and *A. vinealis* (see under that species). In all cases the hybrids are intermediate between their parents and highly sterile. They are all widely scattered and probably under-recorded. For hybrids with *A. castellana* see under that species.

344

102. **Agrostis gigantea** Roth

Illustration, page 347

Black Bent

New Atlas: 775

Loosely tufted rhizomatous perennial, up to 100(120)cm, often branched from the lower nodes; ligules of culm-leaves 2 – 7.5mm, broadly rounded to truncate (and often lacerate), those of the tillers a little shorter, truncate and as long as or longer than wide; blades of culm-leaves flat, (2)3 – 7mm wide, firm, scabrid, dull green. Panicle (8)11 – 25cm, open with spreading branches after flowering but the branchlets and pedicels usually clustered at the branch-tips, the branches and branchlets bare in the lower half; branches, branchlets and pedicels coarsely scabrid or the swollen pedicel-tips rarely smooth. Spikelets 2 – 3mm; glumes subequal or unequal, 1-nerved, scabrid on the keel, acute; lemma 1.5 – 2.2mm, 5-nerved with the nerves sometimes prominent and often excurrent, or rarely 3-nerved with the nerves neither prominent nor excurrent, glabrous on the back, rarely pubescent at the base with hairs 0.05 – 0.3mm (but only when 5-nerved); palea well-developed, 0.8 – 1.4mm, 1/2 – 3/4 the length of the lemma; awn variable and only on the 5-nerved lemmas, 0.5 – 4mm, or usually quite absent; anthers 0.9 – 1.6mm. $2n = 42$. Flowering and fruiting mostly late June to mid-August, but often continuing until early October.

A. gigantea is widely distributed throughout lowland Britain, being most common in England, especially in southern and central counties, scattered in Wales, and uncommon in Scotland outside the central lowlands and the southern shore of the Moray Firth (N Aberdeen, Banffs & Moray). It is very scattered in Ireland, and has been recorded from Guernsey (but not Jersey), the Isles of Scilly and the Western Isles and Orkney (but not recently from the Shetland Isles). It is most common as a weed of cereal fields on light sandy soils and occurs in a range of peri-agricultural habitats such as headlands, roadsides, hedgerows, abandoned fields and waste ground. It is less common in wet grassy areas and in open, generally damp, woodland. However, the exact distribution and ecological range of *A. gigantea* is uncertain because it may easily be confused with other *Agrostis* species, especially *A. stolonifera* and *A. capillaris,* with which it freely hybridizes, and the hybrids may also be widespread (Stace, 1975). Black Bent prefers nutrient-poor sandy or gravelly soils and thrives best where these are disturbed by cultivation. It also occurred as a wool alien, may be cultivated from birdseed (AGB: 39), and was sown in amenity grassland in the past.

Like its close relatives, *A. gigantea* has a variety of regenerative strategies, spreading both by seed and by rhizomes, both of which can be transported in soil during cultivation. It combines high seed production (about 1000 seeds per panicle) with vigorous rhizomatous growth and a deep root system which (unlike *A. stolonifera*) allows it to survive in taller closed vegetation. For this reason it can be a serious weed in cereal crops. The reproductive biology of Black Bent has been less well studied than that of its relatives but it is believed to be largely outbreeding and to found most new populations from autumn germination.

A. gigantea is classified as an archaeophyte in the New Atlas (although labelled as native in most Floras). It has a Eurasian southern-temperate distribution and is naturalized in N America. The species has increased quite substantially since the 1962 Atlas despite the use of herbicide to control it. The general consensus is that, because of the taxonomic problems referred to above, it may continue to be under-recorded.

In many respects the species is similar to *A. capillaris*, but can usually be readily distinguished by its greater size and by its relatively longer ligules. The spikelets are nearly always contracted about the tips of the primary panicle-branches, something that *A. capillaris* does only occasionally. It can be a rather small plant with relatively narrow leaves, mimicking some variants of *A. capillaris*, but the ligule will always settle its identity. It is far less prone to producing awns than is *A. capillaris* but this feature cannot be relied upon as a means of distinguishing the species.

A. gigantea hybridizes with *A. stolonifera*; the resultant hybrid is vigorous but highly sterile. It also hybridizes with *A. capillaris* (see under that species). Both hybrids are widely scattered and probably under-recorded.

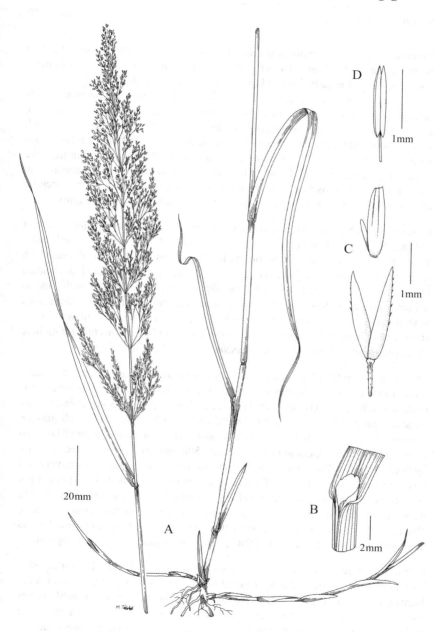

Agrostis gigantea: A, habit; B, ligule; C, spikelet with floret detached from glumes;
D, anther.

103. **Calamagrostis scotica** (Druce) Druce

Scottish Small-reed   New Atlas: 778

Compactly tufted rhizomatous perennial up to 100cm; sheaths smooth; ligule a blunt membrane 1 – 2mm; blades flat or inrolled, up to 2.5mm wide, shortly hairy above, glabrous beneath. Panicle lanceolate to narrowly oblong, fairly dense, 6.5 – 16cm, the branches densely scabrid. Spikelets 4.5 – 6mm; glumes narrowly lanceolate in profile, equal or nearly so, firmly membranous, scabrid on the keel, scaberulous on the flanks, acuminate, the lower 1(3)-nerved, the upper 3-nerved; lemma firmly membranous, ovate, 3 – 4mm, 5-nerved, scaberulous, the callus with hairs 1.5 – 2.5mm, the tip blunt and minutely toothed; awn arising from the lower third of the lemma, almost as long as to slightly exceeding the lemma-tip; palea about two-thirds the length of the lemma; anthers 1.6 – 2.2mm; rhachilla extension 0.7 – 1(1.4)mm, pilose. Flowering and fruiting July and August.

C. scotica is a British endemic species known only from one location, Loch of Durran, Caithness. It was first discovered there in 1863 by Robert Dick (who also found *Anthoxanthum nitens* on the R. Thurso) and to date this drained loch remains its only confirmed site. The grass occurs in wet grazing marsh dominated by *Juncus* species, especially along the edge of deep drainage channels, and in adjacent fen dominated by *Filipendula ulmaria*, and willow carr interspersed with a tall-herb community. The site is flooded in the winter and wet in the summer and is grazed by cattle, sheep and roe deer. Other grasses present include *Deschampsia cespitosa, Phalaris arundinacea* and *Agrostis canina.*

The exact size of the *C. scotica* population is difficult to assess because the site is often flooded, grazing reduces the plant (except where it grows in dense clumps of *Juncus effusus* which partly protects it), and individual tufts are connected by slender hidden rhizomes. Possible hybridization with *C. stricta*, which may be present or have formerly been present, is also a complication. Butler (RDB: 66) estimates the total population to be between 500 and 1500 plants. A recent study by Foley & Porter (2006) (who also review the history of the plant's discovery and taxonomy and give a full list of associated species) suggests that the population comprises several genetic individuals (genets) and is not a single clone, as has been surmised. Their preliminary genetic analysis of offspring from six plants also indicates that *C. scotica* is genetically very similar to *C. stricta* (or at least is not highly divergent from it), and that *C. epigeios* is genetically quite separate.

One of only three endemic British grasses, *C. scotica* is classified as **vulnerable** by Cheffings & Farrell (2005). Unconfirmed records of *C. scotica* from other locations in Caithness and elsewhere must be evaluated but are probably errors for *C. stricta*; the 2 species were lumped together as *C. neglecta* agg. in the 1962 Atlas. The future management of the site of this extremely rare endemic, particularly of the grazing and drainage, is an obvious concern.

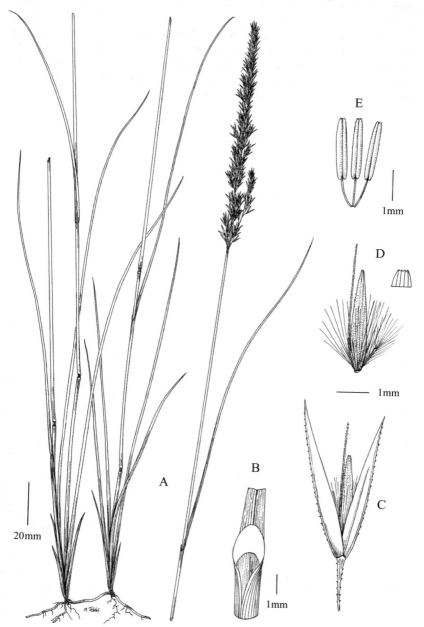

Calamagrostis scotica: A, habit; B, ligule; C, spikelet; D, floret with flattened lemma tip shown separately; E, anthers.

The species belongs in sect. *Deyeuxia* which is circumscribed by the combination of firmly membranous (to indurated), scaberulous (to scabrid) lemma, callus-hairs considerably shorter than the lemma and pronounced rhachilla-extension. In these respects it is similar to *C. stricta* from which it is relatively easy to separate by the longer spikelets with more sharply pointed glumes. It may, however, prove to have been derived from *C. stricta* by introgression from another species (probably *C. canescens* and not *C. epigeios*, see above); fertile forms of this hybrid are very similar to *C. scotica* (see under *C. stricta* for more details).

104. Calamagrostis stricta (Timm) Koeler

Illustration, page 353

Narrow Small-reed

New Atlas: 778

Compactly tufted rhizomatous perennial up to 80(110)cm; sheaths smooth; ligule a blunt membrane (1)1.5 – 3.5(4)mm; blades flat or inrolled, up to 5mm wide, shortly hairy above, glabrous beneath. Panicle lanceolate to narrowly oblong, dense to rather loose, 6.5 – 18cm, the branches densely scabrid. Spikelets 3 – 4(4.5)mm; glumes lanceolate in profile, equal or nearly so, firmly membranous, scabrid on the keel, scaberulous on the flanks, subacute, the lower 1-nerved, the upper 1(3)-nerved; lemma thinly to firmly membranous, oblong-ovate, 2.5 – 3.5mm, 5-nerved, minutely scaberulous to scabrid, the callus with hairs 1.5 – 2.5mm, the tip blunt and minutely toothed; awn arising from the lower third of the lemma, as long as or slightly exceeding the lemma-tip; palea about two-thirds the length of the lemma; anthers 1.4 – 1.9(2.4)mm; rhachilla-extension up to 1mm, short and glabrous to long and pilose, occasionally absent. $2n = 28$. Flowering and fruiting late June to mid-September.

C. stricta is a rare grass of wetlands which occurs in a small number of widely scattered sites in the British Isles, mainly in northern England and Scotland, and around Lough Neagh in N Ireland. Its habitats include marshes and fens and edges and shallows of lakes, a mere and a canal. It grows in areas of permanently high water table or among emergent aquatic plants in neutral soils ranging in pH from 5.9 to 6.6. Associated species include *Deschampsia cespitosa, Filipendula ulmaria, Juncus effusus* and *Phalaris arundinacea* (SPB: 65) and, at its location in E Yorks, *Calamagrostis canescens* with which it has formed hybrids (Crackles, 1995). The records of *C. stricta* are mostly from lowland sites but it reaches 340m at Kingside Loch (Selkirks).

Although rare, and classified as **vulnerable** by Cheffings & Farrell (2005), *C. stricta* can be locally dominant, forming tufted stands of narrow, firm leaves at the water's edge. It is a rather variable species possibly due to past hybridization with other *Calamagrostis* species (see below). Plants at one site, Alemoor Loch in the Scottish borders, show similarities to *C. scotica* but are more than 300km south of the latter's single location. Little seems to be known about the reproductive biology of *C. stricta*; it is said to be normally cross-pollinating (Fryxell, 1957) but E Yorks plants set some seed by self-fertilization. It spreads both by seed and vegetatively via slender creeping rhizomes. Plues (1867) noted that it was not only smaller, stiffer and 'less elegant' than other British *Calamagrostis* species but that it requires moister situations, affecting bogs and marshes. (RDB (based on SPB): 67).

C. stricta is a native species in the British Isles and has a circumpolar distribution, occurring widely in the boreal zones of Europe, Asia and N America, and locally in montane areas futher south (the Circumpolar Boreo-arctic Montane element; P&H 1997). Recorded in 22 tetrads within a total of 15 km squares since 1970, it is difficult to assess changes in *C. stricta*'s distribution in the British Isles because of hybridization and taxonomic confusion. Although known to be lost from some sites by drainage, it is the easiest *Calamagrostis* to overlook and may still be refound in some of its old localities.

C. stricta is very similar to *C. scotica* but with blunter glumes and shorter spikelets, and morphologically much more variable. It introgresses with *C. canescens*, forming both tetraploid and octoploid hybrids (**C.** ×**gracilescens** (Blytt) Blytt which has been classified as **vulnerable** by Cheffings & Farrell). The octoploid is more or less intermediate between the parents in a number of characters (see Crackles (1994) for full details) and can survive for a number of years; it spreads vegetatively but is often partially fertile. The tetraploids are probably backcrosses to *C. stricta* and are largely sterile. Hybridization and backcrossing may account for much of the variation seen in *C. stricta* which is expressed in the size and shape of the panicle, the length and position of the awn, the texture and indumentum of the lemma and the length and hairiness of the rhachilla-extension (see Crackles (1997) for more detailed discussion). The hybrid is known for certain only from a canal-bank in SE Yorks, but male-fertile plants from scattered localities in Scotland may also be referable to it. Male-sterile plants from elsewhere (Scotland and NW England) are likely to be *C. purpurea*.

The membranous, almost smooth lemma and occasionally missing rhachilla-extension indicate just how close together are sections *Calamagrostis* and *Deyeuxia*. The species occupies an intermediate position between *C. scotica* (a 'typical' *Deyeuxia*) and *C. canescens* (a 'typical' *Calamagrostis*) and is just one example among several worldwide that demonstrate the difficulties of separating *Deyeuxia* from *Calamagrostis*.

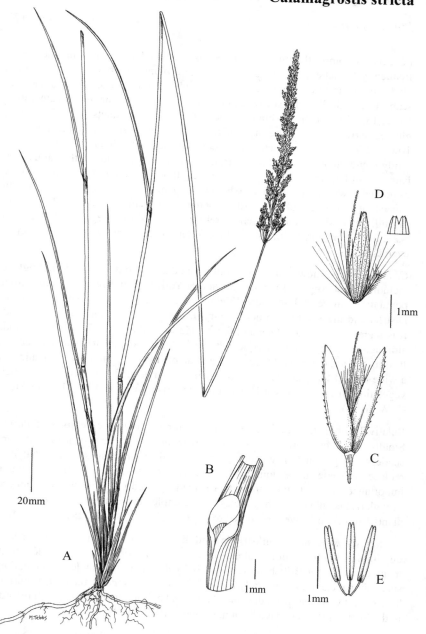

Calamagrostis stricta: A, habit; B, ligule; C, spikelet;
D, floret with flattened lemma tip shown separately; E, anthers.

105. Calamagrostis canescens (F.H.Wigg.) Roth

Purple Small-reed   New Atlas: 777

Loosely to compactly tufted rhizomatous perennial up to 150cm, the culms frequently branched; sheaths smooth; ligule a blunt membrane 1 – 4.5(6)mm; blades flat or inrolled, up to 5.5mm wide, pubescent to pilose above, smooth to scabrid beneath. Panicle narrowly lanceolate to oblong or narrowly ovate, rather loose, 13 – 21(26)cm, the branches densely scabrid. Spikelets 4.5 – 6(6.5)mm; glumes narrowly lanceolate in profile, equal or nearly so, firmly membranous, 1-nerved, scabrid on the keel, scaberulous on the flanks, finely pointed; lemma thinly membranous, ovate, 2.2 – 3.1mm, 3- or 5-nerved, smooth, the callus with hairs 3 – 4(4.5)mm (1.2 – 1.8 times the length of the lemma), the tip narrowly 2-toothed; awn arising from just below the lemma-tip, as long as or slightly exceeding it; palea about two-thirds the length of the lemma; anthers 1.2 – 1.8mm; rhachilla-extension usually absent, rarely a small glabrous peg up to 0.2mm. 2*n* = 28. Flowering and fruiting early June to late August, rarely into September or even October.

C. canescens is now most commonly found in central and eastern England including East Anglia, Lincolnshire and S Yorkshire and has scattered outlier populations in central southern England, the west midlands, Wales, the Lake District and the Scottish border country. It has not been recorded from Ireland. It is a grass of marshes, fens and fen-meadows, and alder and willow carr and, although generally rather infrequent, it may be locally abundant in suitable habitat. It occurs in a range of soil types over a wide pH range (from 3.0 to 7.5), and has a wide range of associated wetland species, often occurring in very species-rich vegetation. It is generally a lowland species, rising to 335m on Malham Moor (MW Yorks).

Relatively little detailed information is available about the ecology of Purple Small-reed. It can form extensive dense stands and is clearly tolerant of light shade when growing in woodland carr. Casual observation suggests that it is replaced in some successions by the taller *Phragmites australis*, but the relative importance of vegetative spread and spread by seed (which may be produced irregularly) is unknown. The species has a complex breeding system (see below); plants from E Yorks were observed to be self-fertile (Crackles, 1994).

C. canescens is native in Britain and has a Eurosiberian Boreo-temperate distribution (with a continental distribution in W Europe). It has been lost from many of its former British sites, probably by drainage of suitable habitat and by successional changes, especially in localities outside its main area of distribution. This retreat was clear from the 1962 Atlas and has continued, although all records in the Scottish Borders have been made since 1962 (see New Atlas).

The species seems to be a complex of sexual plants, facultative apomicts (part sexual, part apomictic) and obligate apomicts (fully apomictic). The latter are

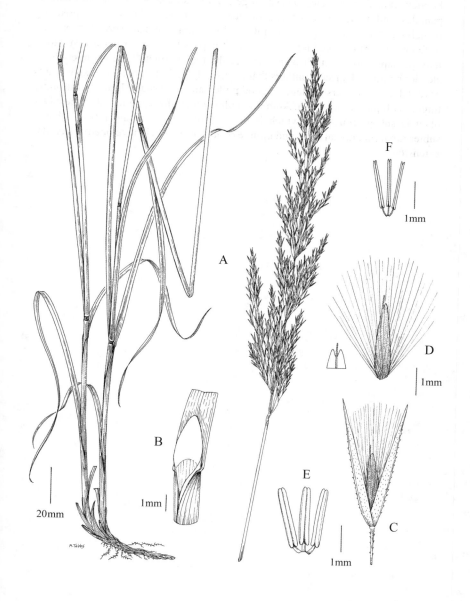

Calamagrostis canescens: A, habit; B, ligule; C, spikelet; D, floret with flattened lemma tip shown separately; E, anthers from fertile floret; F, anthers from apomictic floret.

distinguished from *C. purpurea* by the length of the ligule. As with many part sexual/part apomictic complexes there are many elements that could conceivably be viewed as microspecies. These range from small slender plants with narrow panicles and tightly inrolled scabrid leaves to robust plants with spreading panicles and flat leaves. The morphological variation is evenly spread among the different classes of breeding system, and it is possible that further investigation may perhaps show that all plants are facultative apomicts. The apomicts have slender empty indehiscent anthers that are usually yellow in colour; sexual plants have dehiscent anthers containing good pollen and are usually lightly to strongly tinged with purple or brown. Anther length is much the same in both types. Our plant is subsp. **canescens** which is distinguished by its slender (not robust), subterminal (not dorsal) awn and minute or absent (not well developed) rhachilla-extension.

106. **Calamagrostis epigeios** (L.) Roth

Illustration, page 359

Wood Small-reed

New Atlas: 777

Loosely to compactly tufted rhizomatous perennial up to 160(200)cm, the culms usually unbranched; sheaths smooth; ligule a blunt to pointed, often lacerate, membrane 5 – 12mm; blades flat or inrolled, up to 10mm wide, scabrid on both surfaces. Panicle lanceolate to oblong, very dense (looser during anthesis), (12)16 – 30(35)cm, the branches densely scabrid. Spikelets (4.5)5 – 6.5(7)mm; glumes very narrowly lanceolate in profile, equal or nearly so, firmly membranous, scabrid on the keel, scaberulous on the flanks, finely pointed, the lower 1-nerved, the upper 1- to 3-nerved; lemma thinly membranous, oblong-lanceolate, 2 – 3mm, 3-nerved, smooth, the callus with hairs 3.5 – 5mm (1.5 – 1.8 times the length of the lemma), the tip narrowly 2-toothed; awn arising from above the middle of the lemma and exceeding its tip; palea about two-thirds the length of the lemma; anthers (1.3)1.5 – 2.1mm; rhachilla-extension absent or a small glabrous peg up to 0.2mm. $2n = 28, 56$. Flowering and fruiting late June to mid- or late September.

C. epigeios occurs throughout the British Isles but is only common in S & E England southeast of a line from Yorkshire to Somerset. It is rare in the Southwest Peninsula, scattered and mainly coastal in Wales, northern England and Scotland, and very rare in Ireland. It seems to occur in two quite distinct types of semi-natural habitat: either damp shady woodlands and wood margins, ditches and fens on heavy soils, or open grassland, usually ungrazed, on or near sand-dunes and sea cliffs mostly on light sandy soils. It can also be found in a range of artificial habitats including road verges, quarries and railway banks. The soils on which it grows can be heavy clays or almost pure sands and range in pH from 3.7 to 7.4. It has a range of associates across its very different habitats and is mainly a lowland plant, reaching 370m at Great Asby (Westmorland).

Capable of forming a phalanx of tall dense monospecific stands in the manner of *Phragmites*, *C. epigeios* is the most familiar and easily-recognized of our *Calamagrostis* species. It spreads both vegetatively and by seed, being free-flowering and setting viable seed by cross-pollination (the species is reportedly self-incompatible). Seed are dispersed from the end of August onwards. It is susceptible to any but the lightest grazing or mowing and stands which suddenly appear on roadsides or disturbed land, such as coastal reclamations, may persist for some years before disappearing completely if the grassland is grazed or managed. Casual observation suggests that such populations on open grassland and waste places have increased in abundance in the past 3 or 4 decades. Certainly most of the older Floras describe the species, as might be expected from its English name, only as a grass of 'damp woods, ditches and fens', 'marshy woods and shady places' or 'among bushes in shady places'. Even Hubbard (1968) fails to mention the grassland and dune habitats (although the first record in 1629 from the Isle of Sheppey is likely to have been from coastal grassland). Yet it has long been known as a grass of dune slacks and coastal grassland (in which habitat it hybridizes with Marram, *Ammophila arenaria*; see that species) occurring throughout the Baltic and northern European coasts. It is interesting to speculate to what extent the divergent habitats and soil types are reflected in ecological and genetic differences in *C. epigeios* populations and if the apparent increase in open grassland and colonizing populations has occurred.

C. epigeios is native in the British Isles, and part of the Eurasian Boreo-temperate element of our flora (P&H 1997). A variety is reported from mountains in eastern and southern Africa and various forms are occasionally used as an ornamental grass for lakesides and water gardens. Its spread, since the 1962 Atlas, may be due to better recording, a relaxation of grazing or, as implied above, an expansion of its habitat range by colonizing ecotypes.

C. epigeios is a sexual species differing from *C. purpurea* by the dehiscent anthers full of good pollen, and from *C. canescens* by the density of the panicle and the length of the ligule. These three species belong in *Calamagrostis* sect. *Calamagrostis* which is distinguished, albeit not very well, from sect. *Deyeuxia* by the combination of membranous, perfectly smooth lemma, callus-hairs much longer than the lemma and obscure or quite absent rhachilla-extension. Note the spelling of the epithet.

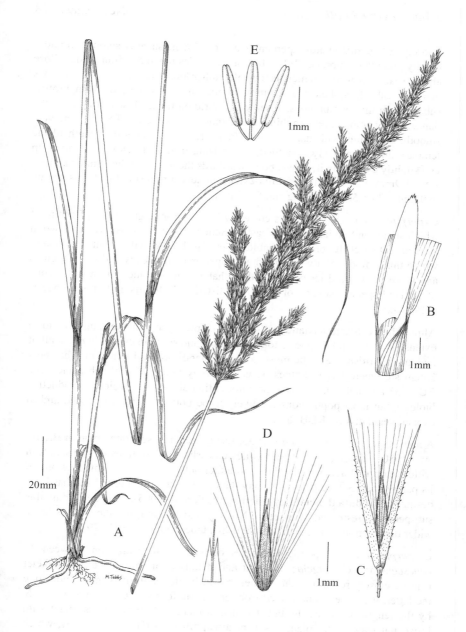

Calamagrostis epigeios: A, habit; B, ligule; C, spikelet; D, floret with flattened lemma tip shown separately; E, anthers.

107. Calamagrostis purpurea (Trin.) Trin.

Scandinavian Small-reed New Atlas: 778

Loosely tufted rhizomatous perennial up to 150cm; sheaths smooth; ligule a bluntly pointed membrane (7)9 – 10(14)mm; blades flat, 4.5 – 5mm wide, pilose above, scabrid beneath. Panicle lanceolate, rather loose, 17 – 22cm, the branches densely scabrid. Spikelets 5 – 6mm; glumes narrowly lanceolate in profile, subequal, firmly membranous, 1-nerved, scabrid on the keel, scaberulous on the flanks, finely pointed; lemma thinly membranous, ovate, 3.2 – 3.8mm, 5-nerved, smooth, the callus with hairs 4.3 – 4.7mm (1.3 – 1.5 times the length of the lemma), the tip narrowly 2-toothed; awn arising from just below the lemma-tip and slightly exceeding it; palea about two-thirds the length of the lemma; anthers 1.5 – 1.9mm, indehiscent; rhachilla-extension absent or a small glabrous peg up to 0.2mm. $2n = 56$. Flowering and fruiting in July.

C. purpurea is a very rare grass currently known from eight sites in Britain, of which six are in Scotland (five in eastern Scotland and one in Argyll) and two in the Lake District. Its preferred habitat seems to be wet willow carr, especially where this is flooded in winter, and also open marsh, ditches, old peat diggings and more rarely on drier banks. In these habitats it is found with a wide range of wetland species, several of which are listed in RDB. Its altitudinal range is unknown.

Although rare, Scandinavian Small-reed, like other species in the genus, can form extensive stands and it appears to be vigorous, and sometimes dominant, at all of its known British sites. The most extensive stands are in the Insh marshes near Kingussie where large swathes occur (this may be a different subspecies; see RDB: 65 and below). We have no information about the species' reproductive biology, but most populations are likely to be both recruited from seed and to expand vegetatively (RDB: 65).

A native species, *C. purpurea* was not recognized as a separate taxon in Britain until 1980 – although it had been collected earlier (e.g. from extensive stands in willow carr at Braemar in 1941) – and either not named or thought to be one of its parent species (see below). It may therefore be under-recorded and has been designated as **data deficient** by Cheffings & Farrell (2005). Outside Britain, this subspecies is restricted to Sweden, Norway and Finland, but the species has a wider distribution (Eurosiberian Boreal-montane element; P&H 1997).

C. purpurea is an apomictic species derived by hybridization between *C. canescens* and *C. epigeios*. In habit and details of inflorescence and spikelet it more closely resembles the former, but in ligule length it is much more like the latter. It can be distinguished from apomictic forms of *C. canescens* mainly by the length of the ligule, but it is also a marginally more robust plant with broad flat leaves. Our plant is subsp. **phragmitoides** (Hartm.) Tzvelev, which is distinguished from other subspecies by the combination of callus-hairs longer

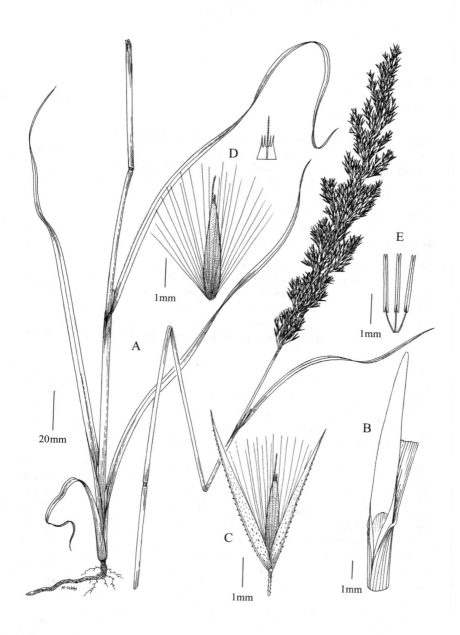

Calamagrostis purpurea subsp. *phragmitoides*: A, habit; B, ligule; C, spikelet;
D, floret with flattened lemma tip shown separately; E, anthers.

than lemma, glumes no more than scaberulous on the flanks, rhachilla scarcely prolonged, spikelets less than 6mm and other minor features of glume shape and awn position. The subspecies are not very well circumscribed and may be better regarded as varieties.

108. **Ammophila arenaria** (L.) Link

Marram   New Atlas: 779

Tufted perennial with extensive, deeply penetrating rhizomes; culms rather stout, up to 90(120)cm; ligule a narrow acuminate membrane 10 – 30(35)mm; blades greyish green, tightly inrolled, stiff and pungent. Panicle spike-like, narrowly oblong to lanceolate-oblong, 10 – 20cm, tapering at the tip. Spikelets narrowly oblong, eventually gaping, 10 – 15mm; glumes subequal, as long as the spikelet; lemma lanceolate, 7.5 – 11mm, obtuse but with a projecting mucro 0.2 – 0.8mm long from just below the tip, bearded at the base with hairs (2.5)3 – 4.5mm; anthers 3, 4.5 – 7mm. $2n = 28$. Flowering and fruiting mid-June to late August.

Marram occurs around the entire coastline of the British Isles, and all offshore islands, wherever there is suitable sand-dune habitat. It is abundant and usually dominant in the mobile stages of almost all dune systems and can be found as scattered non-flowering plants in fixed dunes and dune pasture. Dune soils in which it grows typically comprise loose, unconsolidated sands, low in nutrients, organic matter and water content, and ranging in pH from 6.0 to 9.0 (rarely down to 4.5). The salt content of the sand is also generally low; Marram is not very salt tolerant and does not withstand frequent tidal flooding. It is often preceded in sand-dune successions by two grasses which are salt tolerant, *Elymus farctus* and, to a lesser extent, *Leymus arenarius*, both of which can grow on the driftline marked by the limit of the highest tides. Huiskes (1979) provides a list of plant species commonly found in the *A. arenaria* zone of sand-dunes. The species is also widely planted (including inland sites) to prevent sand-dune erosion.

Among the grasses *A. arenaria* is the ecosystem engineer *par excellence* (rivalled perhaps by *Spartina anglica* on saltmarsh). Vast areas of coastal dune have been built by its ability to stabilize wind-blown sand. Its culms and leaves enhance sand deposition by slowing the wind and the rapidly spreading rhizomes stabilize the sand by branching and rooting at the nodes and producing more erect shoots capable of growing through the accreting layers of sand. It can tolerate up to 1m of sand accretion per year in the most active systems. In these early stages of dune succession Marram is vigorous and flowers freely, but it loses its dominance as the dunes become fixed and other plants colonize, when it ceases to flower and becomes moribund (although often long-lived and persistent). Whilst this loss of vigour can be ascribed to competition with other species, Van der Putten and his colleagues have shown that freshly accreted sand enables new rhizome and root growth and a temporary escape from soil-borne pathogens, including nematodes,

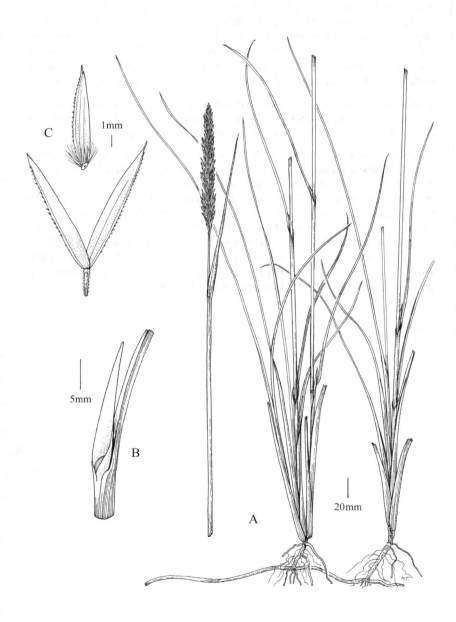

Ammophila arenaria: A, habit; B, ligule; C, spikelet with floret detached from glumes.

which can reduce growth (Van der Putten, 1993). Individuals from fore dunes also respond more rapidly to increased nutrients than those from fixed grey dunes (Gray, 1993). Although vegetative spread predominates in Marram populations, viable seed are produced (>20,000 seeds per clump per annum) and seedlings may occasionally be encountered in the field, usually in April or May. However, seedling mortality is often high due to desiccation, burial or erosion. Newly established plants first flower two or more years after germination, the species being protandrous and principally outbreeding. (Biol. Flora: Huiskes, 1979).

A. arenaria is native (a European Southern-temperate species occurring also on the coasts of W Europe to about 62°N in Norway and southwards to Spain). It has been widely introduced for sea defences outside its native range.

In places Marram hybridizes with *Calamagrostis epigeios* and the resultant hybrid (×**Calammophila baltica** (Flugge ex Schrad.) Brand) is quite sterile. Our plant (sometimes referred to as var. *subarenaria*) is most like Marram, having the greater genomic contribution from that parent, and is found in two areas, the East Anglian coast from N Norfolk to E Suffolk and around Holy Island and Ross Links in S Cheviot (Rihan & Gray, 1991). Morphometric studies indicate that these are plants from just two different hybridization events. Those at Milford-on-Sea in S Hants were taken there from Winterton, Norfolk to stabilize the beach. The hybrid reported from Handa Island off the NW Scottish coast has not been confirmed, although the parents can be found a few metres apart.

109. **Gastridium ventricosum** (Gouan) Schinz & Thell.

Nit-grass

Illustration, page 367

New Atlas: 779

Slender plant with culms erect or geniculately ascending, up to 35(60)cm; ligule a bluntly pointed membrane 1.5 – 3(4)mm; blades flat and glabrous, smooth or scaberulous. Panicle contracted, narrowly lanceolate to narrowly oblong, (2)3 – 10.5cm, spreading at anthesis but contracted again afterwards. Spikelets 3.4 – 4.6(5.3)mm; lower glume as long as the spikelet; upper glume 2.8 – 3.6mm; lemma broadly elliptic, 1.1 – 1.3mm, obtuse with minutely toothed tip, shortly hairy at the base and on the sides, awned from the back above the middle or awnless, the two sorts mixed in the same panicle; awn slender, geniculate, twisted below, 3 – 4.5mm; rhachilla not or scarcely produced, glabrous if the latter; anthers 3, 0.6 – 0.7(0.8)mm. $2n = 14$. Flowering and fruiting late June to mid-August, sometimes persisting until early October.

G. ventricosum is a rare grass probably limited in its native habitat to fewer than 30 locations in SW Britain from the Isle of Wight and Dorset westwards to Cornwall and the Gower Peninsula in S Wales. It occurs in the Channel Islands (on Guernsey and Sark) in ruderal, possibly non-native, habitats and was formerly widespread in S & E England as an arable weed. One relic weed population, known for over 100 years, may still exist in S Hants (and another may have recently established itself from a nearby native site). Its native habitat comprises open turf of short calcareous grasses and herbs on shallow well-drained soils over chalk and limestone. Patches of bare ground, in some sites created by rabbits, are common and the soils are silty clay loams or sandy loams often on a stony matrix and ranging in pH from 6.5 to 7.0 (slightly higher at Clifton, lower in some arable sites (Trist, 1983)). Most populations are on south-facing slopes and relatively near the coast (except a few in Somerset). Such grasslands may be very species-rich. A list of associates from a range of sites is given by Trist (and those from Avon Gorge by Lovatt, (1981)), who records the four most frequent as *Koeleria macrantha, Pilosella officinarum, Sanguisorba minor* and *Thymus polytrichus* (Trist, 1986b; RDB: 168).

Nit-grass is a winter annual, germinating in the autumn (September/October) shortly after the seed are shed, and overwintering as a small, often single-leaved seedling before growth begins again in April. It is, however, frost sensitive, a fact which may partly explain why the species is limited to sites near the sea. Interestingly, such sites, in which bare soil is common and surface temperatures can be extremely high in summer, also provide a niche with the exacting microclimatic conditions required by a range of other organisms, including some ant and butterfly species, which are at their northern limits in southern Britain and have (like *G. ventricosum*) a wider ecological amplitude further south in Europe. The number of inflorescences in British populations varies from year to year but seed production appears to be favoured by hot dry summers and the ideal conditions for population maintenance and expansion are probably a mild winter, a damp warm spring and a hot summer. Seed set is usually high (>80% in experimental conditions) and the species is self-fertile and like most annual grasses, probably predominantly inbreeding. The longevity of the seed bank is unknown. Competition and shading from other plants reduces the amount of flowering and grazing and surface disturbance by rabbits or sheep are important for maintaining favourable habitat conditions. Caryopses with awned lemmas are capable of self-burial by the hygroscopic awn whilst those with unawned lemmas may be mainly dispersed by wind and rain water. (RDB: 168).

First recorded in 1690, *G. ventricosum* is thought to be native in its British calcareous grassland locations, where it may yet be more widespread (as increased recording since the 1962 Atlas has suggested). It is regarded as a casual in other sites, opportunistically occupying a relatively open niche in cornfields where the crop was less dense and also occurring as a wool or grain alien. Improved seed-cleaning, the use of herbicides and the switch to plastic from hessian sacks led to its disappearance from almost all arable sites by the 1950s. Plants from arable habitats were taller, had fewer tillers and unbranched culms compared to those from native sites, but these differences largely merge in cultivation. *G. ventricosum* is a Mediterranean-Atlantic species (P&H 1997) occurring eastwards to Iraq.

As a genus *Gastridium* can be recognized by the peculiar glumes which are swollen, hardened and shining below where they enclose the floret, but membranous, keeled and narrowed above producing the small, hard 'nit' (as in headlice eggs) of the English name. The pale green panicle with its silvery lustre is also unmistakeable.

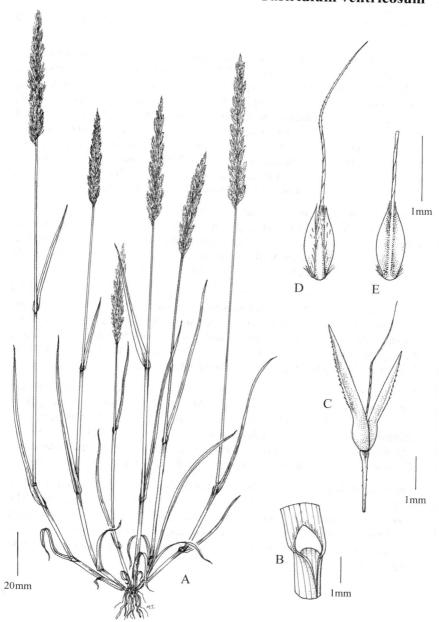

Gastridium ventricosum: A, habit; B, ligule; C, spikelet; D, floret in ventral view; E, floret in dorsal view.

110. Lagurus ovatus L.

Hare's-tail   New Atlas: 779

Greyish green softly hairy plant up to 60cm; sheaths loose, the upper slightly inflated; ligule a blunt membrane 1 – 3.5mm. Panicle a densely fluffy spike-like, globose to ovoid or oblong-cylindrical head, 1 – 4cm, erect or eventually nodding, with projecting bristly awns. Spikelets (7)8 – 10(12)mm; glumes persistent, equal, as long as the spikelet, with narrowly lanceolate body tapering to a long fine bristle, densely pilose with long spreading hairs; lemma rounded on the back, elliptic, the body (3.6)4 – 5(5.4)mm, narrowed into 2 teeth each tipped with a bristle 2.5 – 4(5.5)mm, shortly hairy towards the base, awned from the back in the upper third; awn geniculate with twisted column, 8 – 16(20)mm; anthers 3, 1.2 – 2.6mm. $2n = 14$. Flowering and fruiting late May to mid-August.

Established populations of *L. ovatus* occur in sand-dunes and sandy places on the coast in the Channel Islands and infrequently in southern England, but most other records are of casual plants, scattered mainly thoughout southern England, on rubbish tips, pavements, walls, car parks and waste places. It has only rarely been recorded in Wales, Scotland and Ireland. It is a lowland species.

Hare's-tail is a short-lived annual grass which may germinate in the autumn or the spring, but young plants are frost-sensitive and may rarely survive our winters. It is both self- and cross-pollinating. Many plants in the wild are escapes from garden cultivation or wool or grain aliens and the sand-dune populations along the English south coast (e.g. at Dawlish Warren, Devon and Littlehampton, W Sussex) are known to have been introduced. (AGB: 43).

A neophyte, *L. ovatus* was cultivated in Britain by 1640 and the Guernsey populations were first recorded from the wild in 1791. It has long been naturalized on Guernsey and was finally naturalized on Jersey by the 1860s. The number of established populations in sand-dunes in southern England is said to be increasing. A Mediterranean-Atlantic species, found in Madeira and the Canary Islands, *L. ovatus* is widely naturalized in Mediterranean climatic regions round the world.

A very beautiful grass commonly cultivated for its inflorescence which is widely used in flower arrangements, dried and sometimes dyed bright colours. The densely fluffy white hairs adorning the glumes make the structure of the spikelet very hard to see clearly, but it is unlikely that *Lagurus* will be confused with any other grass except some of the more ornamental species of *Pennisetum*, but these are perennial.

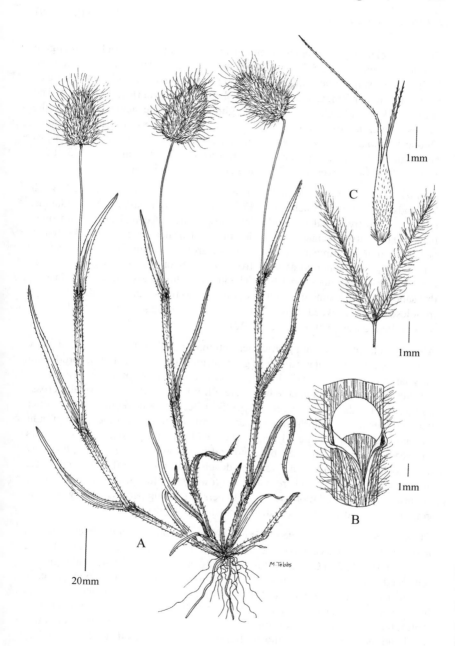

Lagurus ovatus: A, habit; B, ligule; C, spikelet with floret detached from glumes.

111. Apera spica-venti (L.) P.Beauv.

Loose Silky-bent

Slender to relatively stout, erect or geniculately ascending, 30 – 100(135)cm; ligule an oblong membrane (2.5)3.5 – 8.5(10)mm; blades flat, glabrous, scaberulous on both sides or smooth beneath. Panicle ovate or oblong, open and very diffuse or sometimes rather congested, 15 – 35cm, the branches whorled, capillary, naked below. Spikelets (2.2)2.5 – 3.1(3.4)mm; glumes lanceolate, acute, scabrid on the nerves above, the lower 1.7 – 2.5mm, the upper as long as the spikelet; lemma oblong-lanceolate, 2 – 2.7(2.9)mm, acute, asperulous above, awned from just below the tip; awn straight or slightly flexuous, 4.5 – 10mm; anthers 3, 1.2 – 1.7mm. $2n = 14$. Flowering and fruiting late June to mid-August.

A. spica-venti has been recorded from widely scattered locations in the English lowlands but is most frequent in SE England, East Anglia and the NE Midlands. Here it is mostly found in arable fields, especially of cereal crops, and open marginal habitats associated with agriculture such as headlands and tracks. It also occurs from time to time as a casual on waste ground and similar habitats and has infrequently been reported as such from Wales, Scotland and Ireland (a single record from Dublin docks in 1994). The grass is almost exclusively confined to dry sandy or light loam soils and in optimal conditions can be an abundant and troublesome arable weed. It is a lowland species but has been recorded from a path on Ingleborough at 690m (SPB: 48).

A winter annual germinating in either autumn or spring, the elegant and aptly named Loose Silky-bent is capable of growing more than a metre tall and producing very large numbers of small, light, long-awned seed in a single year (there are conflicting accounts of the breeding system from 'apomictic' to 'normally cross-pollinating' but the species is certainly self-fertile). The seed require high summer temperatures to break dormancy and can germinate both in darkness and in light (when the germination rate is higher). The seed bank may persist for up to 5 years and seed are easily dispersed by wind and transported in the soil. In this way dense local populations of the grass can develop and become difficult to eradicate in cornfields, especially where wheat is grown year after year. However, in the majority of sites populations seem not to persist for long periods, even where the grass is quite widespread, as in the Breckland (SPB: 48).

Classified as an archaeophyte in the New Atlas, *A. spica-venti* has been regarded in some Floras as native. It is certainly an ancient introduction, first recorded in the 17th Century (1632 in Clarke (1990), 1670 in Perring *et al.,* (1964)) and regularly remarked upon, largely because of its distinctive and attractive appearance, in the older Floras (e.g. Graves (1822) saw it to the west of London 'accidentally in brickfields' and to the east 'plentifully in corn fields'). However, it does not have a 'natural' habitat in Britain; it is mostly found as a garden escape, casual or arable weed and its populations are mostly transient (it is listed as **near threatened** by Cheffings & Farrell (2005)). It may have been originally introduced with grain

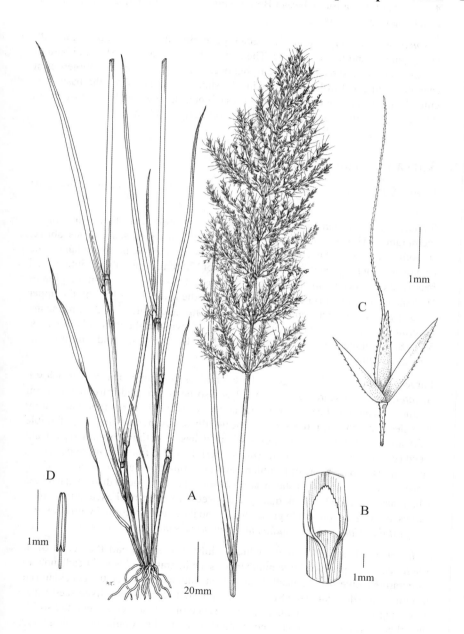

Apera spica-venti: A, habit; B, ligule; C, spikelet; D, anther.

and clover (AGB: 43) but has long been cultivated in gardens as an ornamental. *A. spica-venti* has a Eurosiberian Boreo-temperate distribution as a native and is widely naturalized outside this range.

A. spica-venti is a very distinctive species, generally taller than *A. interrupta* with looser panicle and longer anthers. The panicle branches are whorled and bare of spikelets below in typical specimens, but occasionally they are very numerous at each node, unequal in length and with the shorter spiculate from the base. It is unlikely, however, that even extreme cases of congestion would be confused with *A. interrupta*; anther length will always resolve any problems.

112. Apera interrupta (L.) P.Beauv.

Dense Silky-bent   New Atlas: 780

Slender, erect or geniculately ascending, 15 – 50(80)cm; ligule an oblong membrane (2)2.5 – 4.5(5)mm; blades flat, puberulous or scaberulous above, smooth and glabrous beneath except towards the tip. Panicle narrowly lanceolate or narrowly oblong, contracted, (4)6.5 – 12.5(17.5)cm, dense above, interrupted below, the branches spiculate from the base. Spikelets 2 – 2.6mm; glumes lanceolate, acute, scabrid on the nerves above, the lower 1.5 – 1.9mm, the upper as long as the spikelet; lemma narrowly oblong-lanceolate, 2 – 2.4mm, acute, asperulous above, awned from just below the tip; awn straight or slightly flexuous, 5.5 – 8mm; anthers 3, (0.2)0.3 – 0.4mm. $2n = 14$. Flowering and fruiting mid-June to late July.

Largely restricted to East Anglia, where it may or may not be native (see below), *A. interrupta* is a scarce grass which has also been recorded infrequently from southern, central and eastern England as far north as NE Yorks (and very rarely in Wales and Scotland). It occurs in dry, usually sandy, habitats in areas of arable cultivation and within arable fields where it has sometimes been a significant weed (but less frequently than *A. spica-venti*). It is also found as more persistent populations in bare areas of heathland and poor thin grassland, especially where closely grazed by rabbits or sheep, and as a colonist of a range of disturbed habitats which have included a chalk quarry, a disused railway, gravel excavations, road verges and waste ground. On grassy heathland it has been recorded with *Arenaria serpyllifolia, Catapodium rigidum* and *Sagina procumbens* (SPB: 47).

A. interrupta is a winter annual which, whilst growing to half the height of *A. spica-venti*, can produce large numbers of seed in arable fields and headlands. In its putative native sites on heathlands in East Anglia (centred on the Breckland) it is a much smaller plant (see SPB: 47). It appears to have a long-lived seed bank, appearing in established areas after an absence of several years when the soil is disturbed. Little seems to have been reported about the population ecology and reproductive biology of this species.

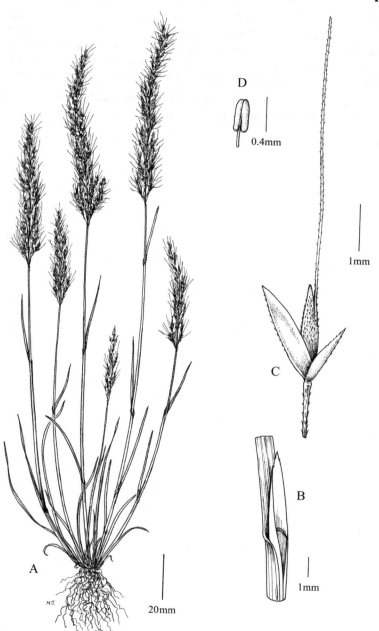

Apera interrupta: A, habit; B, ligule; C, spikelet; D, anther.

A. interrupta is classified as a neophyte in the New Atlas and was first recorded from the wild at Thetford, Suffolk in 1848. Easy (1992) suggests that it is a native species on the light soils of eastern England where it may have grown on sheepwalks on sands and chalklands. Elsewhere it is almost certainly casual, originating from grass-seed, wool shoddy or soils and aggregates from its native area. It is a Eurosiberian Southern-temperate species and has been introduced into N America. Its distribution in Britain appears to be stable or even increasing.

A. interrupta is a plant of generally smaller stature than *A. spica-venti*, with narrow contracted panicle and very small anthers.

113. **Mibora minima** (L.) Desv.

Illustration, page 377

Early Sand-grass

New Atlas: 780

Delicate plant 1.5 – 12(15)cm; ligule a blunt membrane 0.7 – 1.1mm; blades flat or inrolled, smooth and glabrous. Raceme unilateral, 0.6 – 1.6cm, the spikelets ± sessile. Spikelets 1.8 – 2.6mm; glumes persistent, subequal, as long as the spikelet, oblong or elliptic-oblong, very obtuse, smooth and glabrous; lemma 1.1 – 1.6mm, broadly elliptic, truncate or minutely toothed at the tip, densely hairy on the back, awnless; anthers 3, 0.9 – 1.7mm. $2n = 14$. Flowering and fruiting mainly mid-March to early May but, depending on the weather, flowering may start as early as late December and continue, with or without a break, until mid-June or even early July.

M. minima is a rare grass confined to coastal sand-dunes in Wales (in several places in Anglesey and at Whiteford in the Gower Peninsula) and to cliff tops in the Channel Islands, in all of which localities it is thought to be native. It is known from three other dune sites, two recently-discovered populations in England at Studland, Dorset and Sefton, Lancashire (where it may or may not be native) and one older site in Scotland at Dirleton, E Lothian where it is known to have been deliberately introduced. It has also been recorded as a weed of nurseries (it is no longer present at Ferndown, Dorset in this habitat) and may be naturalized in other sites (as at the Firs Botanic Garden in Manchester). In dunes it grows on nutrient-poor bare sand which is moist in winter and not too mobile, preferring patches of open ground in sandy grassland such as rabbit scrapes and path sides, and on cliff slopes in Jersey and Guernsey it is found on thin gravelly soils. It tolerates a wide range of pH levels. Associates of *M. minima* in a range of sites include *Anthyllis vulneraria*, *Aira praecox*, *Cerastium diffusum*, *C. semidecandrum*, *Erophila verna*, *Ononis repens* and *Thymus polytrichus*, but it is frequently found on its own or in a moss carpet among *Ammophila arenaria* or *Carex arenaria*.

As indicated by its specific name, *M. minima* is a tiny grass (arguably the smallest grass in the world (Rich, 1997)) and, as a former epithet *verna* indicates, it is also one of the earliest to come into flower. Even individuals in cultivation rarely average more than 5cm tall and plants <2cm tall are common. In the glasshouse the plant may grow to 15cm and flowering may extend over several months to produce >100 panicles, some occasionally displaying pseudovivipary (the proliferation of the lemma to form a new plant). Plants vary considerably in panicle production in the field as well as in the number of spikelets per panicle. The spikelets are markedly protogynous and, unusually for a short-lived annual grass, *M. minima* is habitually outbreeding. Fewer than 5% of seed on isolated plants are viable, compared to between 22 and 47% of seed on open pollinated plants. Interestingly (for students of evolution) the genetic recombination which normally occurs in outbreeders is restricted in *M. minima* by its meiotic system, the chiasmata being localized to near the centre of the chromosome or the ends of the chromosome arms, and thus preserving intact most of the genetic variation of the parental genotypes, as happens in inbreeders (see Gray, 1986). Seed dispersal is often limited, germination usually occurring in late summer or autumn and a period of temporary chilling being required to initiate flowering (RDB: 246).

As indicated above, *M. minima* is regarded as native in its Welsh and Channel Island locations, but it is not possible to say whether it is native or alien in its newly discovered sand-dune sites. Its diminutive size and early flowering (all traces of the plants can have gone by April) may mean that it has been overlooked. It is not known how long seed survive but the new population at Sefton has certainly expanded. Continual creation of bare sand patches is necessary for population survival. It is a Suboceanic Southern-temperate species, occurring in both coastal and inland sites in the main part of its range. It has been introduced into Australia and N America.

Among British grasses the combination of tiny, one-sided racemes of subsessile, 1-flowered spikelets is unique to *Mibora*. A recent paper by Ortiz *et al.*, (1999) has indicated that populations of this species can be segregated into two distinct subspecies, the segregate being subsp. *littorea* (Samp.) S.Ortiz, J.Rodr.-Oubiña & P.Guitián. Subsp. *littorea* has relatively larger spikelets (2.5 – 3.5(4)mm) than those of subsp. *minima* (2 – 2.5(2.8)mm) and they are more densely packed with some degree of overlap between the first and third spikelets giving a biseriate appearance to the raceme (in subsp. *minima* the first and third spikelets do not overlap and the raceme appears uniseriate). There are other minor differences which are harder to evaluate. Specimens from Dorset (Vc 9), S Hants (Vc 11), E Suffolk (Vc 25) and elsewhere are all clearly subsp. *minima*, but a large proportion of those from Anglesey (Vc 52) are very obviously subsp. *littorea*. It is unclear how important the differences are and for now it is not recommended that the segregate element be given formal recognition.

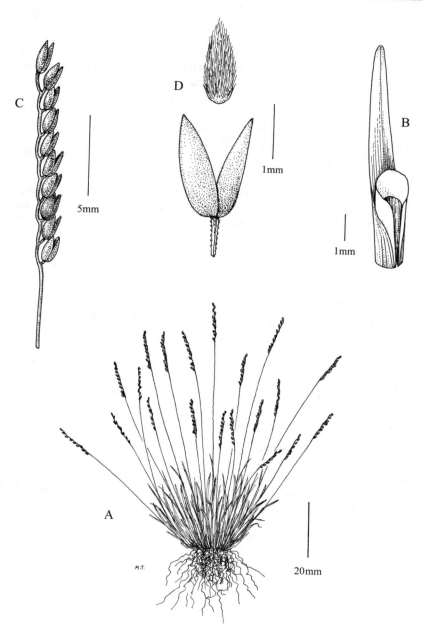

Mibora minima: A, habit; B, ligule; C, raceme;
D, spikelet with floret detached from glumes.

377

114. **Polypogon viridis** (Gouan) Breistr.

Water Bent   New Atlas: 781

Annual or short-lived perennial up to 60cm; culms trailing, rooting at the nodes, geniculately ascending; sheaths loose but not inflated; ligule an oblong membrane 1.5 – 3(5.5)mm. Panicle densely contracted, oblong or ovate, conspicuously lobed, sometimes interrupted below, (2.5)4 – 7.5(13)cm. Spikelets 1.6 – 2.1mm excluding the 0.3 – 1.4mm stipe; glumes equal, rounded on the back below, keeled above, narrowly oblong or narrowly elliptic in profile, scaberulous all over, obtuse, awnless; lemma smooth, broadly elliptic, 0.9 – 1.2mm, minutely toothed at the tip, awnless; anthers 3, 0.4 – 0.7mm. $2n = 28$. Flowering and fruiting early or mid-June to mid-September.

P. viridis occurs in the Channel Islands and the Isles of Scilly and is scattered across southern England, especially below a line from the Bristol Channel to the Thames. It is rare elsewhere in the British Isles. The grass is naturalized and well established in the Channel Islands, generally in open damp habitats. In England it occurs in a range of waste ground and built up habitats including gardens, nurseries, pavement cracks and the base of walls, road- and kerbsides and rubbish tips. These are often in damp situations. It occurs with a wide range of ruderal associates, including other alien species. It is confined to the lowlands.

A neophyte, *P. viridis* is considered to be naturalized in Guernsey, where it was first recorded in 1897, and Jersey, where the first record was 1906. It was introduced into cultivation in Britain in 1800 and was first recorded from the wild in 1876 in Cardiff. Several of its English populations appear to be persistent and the grass appears to be spreading in some areas (e.g. Somerset, where the first record was 1989 and where it was known from nine 10km squares in 2002). It is a native of southern Europe, the Mediterranean, SW & C Asia and N Africa, and has been widely naturalized elsewhere.

On account of the awnless glumes, this species was, for a long time, included in *Agrostis* (as *A. semiverticillata* (Forssk.) C.Chr.), but it now seems that the generic division at this point is unsatisfactory. Modern revisions (e.g. Clayton & Renvoize, 1986) have redefined the distinction and all species with deciduous, stipitate spikelets are now accommodated in *Polypogon*. A male-sterile hybrid between this species and *Agrostis stolonifera* (×**Agropogon robinsonii** (Druce) Melderis & D.C.McClint.) has been recorded from Guernsey.

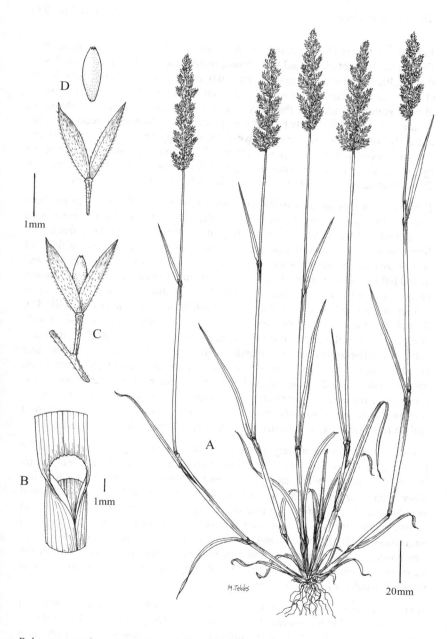

Polypogon viridis: A, habit; B, ligule; C, spikelet attached to panicle branch;
D, spikelet with floret separated from glumes.

115. **Polypogon monspeliensis** (L.) Desf.

Annual Beard-grass   New Atlas: 781

Annual up to 60(75)cm; culms erect or geniculately ascending; uppermost sheaths slightly inflated; ligule an oblong membrane 3 – 11(15)mm, toothed at the top. Panicle densely contracted, narrowly ovate to oblong, sometimes lobed, (1.5)3 – 10.5(15)cm. Spikelets 1.8 – 2.9mm including the 0.2 – 0.3mm stipe; glumes equal, rounded on the back below, keeled above, narrowly oblong in profile, obtuse and shallowly bifid at the tip, scabrid on the body especially below, minutely ciliolate on the margins, awned from the tip, the awn 4.5 – 7.5(9)mm; lemma smooth and glossy, broadly elliptic, 1 – 1.5mm, minutely toothed at the tip, awnless or with a subapical awn up to 1.5mm; anthers 3, 0.3 – 0.6mm. $2n = 28$. Flowering and fruiting mid-June to mid-October or early November.

P. monspeliensis is found in its native coastal habitat along the coasts of southern and eastern England from Dorset to N Norfolk, with centres of distribution around the Solent and the Thames estuaries (e.g. it has been recorded very frequently from the Isle of Grain). It also occurs westwards to Guernsey and Wales and northwards into Scotland as a casual of both coastal sites such as docklands and inland habitats such as rubbish tips, waste ground, disused gravel pits and around gardens (where it is sometimes cultivated for its attractive silky panicles). It arrives in many of these latter habitats as a birdseed or esparto alien (AGB: 45). As a scarce native plant *P. monspeliensis* occurs on open, frequently saline soils in places such as the edges of pools, creeks or recently cleared ditches, the open parts of cattle-poached grazing marsh, or in bare patches along the banks and contour dykes behind sea walls. It is very rarely found on intertidal saltmarshes. Its associates include other short-lived grasses such as *Hordeum marinum, Puccinellia distans, P. fasciculata* and *P. rupestris*, as well as *Aster tripolium, Bolboschoenus maritimus, Juncus gerardii, Salicornia* spp., *Spergularia marina* and, in less saline areas, *Agrostis stolonifera* and *Ranunculus sceleratus*.

An annual reproducing entirely by seed, *P. monspeliensis* requires bare ground for the successful establishment of seedlings. Seeds seem to survive for many years in the soil as new populations often reappear suddenly at, or near to, former sites when ditches are cleared or new sea walls are constructed. Newly established populations often contain large free-flowering plants but over the following two or three years the vigour and seed output of individuals decline as perennial vegetation (often *Bolboschoenus maritimus* or *Elymus athericus*) takes over. The species is self-compatible and predominantly inbreeding, and much of the variation between plants in growth habit, tillering and inflorescence production is retained in cultivation (SPB: 325).

P. monspeliensis is native in SE England (see above) where it reaches its northern limit and is a Mediterranean-Atlantic species widely naturalized outside its native range, including N America and in the Mediterranean climate of southern California it has become something of a pest. Native British populations are

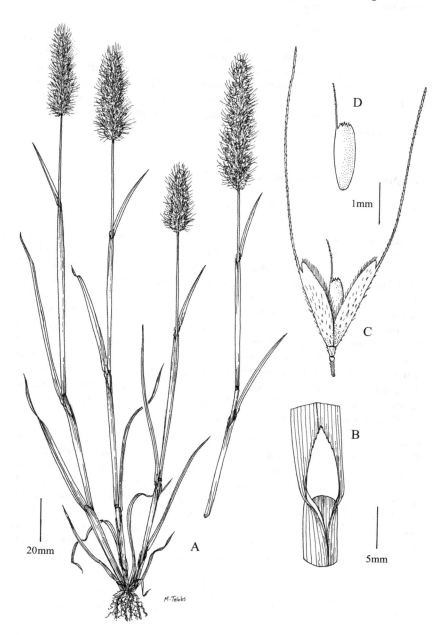

Polypogon monspeliensis: A, habit; B, ligule; C, spikelet with stipe; D, floret.

probably declining as a result of the conversion of coastal grazing marshes to arable and the draining and infilling of brackish ditches and pools.

The combination of long-awned glumes and spikelets deciduous with a short stipe make this species immediately recognizable. In larger specimens the lobing of the panicle is more pronounced and gives rise to an alternative name, Rabbitfoot-grass, used in N America. It occasionally hybridizes with *Agrostis stolonifera*, giving rise to the sterile ×**Agropogon lutosus** (Poir.) P.Fourn. (×*A. littoralis* (Sm.) C.E.Hubb. non Lam.) (*Perennial Beard-grass*). This is a short-lived perennial with persistent spikelets and awned glumes; the anthers are indehiscent and seed-set is unknown.

116. Alopecurus myosuroides Huds.

Black-grass   New Atlas: 783

Annual up to 90cm, erect or geniculately ascending; sheaths smooth, the uppermost slightly inflated; ligule a blunt membrane (1.5)2 – 4(5)mm; blades flat, smooth and glabrous. Panicle cylindrical, (4)5.5 – 11(12.5)cm × 3.5 – 6.5(7.5)mm, tapering towards the tip, yellowish green, pale green or purplish. Spikelets ± oblong, 5.2 – 6.6(7)mm; glumes connate below, the edges on the outer side of the spikelet connate in the lower third, those on the inner side connate in the lower half, shortly hairy (<0.5mm) along the keel and on the nerves near the base, narrowly winged on the keel, acute at the tip; lemma as long as the glumes to within 0.3(0.5)mm either way, the margins connate in the lower third to half, blunt at the tip; awn imperfectly demarcated into column and limb, faintly geniculate at the mid-point, exceeding the tip of the lemma by (3)4 – 6.5(8)mm; anthers orange-brown, (2.4)2.8 – 3.8(4.3)mm. $2n = 14$. Flowering and fruiting mid-May to early September, but mostly early June to mid-August.

Black-grass is very common in England southeast of a line from the Humber to the Severn Estuary and is scattered, usually as a casual, in SW England, Wales, northern England and Scotland, and rare in Ireland. It is almost entirely confined to arable land and associated habitats such as field headlands and waste ground. It is particularly frequent as a weed of winter-sown cereals and other crops which are planted in widely-spaced rows, and although it thrives best on heavy soils of poor structure or limited drainage that are wet in winter, it is more sensitive to cropping system than to soil type and can be found in row crops on light soils. It may be associated with a range of arable weeds and is a species of the lowlands.

A. myosuroides is essentially a grass of open habitats and hence of periodically disturbed ground. Its biology pre-adapts it perfectly to the conditions found in winter-sown crops; it is a winter annual germinating mainly in the autumn, and the seed, which have a short period of innate dormancy broken by high summer temperatures, germinate better in the light (when shed onto the surface or brought to the surface by ploughing). The seeds remain viable for at least 4 years in the

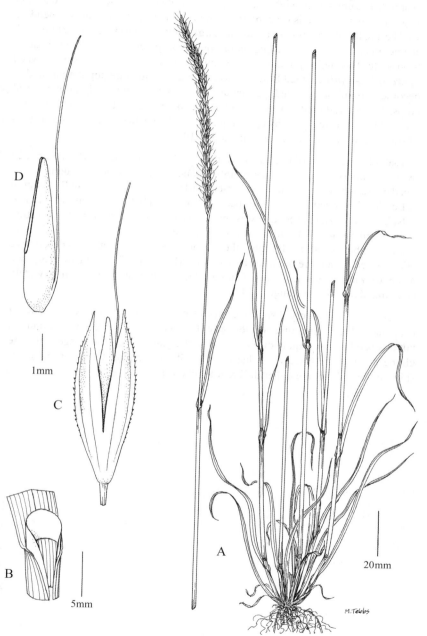

Alopecurus myosuroides: A, habit; B, ligule; C, spikelet; D, floret.

soil, although between 60 and 70% of plants in most populations are from seed <1 year old. The grass over-winters as a small plant, at between the 2-leaf and 5-tiller stage. The mature plant is frost tolerant and flowers through the summer shedding seed before the wheat crop is harvested. Large plants can produce up to 8000 seed, characteristically by outbreeding on protogynous spikelets, but self-fertilization is possible. This biology and life-cycle (almost exactly like that of a similar weed *Apera spica-venti*) enabled Black-grass to rapidly build large populations and to become a troublesome weed, particularly in areas of continuously grown cereal crops. It has additionally acquired tolerance to several herbicides and remains difficult to eradicate except by changing agronomic practice (such as a succession of spring-sown crops). (Biol. Flora: Naylor, 1972).

Classified in the New Atlas as an archaeophyte, *A. myosuroides* has been regarded by most authors as native. It is probably an ancient introduction, brought in as a weed of crops by early farmers. The first record in Britain is 1597 from Paddington in London. The occurrence of the species (also called 'Black Twitch') as a casual outside its core range in Britain was mainly as a wool alien or from a cultivation of birdseed (AGB: 46); birds such as pheasant are said to "eat its seeds with avidity but being disliked by cattle there is no hope of exchanging its descriptive title of weed for a more dignified appellation" (Plues, 1867). As an archaeophyte *A. myosuroides* has a European Southern-temperate distribution and is widely naturalized outside this range.

A. myosuroides is a very distinctive species of *Alopecurus* on several counts: it is annual (of the remaining species only *A. aequalis* can sometimes be annual, but this is otherwise a quite different plant); the glume-keels are winged; and the glume-margins are fused for at least a third of their length (the inner and outer sides of the spikelet are rather different in this respect, see above).

117. **Alopecurus bulbosus** Gouan

Illustration, page 387

Bulbous Foxtail

New Atlas: 782

Tufted perennial up to 45(55)cm, erect or sometimes geniculately ascending; culms bulbous at the base, the 'bulbs' 1.5 – 5(6)mm wider than the culm itself; sheaths smooth, the uppermost slightly inflated; ligule a blunt membrane 2 – 4(5)mm; blades flat or inrolled, smooth and glabrous (except for the scabrid margins). Panicle cylindrical, (1.5)2 – 5.5(7)cm × 2.5 – 5.5(6)mm, green tinged with grey or purple. Spikelets oblong, 2.7 – 3.4(3.8)mm; glumes connate only at the extreme base, shortly hairy (<0.5mm) along the keel and pubescent on the flanks below, wingless on the keel, acute at the tip; lemma c.0.5mm shorter than the glumes, the margins connate only at the extreme base, very blunt at the tip; awn ± demarcated into column (this slightly twisted) and limb, ± geniculate at the mid-point, exceeding the tip of the lemma by 2 – 4.5mm; anthers light brown, 1.5 – 2.4mm. $2n = 14$ (and rarely 21, 28). Flowering and fruiting early May to early August.

A. bulbosus is a scarce coastal grass in southern Britain, occurring in scattered locations along the south coast of Wales, around the Bristol Channel and along the south and east coasts of England north to N Lincs. It is also found on Guernsey. Its habitat is damp brackish grassland close to the sea, especially unimproved grazing marsh and habitats associated with it such as banks below sea and river walls and depressions and hollows which are the sites of former saltmarsh creeks and pans. It particularly favours areas which may be flooded in winter but is not found on tidally-inundated saltmarsh. In general it grows on the edges rather than the centre of hollows and can be found in cattle-poached areas around pools and drinking troughs. Soils tend to be brackish rather than saline, although it will grow alongside more salt tolerant species such as *Aster tripolium, Plantago maritima, Puccinellia distans* and *Spergularia marina*. More typical associates across a range of locations are *Carex divisa, Festuca rubra, Juncus gerardii, Poa pratensis* subsp. *irrigata, P. pratensis* subsp. *pratensis, Ranunculus sardous* and *Trifolium fragiferum* (SPB: 43). It also occurs with *Alopecurus geniculatus* which tends to grow in wetter areas but with which it hybridizes (see below).

Although generally uncommon, *A. bulbosus* can be locally abundant and sward-forming in suitable habitats. It is inconspicuous among other grasses once the small dark narrow flowering spikes have disappeared, usually from early June onwards. New leaves are produced in August and September and a period of slow or inactive winter growth follows before growth and flower production begin in mid-April. Regeneration is by seed (the breeding system is unknown), and occasionally by the swollen pinkish 'bulbs' which can survive tidal inundation and ploughing (Trist, 1981) but are probably not a habitual means of dispersal as in *Poa bulbosa*. Some populations are known to contain diploid, triploid and tetraploid individuals, the last two being true autopolyploids.

A. bulbosus is native in Britain where it is near the northern limit of its Suboceanic Southern-temperate distribution. It was formerly a Red Data Book species having apparently been lost from many former sites, especially in the north and east. More recent surveys showed that the species persists at many of its known locations – in Sussex and Kent (FitzGerald, 1989), Dorset (Pearman, 1990) and E Suffolk (Trist, 1981) – and could easily be overlooked outside the 2 or 3 weeks it is in flower. However, it remains a scarce and threatened plant, as does its habitat which is home to some other uncommon or scarce grasses (see *Puccinellia fasciculata, P. rupestris, Polypogon monspeliensis* and *Hordeum marinum*).

The 'bulbs' comprise the lowermost one or two globose or pear-shaped internodes of the stem swollen with food reserves and clothed in decaying sheaths. The species is most likely to be mistaken for *A. geniculatus* from which it can be distinguished by the acute glumes, the less positively geniculate stems and the more obvious bulbous swellings at the base. The two species occasionally hybridize; the resultant hybrid (**A. ×plettkei** Mattf.) is intermediate, particularly with respect to the size of the 'bulbs,' and is highly sterile with indehiscent anthers. Its distribution and ecology are described by Trist & Wilkinson (1989) who conclude that it does not threaten the survival of *A. bulbosus*.

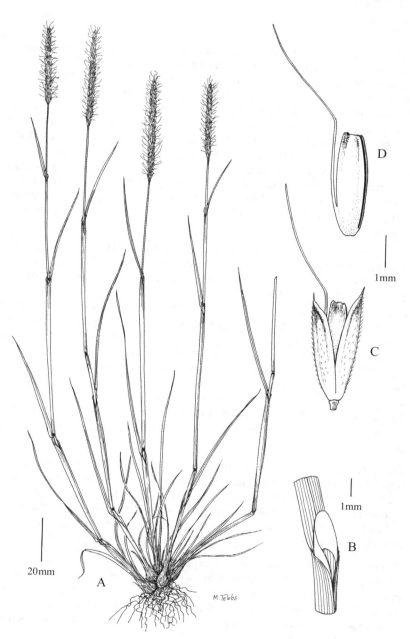

Alopecurus bulbosus: A, habit; B, ligule; C, spikelet; D, floret.

118. **Alopecurus aequalis** Sobol.

Orange Foxtail   New Atlas: 783

Annual, biennial or tufted perennial; culms up to 40(65)cm, sometimes prostrate and rooting from the nodes below, geniculately ascending, not bulbous at the base; sheaths smooth, the uppermost pale and slightly inflated; ligule a blunt membrane 2 – 5.5mm; blades flat, glabrous, faintly scabrid on the nerves, green. Panicle cylindrical, 2.5 – 5cm × 3.5 – 5.5mm, pale green or greyish, sometimes bluish. Spikelets elliptic or oblong, 1.9 – 2.4mm; glumes connate only at the extreme base, shortly hairy (<0.5mm) along the keel and pubescent on the flanks, wingless on the keel, blunt at the tip; lemma as long as the glumes or up to 0.3mm longer, the margins connate in the lower third to half, very blunt at the tip; awn slender, not demarcated into column and limb, shorter than the lemma or exceeding the tip by less than 0.5mm; anthers bright orange or golden yellow, rarely pale brown, (0.7)0.8 – 1(1.2)mm. $2n = 14$. Flowering and fruiting early June to mid-September.

A. aequalis is widely scattered in eastern and central England as far north as Yorkshire and the Isle of Man, and is rare in SW England, Wales, Scotland (where it is probably not native) and Ireland (where it was not discovered until 1992). It has been recorded from Jersey and Lundy Island. It is a grass of rather local occurrence in marginal freshwater wetland habitats such as the edges and shallows of ponds, ditches, pools in wet meadows, reservoirs and gravel pits. It can be especially abundant on drying mud in the summer drawdown zone of water bodies such as village ponds and meres. It occurs in the latter habitat in Breckland where its associates include *Agrostis stolonifera*, *Chenopodium rubrum*, *Juncus articulatus*, *Mentha aquatica*, *Myosoton aquaticum*, *Oenanthe aquatica*, *Persicaria amphibia*, *Phalaris arundinacea*, *Potentilla anserina*, *Rorippa amphibia*, *R. palustris*, *Rumex maritimus* and *Sagina nodosa* (SPB: 40). In recent times Orange Foxtail has been recorded as a weed in several aquatic garden centres.

There appears to be little information available on the reproductive and population biology of this species. Populations vary greatly in size from year to year depending on the extent to which the edges of freshwater bodies recede in a particular summer. In areas of drying mud where dense populations form, it is difficult to count individual plants as culms root at the nodes. In years when water levels are high the plant may only be present as dormant seed (SPB: 40).

A. aequalis is native and has a Circumpolar Boreo-temperate distribution. Changes in distribution are difficult to assess because of annual fluctuations in population size and its virtual disappearance in some years, but the infilling of old ponds and general drainage of wetlands may be seen as a threat. Its ability to colonize garden centres and new open habitats such as abandoned gravel pits may enable it to spread in some areas.

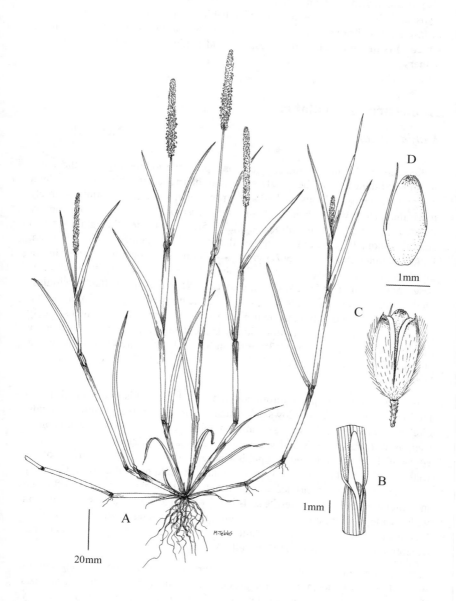

Alopecurus aequalis: A, habit; B, ligule; C, spikelet; D, floret.

389

The bright orange or golden yellow anthers are characteristic of the species and immediately distinguish it from the more common *A. geniculatus*. The species are also distinguished by the markedly shorter anthers, the shorter, less conspicuous awns and the less positively perennial habit of *A. aequalis*. However, they occasionally hybridize; the resultant hybrid (**A. ×haussknechtianus** Asch. & Graebn.) is intermediate in most respects and is highly sterile with indehiscent anthers.

119. Alopecurus geniculatus L.

Marsh Foxtail   New Atlas: 782

Tufted perennial; culms up to 50(65)cm long, prostrate and rooting from the nodes for most of their length, the distal one or two internodes geniculately ascending, not or indistinctly bulbous at the base, in the latter case the swellings scarcely more than 1mm wider than the culm; sheaths smooth, the uppermost slightly inflated; ligule a blunt membrane (2)2.5 – 5(6)mm; blades flat, glabrous and smooth or sometimes slightly rough on the nerves below, green or greyish green. Panicle cylindrical, 2.5 – 5.5(7.5)cm × 4 – 7mm, green or tinged with blue or purple. Spikelets oblong, (2.2)2.6 – 3.3mm; glumes connate only at the extreme base, shortly hairy (<0.5mm) along the keel and pubescent on the flanks, wingless on the keel, blunt at the tip; lemma as long as the glumes or up to 0.2mm shorter, the margins connate only at the extreme base, very blunt at the tip; awn scarcely demarcated into column and limb, faintly geniculate at the mid-point, exceeding the tip of the lemma by 1.5 – 3(3.5)mm; anthers yellowish brown, dark brown or purplish, 1.3 – 1.9mm. $2n = 21$. Flowering and fruiting late May or early June to late August.

A. geniculatus is widespread throughout the British Isles. It is frequently found in the lower parts of wet meadows and grazing marshes, on the margins of ponds, ditches and rivers, and also, less commonly, in a range of disturbed wet habitats such as wet arable fields and waste places. It may be abundant on the muddy edges of shallow ponds and still pools where it often floats on the surface of the water, rooting at the nodes and 'geniculating' or bending at the nodes in a very characteristic fashion to produce its erect panicles. Its habitats are typically flooded in winter and tend to be on fertile soils in the pH range 5.5 – 7.0. The grass occurs with a wide range of plant species including, at many sites, *Agrostis stolonifera*. It is most common in lowland Britain but reaches 595m in Northumberland and, exceptionally, 845m on Great Dun Fell (Westmorland).

Marsh Foxtail, although low-growing, can form extensive carpets of long stolons which root at the nodes, and if shoots are detached by disturbance or grazing animals they often re-root to form new plants. The relative importance of regeneration by this means or by seed is not known. Seed may germinate throughout the summer months and presumably provide a means of spreading to more distant disturbed

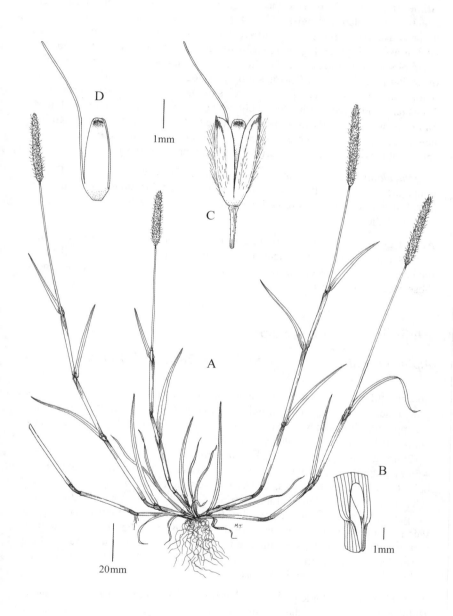

Alopecurus geniculatus: A, habit; B, ligule; C, spikelet; D, floret.

or drawn-down areas of bare mud. A persistent seed bank has been found by some authors, but not others. In fact, considering it is a relatively common species, Grime *et al.,* (2007) remark that *A. geniculatus* has not received sufficient attention from plant ecologists (CPE: 104). They draw attention to its similarity in many aspects to *Agrostis stolonifera* and compare its ecology with that of the latter grass, noting that *A. geniculatus* better exploits the drawn-down margins of reservoirs, flowers and sets seed earlier, and generally occupies a narrower range of habitat types. *A. geniculatus* is strongly protogynous, and is probably mostly outbreeding, but is self-compatible. Studies of DNA variation (Wentworth *et al.,* 2004) have indicated that it is probably derived from the (much rarer) diploid *A. bulbosus,* with which it can form hybrids (see that account), but from which it is now largely separated, both ecologically (*A. geniculatus* is found in wetter, non-saline habitats) and in evolutionary terms (the hybrid is sterile).

A. geniculatus is native in the British Isles and has a wide European Boreo-temperate distribution. It is widely naturalized outside this range, for example in N & S America and in Australia. It may have occurred rarely in the British Isles as a wool alien.

At first glance this species may be confused with *A. bulbosus* but it has blunt glumes, a more positively geniculate habit and less obvious bulbous swellings at the base. It hybridizes with *A. aequalis, A. bulbosus* and *A. pratensis*; see under those species for details.

120. Alopecurus ovatus Knapp

Alpine Foxtail   New Atlas: 783 (as *Alopecurus borealis*)

Loosely tufted perennial with slender stolons; culms up to 45cm, erect or geniculately ascending, without bulbous swellings at the base; sheaths smooth, the uppermost inflated; ligule a blunt membrane 1 – 2(3)mm; blades flat, glabrous, faintly scaberulous above. Panicle broadly cylindrical to ovoid, 1.5 – 3cm × 7 – 12mm, greyish green or tinged with purple. Spikelets elliptic or ovate, 3 – 4.5mm; glumes connate only near the base (less than a quarter their length), silky-hairy (>1mm) along the keels, shortly hairy on the flanks, wingless on the keel, subacute at the tip; lemma as long as or very slightly longer than the glumes, the margins connate only near the base (less than a quarter their length), very blunt at the tip; awnless or with a slender awn ± demarcated into a slightly twisted column and straight limb, faintly geniculate at the mid-point and exceeding the tip of the lemma by 1 – 2mm; anthers brown, 1.8 – 2.7mm. $2n = 100$, c.112, 117. Flowering and fruiting late June to early August.

A. ovatus is a rare alpine grass recorded from scattered locations in the Scottish Highlands and from southern Scotland and northern England. It occurs on the banks of mountain streams and in flushes, on mud and rocks in the stream or on wet mossy and grassy slopes (often associated with late lying snow). It is found

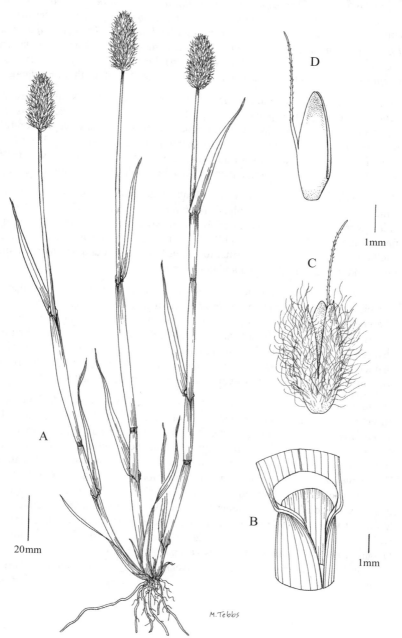

Alopecurus ovatus: A, habit; B, ligule; C, spikelet; D, floret.

393

over a range of acidic or slightly basic substrates where its associates include *Caltha palustris, Chrysosplenium oppositifolium, Epilobium anagallidifolium, Montia fontana, Saxifraga stellaris, Stellaria uliginosa* and *Veronica serpyllifolia* (SPB: 41). Among the bryophytes in such habitats are *Dicranella squarrosa, Philonotis fontana* and *Scapania uliginosa*. It mainly occurs above 600m and ascends to 1220m on Braeriach (S Aberdeen), but is found at lower elevations down to 450m on Widdybank Fell (Durham) in the fells of northern England.

Little seems to be known about the ecology and biology of this rather rare and generally inconspicuous patch-forming grass. It is often heavily grazed by sheep and deer and inflorescences can then be found only among taller vegetation (e.g. in *Carex nigra* or *Eriophorum angustifolium*) along the edges of flushes and streams. Flower production is said to vary considerably from year to year (SPB: 41). Many records report single plants or patches with very few inflorescences.

A. ovatus has a Circumpolar Arctic-Montane distribution, being present in N America and to 83°N on Greenland. In Europe it is native in Britain, Svalbard, arctic Russia and the Urals. First found in Britain in 1794, the species was unknown outside the Scottish Highlands until 1956 when it was discovered in the southern uplands. Since then further localities have been found within its existing range and in southern Scotland and northern England.

A. ovatus is a variable species in which the lemma may be either awnless or conspicuously awned; the complete absence of awns is unusual in *Alopecurus*. The species is usually recognized by the broadly cylindrical or ovoid panicle and awnless lemmas. Awned forms can resemble *A. pratensis* and are then best distinguished by the degree of fusion of the lemma margins. This is a very difficult character to see since it is not easy to remove a lemma from between the glumes without damaging it; it is, however, reliable when other characters fail.

The familiar name *A. alpinus* Sm. (1803) is predated by *A. alpinus* Vill. (1786), a different species, and cannot be used. The unavailable name has been replaced by *A. borealis* Trin. (1820) in most recent texts. However, Knapp (1804), in a much neglected publication, was apparently aware of the problem of Smith's epithet and coined a new name, *A. ovatus*, to replace it, citing the same type material. This name predates *A. borealis* and must therefore replace it. There is, however, another species in the Antarctic region, known locally as *A. magellanicus* Lam., that may be conspecific; it seems to differ by little more than its longer awn. Should it turn out to be the same as our species then the name *magellanicus*, which dates from 1791, would have to be used. In a revision of *Alopecurus* by Doğan (1999) the epithet *borealis* is accepted, with *magellanicus* in synonymy without further comment (an obvious error); the range of *magellanicus* was not included in that of *borealis*.

121. **Alopecurus pratensis** L.

Illustration, page 397

Meadow Foxtail   New Atlas: 781

Tufted perennial up to 100(135)cm, erect or geniculately ascending, not bulbous at the base; sheaths smooth, the uppermost slightly inflated; ligule a blunt membrane 1 – 2.5(3)mm; blades flat, glabrous, smooth or scabrid, green. Panicle cylindrical to broadly cylindrical, 3.5 – 9.5(13)cm × 6.5 – 11.5mm, green or purplish. Spikelets elliptic, (4)4.5 – 6(6.5)mm; glumes connate in the lower quarter, ciliate (c.1mm) on the keel, pubescent on the flanks, wingless on the keel, acute at the tip; lemma as long as the glumes to within 0.3mm either way, the margins connate in the lower third to half, acute at the tip; awn clearly demarcated into column (this slightly twisted) and limb, geniculate at the mid-point, exceeding the tip of the lemma by 3 – 6.5mm; anthers brown, 2 – 3.5mm. $2n = 28$. Flowering and fruiting mid-May to late July; some strains beginning in early April and some lasting at least until mid-August.

Widespread throughout the British Isles, *A. pratensis* is absent only from the mountains of NW Scotland and from parts of western Ireland. It is a common component of moist grassland on fertile soils throughout the lowlands, and is also abundant in upland pastures and hay meadows. To a lesser extent it occurs in other grassy habitats such as road verges, parks, hedgerows and woodland margins but is not found in very dry situations on light or infertile soils, in grassland which remains waterlogged through the summer, or in frequently disturbed habitats including arable fields. It is most frequent on mildly acidic soils in the pH range 5.0 – 7.0. Being essentially a grass of grasslands, Meadow Foxtail tends to occur with other meadow grasses (some with similar appellations) such as *Anthoxanthum odoratum, Cynosurus cristatus, Festuca pratensis* and *Phleum pratense*, but has a wide range of associates, particularly in older species-rich hay meadows and pasture. It reaches 610m in Dumfries and, exceptionally, 845m on Great Dun Fell, Westmorland.

A. pratensis remains green through the winter and begins to grow early in the spring. It is early flowering, following *Anthoxanthum odoratum* as one of our earliest meadow grasses. It displays the clear protogyny typical of its genus which undoubtedly facilitates outbreeding and hybridization not only between other *Alopecurus* species, but also among the various strains of indigenous plants and imported cultivars of *A. pratensis*. The variation between 'leafy' and 'stemmy' genotypes seen in other grasses (e.g. *Lolium perenne*) can be found among these strains. Seed is set in June and July and regeneration appears to be mainly by the autumn colonization of gaps in the vegetation, there being no persistent seed bank. *A. pratensis* is frost tolerant, can tolerate grazing and cutting, but not heavy trampling, and is moderately shade tolerant. It was formerly a favoured constituent of pasture and hay meadows on moist productive soils (see below) and can be most frequently found in older permanent grassland. (CPE: 106).

A. pratensis is native in the British Isles and has a circumpolar Boreo-temperate distribution, in part of which it is native. It has been widely naturalized and, at least until the middle of the last century, was traded as a forage grass. Indeed, it was probably the first forage species to be sown in Britain, seed from indigenous strains being collected for cultivation (and prizes offered for their quality) as early as 1766. Early authors and agronomists extol the virtues of the species, especially the native genotypes, which with its early growth, high production, nutrition and palatability, and plentiful aftermath, achieved the triple goals of 'quality, quantity and earliness'. For example, Graves (1822) hails it "the best of all our English grasses for two crops where the land is rich" and Curtis (1805) notes "it bears the scythe twice a year to advantage". However, it has declined in agricultural importance probably because it takes 2 – 3 years to develop a productive sward and cannot be used in short-term leys. An excellent companion grass, rather than a dominant, it is among the species recommended for creating wild flower meadows.

Apart from the great diversity of native strains, numerous varieties have been imported to improve yields for grazing; often these flower earlier than the native strains or persist until much later, sometimes staying green all year. On rare occasions the species bears proliferous spikelets. Forms with coloured or variegated leaves are sometimes cultivated in gardens, among them 'Aureo-variegatus' with leaves striped green and golden-yellow, and 'Aureus' with wholly golden-yellow leaves. The species hybridizes with *A. geniculatus* almost wherever the two species grow together. The resultant hybrid (**A. ×brachystylus** Peterm. (*A. ×hybridus* Wimm.)) is intermediate in most respects, especially in the fusion of the lemma and glume margins and spikelet length (this generally in the range of 3 – 4.5mm); it is usually highly sterile with indehiscent anthers (New Atlas: 782). On rare occasions the hybrids may show a low level of fertility, in which case recognition is a matter of assessing the degree of intermediacy between the parents.

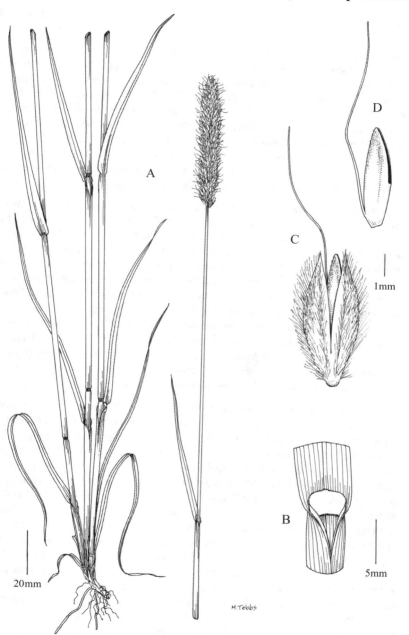

Alopecurus pratensis: A, habit; B, ligule; C, spikelet; D, floret.

122. Phleum arenarium L.

Sand Cat's-tail   New Atlas: 785

Annual up to 15(30)cm, erect or geniculately ascending; sheaths smooth, the uppermost slightly inflated; ligule a blunt membrane (1)2 – 4(7)mm; blades glabrous, 1.5 – 4mm wide, usually flat, sometimes folded. Panicle subcylindrical to narrowly ellipsoid, (0.5)1 – 5cm × (4)5 – 7.5mm, narrowed at the base, rounded at the tip, the branches free. Spikelets lanceolate to oblong-elliptic, 3 – 4mm; glumes acute or subacute and gradually narrowed into a scabrid mucro 0.2 – 0.4mm, stiffly pectinate-ciliate on the keel above, ciliolate on the margins, scaberulous on the flanks; lemma one-third the length of the glumes, very blunt at the tip, minutely hairy; palea as long as the lemma; anthers 0.5 – 0.9mm. $2n = 14$. Flowering and fruiting mid- or late May to early August.

P. arenarium is a grass of sand-dunes widely distributed around the English, Welsh and Irish coasts (except SW Ireland) and in the Channel Islands, but confined in Scotland to scattered locations on the east coast and to the north Solway coast. It also occurs inland on open heathland in Breckland and rarely in other disturbed sandy areas. In coastal dunes it grows on open, infertile, free-draining calcareous sands or sandy shingles which are likely to be mobile or semi-mobile. These range in pH from 5.6 to 8.8 and the plant is absent from acidic sands and dune systems and from wet dune slacks. It is found mostly in open areas within semi-fixed dunes dominated by *Ammophila arenaria* and *Festuca rubra* and associates in this habitat include other winter annuals such as *Aira praecox, Arenaria serpyllifolia, Cerastium diffusum, C. semidecandrum, Myosotis ramosissima, Viola tricolor* and *Vulpia fasciculata*. The moss *Tortula ruraliformis* is a common associate; a full list is given by Ernst & Malloch (1994).

P. arenarium is a winter annual reproducing entirely by seed which germinate in the dunes from late August up to late November whenever the sand is sufficiently moist and temperatures fall below 10°C. The overwintering leaves lie near the sand surface but young seedlings are susceptible to both autumn and spring droughts and episodic dry spells can cause severe mortality. Early spring drought may kill more than 90% of plants. Growth resumes from March onwards, depending on frosts, and the inflorescences start to develop in mid-April and to flower from May onwards. *P. arenarium* has relatively small anthers, is fully self-compatible and populations are likely to be highly inbreeding (bagged heads produce as many seed as unbagged heads). Nearly all caryopses are shed by early September and the fairly shallow-rooted plants turn straw coloured and quickly disappear. In the field there appears to be little or no carry over of seed from year to year although seed remain viable in storage for up to 7 years (>50% do not survive 4 years). Seed can withstand sand burial by 2cm but only a few seedlings emerge from 5cm deep. Adult plants can withstand 5cm of accreting sand, but lose recently initiated tillers, and display considerable phenotypic plasticity in height, the number of tillers, the number of spikelets per inflorescence and the

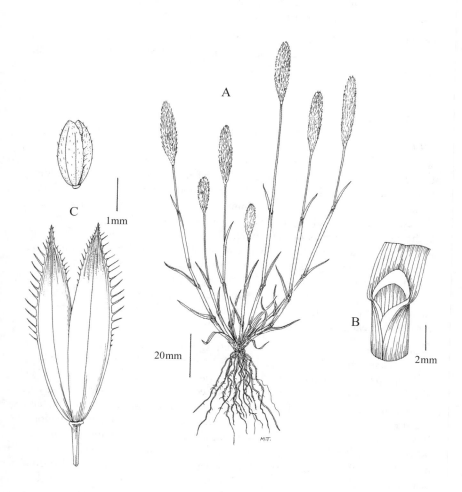

Phleum arenarium: A, habit; B, ligule; C, spikelet with floret detached from glumes.

weight of caryopses. The adult plant can be less than 2cm high but responds dramatically to fertilizer additions. Susceptibility to aluminium may explain the species' restriction to calcareous sands. (Biol. Flora: Ernst & Malloch 1994).

A native in the British Isles, *P. arenarium* occurs along the European coast from Sweden southwards (a European Southern-temperate plant). It has declined in Breckland, possibly because of a decrease in mobile sandy habitats (it does not compete well in perennial vegetation).

The only annual in the genus native to the British Isles, further distinguished by the acute or subacute glumes gradually tapered into a short mucro, and by the short anthers.

123. Phleum alpinum L.

Alpine Cat's-tail   New Atlas: 785

Loosely tufted, shortly rhizomatous perennial up to 50cm, erect or ascending from a curved or geniculate base; sheaths smooth, the upper slightly inflated; ligule a very blunt membrane 0.5 – 2mm; blades glabrous, 2.5 – 5mm wide, flat. Panicle ovoid to broadly cylindrical, 1 – 3(5)cm × 8.5 – 12mm, not narrowed at the base, the branches free but extremely short. Spikelets oblong, 4.5 – 6mm including the awns; glumes stiffly pectinate-ciliate on the keel, scaberulous on the flanks, the lower ciliolate on the margins, truncate at the tip and produced into a straight or curved scabrid awn 2 – 3mm; lemma about two-thirds the length of the glume-body, very blunt at the tip, minutely hairy on the nerves; palea a little shorter than the lemma; anthers 1 – 1.6mm. $2n = 14, 28$. Flowering and fruiting early July to early or mid-August.

P. alpinum is a scarce alpine grass occurring above 600m in the mountains of northern and central Scotland and in two sites in northern England. It grows both in damp open rocky habitats and in closed swards on wet grassy slopes with other grasses, sedges and mosses, mainly on calcareous substrates but in some areas on more acidic rocks enriched by flushing or downwashed base-enriched sediment. It grows in cliff gullies and on dry rock faces but is usually in damp situations. It is often associated with *Carex bigelowii, C. saxatilis, Deschampsia cespitosa, Festuca rubra, Juncus castaneus, Luzula multiflora, Nardus stricta* and a variety of small herbs and mosses (SPB: 309). *Alopecurus ovatus* has been recorded from nearby flushes in several of its central Scottish sites but not further west. The altitudinal range of *P. alpinum* in Britain is from 610m on Braeriach to 1220m on Cairntoul (both in S Aberdeen).

Little seems to be known about the population biology of Alpine Cat's-tail in its British stations, although the species has been studied in Antarctica; populations from different micro-environments on South Georgia were shown to vary in reproductive output as measured by the number of inflorescences, florets and seed

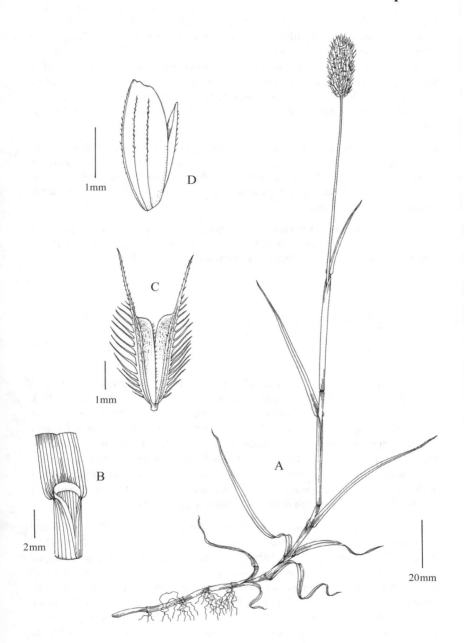

Phleum alpinum: A, habit; B, ligule; C, glumes; D, floret.

which were related directly to the severity of each habitat. Vegetative performance was remarkably similar across the habitats (Callaghan & Lewis, 1971a, 1971b). During the winter plants undergo a period of dormancy broken by the retreat of overlying snow. Flowering tillers are produced after floral initiation of vegetative tillers at least one year old. Seed have no innate dormancy. It is probable that the British populations, like some of those on South Georgia, fail to set viable seed in several years, and that existing populations are mostly maintained by vegetative growth. In most British habitats it is ungrazed or lightly grazed and heavy grazing may partly be responsible for restricting the plant's spread in some areas (SPB: 309).

P. alpinum is native in Britain and is the most widespread of the *Phleum* species, having a Circumpolar Boreo-arctic montane distribution in the northern hemisphere and being found on high mountains in Chile and Argentina, and in Antarctica. It is probably still present at some of the British sites which have not been revisited since before 1987.

Our plant is subsp. **alpinum** (at one time known as *P. commutatum* Gaud.) which is tetraploid ($2n = 28$) and has scabrid awns. In the mountains of central and southern Europe is subsp. **rhaeticum** Humphries which is diploid ($2n = 14$) and has ciliate awns.

124. Phleum phleoides (L.) H.Karst.

Purple-stem Cat's-tail   New Atlas: 785

Tufted perennial up to 60(70)cm, usually erect; sheaths smooth; ligule a very blunt membrane 0.5 – 1.5(2)mm; blades glabrous, 1.5 – 3mm wide, flat or inrolled. Panicle cylindrical, 2.5 – 6.5(9)cm × 5 – 7.5mm, not narrowed at the base, the branches free. Spikelets oblong, 2.2 – 3.4mm including the awns; glumes abruptly narrowed at the tip into a scabrid mucro or short awn 0.2 – 0.5(0.7)mm, scabrid to pectinate-ciliate on the keel above, glabrous on the margins, scaberulous on the flanks above; lemma two-thirds to three-quarters the length of the glumes, blunt at the tip, glabrous or minutely hairy; palea about as long as the lemma; anthers 1 – 1.3(1.5)mm. $2n = 14$. Flowering and fruiting mid-June to early August.

P. phleoides is a rare grass of dry sandy and chalky soils in SE England and is now almost entirely confined to the Norfolk and Suffolk Breckland. Here it occurs in a range of open habitats including grazed open grassland and heathland, wide sandy road verges within forest plantations, the edges of tracks and chalk pits, and near rabbit warrens and on other disturbed ground. Soils are generally shallow, free-draining, light and infertile. It occurs outside Breckland in Hertfordshire on glacial sand overlying chalk and at a relatively recently discovered site in E Suffolk. Typically among a wide range of associates are the grasses *Festuca ovina, Helictotrichon pratense, Koeleria macrantha* and *Phleum*

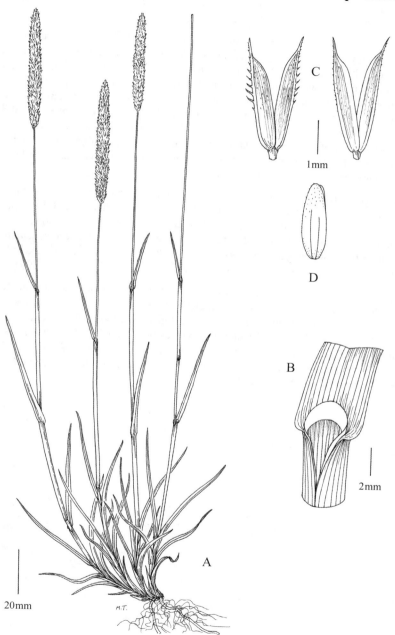

Phleum phleoides: A, habit; B, ligule; C, glumes of two sorts; D. floret.

bertolonii as well as *Achillea millefolium, Galium verum, Lotus corniculatus, Luzula campestris, Plantago lanceolata, Ranunculus bulbosus, Sagina nodosa* and *Scabiosa columbaria* (RDB: 277).

Although nationally rare, the Breckland colonies of *P. phleoides* appear to be thriving (a 1993 survey reporting 40 sites in Norfolk and Suffolk). It is a remarkably drought-tolerant grass, remaining green when other grasses are withered and brown. Flowering in Breckland mainly in June, it is protogynous and self-incompatible. Where it is heavily grazed by rabbits it may fail to flower and lack of flowering spikes may have caused the species to be overlooked in the past. It is not known whether seed germinate mainly in autumn or spring but establishment of seedlings on bare ground suggests that autumn germination is important. The species is said to be susceptible to the addition of fertilizer, being outcompeted by more vigorous species.

A native in Britain, *P. phleoides* is a Eurosiberian Temperate species with a continental distribution in W Europe. It was first recorded around 1775 near Newmarket and in 1780 at Swaffham. Disappearing from many locations before 1930, new populations have been found recently, most of which are considered to have been overlooked (see above), and its known range has been extended eastwards; its easternmost site at Stuston (E Suffolk) was discovered in 1991.

P. phleoides is a relatively easy species to recognize on account of the combination of perennial habit and cylindrical panicle with free branches. Gordon (undated) noted that "Sinclair pointed out that the inflorescence looks like a spike, until pressed between the fingers when it proves to be a panicle". *P. alpinum* has a shorter, broader panicle and longer awns on the glumes, and is found in quite different places. *P. pratense* and *P. bertolonii* have truncate glumes and the panicle branches are adnate to the main axis.

125. Phleum pratense L.

Illustration, page 407

Timothy

New Atlas: 784

Loosely to densely tufted perennial up to 100(150)cm, erect or geniculately ascending, the basal 1 – 3 internodes short and usually swollen and bulb-like; sheaths smooth, not inflated; ligule a rounded or sometimes bluntly pointed membrane 2 – 5.5mm; blades glabrous, 4 – 8mm wide, usually flat, scabrid all over or only in the upper part and on the margins, green or greyish green. Panicle cylindrical, (3)5 – 14(20)cm × 6.5 – 10mm, the branches adnate to the axis. Spikelets oblong, (3.5)4 – 5(5.5)mm including the awns; glumes stiffly pectinate-ciliate on the keel, scaberulous on the flanks, the lower ciliolate on the margins, truncate at the tip and produced into a straight or curved scabrid awn 0.8 – 1.7(2)mm; lemma two-thirds to three-quarters the length of the glume-body, very blunt at the tip, minutely hairy on the nerves and flanks; palea about as long as the lemma; anthers (1.4)1.7 – 2.2(2.4)mm. $2n = 42$. Flowering and fruiting mid-June to mid-August, sometimes persisting until late September.

P. pratense is widespread and common throughout most of the British Isles except NC & NW Scotland. It occurs on the Outer Hebrides and the Orkney and Shetland Isles where it is classified as an introduction (see below). The species is a common constituent in a wide range of grass-dominated habitats including hay meadows, pastures and rough grassland as well as waste places, field margins, road verges and arable fields. It is widely sown in grasslands for hay, silage and pasture and occurs as a casual from birdseed and other sources. It is most frequent on moist, relatively fertile, heavy or peaty soils and is restricted to those with a pH >5.0. Its most faithful associates are other meadow grasses (e.g. *Alopecurus pratensis, Anthoxanthum odoratum, Cynosurus cristatus* and *Festuca pratensis*) but it may be found with a wide range of herbs. Charting the exact distribution, ecological amplitude and changing status of *P. pratense* is complicated not only by its widespread introduction and cultivation but also by confusion with *P. bertolonii* (also introduced and cultivated) and the frequent inclusion of both species within an aggregate taxon (*P. pratense* sens. lat.).

A familiar grassland plant, Timothy is actually an extremely variable species comprising a great many cultivars which have been introduced for hay or grazing. Like other grasses selected in this way it includes short-lived 'stemmy' types and more persistent 'leafy' types. Some individuals may be very long-lived (>20 years) whilst others are quite transient. *P. pratense* is a cold tolerant species which is generally green in winter and produces tillers in both spring and autumn. Its tall nodal stems and relatively shallow root system suit it best to infrequent cutting or grazing and it is especially vulnerable to heavy summer grazing and trampling. It flowers in the summer following germination (unusually among British pasture grasses it does not have a chilling requirement for floral induction) and is protogynous and self-incompatible. Although a proportion of the seed remains viable for 20 years in storage evidence for a persistent soil seed bank is equivocal.

Nevertheless, populations must be maintained by seed, most individuals being virtually incapable of lateral vegetative spread (CPE: 462).

P. pratense is native in the British Isles, although truly native genotypes may be restricted to moist soils in water meadows and other low-lying grasslands, and may now be quite rare. Actual introductions have only been recognized in SW Ireland and the Northern Isles but must be widespread throughout lowland Britain where the first introductions date from the early part of the 18th century (including those brought in around 1720 by Timothy Hanson who cultivated the species widely in N America and from whom it received its common name). A Eurosiberian Temperate species, *P. pratense* has been widely naturalized so that its distribution is now circumpolar.

An immensely variable species overlapping in almost all characters with *P. bertolonii*. The most reliable means of separation is by considering a combination of features including: height of plant (mostly over 70cm; *bertolonii* mostly less than 70cm); width of leaf (mostly more than 4mm; *bertolonii* mostly less than 5mm); length of anther (mostly more than 1.7mm; *bertolonii* mostly less than 1.7mm); width of panicle (mostly more than 7mm; *bertolonii* mostly less than 7mm); length of spikelet including awn (mostly more than 4mm; *bertolonii* mostly less than 4mm); length of awn (mostly 1.2mm or more; *bertolonii* mostly less than 1mm). No single character, except chromosome number (*pratense* hexaploid, $2n = 42$; *bertolonii* diploid, $2n = 14$), is wholly reliable and such characters as panicle length and ligule shape are of very little help. Nevertheless, the rank of species does seem appropriate for the two elements.

An artificial hybrid raised at the Experimental Station of the Scottish Society for Plant Breeding at Corstophine in about 1937 (specimens in the Kew Herbarium) between *P. bertolonii* ($2n = 14$) and *P. alpinum* ($2n = 28$), which is apparently hexaploid ($2n = 42$) and quite fertile, resembles *P. pratense* in just about every feature. No natural hybrids, however, have been detected in the British Isles.

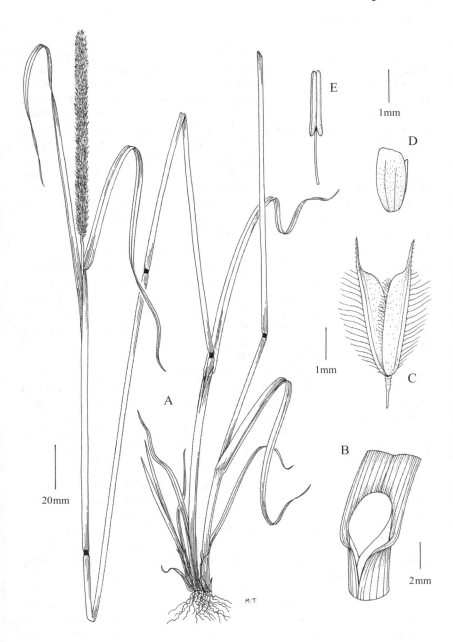

Phleum pratense: A, habit; B, ligule; C, glumes; D, floret; E, anther.

126. **Phleum bertolonii** DC.

Smaller Cat's-tail New Atlas: 784

Loosely to densely tufted perennial up to 65(80)cm, erect or geniculately ascending, the basal 1 – 2 internodes short, swollen and bulb-like; sheaths smooth, the uppermost slightly inflated; ligule a bluntly pointed, sometimes broadly rounded, membrane 1 – 3(4)mm; blades glabrous, 1.5 – 4(5)mm wide, usually flat, scaberulous on the margins, sometimes also on the nerves, green or greyish green. Panicle cylindrical, 1 – 6.5(8.5)cm × 4.5 – 7mm, the branches adnate to the axis. Spikelets oblong, 2.3 – 3.8mm long including the awns; glumes stiffly pectinate-ciliate on the keel, scaberulous or minutely hairy on the flanks, the lower ciliolate on the margins, truncate at the tip and produed into a straight or curved scabrid awn 0.3 – 0.9(1)mm; lemma two-thirds to three-quarters the length of the glume-body, very blunt at the tip, minutely hairy on the veins; palea almost as long as the lemma; anthers 1 – 1.7mm. $2n = 14$. Flowering and fruiting mid-June to mid-August, sometimes to early September.

P. bertolonii is predominantly a lowland species, being widespread and generally common in England and most of Wales. becoming more scattered in Scotland, especially in the north and west where it is rare, and occasionally introduced. It is scattered, although almost certainly under-recorded, in Ireland. Its exact distribution is difficult to map because of confusion with *P. pratense* and its inclusion for many years within that taxon. *P. bertolonii* is found in old pasture and meadows, particularly semi-natural short-turf grassland of the downs and hills in England, but also in short rough grassland on roadsides, waysides and waste ground. It occasionally occurs as an alien on rubbish tips. Although its ecological range overlaps that of *P. pratense, P. bertolonii* tends to be found in shorter thinner vegetation on drier less fertile calcareous, sandy or rocky soils both in natural grasslands and in the relatively small number of waste ground sites it occupies. But it can occur on clay. As the species usually grows in less productive grassland and more often in ancient grassland than Timothy, it has a wide range of associates.

The population biology of *P. bertolonii* is similar to that of *P. pratense* although it seems to have a greater capacity for persistence and vegetative spread. Individual plants may be very long-lived and seed may persist in the seed bank for >20 years. Smaller and more slender than Timothy, it generally has more basal growth and sometimes develops leafy non-rooting stolons. It does, however, display a wide range of variation, from prostrate leafy plants (which can be high yielding and extremely palatable and thus thrive in permanent pasture), to more stiffly erect types similar to *P. pratense*. Indeed, some bred varieties of *P. bertolonii* can only satisfactorily be distinguished from small *P. pratense* by their different chromosome number. Although cultivars of *P. bertolonii* have been fairly widely introduced, *P. pratense* has been the preferred species for short- and mid-term leys, responding well to the conditions in modern high production grassland.

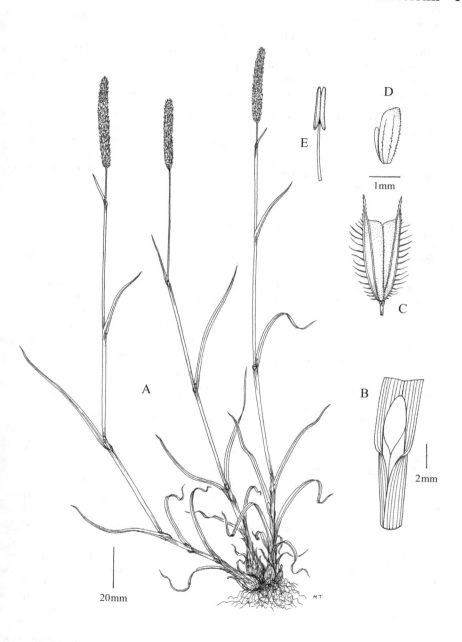

Phleum bertolonii: A, habit; B, ligule; C, glumes; D, floret; E, anther.

P. bertolonii is native to the British Isles and has a European Southern-temperate distribution. As a native it is probably more widespread than *P. pratense*. It is widely naturalized outside its native range including N America. Because of taxonomic confusion it is not possible to assess changes in its distribution in the British Isles in recent decades, but it is probably under-recorded (as *P. pratense*). Older texts which did not recognize the taxon, even as a variety or subspecies, often describe how *P. pratense* becomes much smaller on dry soils and develops bulbous basal internodes; many of these plants will have been *P. bertolonii*.

P. bertolonii is difficult to distinguish from *P. pratense*; see under that species for guidance. The exact affinities of our plant to a similar non-British tetraploid ($2n$ = 28) are unclear. It is possible that the epithet *bertolonii* properly belongs to this non-British element, and if this and the British plant are deemed to be distinct at species level then our plant would require another name; the next epithet available is *serotinum* Jord.

127. Glyceria maxima (Hartm.) Holmb.

Reed Sweet-grass   New Atlas: 763

Stout rhizomatous plant; culms erect, up to 250cm, fully self-supporting; sheaths eventually splitting, keeled above; ligule a narrow, firmly membranous rim, 3 – 6.5mm, elongated to a central point; blades with cross-nerves. Panicle broadly ovate to oblong, 20 – 35(45)cm, loose and open or becoming contracted and rather dense. Spikelets oblong to narrowly oblong, 6 – 9.5mm, 4- to 7(9)-flowered; glumes broadly ovate to oblong or elliptic, membranous, 1-nerved, the lower 2 – 3(3.4)mm, the upper 2.5 – 4mm; lemmas elliptic to ovate-elliptic, 3.2 – 4mm, prominently 7-nerved, very blunt but not toothed or lobed; palea wingless on the keels, shallowly notched at the tip, about as long as the lemma; anthers 1.2 – 2mm. $2n = 60$. Flowering and fruiting late June to early September.

G. maxima occurs throughout most of England, being particularly common in the south and east lowlands, but is scattered or rare in the southwest (Devon and Cornwall) and the north (in counties north of S Lancs and Yorks). It occurs mainly in the south and east in Wales and in Scotland it is largely restricted to the southwest, central lowlands and Aberdeenshire. It is scattered in Ireland, mainly in central districts. *G. maxima* is confined to the margins of freshwater bodies such as ponds, rivers, ditches, lakes and canals and to wet marshy areas, such as water-meadows, which are flooded in winter. It is most commonly found on waterlogged alluvial soils of high fertility and pH (6.0 – 8.0) close to still or slow flowing water where it often grows in tall dense luxuriant stands, and may form thick floating peaty mats across the water's surface. In these situations it excludes most other species, forming a distinct zone in the riparian community often with a *Phalaris arundinacea*-dominated zone to landward and a *Sparganium erectum*-dominated zone in deeper water. Lambert (1947) lists some of the associates of *G. maxima* in its main habitats. It is chiefly a lowland plant but reaches 600m at Sprinkling Tarn (Cumberland).

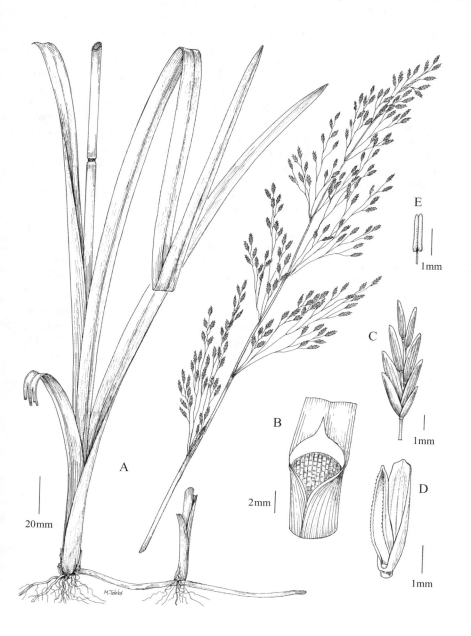

Glyceria maxima: A, habit; B, ligule; C, spikelet; D, floret; E, anther.

Plants from British populations of *G. maxima* are morphologically very similar and most populations are maintained, and established, vegetatively. Detached pieces of rhizome may be dispersed by water to found new populations, the grass spreading by this means along canals, rivers and interconnecting water bodies, such as the Norfolk Broads. Early spring growth enables *G. maxima* to compete successfully with Common Reed, *Phragmites australis*, although not in more anaerobic soils or deeper water (*G. maxima* growing to 80cm depth). Erect stands die back by November but plants in the floating rafts may remain green over winter. Newly established plants take 2 – 5 years to flower and despite the large panicles, seed set appears to be generally poor (between 3 and 18%) and establishment from seed may be a rare event. Most seeds germinate in the spring. In some parts of lowland Britain there is a long history of cultivation of this species as a fodder plant and to prevent bank erosion. It is eagerly grazed by cattle and is tolerant of fairly frequent mowing. Many of the populations from isolated water bodies may be from deliberate plantings, although water fowl may occasionally disperse the seed. (Biol. Flora: Lambert, 1947; CPE: 338).

A native species with a Circumpolar Temperate distribution, *G. maxima* has been widely naturalized outside its native range including Australia and New Zealand where it has become something of a nuisance in choking waterways. The increase in its British range since the 1962 Atlas, especially in the north, may be partly by deliberate introductions.

G. maxima is a very distinctive species unlike any other in the genus in our area. Apart from the lack of wing on the keels of the palea, it is the only species to be robust and fully self-supporting and to have cross-nerves on the leaves. A form with green and yellow striped leaves is often planted beside ponds and lakes as an ornamental.

128. Glyceria fluitans (L.) R.Br. Illustration, page 415

Floating Sweet-grass   New Atlas: 763

Loosely tufted and forming loose masses in shallow water; culms decumbent to ascending, sometimes with prostrate or floating base and erect panicle, up to 115(140)cm; sheaths not keeled; ligule a very delicate, narrowly triangular membrane (5)7.5 – 11(16)mm, but often torn or crumpled; blades without cross-nerves. Panicle contracted, erect or curved and nodding, 20 – 50(55)cm, sparingly branched below, the branches usually in pairs, the longer with up to 4 spikelets, the shorter with 1 spikelet. Spikelets narrowly oblong, (13)18 – 36mm, (6)9- to 14(16)-flowered; glumes elliptic-oblong to oblong, thinly membranous, 1- to 3-nerved, blunt, the lower 2 – 3.5(4)mm, the upper 3 – 5(5.5)mm; lemmas elliptic-oblong to oblong, 6 – 7.5(8.7)mm, prominently 7-nerved, blunt or bluntly pointed but not toothed or lobed; palea winged on the keels, sharply 2-toothed at the tip, the teeth projecting beyond the tip of the lemma or not; anthers (1.5)1.8 – 3mm. $2n = 40$. Flowering and fruiting early June to early September.

The most widespread of our *Glyceria* species, *G. fluitans* occurs throughout the British Isles including the Channel Islands, the Isles of Scilly, the Western Isles and Orkney and Shetland. It is generally common in a range of aquatic habitats including the edges of ditches, rivers, ponds and lakes, and in marshland and water-meadows. It grows on the muddy edges of water bodies and in shallow, still or slow flowing water where it forms loose floating rafts. Never in such dense erect stands as *G. maxima*, or extending into such deep water, *G. fluitans* may nonetheless form sprawling stands, especially in wet depressions in pastures and on pond margins to which nutrients are added by cattle. It grows in a range of soils but is most abundant within the pH range of 5.0 – 6.5, being absent from very acidic or highly calcareous waters. Whilst most species are excluded from dense stands, common associates in the north of England include *Apium nodiflorum, Callitriche stagnalis, Equisetum palustre* and *Ranunculus flammula* (CPE: 336). It has been recorded from sea-level to 720m on Knock Fell (Westmorland).

G. fluitans is tolerant of seasonally-fluctuating water levels, of nutrient enrichment, of a degree of shading and of high levels of disturbance such as trampling and ditch-clearing, although it seems remarkably fragile (as Plues (1867) noted "the graceful panicles are unsuitable for a bouquet" as "the stems break before you have carried it a dozen yards"). It forms extensive patches by creeping shoots which, if detached, easily re-root and may be carried by water to establish new populations. Although it may reproduce mostly vegetatively, and is winter green, seed appears to be set regularly. *G. fluitans* is slightly protandrous and normally cross-pollinating, although different populations or races have different degrees of self-compatibility. The seed, shed in August and September, are likely to be dispersed by birds and form a persistent buried seed bank in peaty soils from which new populations may arise (usually from spring germination although the frequency of this means of regeneration is not known). *G. fluitans* is the most variable of our Sweet-grass species and experimental studies have established that there are heritable differences in growth habit and the number of florets per spikelet. (CPE: 336; also Preston & Croft, 1997).

G. fluitans is a native species and is part of the European Temperate element in our flora which also extends into the Boreal zone (P&H 1997). It has been widely naturalized in N & S America, Australia and New Zealand. Its distribution in the British Isles, where it may have also occurred as a rare wool alien, appears to be stable. Also known as 'Manna Grass' the long slender yellow seeds were at one time harvested for 'Manna croup' to include in soup or cook for porridge.

It is distinguished from the other floating sweet-grasses mostly by the size of the spikelet parts. It readily hybridizes with *Glyceria notata* and less readily with *G. declinata* (see under *G.* ×*pedicellata* for details of both).

Glyceria fluitans: A, habit; B, ligule; C, spikelet; D, floret; E, anther.

129. **Glyceria notata** Chevall

Plicate Sweet-grass   New Atlas: 764

Plant tufted or forming loose patches; culms slender to stout, spongy, ascending from a prostrate base and usually rooting from the nodes, up to 120cm; sheaths keeled; ligule an oblong, bluntly pointed membrane (5)6 – 12mm; blades without cross-nerves. Panicle rather broad, lanceolate or oblong to ovate, loose, (12)20 – 40(50)cm, the branches in clusters of 2 – 5 with one branch longer than the rest. Spikelets narrowly oblong, 12 – 20(22)mm, 7- to 14-flowered; glumes oblong to broadly elliptic, membranous, 1-nerved, very blunt, the lower 1.4 – 2.7mm, the upper 2.3 – 4(4.5)mm; lemmas broadly elliptic to broadly obovate-oblong, (4.2)4.5 – 5(5.5)mm, prominently 7-nerved, scarcely to very bluntly toothed or lobed at the tip; palea winged on the keels, very blunt and shallowly notched at the tip, as long as or shorter than the lemma; anthers (0.8)1 – 1.4(1.6)mm. $2n = 40$. Flowering and fruiting late May to early September.

G. notata is widely distributed throughout England but is scattered in Wales and largely confined to the south and east of Scotland. It is reasonably common in northern and central Ireland but scattered elsewhere, generally along the coast. It occurs in similar habitats to *G. fluitans*, i.e. shallow ditches, streams and the muddy margins of ponds. It is found in more base-rich soils and waters than other Sweet-grass species and may be locally dominant along rivers fed by limestone streams. It occurs in marshland but is less common in areas with fluctuating water levels and avoids nutrient-poor and acidic soils. It is found with a range of wetland species and occurs from sea-level to 380m at Malham Tarn (MW Yorks).

Apart from being more calcicolous, *G. notata* has a rather similar ecology to *G. fluitans*, populations reproducing vegetatively and new populations being established from detached pieces of plant (in the case of *G. notata* from stolons). However, *G. notata* is inbreeding and produces smaller seed than *G. fluitans*. These may enter a persistent seed bank, remaining viable for a minimum of 5 years, and new populations may be established from seed. The seed are eaten and dispersed by water fowl. The succulent foliage, like that of all Sweet-grass species, is eagerly grazed by cattle. Experimental studies have shown that populations differ genetically in reproductive allocation, some producing flowers in the first season and others flowering in later years in favour of high initial vegetative production.

G. notata is a native species in the British Isles, part of our large European Temperate flora, and is also found eastwards to C Asia and in N Africa. It may be under-recorded in the British Isles, partly because of confusion with *G. declinata* (from which it may be derived by autoploidy), but has probably declined in southern England along with other perennial grasses of similar habitat, such as *Catabrosa aquatica* and *Poa palustris*, which are sensitive to improved drainage. It has been recorded in the past as a wool alien (AGB: 28).

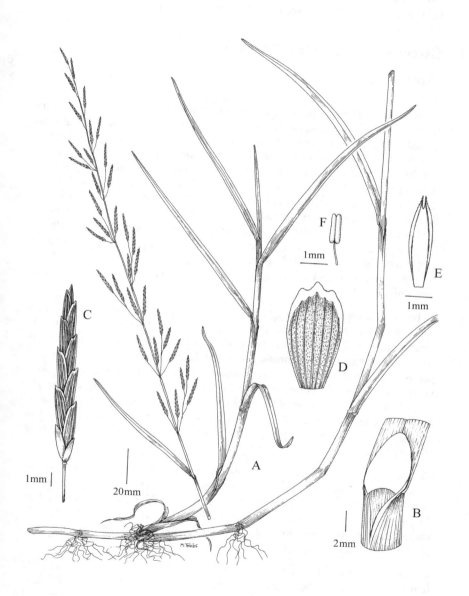

Glyceria notata: A, habit; B, ligule; C, spikelet; D, lemma, flattened; E, palea; F, anther.

The species is rather similar in spikelet dimensions to *G. declinata* but lacks the prominent palea teeth exceeding the tip of the lemma. The lemma-tip is at most bluntly toothed, but usually merely somewhat undulate or broadly lobed. It hybridizes with *G. fluitans* (see under *G.* ×*pedicellata* for details).

130. Glyceria ×pedicellata F.Towns.

Hybrid Sweet-grass   New Atlas: 763

Plant forming extensive patches; culms slender to fairly stout, fleshy, ascending from extensively creeping or floating runners, up to 100(150)cm; sheaths not keeled; ligule a delicate, narrowly triangular membrane 7 – 16mm, but often torn or crumpled; blades without cross-nerves. Panicle lanceolate to oblong, loose, (14)20 – 50(55)cm, the branches mostly in groups of 2 or 3 (but usually solitary in the upper part), the longest bearing up to 9 spikelets, the shortest with just 1 or 2 spikelets. Spikelets narrowly oblong, 14 – 25(32)mm, (6)9- to 12(16)-flowered, the florets persistent; glumes broadly oblong to broadly elliptic, 1-nerved, blunt, the lower (1.5)2 – 3.5mm, the upper (2.5)3 – 4.5(5)mm; lemmas oblong-elliptic, (4.5)5.3 – 6.5mm, prominently 7-nerved, blunt at the tip and without teeth or lobes; palea shortly 2-toothed at the tip, as long as the lemma; anthers 1.2 – 1.7mm, indehiscent and without good pollen. $2n = 40$. Flowering mid-June to mid-August.

Hybrid Sweet-grass is the male-sterile hybrid between *G. fluitans* and *G. notata* and is widely scattered over the geographical range of its *G. notata* parent. It is most frequent in England and in the south. It occurs with either, both or neither parent in the same range of aquatic and wetland habitats including the margins of ponds, ditches and lakes, around rivers and streams and in wet muddy depressions in pastures. It has often been recorded from swiftly-flowing streams and beside rivers in upland Carboniferous Limestone, habitats not favoured by either parent. Soils are generally nutrient-rich and often calcareous, and *G.* ×*pedicellata* has a wide range of associated species. It is found from sea-level to 550m at Moor House (Westmorland).

Completely sterile, this grass illustrates well the phenomenon of hybrid vigour, often forming extensive patches by a system of long runners, and spreading to new sites by fragments carried in flowing water. It is probably overlooked or mistaken for one of its parents. Variation between different clones, some resembling *G. fluitans* and others being more like *G. notata*, suggests that hybrids have been produced on several occasions.

G. ×*pedicellata* is a native plant in the British Isles and is widespread in the temperate parts of Europe. Apparent changes in its distribution since the published map in the Critical Supplement to the 1962 Atlas are likely to be due to improved recording, especially in Ireland, but it is probably still under-recorded.

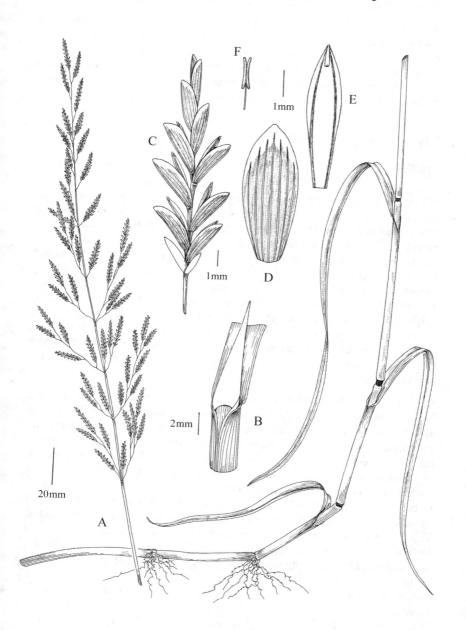

Glyceria × pedicellata: A, habit; B, ligule; C, spikelet; D, lemma, flattened; E, palea; F, anther.

The spikelets are intermediate in size between the parents, but the empty anthers and persistent, gaping florets are an adequate means of recognition.

G. fluitans also hybridizes with *G. declinata*. This hybrid is male-sterile and is likewise intermediate in spikelet dimensions between its parents. It is much rarer than *G.* ×*pedicellata* being much more difficult to form. It is best recognized by the obvious contribution from *G. declinata* in which the palea-teeth are produced beyond the tip of the lemma and by the lemma-tip itself being rather obscurely toothed. It also differs by its chromosome number ($2n = 30$).

131. Glyceria declinata Bréb.

Small Sweet-grass   New Atlas: 764

Culms loosely tufted, erect or ascending from a curved or geniculate base, or prostrate, up to 70(90)cm; sheaths keeled; ligule a delicate, narrowly triangular membrane (3.5)5 – 9(10)mm, but often torn or crumpled; blades without cross-nerves. Panicle linear to lanceolate, straight or curved, (7)12 – 33cm, often 1-sided, sparingly branched, the branches solitary or in groups of 2 or 3, the longest branch with up to 4 spikelets, the shortest with 1 spikelet. Spikelets narrowly oblong, 12 – 22mm, 7- to 14-flowered; glumes ovate to oblong, membranous, 1-nerved, blunt, the lower 1.5 – 2.5mm, the upper 2.7 – 3.7mm; lemmas broadly elliptic-oblong, (3.8)4.2 – 5.3mm, prominently 7-nerved, conspicuously 3- to 5-toothed at the tip, the teeth acute; palea winged on the keels, narrowed to a sharply 2-toothed tip, the teeth projecting beyond the tip of the lemma; anthers 0.8 – 1.1(1.3)mm. $2n = 20$. Flowering and fruiting early June to late September or even late October.

G. declinata is widely distributed in the British Isles as far north as southern Scotland and with a markedly more westerly distribution in Great Britain than all others in the genus except *G. fluitans*. It is scattered in northern Scotland and in Ireland but here, and throughout the British Isles, its exact range is unclear because of under-recording and possible confusion with other Sweet-grasses. Typical habitats include the muddy margins of ponds, ditches and rivers and in cattle-poached areas of marshy grassland. It occurs in shallow water but tends to be less frequently found in the permanently waterlogged habitats favoured by other *Glyceria* species. It has even been recorded from damp arable fields. The species occurs on a wide range of acidic or near-neutral soils (pH 4.0 – 7.0) including peat, clay, sand, gravel and river shingle, and tends to replace *G. fluitans* in base-poor sites, especially where these are heavily trampled. It does not occur in the highly calcareous sites favoured by *G. notata*. Characteristic associates include *Agrostis stolonifera, Isolepis setacea, Juncus articulatus, J. bufonius, Lotus pedunculatus, Ranunculus flammula, R. repens* and *Stellaria uliginosa* (see Preston & Croft, 1997). It occurs from sea-level, including the upper edge of saltmarshes in Scotland, to 500m at Lyn Crugnant (Cards).

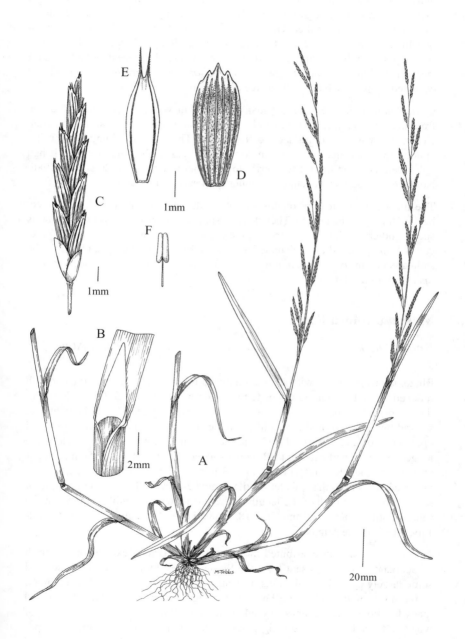

Glyceria declinata: A, habit; B, ligule; C, spikelet; D, lemma, flattened; E, palea; F, anther.

As its common name implies, *G. declinata* may easily be overlooked, especially in heavily trampled mud and, having a more diffuse growth habit, does not form extensive stands (although it can easily be detected by its glaucous appearance, as another common epithet 'Glaucous Sweet-grass' suggests). Like *G. notata*, of which it may be the diploid progenitor, it is highly inbreeding, the anthers and stigmas barely protruding from the floret. It spreads by seed and although it lacks the stolons of *G. notata* and *G. ×pedicellata* it also spreads vegetatively by detached stems which either float free or are uprooted by cattle.

G. declinata is native in the British Isles and in western and central Europe from the Azores northwards to southern Scandinavia (the Suboceanic Temperate element). It has been introduced to N America. The problem of under-recording alluded to above may be acute in some areas, e.g. in N Ireland where it had only been recorded from 2 sites prior to 1980 but was found in 20 sites in 1986. Nonetheless, there is a decline in frequency in eastern England.

The most obvious feature of this species is the teeth of the palea that project beyond the tip of the lemma. They do so to some extent also in *G. fluitans*, but this species otherwise has much larger spikelet parts. The plant often has semi-erect culms from a curved or geniculate base but these do not otherwise resemble the stout erect culms of *G. maxima*. It rarely hydridizes with *G. fluitans* (see under *G. ×pedicellata* for details).

132. Melica uniflora Retz.

Wood Melick   New Atlas: 765

Rhizomatous perennial with slender culms up to 70cm; sheaths glabrous or with reflexed hairs, terminating opposite the ligule in a bristle (1.5)2.5 – 4.5(7)mm; ligule a blunt membrane 0.4 – 1mm; blades thin, bright green, shortly hairy above, scabrid beneath and on the margins. Panicle sparingly branched, very loose and open, erect or nodding, 9 – 19(23)cm, the branches bare of spikelets below, the longest 3 – 8cm and bearing (1)2 – 4(6) spikelets. Spikelets 4 – 7.5mm, with 1, very rarely 2, fertile florets; lower glume 3-nerved, (3)4 – 5.5(6)mm; upper glume 5-nerved, as long as the spikelet; fertile lemma 7-nerved, 4.5 – 5.5mm; clump of sterile lemmas about half the length of the fertile, on a rhachilla joint about the same length; anthers 1 – 2mm. $2n = 18$. Flowering and fruiting early May to mid-July, rarely to late August.

M. uniflora is widely distributed throughout Great Britain except for the north of Scotland (it is also absent from the Western Isles, Orkney and Shetland) and some largely agricultural districts of central and eastern England. It is common in the north of Ireland where better recording since the 1962 Atlas has added many locations, but appears scattered in the south. It is a locally common grass of woodland, shady banks and hedgerows, occurring in a range of woodland types including oak/ash woodland where it is most common in rides and glades, and

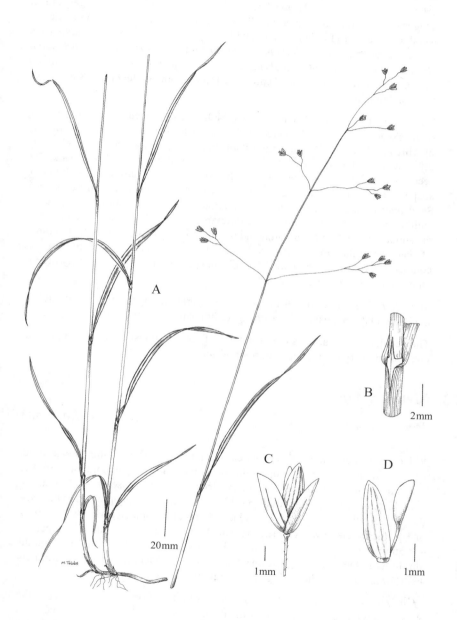

Melica uniflora: A, habit; B, bristle opposite ligule; C, spikelet; D, florets.

open beech woods, where it is often abundant as a loose patchy carpet. Largely found on free-draining, comparatively infertile, base-rich soils (mostly in the pH range of 5.5 – 7.5), *M. uniflora* may occur on shaded rock ledges and in hedgebanks as a relic of former woodland. It is regarded as an indicator of ancient woodland in eastern England. It has a wide range of woodland plants as associates including the grass *Brachypodium sylvaticum* and herbs such as *Geum urbanum, Hyacinthoides non-scripta, Moehringia trinervia, Mercurialis perennis, Sanicula europaea* and *Teucrium scorodonia*. It is found from sea-level to 485m in the Scottish Highlands.

The striking bright green leaves of Wood Melick tend to occur in distinct patches, often several metres in diameter, which suggests that regeneration is mainly by rhizomatous growth and that establishment from seed may be relatively infrequent. Seed is set from July to August and forms a persistent seed bank. The seed are sometimes dispersed by ants that are apparently attracted by the club-shaped mass formed by the sterile lemmas (which may function as an elaiosome). Seed may be heavily predated. Germination occurs in the spring, a period of chilling being required to break seed dormancy. Unusually for a woodland grass the shoots die back in the autumn and the plant is not winter green. Its tolerance of shade and relatively infertile soils enables it to occupy sites where it avoids competition from taller potentially dominant species. However, relatively little is known about its ecology (CPE: 422).

M. uniflora is a native species throughout temperate Europe and its distribution in the British Isles appears to have changed little since the 1962 Atlas.

The peculiar bristle at the summit of the leaf-sheath opposite the ligule is a most unusual and very distinctive feature of *M. uniflora*.

133. Melica nutans L.

Mountain Melick   New Atlas: 764

Rhizomatous perennial with slender culms up to 80cm; sheaths minutely scabrid, not terminating in a bristle opposite the ligule; ligule a membranous rim 0.1 – 0.2mm; blades bright green, shortly hairy above, otherwise minutely scabrid. Panicle narrow, 1-sided, nodding, 3 – 13cm, the branches ± appressed to the axis, the longest 0.5 – 3cm and bearing (1)2 – 4 spikelets. Spikelets 6 – 8mm, with 2 or 3 fertile florets; lower glume 5-nerved, 4 – 6.5mm; upper glume 5-nerved, 4.5 – 7.5mm; fertile lemma 7- to 9-nerved, as long as the spikelet; sterile lemmas almost half as long as the fertile on a rhachilla joint about the same length; anthers 1 – 1.6mm. $2n = 18$. Flowering and fruiting mid-May to late July.

M. nutans is scattered in NW Britain north of a line from the R. Humber to the R. Severn with outlier populations in Gloucestershire and Northants. It occurs in mainly hilly districts in northern England, Wales and mainland Scotland, but is absent from all offshore islands and from Ireland. A generally uncommon grass, it

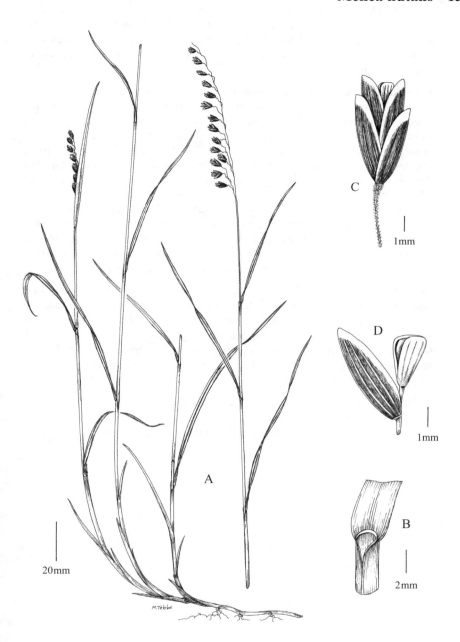

Melica nutans: A, habit; B, ligule; C, spikelet, D, uppermost florets.

can be locally frequent in and around deciduous woods, in shady scrub (typically of birch, alder or hazel) and in the grikes of limestone pavement. It is confined to basic infertile soils over limestone and other base-rich rocks and to shady habitats, as much on the borders of woodland as in the woods themselves. It occurs with a range of woodland associates and is found from a few lowland sites to 820m in Glen Isla (Angus).

Remarkably little appears to have been published on the reproductive biology and ecology of this attractive little grass. It clearly maintains its current populations, which can be quite small and isolated, by means of the persistent spreading rhizomes. Seed are set in July and August and appear to have little or no innate dormancy. They germinate fully in the light (100%) but not in the dark (10%) and produce only a short-term transient seed bank. Studies of old forest stands in Europe, which appear to have restricted dispersal abilities at the present day and which may be affected by acidification of the soils, indicate fairly low genetic diversity in the species. Its tolerance of shade and also of low fertility clearly enables it to avoid competition from potential dominants. In common with other woodland grasses such as *Brachypodium sylvaticum, Melica uniflora* and *Milium effusum* the leaves of *M. nutans* have stomata only on the upper (adaxial) surface and are reversed at the base so that this surface faces the ground.

M. nutans is native in Great Britain and has a Eurasian Boreo-temperate distribution (with a continental distribution in Europe; P&H, 1997). A decline before 1930, especially in southern Scotland, was noted in the 1962 Atlas but other than local losses the distribution is unchanged. Graves (1822) remarked of the Mountain Melick that "from its elegance it merits a place in the gardens of the curious … but it has no pretentions to the notice of the cultivator". And few, it seems, to that of the ecologist.

M. nutans is distinguished from *M. uniflora* mainly by the number of fertile florets (2 or 3 compared with usually just 1), the narrow panicle of slightly larger spikelets and the absence of a bristle at the summit of the leaf-sheath.

134. **Brachypodium sylvaticum** (Huds.) P.Beauv.

Illustration, page 429

False Brome

New Atlas: 793

Tufted perennial with only weakly formed rhizomes; culms erect or spreading, up to 90(115)cm, hairy at and towards the nodes, otherwise smooth and glabrous; leaves bright green; sheaths usually pilose with spreading or reflexed hairs, sometimes the uppermost, or rarely all, glabrous; ligule a blunt membrane with ciliolate margin, 1.5 – 5(6)mm; blades usually flat, 4 – 12mm wide, narrowed towards the sheath, mostly loosely hairy, sometimes scaberulous or smooth. Raceme (5)6 – 12.5(14)cm, usually nodding at the tip, bearing 5 – 12 spikelets. Spikelets lanceolate to narrowly oblong, 20 – 40(55)mm, 7- to 16(21)-flowered; glumes lanceolate to narrowly oblong, the lower 6 – 10(12.5)mm, the upper 8.5 – 15mm; lemmas oblong-lanceolate, 9 – 13mm, usually shortly and stiffly hairy, sometimes only scabrid or smooth, acute at the tip and extended into an awn 8 – 14mm; anthers (2.5)3 – 4.5(5)mm. $2n = 18$. Flowering and fruiting late June to mid-September, rarely to late October.

B. sylvaticum is widespread and common throughout the British Isles except for large areas of northern Scotland (it is not recorded on the Shetland Islands). It is principally a grass of woodland rides and margins, copses, thickets, hedgerows and other shady habitats including railway banks and roadsides. It is often found in coppiced woodland. It is also frequent in more open habitats especially in the uplands and in the north, and may be found in base-rich grassland, limestone pavement, scree slopes, rocky cliffs, and on quarry and mine waste. It colonizes chalk and limestone downs which have been invaded by scrub and may persist in former areas of scrub and woodland. It has also been recorded from sea cliffs and fixed sand-dunes. False Brome occurs on a wide range of substrates but is most frequent on well-drained, less fertile, neutral to calcareous soils in the pH range of 6.0 – 8.0 and is absent from very acidic soils. Across its range of habitats it has many associates including, in woodland, a number of calcicolous herbs (see the list for *Melica uniflora*). It occurs from sea-level to 465m at Highfolds Scar, Malham (MW Yorks).

Although our plant is deemed to be a single taxon (a further subspecies occurs in Europe) it can vary quite considerably in growth and general appearance. Plants growing in patchy scrubland often produce tall, clambering shoots and inflorescences, those in the shadier parts of woodland rarely produce inflorescences and plants from open habitats are often shorter with much paler yellow-green leaves. Absent from deep shade, *B. sylvaticum* does not produce much seed in woodland but single individuals may produce as many as 2700 seeds in upland grassland (CPE). Seed is set from August to October and most germinates in the spring, although autumn germination is possible. The species probably regenerates mainly by seed and, although no persistent seed bank has been reported, buried viable seed have been found in one survey. It is a grass of no agricultural value and is usually absent from heavily grazed grassland (rabbits, deer and sheep will eat it). However, it can persist in rough grassland where burning is used to control scrub. The species is probably self-compatible (CPE: 156).

A native in the British Isles, *B. sylvaticum* is part of the European Temperate element in our flora. It also occurs in temperate Asia and has been widely naturalized outside its native range. It is sometimes found as an alien on tips (AGB: 56).

A distinctive species unlikely to be confused with any other. The loose racemes with nodding tips and cylindrical spikelets will separate it at once from *Elymus*. For notes on the putative hybrid with *B. pinnatum* see under that species.

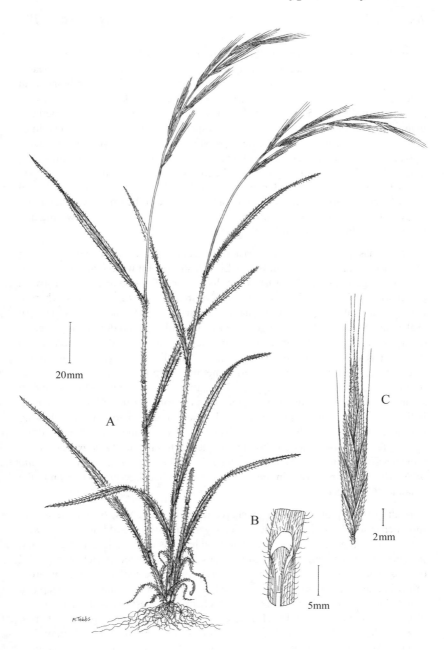

Brachypodium sylvaticum: A, habit; B, ligule; C, spikelet.

135. **Brachypodium pinnatum** (L.) P.Beauv.

Tor-grass   New Atlas: 793

Strongly rhizomatous perennial, scarcely forming tufts; culms erect, up to 120(150)cm, usually glabrous; leaves light or dark green to glaucous; sheaths glabrous or the lower sometimes shortly pilose; ligule a blunt membrane with ciliolate margin, 0.6 – 2.5(3.5)mm; blades inrolled and 0.7 – 2mm across, or sometimes flat and (2.5)3.5 – 8.5(11)mm wide, mostly loosely hairy, sometimes glabrous, scabrid or scaberulous beneath especially towards the tip, sometimes quite smooth. Raceme 3 – 16(17.5)cm, usually erect, bearing (3)5 – 14 spikelets. Spikelets lanceolate to narrowly oblong, 17 – 35(70)mm, 7- to 24(36)-flowered; glumes lanceolate to narrowly oblong, the lower (4)4.5 – 7(9)mm, the upper (5)6 – 8.5(9)mm; lemmas oblong-lanceolate, (7)8.5 – 11(13)mm, usually shortly and stiffly hairy, sometimes only scabrid or smooth, acute at the tip and extended into an awn (0.5)1.5 – 4.5(6)mm; anthers 3 – 5(5.5)mm. $2n = 28, 36$. Flowering and fruiting early June to late September.

Tor-grass has a pronounced southeastern distribution in Great Britain, occurring in a broad band from Yorkshire and Lincolnshire southwestwards, tracing the calcareous geology to Oxfordshire, Wiltshire and Dorset, and with eastward projections in East Anglia and along the North and South Downs. Elsewhere it is very scattered, being rare or casual in Cornwall, the Channel Islands, western Wales and Scotland. It is very scattered in Ireland. It is predominantly a grass of dry, relatively infertile calcareous grasslands, especially those where sheep grazing has been abandoned. Here it may form distinctive patches of foliage often several metres in diameter and sometimes dominating large areas. It also occurs on rocky outcrops, quarry spoil, road and railway embankments, and in scrub, hedgerows, woodland and plantations (in some of these latter habitats it is likely to be the true *B. pinnatum*; see below). Found on soils with a pH >5.0 it is most frequent on those from 7.5 to 8.0. Dense stands of the grass often contain few or no other species but it is frequently found with *Bromus erectus* and typical associates include *Centaurea nigra, Hypericum perforatum* and *Valeriana officinalis*. It occurs mostly in the lowlands but has been recorded at 380m in the uplands. (CPE: 154).

Spreading mainly by means of extensive creeping rhizomes, *B. pinnatum* may form dense stands often including a thick layer of persistent leaf litter. Such stands exclude most other species and in its optimal habitats of dry calcareous grassland the species has become a threat to the conservation of species-rich swards and their associated invertebrate faunas. It clearly became established in many areas following changes in grazing practice and the advent of myxomatosis, sheep and rabbits having formerly held the grass in check. Once established it has proved difficult to eradicate or control. It is tolerant of frost and trampling and its buried rhizomes survive burning rather better than *Bromus erectus*, which it may then replace. Although vegetatively vigorous, seed set is poor and variable, averaging

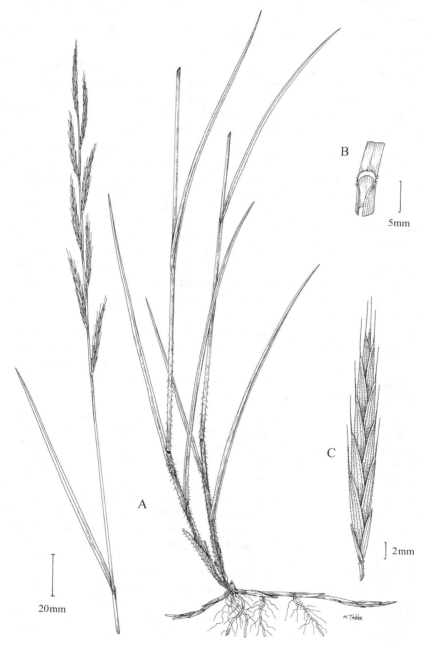

B

5mm

C

2mm

A

20mm

M.Tebbs

Brachypodium pinnatum: A, habit; B, ligule; C, spikelet.

around 20% at best, and populations in upland sites, where it is largely confined to south-facing slopes, rarely produce any seed. Where viable seed is produced (the species is protogynous and normally cross-pollinating) it is shed from September onwards but some may overwinter on the plant. Seeds germinate in spring and appear not to form a persistent seed bank (CPE: 154).

B. pinnatum is native in the British Isles and belongs to the Eurosiberian Temperate element in our flora. As detailed above, it is spreading in many of its long-established sites in chalk grassland and also along railway banks and roadsides in the uplands where it may largely be introduced. It is also increasing as an alien, when it is not completely restricted to calcareous soils.

B. pinnatum is a complex of taxa, two of which are said to occur in the British Isles. The genus has been revised by Schippmann (1991) who, following on from earlier work by Scholz (1968), D'Ovidio & Lucchese (1986) and Schippmann (1986), divided the species into two (one with two subspecies, but one of these absent from our area). The second taxon, *B. rupestre* (Host) Roem. & Schult., had not previously been mentioned as a British plant but the implication is that the common Tor-grass of calcareous grasslands should, in fact, be this species. Plants of semi-shade, marginal sites and clay soils are apparently the true *B. pinnatum* and are much the rarer (see Chapman & Stace, 2001). Almost no mapping data recognising the distinction are available and the species have been placed on the **waiting list** by Cheffings & Farrell (2005). The discriminating characters can be summarized as follows:

B. pinnatum: vegetative parts mostly pubescent; ligule (of second leaf) (0.4)0.6 – 1.8(2.4)mm; blade dark green, flat, dull, covered all over below with prickle-hairs (on both costal and intercostal regions), mostly hairy above; spikelets 18 – 40mm; lemmas 7 – 11mm, mostly hairy; awn 1 – 6mm; $2n = 28$; in marginal areas, semi-shade and heavy wet clay soils.

B. rupestre: vegetative parts mostly glabrous; ligule (1)1.6 – 2.8(2.9)mm; blade light green, flat or inrolled, glossy, smooth or scaberulous (the prickle-hairs restricted to the costal regions), mostly glabrous above; spikelets 30 – 50mm; lemmas 9 – 11mm, mostly glabrous; awn 1 – 3mm; $2n = 14$, 18 (not in the British Isles), 28, 36; in calcareous grassland.

A proportion of available material has been determined, independently, by U. Schippmann and F. Lucchese but it is still difficult to decide how to apportion the rest of the material between the taxa. There is general agreement that the morphological characters, both qualitative and quantitative, overlap to the point where they cease to be of much practical value and distinction ultimately rests on the distribution of prickle-hairs on the underside of the blade, but this character is difficult to assess and of very little use in the field. It is probably overstating the importance of the distinction by according the rank of species to the elements; Smith in Tutin *et al.,* (1980) treated them as subspecies, and this is probably nearer the mark. Until better discriminating characters can be found, it is wiser not to attempt a distinction.

The inflorescence in this species is particularly unstable. In many instances there may be two or three spikelets at a node, sometimes more on a short branchlet, and on occasion the branching is such that the inflorescence takes on the form of a contracted panicle rather than a raceme. In many cases there are also supernumery glumes at the base of the spikelet. For a fuller discussion see Oliver (1998, 2001a, 2001b).

B. pinnatum is intermediate between *B. sylvaticum* and '*B. rupestre*' and material once thought to have been the hybrid between *pinnatum* and *sylvaticum* (**B.** ×**cugnacii** A.Camus) is now thought to be the true *pinnatum*. However, this does not account for the fact that much of this material is sterile, as would be expected of a hybrid.

136. **Bromus carinatus** Hook. & Arn.

California Brome   New Atlas: 792 (as *Ceratochloa carinata*)

Annual or short-lived perennial; culms stout, erect, up to 95(150)cm; sheaths scabrid to sparsely pubescent; ligule roundly obtuse, 2 – 3.5(6)mm; blades up to 12mm wide, scaberulous on the upper surface, otherwise glabrous to sparsely pubescent. Panicle (8)15 – 30(35)cm, open with long, spreading or drooping branches. Spikelets narrowly lanceolate, (25)30 – 45mm (excluding the awns), (6)7- to 9(12)-flowered, laterally compressed; lower glume lanceolate, 3- to 5-nerved, (8.5)9.5 – 12.5(15)mm, acute, glabrous; upper glume lanceolate, 7-nerved, 11 – 15(16.5)mm, acute, glabrous; lemmas lanceolate, 7- to 9-nerved, (14)15.5 – 17.5(19)mm, firmly laterally compressed and keeled, the margins smoothly curved without an angle, usually scabrid (rarely shortly and sparsely pubescent) on the back, faintly 2-toothed at the tip; awn straight, (5)7.5 – 12.5mm, subterminal (within 0.5mm of the lemma tip); palea almost as long as the lemma (at least ¾ as long); anthers 0.5 – 1(1.5)mm in cleistogamous spikelets, 2.5 – 4.5mm in chasmogamous spikelets. Caryopsis much shorter than the palea, laterally compressed. $2n = 56$. Flowering and fruiting mid-June to early September, sometimes still flowering in late October.

B. carinatus occurs mostly in southern and eastern England south of the Wash and is rare elsewhere. It was recorded from Ireland (Dublin Port) in 1987. It is found on road verges, alongside paths, on the edges of fields and on riverbanks and towpaths. It is abundant in the latter habitats in the Thames Valley, especially in Surrey and Middlesex, having spread from Kew (see below).

A short-lived perennial (3 – 5 years) in its native N America, *B. carinatus* may be annual in Britain spreading both vegetatively and by seed, vigorously outcompeting native waterside flora. Seed are primarily produced by selfing but also by outcrossing and in cleistogamous florets. Hubbard remarked on the difference between flowering times of cleistogamous (late season) and chasmogamous (early season) spikelets, which can be borne on the same plant, but this could not be confirmed for this account. In its native areas along the Pacific coast of the USA it is a common grass of open grassland and shrubland, particularly in secondary successions such as post-fire vegetation, but can also be a pioneer (appearing on the mud flows of Mount St Helens 4 years after the 1980 eruption). It is established there by spring germination but we have no information on its population biology here.

California Brome is a neophyte in the British Isles introduced as a sileage crop and horticultural curiosity, and widely naturalized from both sources. It has spread rapidly since the 1962 Atlas, most famously along the Thames, having first been recorded as an escape from the Royal Botanic Gardens, Kew about 1919. It spread slowly at first but had reached Oxford by 1945. It also occurs increasingly as a casual in docks and on tips.

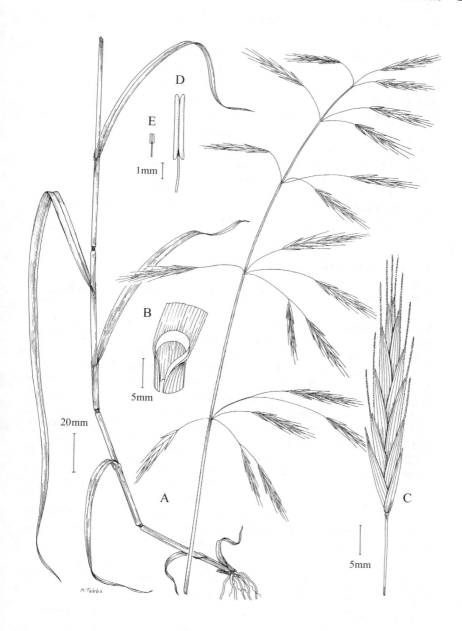

Bromus carinatus: A, habit; B, ligule; C, spikelet; D, anther from chasmogamous floret;
E, anther from cleistogamous floret.

137. **Bromus marginatus** Nees ex Steud.

Western Brome   New Atlas CD (as *Ceratochloa marginata*)

Another N American species that is occasionally introduced. It is very similar to, and may perhaps be conspecific with, *B. carinatus* but has more conspicuously pubescent sheaths, blades and lemmas (especially the last) and a shorter awn not more than 7 mm.

It has been recorded infrequently as a casual in rough and waste ground around docks and may have been naturalized for a few years near Rickmansworth (Herts). Records are mainly from SE England but it was first found in the wild in 1911 in Selkirks. Known in the USA, where it is widely distributed, as Mountain Brome, it was once a more regular wool alien (AGB: 55).

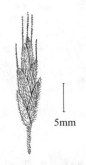

5mm

Bromus marginatus: spikelet.

138. **Bromus catharticus** Vahl

Rescue Brome   New Atlas: 792 (as *Ceratochloa cathartica*)

Annual or short-lived perennial; culms stout, erect or ascending, up to 80(160)cm; lower sheaths shortly hairy, the upper glabrous; ligule roundly obtuse, (1.5)3 – 4(5)mm; blades up to 12mm wide, scabrid on the upper surface, otherwise glabrous to thinly hairy. Panicle (7)11 – 30(35)cm, open with long spreading or drooping branches, or narrower with erecto-patent branches. Spikelets lanceolate to narrowly ovate, (20)25 – 35mm (excluding the awns), 4- to 8(12)-flowered, laterally compressed; lower glume narrowly lanceolate, 3- to 5-nerved, (6)8.5 – 14mm, acuminate, glabrous; upper glume narrowly lanceolate, 7- to 9-nerved, (8)10 – 15(18)mm, acuminate, glabrous; lemmas lanceolate, 9- to 11-nerved, 12 – 18(21)mm, firmly laterally compressed and keeled, the margins smoothly curved without an angle, usually scabrid on the back, faintly 2-toothed at the tip; awn straight, 0.5 – 4.5(5)mm, subterminal (within 0.5mm of the lemma tip), never completely absent; palea half as long to almost as long as the lemma; anthers 0.4 – 1.1mm in cleistogamous spikelets, up to 3.5mm in (rare) chasmogamous spikelets. Caryopsis much shorter than the palea, laterally compressed. $2n = 42$. Flowering and fruiting late May through to mid-November.

B. catharticus may occur as a casual mainly in England and mainly in the south where it can become naturalized on roadsides and waste ground and in arable fields, especially in the Isles of Scilly and the Channel Islands.

A neophyte first recorded in the wild in 1870, Rescue Brome was first introduced for fodder in 1788. As well as escapes from cultivation it may also occur as an alien of grain and (formerly) wool. Considered to be an invasive species in N America, it appears to be slowly increasing here (AGB: 54).

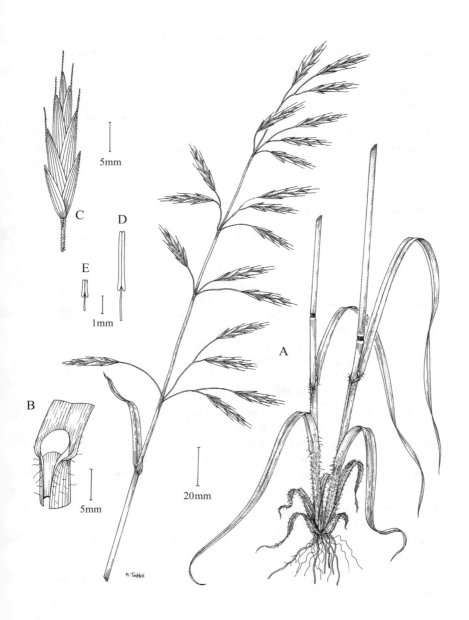

Bromus catharticus: A, habit; B, ligule; C, spikelet; D, anther from chasmogamous floret; E, anther from cleistogamous floret.

437

B. catharticus is part of a S American species-complex that is not, as yet, fully resolved. Two genotypes were introduced to N America from whence they were carried around the world and widely sown as fodder grasses. These two variants have been known as *B. unioloides* Kunth and *B. willdenowii* Kunth. The name *B. catharticus* was for a long time regarded as a taxon of unknown identity within the complex, but this particular problem has been resolved and the name is now correctly applied in a broad sense to the complex.

Rescue Brome is clearly very closely related to *B. carinatus*, and the two are distinguished by scarcely more than awn length. Sometimes a distinction is drawn between the relative lengths of lemma and palea, but this seems to be extremely unreliable (*B. carinatus* palea as long as lemma; *B catharticus* palea half as long as lemma). The variability of and distinction between the two species need to be re-examined.

139. Bromus stamineus E. Desv.

Southern Brome   New Atlas CD (as *Ceratochloa staminea*)

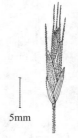

Very similar to *B. catharticus* but usually has hairier vegetative parts. The spikelets are smaller (12 – 20(23)mm), as are the lower glume (3.5 – 6mm), upper glume (5 – 7.5mm) and lemmas (8 – 10.5mm). The awn is longer in relation to the length of the lemma (3.5 – 5.5mm) and the palea is as long as the lemma, sometimes slightly longer. The lemmas, in particular, are shortly pubescent on the back although the hairs are often so short and slender as to be barely visible without the aid of strong magnification.

5mm

Bromus stamineus: spikelet.

B. stamineus has been found in the past in a few places in southern England on rubbish tips, rough ground, a sewage works and on waysides; it is known as 'Roadside Brome' in N America. Another common name, 'Grazing Brome', reflects its use there as a dryland pasture grass where it persists under close grazing by sheep and provides out-of-season forage.

A neophyte, it is not known when *B. stamineus* was introduced to Britain. It is a native of S America and was at one time widely naturalized but it is now a rare casual and is occasionally grown in gardens from which it readily self-seeds (AGB: 55).

It is likely that the correct name of this species is, in fact, *B. cebadilla* Steud. This name was published on 12 or 13 April 1854 whereas *B. stamineus* was probably published after mid-1854. Further research may be necessary to resolve this; in the meantime, the more familiar name is retained.

140. **Bromus ramosus** Huds.

Illustration, page 441

Hairy-brome

New Atlas: 789 (as *Bromopsis ramosa*)

Tufted perennial with erect or ascending culms up to 190cm; sheaths loosely to densely hairy with soft reflexed hairs (especially the lower; the upper sometimes minutely hairy or glabrous) and with short pointed auricles; ligule blunt, 1 – 4.5(5.5)mm; blades flat, up to 15mm wide. Panicle 8 – 40cm, narrow to broad, the slender scabrid branches suberect and drooping to one side to broadly spreading and pendent, 1 – 4 together at the lowest node, the longest of these with 1 – 11 spikelets; scale at lowest panicle-node glabrous or pubescent to long-ciliate on the upper edge (rarely with a short blade). Spikelets narrowly lanceolate to narrowly oblong, (14)16 – 38(41)mm (excluding the awns), 3- to 12-flowered; lower glume narrowly lanceolate, 1-nerved, (5.5)6.5 – 9(9.5)mm, acute; upper glume oblong-lanceolate, 3-nerved, 7.5 – 11.5(13)mm, obtuse and mucronate to acute; lemma 5-nerved, (9.5)11 – 15.5mm, pubescent near the margins, scabrid on the back, shortly bifid at the tip; awn straight, 5 – 9.5mm; anthers (1.8)2.1 – 4.3(5.3)mm. Flowering and fruiting mid-June to early September.

A complex of intergrading entities that are most appropriately recognized at subspecies level. Two of these occur in our area:

140a. subsp. **ramosus**. Culms up to 190cm (and rarely less than 90cm); lower and upper sheaths usually hairy; ligule 1.5 – 4.5(5.5)mm; panicle 16 – 40cm, the branches widely spreading, pendent, almost invariably in a pair at the lowest node, the longer of the pair with up to 11 spikelets; scale at the base of the panicle thinly to densely ciliate on the upper edge (but usually glabrous in the middle); spikelets (22)25 – 38(41)mm, (5)8- to 12-flowered; anthers (2.7)3 – 4.3(5.3)mm; $2n = 42$.

B. ramosus subsp. *ramosus* is frequent and widespread throughout mainland Britain except for the Fens, mid-Wales and central and northern Scotland. It is absent from the Channel Islands, the Isles of Scilly, the Outer Hebrides and Orkney and Shetland. It is also absent from much of the west and south of Ireland but is scattered elsewhere. A grass of shaded habitat, especially woodland margins and hedgerows, usually on moist base-rich soils, Hairy-brome can sometimes be found on ditch banks and other habitats in originally wooded areas. It grows mostly on soils with a pH value >5.0 and often occurs in open ground in woods with moderate amounts of bare soil and some tree leaf litter or a bryophyte mat. It commonly occurs with *Festuca gigantea* which has a similar ecology (CPE: 162). It is almost exclusively a grass of lowland woodlands and hedges but reaches 420m at Carrigill (Cumberland).

Among our tallest native grasses the winter-green leaves and elegant nodding panicles of Hairy-brome (which may also persist in a dried state over winter) are an unmistakable feature of many woodland borders and shaded lanes in lowland Britain. However, we appear to know relatively little about its ecology. A polycarpic perennial, the grass has no means of effective regeneration other than tillering, and population expansion and establishment is entirely by seed. The seed are probably dispersed by mammals and humans, attached to fur and clothing, and germinate in the spring. In one study 25% of the seed surviving in soil were viable after 6 years. The species is self-compatible. As mentioned above, Grime *et al.*, (2007) point out that *B. ramosus* subsp. *ramosus* shares many attributes with *Festuca gigantea*, although it is found more often in deep shade and in somewhat drier habitats. Both successfully colonize secondary woodland.

B. ramosus subsp. *ramosus* is native in the British Isles and is part of the European Temperate element in our flora. Its distribution appears unchanged since the 1962 Atlas.

140b. subsp. **benekenii** (Lange) H.Lindb. (*Lesser Hairy-brome*). Culms 40 – 125cm (rarely more); lower sheaths hairy, the upper usually glabrous; ligule 1 – 3mm; panicle 8 – 20cm, the branches suberect, drooping to one side, 1 – 4 together at the lowest node, the longest with 1 – 4 spikelets; scale at the base of the panicle pubescent (but usually glabrous in the middle), rarely glabrous or thinly to densely ciliate on the upper edge; spikelets 14 – 19(21)mm, 3- to 5-flowered; anthers 1.8 – 3.3mm. $2n = 28$. New Atlas: 789 (as *Bromopsis benekenii*).

B. ramosus subsp. *benekenii* is a scarce grass occurring in a few widely scattered locations in Great Britain from the North Downs and the Chiltern Hills northwards to Perthshire. It has been most frequently recorded from beech woods on calcareous soils but occurs in other deciduous woodland and in scrub and hedgerows. It prefers light shade and is found among other woodland herbs on shallow, often humus-rich, soils over chalk or limestone. It tends to be found on sloping ground in small or medium-sized patches, sometimes growing with subsp. *ramosus* (and possibly overlooked as a consequence). Little is known about its reproductive biology or ecology (SPB: 63).

A native taxon in Great Britain, subsp. *benekenii* is part of our European Temperate flora. It has a continental distribution in western Europe and is found in scattered localities in C Asia eastwards to China. Although now better recorded than for the 1962 Atlas, it is probably still under-recorded and thus any changes in distribution are difficult to assess.

The only wholly reliable character for separating the two subspecies is chromosome number. Compared with subsp. *ramosus*, subsp. *benekenii* is likely to have less hairy upper leaf-sheaths and a shorter, narrower panicle drooping to one side. It shows greater variation in the number of branches at the lowest node of the panicle, and the longest of these is inclined to bear fewer, marginally shorter spikelets. There is little else of real help in the morphology except for the less ciliate (usually pubescent and seldom completely glabrous) scale at the base of the panicle and the very slightly shorter anthers. European material of subsp. *benekenii* shows more variation than ours in ligule length, panicle length, spikelet length, number of florets (3 – 5 in ours, 4 – 7 in Europe), awn length and anther length. It can therefore be even harder to distinguish from subsp. *ramosus* and confirms the unsuitability of species rank for the two elements.

Bromus ramosus subsp. *ramosus*: A, habit; B, ligule; C, scale at base of panicle; D, spikelet; E, anther. *Bromus ramosus* subsp. *benekenii*: F, panicle; G, scale at base of panicle.

141. **Bromus erectus** Huds.

Upright Brome   New Atlas: 790 (as *Bromopsis erecta*)

Densely tufted perennial with very short rhizomes; culms erect or ascending, up to 130cm; tillers with leaves inrolled or folded along the long axis; sheaths glabrous or the lower sometimes with loose spreading hairs, without auricles; ligule blunt, 0.5 – 2mm; blades usually inrolled. Panicle 7 – 17(20)cm, erect or rarely somewhat nodding, loose to fairly dense, the scabrid branches mostly short, clustered, erect or somewhat spreading; scale glabrous or pubescent. Spikelets narrowly lanceolate to narrowly oblong, (15)20 – 35(37)mm (excluding the awns), 4- to 10(13)-flowered, the uppermost floret usually vestigial; lower glume narrowly lanceolate, 1- to 3-nerved, 7 – 12mm, finely acute; upper glume lanceolate, 3-nerved, (8)9 – 13(15)mm, acute; lemma 7-nerved, (10)11 – 15(17)mm, scaberulous to softly hairy on the back, acute or minutely 2-toothed at the tip; awn straight, 4 – 7.5(9)mm; anthers (3.4)4.6 – 6.2(7.7)mm. $2n = 28, 42, 56, 70, 84, 112$. Flowering and fruiting late May to mid-July.

B. erectus is common in England in suitable habitats from Yorkshire and Lincolnshire southwards to Dorset with eastward projections in East Anglia and along the North and South Downs. Although more widespread, extending for example into North and South Wales, this distribution pattern closely resembles that of *Brachypodium pinnatum* with which it shares its optimal habitat of dry calcareous grassland. Northwest of this area *B. erectus* is rare and probably introduced. It is uncommon in central Ireland, where Ryves *et al.,* (1996) suggest it is an introduction (AGB: 53). Most common on well-drained infertile chalk and limestone grassland, it may be dominant where grazing is light or absent, especially on the downs. It can also be found, less frequently, in sand-dunes, on roadsides, on quarry spoil and on waste ground. Soils are almost always base-rich, the grass being most frequent on soils in the pH range 7.0 to 8.0 and absent from acidic, wet and arable sites. It has many associates, especially in species-rich chalk grassland and is principally a grass of the lowlands (but it has been observed at up to 300m on the carboniferous limestone).

A densely-tufted, winter-green perennial, Upright Brome often forms dense or 'fairy-ring' type patches in neglected calcareous grassland, frequently accompanied by *Brachypodium pinnatum*. Like the latter species, *B. erectus* has benefitted from a relaxation of grazing and the decline of rabbits in the 1950s due to myxomatosis. The extent of its suppression by rabbits was revealed by classic early (1920s) experiments on floristically-rich chalk grassland where it invaded rabbit-proof enclosures and dominated such swards after six years, and in shallow calcareous soils in the Breckland where it similarly invaded and dominated plots fenced against rabbits. New populations are established by seed which germinate in the autumn and the largest colonies tend to occur on drier shallower soils in which open areas become available for seedling establishment. Seed set is high, even in the rarer upland populations, and occurs by obligatory cross-pollination.

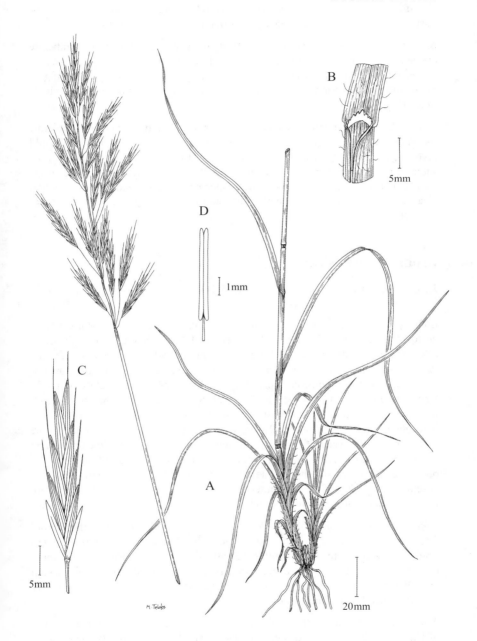

Bromus erectus: A, habit; B, ligule; C, spikelet; D, anther.

The reliance of *B. erectus* on regeneration by seed and its lack of rhizomes may explain why *Brachypodium pinnatum* tends to be more dominant where they co-occur. *B. erectus* is also more easily controlled by burning (CPE: 160).

B. erectus is native, at least in SE England, and part of the European Temperate element in our flora. It is widely naturalized outside its native range. It may be increasing here not only where grasslands are neglected but also by extending its range into waste ground. It was formerly recorded as a weed in sandy cornfields in SE England.

Upright Brome is a distinctive enough species that should present few problems. Its tendency towards glabrous leaf-sheaths is unusual in the genus and could give rise to confusion with *Festuca pratensis*. However, its lack of auricles, its subterminal (rather than terminal) awn and the hairy appendage on the ovary (rather than ovary shortly hairy in the upper part) should make the distinction clear. It is reputed to be responsible for more cases of hayfever than any other grass species in our flora.

142. Bromus inermis Leyss.

Hungarian Brome   New Atlas: 790 (as *Bromopsis inermis*)

Loosely tufted, aggressively rhizomatous perennial; culms erect or ascending, up to 150cm; tillers with flat blades; sheaths glabrous or the lower pubescent, obscurely auriculate; ligule blunt, 0.5 – 1.5(2)mm; blades flat, up to 9mm wide. Panicle 9 – 22(30)cm, erect, dense to rather loose, the scaberulous branches clustered, erect or somewhat spreading; scale pubescent. Spikelets narrowly lanceolate to narrowly oblong, (18)26 – 35(38)mm (excluding the awns), (6)8- to 10(11)-flowered, the uppermost floret usually vestigial; lower glume oblong-lanceolate, 1-nerved, (5)6 – 9(12)mm, with an obtuse hyaline tip; upper glume oblong-ovate, 3-nerved, (6.5)8 – 11(13.5)mm, with an obtuse hyaline tip; lemma 3- to 5-nerved, (9.5)10 – 13.5(14.5)mm, scaberulous to pubescent on the back, obtuse or minutely 2-toothed at the tip; awn straight, 0.5 – 2.5(3)mm, or quite absent (in about 2/3 of cases); anthers (3.3)3.8 – 5.4(7)mm. $2n = 28, 42, 56, 70$. Flowering and fruiting early June to late August.

B. inermis has been recorded as a casual from scattered localities throughout England and in the central lowlands of Scotland. Elsewhere it is rare (western England, Wales, northern and southern Scotland) or absent (Ireland, the Channel Islands, the Northern Isles). It occurs on road verges, field margins and rough ground and has become established in a number of sites in England on dry, sandy or stony soils. It is confined to the lowlands.

Although little studied in the British Isles, the most frequently mentioned feature of Hungarian Brome is its drought resistance and hence the ability to persist in poorer, well-drained sandy soils. In N America, where it is also introduced (but

Bromus inermis: A, habit; B, ligule; C, spikelet; D, anther.

see below), it is considered an invasive species, becoming established in disturbed areas such as roadsides, over-grazed pastures and even the edges of native prairie. There it is very long-lived and able to tolerate cold and salt as well as drought. It spreads by rhizomes, forming distinctive patches, and grows in a wide variety of soil types and habitats (including coal spoil at pH 4.5). The species is normally outbreeding. At the same time as being classed as an invasive it is grown in some areas for fodder or used to rehabilitate damaged and difficult sites because of its soil-binding properties. There is huge variation in phenological and morphological traits across N America (e.g. southern variants are more rhizomatous than those in the north) and the biology of our plant is likely to depend on the source, or sources, of its introduction from Europe.

Classified as a neophyte, *B. inermis* was first cultivated in Britain in 1794 and was widely sown for fodder and pheasant food. It was first recorded in the wild in 1890 and now mostly arrives here as a seed contaminant. Where well established it can be difficult to control because of its strong rhizomes, and is spreading quickly in some areas on verges and waste ground. It is a Eurosiberian Temperate species (as subsp. *inermis*; see below).

Most of our material is pure *B. inermis*, but there are records of a N American species, **B. pumpellianus** Scribn. (sometimes reduced to subspecies, *B. inermis* subsp. *pumpellianus* (Scribn.) Wagnon) from a few places in Essex, Kent and Devon. *B. pumpellianus* is distinguished by its densely pilose lemmas (*B. inermis* at most shortly pubescent, mostly near the margins), a feature not well expressed in British material. In N America the two taxa are known to hybridize, and it is likely that our material was introduced as this hybrid.

143. Bromus diandrus Roth

Great Brome   New Atlas: 790 (as *Anisantha diandra*)

Stout erect or ascending annual up to 100(120)cm; sheaths softly hairy with slightly deflexed hairs, or sometimes glabrous above, or glabrous throughout; ligule rounded, (2)2.5 – 5.5(6.5)mm, often jagged or deeply lacerate. Panicle contracted with ascending branches at first, sometimes becoming very lax and open but often remaining contracted, (5)7 – 16(30)cm; axis densely hairy; branches stout, spreading or erect, longer or shorter than the spikelets, simple or rarely one of the lowermost branched. Spikelets oblong at first, becoming wedge-shaped and gaping at maturity, (28)35 – 48(54)mm (excluding the awns), (5)6- to 11-flowered of which the apical (1)2 – 4 florets are sterile; lower glume narrowly lanceolate to lanceolate, 1(3)-nerved, 14 – 24mm; upper glume lanceolate, 3(5)-nerved, 20 – 32mm; lemma 7-nerved, (21)24 – 32(35)mm, coarsely scabrid on the back, with narrow apical teeth 2 – 5(6.5)mm; awn straight, (3)4 – 5.5cm; callus blunt to sharply pointed with oval to elliptic scar; anthers 0.6 – 1.3(2.6)mm. $2n = 42, 56$. Flowering and fruiting early May to late July but mostly late May to early June.

Bromus diandrus var. *diandrus*: A, habit; B, ligule; C, spikelet; D, callus in front view (left) and side view (right); E, anther. *Bromus diandrus* var. *rigidus*: F, callus in front view (left) and side view (right).

As with the closely related *B. sterilis*, an extremely variable species with a greater range of measurements than those from our material would imply. Sales (1993) records lower glume as 12 – 36mm, upper glume as 18 – 47mm, lemmas as 13 – 53mm and anthers as 0.45 – 5.9mm. Two taxa, formerly distinguished at species level, are included in the description above, *B. diandrus* and *B. rigidus*. Sales (op. cit.) has looked in detail at the characters that were said to separate them and found that none is entirely reliable. Indeed, she reports that variation is continuous, characters often unassociated and recognition at a rank higher than variety untenable. It is probable that the two extremes could be accommodated in subspecies, but certainly no higher. The usual characters for separating the varieties are as follows, although those relating to inflorescence-form are the least reliable:

143a. var. **diandrus**: panicle lax, spreading, broadly ovate; branches mainly longer than the spikelets; base of lemma in profile contracted just above the callus; callus blunt with oval scar; anthers 0.7 – 5.9mm; $2n = 56$.

143b. var. **rigidus** (Roth) Sales (*Rip-gut Brome*): panicle contracted, stiffly erect, narrowly ovate; branches mainly shorter than the spikelets; base of lemma in profile continuous with the callus; callus pointed with elliptic scar; anthers up to 0.7mm; $2n = 42$. New Atlas: 791 (as *Anisantha rigida*).

The relationships between these two taxa and *B. sterilis* have not been fully resolved. One suggestion is that *B. diandrus* has resulted from the hybridization of *B. sterilis* and *B. rigidus*, but experimental proof is lacking.

After reassessment of British material it seems that var. *rigidus* is far less common than at first thought and is established only in East Anglia and the Channel Islands. Much of our material, however, is morphologically intermediate and many immature specimens of var. *diandrus*, with their contracted panicles, have been misidentified as var. *rigidus*.

B. diandrus var. *diandrus* is now scattered as a casual through lowland Britain and is well established in several areas including the Isles of Scilly, the Channel Islands and East Anglia. It is rare in Scotland and Ireland. It occurs on rough and waste ground, road verges, rubbish tips and open grassland or heath on sandy soils. It may also be a weed of cultivated land and has become established in a number of coastal dunes. *B. diandrus* var. *rigidus* has been recorded from a similar range of ruderal habitat types but is particularly associated with sand-dunes and sandy places near the sea. Both varieties are found on a range of light to heavy soils of widely different pH although var. *rigidus* is probably more common on well drained, nutrient-poor, calcareous soils. It is a lowland species.

The biology and ecology of several *Bromus* species, and other grasses which have originated from Mediterranean-type climates, have often been better studied in those countries where they have been introduced and become invasive or weedy (see, e.g. *Avena barbata* or *Bromus tectorum*). *B. diandrus* is a significant, though mostly manageable, weed in parts of southern Australia (where it arrived around 1875), and from studies there we know it to be either a winter or summer annual germinating when soils become sufficiently warm and wet. Seed germination is inhibited by low moisture and high temperatures, and by light, and ungerminated seeds remain viable for at least 2 years. They are produced (from 600 to 3000 per plant) mostly by self-pollination and cleistogamous florets have been observed. Both variants (which have also been found to be difficult to distinguish in other parts of the world) display high phenotypic plasticity and respond by increased tiller production to high nutrients and low competition. This makes them successful weeds in wheat crops in Australia, capable of reducing grain yields by up to 30%. The extensive fibrous root system also confers a degree of drought tolerance, seen in several situations in British populations.

B. diandrus is classed as a neophyte in the British Isles (although at one time it was believed to be native in the Channel Islands). Var. *diandrus* was introduced in 1804 and first recorded in the wild (in Fife) in 1835, and var. *rigidus* was recorded as a wild plant in 1834. The species is a grain, birdseed and formerly wool alien native to the Mediterranean region and SW Asia and widely naturalized in many parts of the world including Europe, N & S America, South Africa, Japan and Australasia. It appears to be spreading in southern England and East Anglia where it may be increasingly experiencing the mild winters and hot dry summers which characterize its native region.

The colourful epithet 'Rip-gut Brome', which is also used for var. *diandrus* in the USA and elsewhere, derives from the propensity of the sharp dry 'seed' to penetrate the soft tissues of animals' mouths, eyes and feet, sometimes causing serious discomfort. The tiny backwards-pointing stiff hairs facilitate the dispersal of the seed in wool, animal fur and clothing (especially socks!). Their effectiveness can be demonstrated by holding the seed of this and some other bromes, such as *B. sterilis*, between finger and thumb and attempting to pull (rather than push) on the awn.

144. Bromus sterilis L.

Barren Brome   New Atlas: 791 (as *Anisantha sterilis*)

Slender erect or ascending annual up to 90(125)cm; sheaths softly hairy with slightly deflexed hairs, or glabrous above, or sometimes glabrous throughout; ligule rounded, 1.5 – 3.5mm, often jagged or deeply lacerate. Panicle contracted with ascending branches at first, becoming lax and very open with drooping branches, (8)11 – 24(26)cm; axis usually glabrous or scabrid, sometimes puberulous above; branches slender, spreading, longer than the spikelets, simple or rarely one of the lowermost branched. Spikelets oblong, becoming wedge-shaped and gaping at maturity, (20)24 – 36(43)mm (excluding the awns), 4- to 12-flowered of which the apical 2 – 4 florets are sterile; lower glume narrowly lanceolate, 1(3)-nerved, (7.5)9 – 13(15)mm; upper glume lanceolate, 3(5)-nerved, (11)12.5 – 19.5(22)mm; lemma 7-nerved, (14.5)16.5 – 23mm, coarsely scabrid on the back, with narrow apical teeth 0.9 – 2.6mm; awn straight, (1.5)2 – 3.5cm; callus blunt with ± circular to sometimes oval scar; anthers 0.9 – 1.8mm. $2n = 28$. Flowering and fruiting mid-May to late July or mid-August.

B. sterilis is widespread and abundant throughout lowland Britain, but is largely confined to the east of Scotland and to the southeast half of Ireland. It is found near and in hedgerows and in a wide range of disturbed habitats such as roadsides, waste ground, field margins, railway embankments, building sites and rough open grassland. It has become a significant arable weed in some areas, especially under conditions of continual winter wheat cultivation. It occurs on a range of substrates from dry sandy banks and stony or even tarmacked wasteland to fertile arable land, but is most frequent in moderately fertile, well-drained soils of pH >6.5. It is found with a wide range of associates and is principally a lowland species, reaching 365m in Derbyshire.

Barren Brome (the 'barren' referring to its agricultural production not its reproductive output) is by far the most successful and widespread of our introduced brome-grasses. It is a winter annual, germinating in the autumn and overwintering as a small green plant, although some spring germination occurs and these plants also flower successfully. The seed are very large and relatively few are produced per plant compared with many successful weeds. Most are produced by self-pollination but some crossing occurs (cleistogamous florets have also been reported). They have little or no innate dormancy, although seed produced earlier in the year tend to have short-lived dormancy, but will not germinate in the light or in conditions of low moisture (i.e. on the surface). There is thus no persistent soil seed bank. Germination tends to be delayed until the autumn but flowering plants can occasionally be encountered in the winter months (e.g. on 7th January by Arber in 1934). Unable to establish seedlings when buried more than about 13cm (a considerable depth nonetheless), *B. sterilis* flourishes under minimum tillage cultivation and came into its own as a weed when this technique was introduced in the 1970s and 1980s, especially for year-on-year winter wheat.

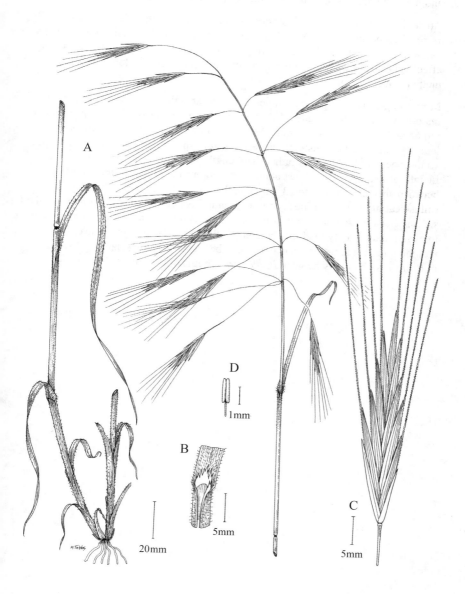

Bromus sterilis: A, habit; B, ligule; C, spikelet; D, anther.

Genetic studies have suggested that nearby hedgerow and boundary populations are a major source of continual re-infestation of arable fields and that boundary and field populations have not become ecotypically differentiated. (CPE: 114).

An archaeophyte (the first historical record in the British Isles is 1597), *B. sterilis* has become widespread throughout Europe and SW Asia and is widely naturalized elsewhere. It was a frequent wool alien (AGB: 53) and is very effectively dispersed by mammals and by man, both on our clothing and by our methods of cultivation.

Morphologically, the species is much more variable than measurements from our material would indicate. Sales (1993) records lower glume as 5.5 – 14.7mm, upper glume as 7.5 – 21mm and lemma as 10.5 – 30mm. Taking these measurements into account, the best distinction between this species and *B. diandrus* would seem to be length of glumes rather than length of lemma as given in most Floras. Length of lemma will still just about work on our material, but the cut-off point between species is nearer to 23 mm than the oft-quoted 20 mm. The shape of the callus-scar at the base of the second lemma is frequently used to distinguish this species from *B. diandrus*, but in fact variation is quite continuous from circular to oval and ultimately to elliptic and is of little help except in extreme cases. The indumentum of the inflorescence axis can be a useful guide (glabrous to scabrid in *B. sterilis*, distinctly hairy in *B. diandrus*) but is not wholly reliable.

145. Bromus tectorum L.

Illustration, page 455

Drooping Brome   New Atlas: 791 (as *Anisantha tectora*)

Slender erect or ascending annual up to 70(85)cm; lower sheaths softly hairy, the upper sometimes glabrous; ligule rounded, (1)1.5 – 3(4)mm, usually jagged to deeply lacerate. Panicle loose to rather dense, (4)6 – 14(18)cm; axis smooth or scabrid to puberulous or thinly pilose, the culm below the panicle similar; branches usually turned to one side, drooping or horizontal, the spikelets nodding or held horizontally, the lower longer than the spikelets and each bearing several (up to 8) spikelets. Spikelets oblong, becoming wedge-shaped and gaping at maturity, 13 – 20mm (excluding the awns), 6- to 11-flowered of which the apical 2 – 6(9) florets are sterile; lower glume linear-lanceolate, 1-nerved, (5)6 – 8mm; upper glume elliptic-lanceolate, 3-nerved, (7)9 – 11(12)mm; lemma 7-nerved, (9.5)10.5 – 13(14.5)mm, thinly to densely pubescent on the back, with narrow apical teeth 0.6 – 1.1(1.7)mm; awn slightly divergent, 1 – 2cm; callus blunt with ± circular scar; anthers 0.5 – 1.1mm. $2n = 14$. Flowering and fruiting late May to late June or sometimes to late July.

B. tectorum is an infrequent casual recorded from scattered localities in the southern part of Great Britain and is apparently naturalized in a few places in East Anglia. It turns up from time to time in places such as railway yards, roadsides, waste ground, rubbish heaps and in newly sown lawns, sports fields and road verges. It has been recorded from Breckland in grass heaths, banks and firebreaks on sandy soils, but has declined in abundance there. It has a range of associates, mostly other casuals, and is confined to the lowlands.

Although a rare species here, Drooping Brome has been quite the most invasive of the annual brome-grasses, especially in N America where it is known as 'Cheatgrass'. Its biology has enabled it to invade and dominate many of the shrub-steppe ecosystems of the western USA and Canada as well as overgrazed grassland, waste areas and even winter crops. The seeds germinate in response to autumn rain and the plants are well established by spring, their deep fibrous root system enabling them to deplete local soil moisture and successfully outcompete the seedlings of the native perennial grasses. Combined with high seed production and a buried viable seed bank (seed remain viable for 1 – 5 years) this enables *B. tectorum* to transform bunchgrass and sagebrush ecosystems into ones dominated by annual grasses and more frequent fires (the dead annual cheatgrass is highly flammable). This encourages more sites for invasion, hence the phrase of one exasperated ecologist that "fire begets cheatgrass and cheatgrass begets fire". In this way vast areas of western N America have been transformed since its introduction (probably accidental, but it does have some qualities as early forage) in the late 1800s and early 1900s. Seed are mostly produced by self-fertilization, require high summer temperatures to break dormancy, germinate to a higher percentage in dark than in light and are dispersed both by wind and by animals, all attributes of a successful weed in disturbed environments.

453

A neophyte in Britain, *B. tectorum* has been known in the wild since 1863, but was first grown in 1776. It is part of the Eurosiberian Southern-temperate flora and extends as a native as far north as northern France and southern Scandinavia. It is widely naturalized outside this native range. It occurs in the British Isles mainly as a casual of grain, grass-seed and (formerly) wool shoddy and is cultivated from birdseed (AGB: 53).

At maturity, the species is instantly recognized by the small glistening spikelets often all held horizontally to one side but sometimes merely drooping to one side. In the more floriferous spikelets the rhachilla above the last fertile floret is often twisted so that the awns of the sterile florets lie in several different planes in the manner seen in *B. rubens*. The look of these plants is rather different from that of the norm but they otherwise appear to be ordinary *B. tectorum* and the feature is of less significance here than it is in *B. rubens*.

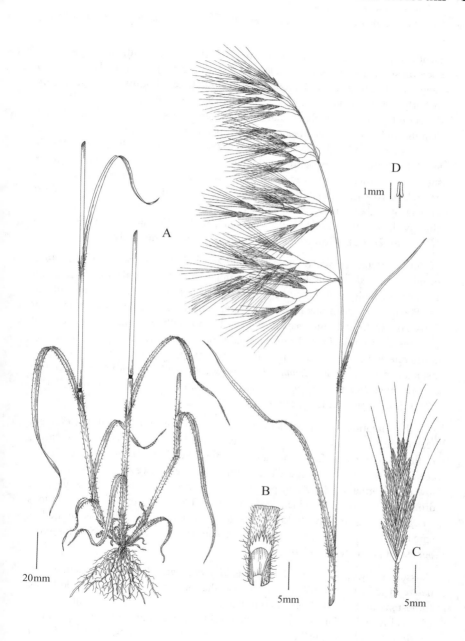

Bromus tectorum: A, habit; B, ligule; C, spikelet; D, anther.

146. Bromus madritensis L.

Compact Brome   New Atlas: 792 (as *Anisantha madritensis*)

Slender erect or ascending annual up to 60(75)cm; lower sheaths softly hairy, the uppermost usually glabrous; ligule rounded, 1 – 2.5(3)mm, usually somewhat jagged to deeply lacerate. Panicle erect or sometimes slightly nodding, loosely to fairly densely contracted, (2)3.5 – 9.5(14)cm; axis thinly hairy to glabrous, the culm below the panicle similar; branches erect or slightly spreading, shorter than the spikelets and each bearing 1 or 2 spikelets. Spikelets oblong, becoming wedge-shaped and gaping at maturity, (19)25 – 40mm (excluding the awns), 7- to 13(15)-flowered of which the apical 1 – 3(4) florets are sterile; lower glume subulate-lanceolate, 1-nerved, 6 – 11mm; upper glume linear-lanceolate, 3-nerved, (8)10 – 14.5(16)mm; lemma 7-nerved, (12.5)13.5 – 18.5(21)mm, scabrid to densely pubescent on the back, with narrow apical teeth 0.7 – 2mm; awn slightly divergent, 1.5 – 2.5cm; callus blunt with ± circular scar; anthers 0.5 – 1(1.3)mm. $2n = 28$. Flowering and fruiting mid-May to mid-July.

Widely scattered across southern England and S Wales, *B. madritensis* has long been established in some localities here and in the Channel Islands. It occurs on the Isles of Scilly and in southern Ireland, but is rare in Great Britain north of the Wash. It has been recorded from a range of dry open habitats such as rocky banks, old walls and ruins, pavements, wasteland, bulbfields and sand-dunes, and as a casual from docks and rubbish tips. It occurs on a range of soils including limestone and coastal sands, and with a range of species. In its semi-natural sites its main associates are *Bromus hordeaceus, Catapodium rigidum, Geranium robertianum, Hornungia petraea, Saxifraga tridactylites* and *Sedum acre* (RDB: 39). It is confined to the lowlands.

A self-pollinating winter annual capable of high seed production and efficient seed dispersal, *B. madritensis* is biologically similar to *B. tectorum*. It is invasive in the grasslands of California and capable, like *B. tectorum*, of altering the ecosystem to an annual grass/fire dominated one. However, it has relatively low seed dormancy there and populations can be wiped out by a few years of drought. There is some evidence of greater seed longevity in British populations (see RDB). It is sensitive to low winter temperatures which may have limited its spread in N America and account for the southwestern distribution of the more persistent populations in Britain.

Classed as a neophyte in the New Atlas, *B. madritensis* is thought by some to be native in some sites in SW Britain such as the rocky slopes on the Carboniferous Limestone of the Avon Gorge and in Pembrokeshire. It may also be native in the Channel Islands. Many of these populations have been known for a long time (it was first recorded in the Avon Gorge in 1773) and appear to be stable, and often large in size (it has been placed on the **Parking List** by Cheffings & Farrell,

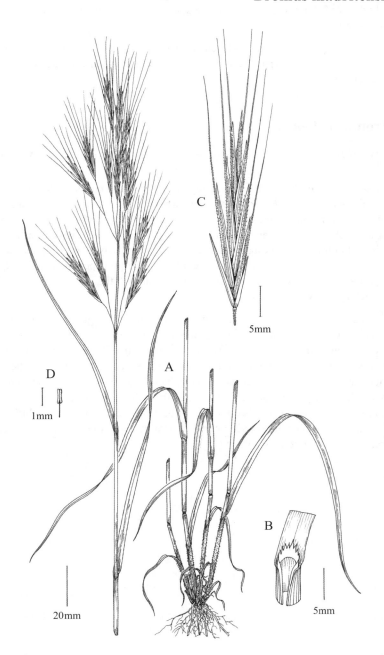

Bromus madritensis: A, habit; B, ligule; C, spikelet; D, anther.

2005). It is a native of the Mediterranean region and SW Asia and is naturalized in both N & S America, Australia and elsewhere. In Britain it was also a casual of wool shoddy, esparto and birdseed.

B. madritensis can be distinguished from *B. sterilis* by its contracted panicle, and from *B. diandrus* (particularly var. *rigidus*) by its smaller spikelet parts and circular callus-scar.

147. Bromus rubens L.

Foxtail Brome   New Atlas CD

Another native of the Mediterranean region and SW Asia occasionally introduced into similar places to *B. madritensis* but where it rarely persists. It is also very similar to it in appearance and can sometimes scarcely be distinguished from it. Its main characteristics are its much denser panicle, densely pubescent panicle axis and culm below the panicle, and the conspicuously twisted upper part of the rhachilla. The last is particularly evident in fruiting specimens because the uppermost florets are noticeably out of alignment with the lower, their awns thus projecting in several planes.

A rather infrequent casual (formerly of wool, latterly of grain and esparto) *B. rubens* is generally found in waste places and around docks. It is another cool-season annual grass which is highly inbreeding (less than 1% outcrossing recorded from some populations) and can grow on shallow dry soils. It has also become widely naturalized outside its native range, including the western USA where it is especially common in Pacific Coast States from Washington to California. Like *B. madritensis* (of which it is often treated as a subspecies) it has very little seed dormancy and no persistent seed bank, making it easier to control and probably limiting its spread to new habitats.

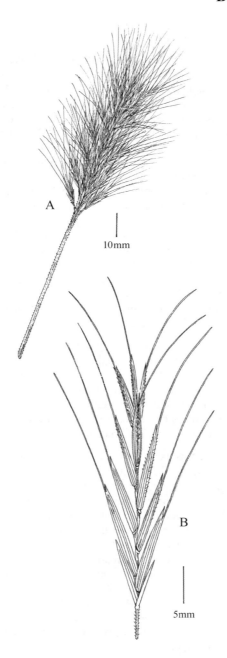

10mm

5mm

Bromus rubens: A, panicle; B, spikelet.

148. **Bromus secalinus** L.

Rye Brome   New Atlas: 789

Annual; culms erect or ascending, up to 120(135)cm; lower sheaths obscurely hairy to densely pubescent, rarely completely glabrous, the upper glabrous; ligule blunt, 0.75 – 1.5(2)mm, jagged or toothed; blades flat, up to 10mm wide, thinly hairy. Panicle erect or eventually slightly nodding, contracted to loose and open, (2)5 – 15(20)cm, the primary branches scabrid or pubescent, unequal, the longest with up to 4 spikelets. Spikelets ovate to oblong, 10 – 20(24)mm (excluding the awns), 5- to 16-flowered; lower glume ovate or oblong, 3- to 5-nerved, (3.3)4.3 – 5.9(6.8)mm, obtuse, glabrous or pubescent; upper glume ovate to elliptic, 5- to 7-nerved, (4)5.2 – 6.7(8.5)mm, obtuse, glabrous or pubescent; lemmas ultimately with inrolled margins, not overlapping, 7-nerved, (5.1)5.9 – 8.3(9)mm, becoming very firm with inconspicuous nerves, the membranous margins smoothly curved or broadening above into a barely perceptible angle, glabrous to densely pubescent on the back, blunt at the tip; awn straight or slightly flexuous, 3.5 – 8mm, occasionally only up to 1.5mm and scarcely projecting beyond the tip of the lemma, inserted 0.4 – 1.2(1.5)mm below the lemma-tip, rarely completely absent (and then usually not from all lemmas in a spikelet); palea equal to or slightly shorter than the lemma; anthers 1 – 2.5mm. Caryopsis shorter than the palea, deeply concavo-convex with inrolled margins wrapped around the palea. $2n = 14, 28$. Flowering and fruiting early June to mid-August.

Formerly common in the south, *B. secalinus* is now patchily, though widely, distributed across the southern half of England and Wales and is rare or absent elsewhere. It may be increasing again in some areas (e.g. Norfolk, Worcestershire) but mainly occurs at present as an infrequent casual in fields of winter wheat and as a contaminant of grass-seed. Its main habitats are the margins of cereal fields, waste ground including roadsides, and occasionally new or improved grass and/ or clover leys. It occurs on various soils and is confined to the lowlands.

Rye Brome is one of the best examples we have in our flora of a crop mimic, i.e. it probably evolved alongside the crop to grow and be dispersed with it. Its seed is very like that of a cereal grain; the size and furrowed shape of the caryopsis closely mimics the rye grain and would have been difficult to separate from it at harvest. The slow disarticulation of the spikelet, the lack of seed dormancy, and the tendency to higher seed germination in the dark are also aspects of the species' biology which are likely to have evolved in primitive agriculture to enable it to become a successful cornfield weed. Frequently found in central and southern England up to the early part of the 20th century, it was an established and often troublesome weed in many areas. Its demise came with the advent of improved seed-cleaning techniques, when not only would it be decreasingly re-sown with the crop but would also be disadvantaged by its lack of dormancy and hence a buried viable seed bank. There is disagreement in the literature about the extent to which *B. secalinus* normally cross-pollinates but it does not appear to be self-incompatible.

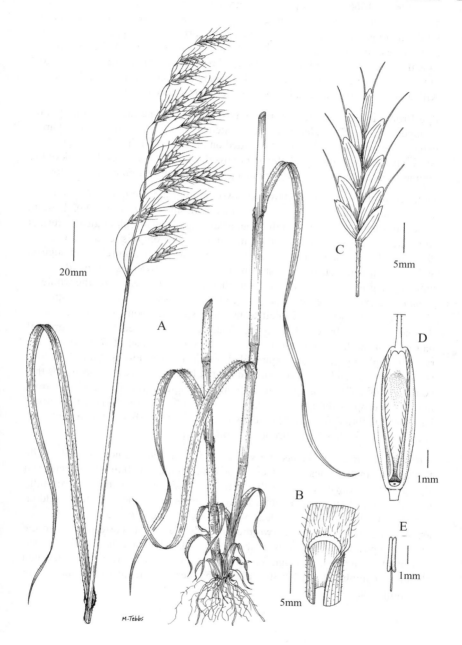

20mm

5mm

A

C

D

B

E

1mm

1mm

5mm

M.Tebbs

Bromus secalinus: A, habit; B, ligule; C, spikelet; D, floret in front view; E, anther.

Classed as an archaeophyte in the New Atlas, *B. secalinus* was first recorded in Britain in 1666 but was probably introduced an extremely long time ago as an arable weed of primitive agriculture. It may also have been an alternative food when the crop failed. When mixed with corn the seed apparently impart a bitter taste to the flour and were given the name 'cheat', probably because at one time they were thought to be produced by the degeneration of rye or other cereal grains. The species' native range is unknown, but it occurs throughout Europe, N Africa and western Asia and has been widely introduced elsewhere.

Rye Brome is a species readily recognized in fruit by the tightly inrolled grain wrapped around the palea and the thickened lemma with imbedded, barely perceptible nerves. The lemma is rounded on the back with inrolled margins and successive lemmas in the spikelet do not overlap (in other species the back of the lemma is partially embraced by the margins of the lemma immediately below).

Included in the description above are two cytotypes: a tetraploid, *B. secalinus* s. str., and a diploid, *B. pseudosecalinus* P.M.Sm. (*Smith's Brome*). Despite indications in the literature that they can be distinguished morphologically, results from the present study have shown that this is very optimistic. It has become clear that the two taxa are not nearly as distinct as the literature would suggest and indeed it is doubtful if any specimens other than extremes can be identified with any degree of certainty. No single character is reliable, but on the whole *B. pseudosecalinus* is interpreted as being the smaller of the two in most spikelet characters, although it is difficult to be more specific about the measurements that should be utilized. That the two can be distinguished by the degree of hairiness of the lower leaf-sheaths is also unreliable; those of *B. secalinus* are rarely completely glabrous despite what is said in most Floras. Smith's Brome is claimed as an endemic to Great Britain and Ireland. However, specimens that could undoubtedly be assigned to it on morphological grounds are known from northern Europe although their chromosme numbers are not known. Diploids have been reported from N America where *B. secalinus* (but not, apparently, *B. pseudosecalinus*) has been introduced from Europe.

Variants with larger spikelets and grains tend to be found among cereals while those with smaller ones mostly occur as contaminants of Italian and Perennial Rye-grass; those with grains in the intermediate size range can be successfully cleaned from both cereals and amenity grass-seed and are thus seldom introduced. This may be why there were thought to be two species but there is, as yet, no certainty that these two morphological elements correspond with the two cytotypes. Ultimately, it is doubtful if the two elements should be regarded as separate taxa at all, although the differences in chromosome number and seed chemistry (Smith, 1968a, 1968b) indicate that perhaps the rank of variety might be appropriate.

149. **Bromus interruptus** (Hack.) Druce

Interrupted Brome

Annual or biennial; culms erect or ascending, up to 100cm; lower sheaths softly hairy, the upper pubescent; ligule blunt, 0.75 – 1.5(2)mm, jagged or toothed; blades flat, up to 6mm wide, softly hairy. Panicle stiffly erect, oblong, dense, (1)3 – 8(9.5)cm, interrupted, the primary branches short to very short, in groups of (1)2 – 4 on alternate sides of the axis, each bearing 1 – 4 sessile or subsessile spikelets. Spikelets broadly ovate to broadly oblong, (9.5)11 – 13.5(16)mm (excluding the awns), (5)7- to 11(13)-flowered; lower glume oblong to elliptic, 3- to 7-nerved, (5)6 – 8mm, blunt or abruptly pointed, sometimes mucronate, pubescent; upper glume obovate to elliptic-obovate, 5- to 9-nerved, 6.5 – 9mm, blunt or abruptly pointed, sometimes with a minute awnlet up to 0.3mm; lemmas closely overlapping, 7- to 9-nerved, 7.5 – 9.5mm, moderately firm with conspicuous nerves, the membranous margins broadening above into a slight angle, thinly to densely pubescent on the back above (often sparsely pubescent to subglabrous below), minutely 2-toothed at the tip; awn straight, (4.5)6 – 8.5(10)mm, inserted (0.6)0.8 – 1.5mm below the lemma tip; palea shorter than the lemma, split to the base between the keels; anthers (0.6)1 – 2(2.7)mm. Caryopsis about as long as the palea, obovate, flat or slightly concavo-convex. $2n = 28$. Flowering and fruiting late May to late June, occasionally to mid-August.

B. interruptus is extinct in the wild. It was formerly present as an arable weed on light chalky soils scattered across southern and eastern counties below a line from the Wash to the Severn Estuary. It was particularly associated with fields of sainfoin (*Onobrychis viciifolia*) but occurred in other crops including rye-grass and clover and on other cultivated land and associated habitats such as waste ground, headland and roadsides. Mostly on calcareous soils, it was also found on more neutral soils, sands and clays. Apart from the crop species, it has been recorded as occasionally associated with other annual brome grasses, *B. racemosus, B. hordeaceus* and *B. sterilis*, and with *Cirsium arvense* and *Sanguisorba minor*.

Although not found in the wild since 1972, this fascinating grass has been quite widely cultivated from seed passed among botanists and therefore we know something of its biology (it was even studied in a PhD thesis examined by AJG!). Like its close relatives it is a winter-annual with some germination also occurring in the spring. Seeds can germinate under conditions of relatively low water availability and germinate more quickly than those of other annual bromes. However, experiments have shown that they cannot survive burial at depths as great as those of *B. sterilis* (fewer *B. interruptus* seedlings emerged from 5cm and none from 10cm) and that young plants are outcompeted by *B. sterilis*. Seed of *B. interruptus* are also naturally dispersed a shorter distance from the parent plant than those of other bromes, within 1.5m. These factors, together with the decline in area of sainfoin, itself a relatively recent crop introduced in the late 17th century, and changes in seed-cleaning techniques and land use, may all have contributed to the species' decline (see below). It is probably mainly inbreeding; Hubbard (1984) noted that pollination frequently occurred within unopened florets as happens in other annual bromes.

B. interruptus is native and endemic to England and is **endangered** (Cheffings & Farrell 2005). Its history has been reviewed a number of times and most recently by Lyte & Cope (1999) and Rich & Lockton (2002) who give a detailed account of its records and ecology and provide full references for those who would like to follow up the intriguing story of this enigmatic species. It was a late addition to the British flora, not being recognized as a distinct species until quite late, and the earliest collections were made in 1849. Once known, it was found to be quite widespread in southern and eastern England and was gathered from fields of sainfoin, clover and rye-grass with whose seeds it had doubtless spread well beyond its original range, wherever that may have been. As seed-cleaning processes became more efficient, and land-use changed, it went into a rapid decline and was last found in a field in Cambridgeshire in 1972. Since then it has been regarded as extinct in the wild and is now the subject of a species recovery programme. It is hoped that one day it may return to some of its native haunts but attempts to regenerate it from the Cambridgeshire soil seed bank have failed. During the latter part of its decline, cultivated material existed in the Royal Botanic Garden, Edinburgh from which it has subsequently been distributed to other botanic gardens. It has been introduced, presumably accidentally, into the Netherlands although it is probably not still surviving. Its claim to native, and therefore endemic, status in Britain has been challenged but until a likely origin for it outside the UK can be demonstrated it must be accepted as both native and endemic.

The species is identified at once by the combination of dense, interrupted inflorescence and split palea. Its relationships to other members of the *B. hordeaceus* group are unclear, although genetic and seed protein studies suggest it is probably derived by mutation from *B. hordeaceus*.

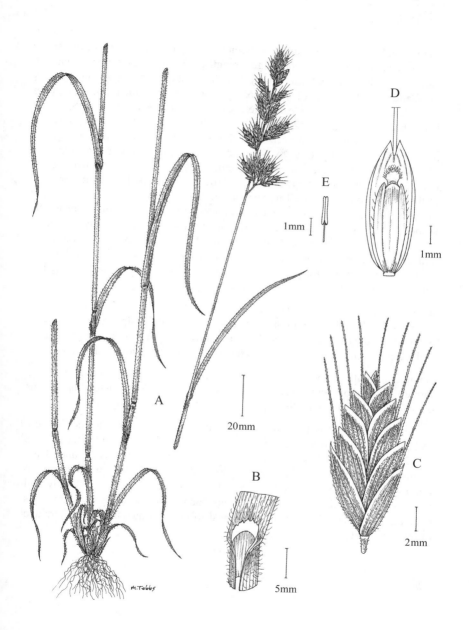

Bromus interruptus: A, habit; B, ligule; C, spikelet;
D, floret in front view to show split palea; E, anther.

150. **Bromus arvensis** L.

Field Brome

Annual; culms erect or geniculately ascending, up to 90cm; lower sheaths softly hairy, the upper usually glabrous; ligule blunt, 1 – 3mm, finely toothed or jagged; blades up to 5mm wide, loosely hairy. Panicle erect or sometimes nodding, very loose and open, (7)10 – 20(25)cm, broadly ovate to elliptic, the primary branches scabrid, the longest with up to 8 spikelets, these on pedicels up to 3cm. Spikelets lanceolate to oblong, 14 – 20(24)mm (excluding the awns), 6- to 11-flowered; lower glume lanceolate, 3-nerved, 3.5 – 5.5(6)mm, acute, glabrous; upper glume narrowly ovate to elliptic, 5- to 7-nerved, 5 – 7(8)mm, acute or shortly awned (the awn up to 1 mm), glabrous; lemmas ultimately with overlapping margins and not inrolled about the caryopsis, 7-nerved, (6)7 – 8.5(9)mm, firmly membranous at first with prominent raised nerves, becoming much firmer and quite hard at maturity, the margins broadened above into an obtuse angle, glabrous or faintly scaberulous, shallowly 2-toothed at the tip; awn straight to slightly curved, 7 – 12mm, arising from the back of the lemma 1.5 – 2.5mm below the tip; palea almost as long as the lemma (at least 4/5 as long); anthers (2.5)3 – 4(4.5)mm. Caryopsis shorter than the palea, almost flat. $2n = 14$. Flowering and fruiting late June to late August.

B. arvensis is now a rare casual mainly in the south and east of England in arable and grass fields and waste ground, or in docks and rubbish tips. It occurs chiefly on infertile light or sandy soils, and was formerly associated with a range of crops including clover, rye-grass, sainfoin and buckwheat. It is a lowland species.

A winter annual with poor seed longevity and weak dormancy, Field Brome was formerly much more common, especially as a weed of cereals or grasses. Populations occasionally persisted for a few years, particularly on open sandy soils.

B. arvensis is classed as a neophyte in the British Isles, and was first recorded here in 1763. It may once have been grown for hay, as it was in Europe, but appears mostly to have arrived as a contaminant of cereals and grass-seed. It underwent a rapid decline during the first half of last century (AGB: 49), probably due to improved seed cleaning, selective herbicides and the decline in wool shoddy, and is nowadays more likely to arrive as a constituent of birdseed. Its native range is uncertain, but it has a European Temperate distribution which it probably attained through cultivation.

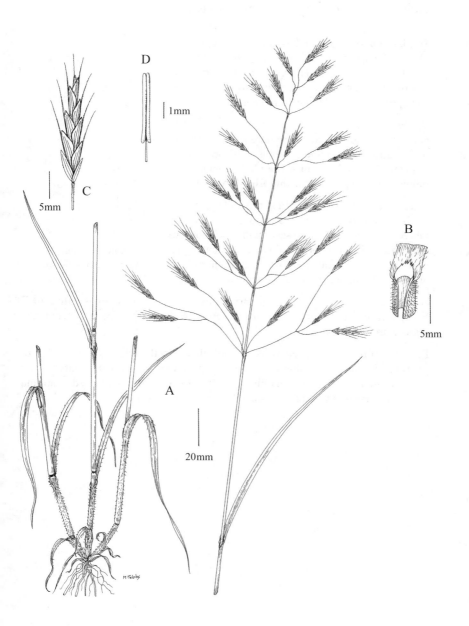

Bromus arvensis: A, habit; B, ligule; C, spikelet; D, anther.

151. **Bromus japonicus** Thunb. ex Murray

Thunberg's Brome   New Atlas CD

Similar to *B. arvensis* but has much shorter anthers (0.5 – 1 .5mm) and longer, sometimes hairy lemmas (8 – 10(12)mm); the awns are rather more strongly divergent; and the panicle, while similarly loose and open, is inclined to be more pendent.

B. japonicus has not been recorded here recently but was formerly widely scattered but sporadic from Cornwall to southern Scotland, but mainly in England. It was found in waste places, docks and rubbish tips, largely originating from birdseed.

A winter annual brome with a very similar biology to *B. arvensis*, Thunberg's Brome is largely inbreeding and produces seed with little or no dormancy. They do not germinate immediately as they tend to be retained on the dead mother plant until the autumn when dispersal begins.

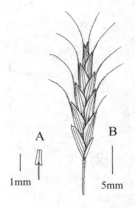

Bromus japonicus:
A, anther; B, spikelet.

A casual, recorded in the wild in Britain by 1863, *B. japonicus* is native in C Europe eastwards to Japan and has become widely naturalized in temperate regions around the world.

Earlier records of the species as a wool alien mostly refer to the similar **B. pectinatus** Thunb., but this has thinner papery lemmas smoothly curved (not obtusely angular) along the margins, the latter being somewhat turned in around the ± flat caryopsis so that successive lemmas do not overlap.

152. **Bromus racemosus** L.

Illustration, page 471

Smooth Brome

New Atlas: 786

Annual; culms erect or ascending, up to 100(140)cm; lower sheaths pubescent to pilose; ligule truncate or broadly dome-shaped, 0.6 – 2.1mm, jagged or toothed; blades flat, up to 9mm wide, softly pilose. Panicle erect or nodding, narrow with ascending branches to broad with drooping branches, (4)6 – 19(22)cm, the longest primary branches (1)2 – 9(13)cm, each bearing 1 to several spikelets. Spikelets lanceolate to oblong, (11)15 – 25(31)mm, (5)6- to 10(13)-flowered (very rarely more), usually glabrous, rarely thinly pubescent; lower glume lanceolate-oblong, 3- to 5-nerved, (4)5 – 8(9)mm, blunt; upper glume ovate to elliptic, 5- to 9-nerved, (4.8)6 – 9(10)mm, blunt, sometimes mucronate or shortly awned (to 1mm); lemmas ultimately with overlapping margins and not inrolled about the grain, 7- to 11-nerved, (6)7.5 – 11(12)mm, becoming very firm with inconspicuous nerves, the membranous margins smoothly curved or broadening above into a very blunt angle, blunt at the tip; awn straight or slightly flexuous, (4)6.5 – 10(11.5)mm, inserted 0.6 – 2mm below the lemma-tip; palea slightly shorter than the lemma; anthers (0.5)1 – 2.5(3.2)mm. Caryopsis shorter than the palea, shallowly concavo-convex to almost flat. $2n$ = 28, 56. Flowering and fruiting late May to late July.

B. racemosus is widespread and locally frequent in southern England below the Wash and is scattered northwards to Yorkshire and in Wales. It is a rare casual in Scotland and the Channel Islands and is scattered and generally uncommon in Ireland. Its best known habitats are pasture and grasslands, especially unimproved and seasonally flooded hay and water meadows and the drier edges of drainage ditches. However, it also occurs on disturbed ground, waysides, road verges, waste land and increasingly as a weed of arable land, especially winter wheat, where it can be troublesome. It is typically found on fertile soils and is generally confined to the lowlands.

Like most annual brome grasses, *B. racemosus* is highly self-fertile and probably mostly inbreeding, pollination often occurring within the unopened floret. The extent to which its ecology and biology differ from those of other species is unclear and is affected by confusion with *B. commutatus* (see below). It is thought to germinate mainly in the autumn and to have seed which are more dormant and longer-lived than those of most winter annual bromes (one experiment reported almost 25% of buried seed remaining viable after six years). However, its occupancy of two quite different habitat types may have led to ecotypic differentiation. Certainly the arable weed forms tend to display more of the '*commutatus*'-type traits than those from damp grassland.

B. racemosus is native in Britain and is part of the European Temperate element in our flora. It is widely naturalized outside its native range and has become a weed problem in some areas of N America. In the British Isles it has declined in the last 50 years because of agricultural improvement and drainage of old meadows, but may be increasing in disturbed habitats and as a casual from grass-seed.

Included in the description above are two extreme elements often regarded as species, the second being *B. commutatus* Schrad. (*Meadow Brome*). There have always been immense difficulties in distinguishing them and many attempts have been made to find adequate characters (e.g. Spalton, 2002). Where the two extremes grow together (for instance as at Chertsey Meads, Surrey Vc17) every possible shade of intermediate can be found and relatively few plants can confidently be assigned to one 'species' or the other. This clearly indicates unrestricted gene-flow between the extremes, strongly suggesting that the rank of species is not appropriate. Since the two elements are sympatric and occur in the same habitats the rank of subspecies is likewise inappropriate. Even resorting to variety would make the task of identification no easier. Their traditional, though unreliable, distinguishing features are as follows:

B. racemosus. Leaf-sheaths pubescent; panicle narrow, drooping to one side; primary panicle branches less than 4cm and each bearing only 1 or 2 spikelets; spikelets 10 – 16(18)mm; lowest rhachilla-internode 0.7 – 1mm; lemmas 6.5 – 8(9)mm; awns 5 – 9mm; anthers 1.5 – 3(3.5)mm.

B. commutatus (Schrad.) Coss. & Dur. Leaf-sheaths pilose; panicle broad, spreading; primary branches more than 4cm and each bearing several spikelets; spikelets 15 – 28(30)mm; lowest rhachilla-internode 1.3 – 1.7mm; lemmas (7.5)8 – 11mm; awns (3)5 – 10mm; anthers (1)1.3 – 1.5(2.5)mm. New Atlas: 786.

In practice, it has been found that all measurable characters vary quite independently and show a normal distribution without trace of bimodality. The limits used to circumscribe the taxa are therefore almost entirely arbitrary and in some cases little short of fanciful. Only those individuals with a certain suite of character-states can be assigned to one or other taxon with certainty.

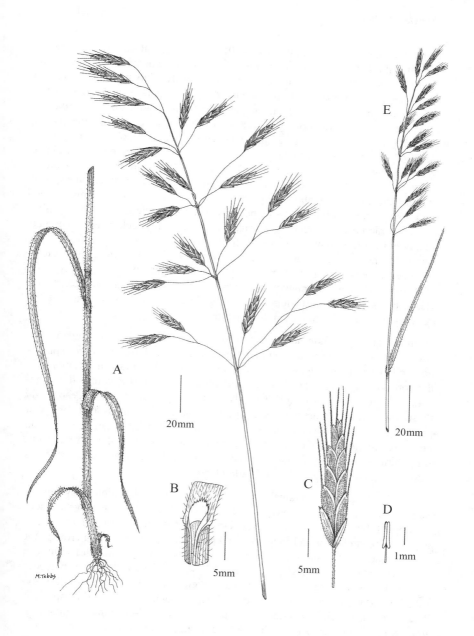

Bromus racemosus ('*commutatus*'): A, habit; B, ligule; C, spikelet; D, anther.
Bromus racemosus ('*racemosus*'): E, panicle.

471

153. **Bromus lepidus** Holmb.

Slender Soft-brome New Atlas: 788

Annual; culms usually erect, up to 70(100)cm; lower sheaths densely pubescent, the upper thinly pubescent or sometimes glabrous; ligule blunt, 0.5 – 1.3(1.7)mm, finely toothed; blades flat, up to 5mm wide, softly hairy. Panicle erect and contracted at first, becoming looser and nodding with maturity, (1.5)3 – 8(10)cm, the primary branches pubescent, unequal, the longest with up to 3 spikelets. Spikelets lanceolate to oblong, (6.5)9 – 15(16.5)mm (excluding the awns), 5- to 10(12)-flowered; lower glume ovate to oblong, 3- to 7-nerved, (3.1)3.6 – 5.2(5.7)mm, subacute to acute, usually glabrous, rarely pubescent; upper glume ovate-elliptic to broadly elliptic, 5- to 7-nerved, (3.9)4.3 – 6(7)mm, subacute to acute, usually glabrous, rarely pubescent; lemmas ultimately with overlapping margins and not inrolled about the grain, 7-nerved, (4.9)5.5 – 6.6(6.9)mm, papery with conspicuous raised nerves (especially when dry), the margins broadening above the middle into a slight angle, usually glabrous on the back, rarely pubescent, deeply bifid at the tip with a broad V-shaped sinus; awn straight, 4 – 7(8.5)mm, inserted at the base of the sinus; palea a little shorter than the lemma (3/4 as long or more); anthers 0.5 – 1.8(2.1)mm. Caryopsis longer than the palea, rarely equal to it, shallowly concavo-convex to almost flat, the terminal appendage usually visible beyond the tip of the lemma. $2n = 28$. Flowering and fruiting late May to early August, rarely as late as mid-September.

Formerly quite common and widespread in the southern half of England and widely scattered throughout the remainder of the British Isles, *B. lepidus* appears now to have a rather patchy distribution in the south and is rare and scattered in the north of England and in Wales, Scotland and Ireland. It is confined to man-made habitats, occurring mainly in newly sown or improved grasslands, especially those sown with rye-grass and fescue species. These include grasslands for hay or pasture, lawns, amenity areas and roadside banks and verges. It can also be found on waste ground and the edges of arable fields and on a range of cultivated soils. It is mainly found in sown grassland with *Lolium multiflorum* and *L. perenne* and *Festuca pratensis* and *F. rubra*. It is a lowland species.

B. lepidus is a winter annual which is probably similar biologically to *B. hordeaceus*, to which it is very closely related. It is known to have no self-incompatibility system and is possibly largely inbreeding, but we are unaware of any detailed studies of its life history and population ecology. It is a crop mimic in the broadest sense in that it is successfully dispersed, by man, with a range of small-seeded grasses. Indeed, its first record from the wild in 1836 was preceded in 1831 by the first large-scale imports of rye-grass and other seeds for grass leys (although it was nearly 100 years before it was recognized as a distinct species). The extent to which its decline is due to improved seed-cleaning techniques is unknown, but the New Atlas points out that changes in recorder recognition may have obscured the actual change in distribution.

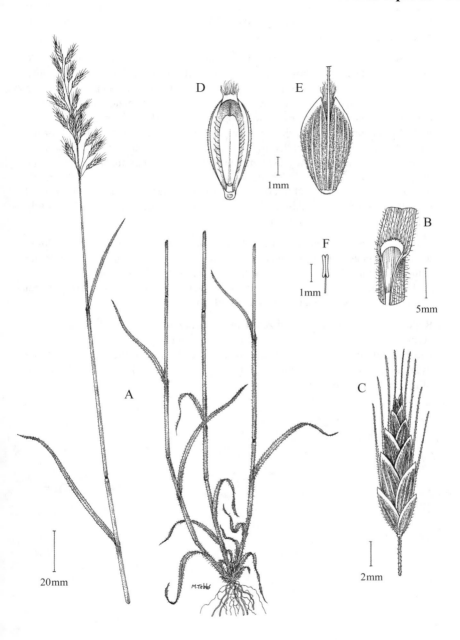

Bromus lepidus: A, habit; B, ligule; C, spikelet; D, floret from the front;
E, floret from the back; F, anther.

A neophyte in the British Isles, the origin and native range of *B. lepidus* are uncertain. It has been introduced as a contaminant of grass-seed to other parts of Europe and elsewhere, including N America, and is not known outside the man-made habitats in which it may have evolved.

The species is very closely related to, and often not very different from, *B. hordeaceus*. There are, however, several reliable features that will distinguish them: length of lemma, length of caryopsis in relation to the palea, and position of insertion of the awn. The latter is very positively correlated with the other two but is prone to misinterpretation. The awn is clearly at the base of the sinus in *B. lepidus* and this is visible even in side-view because of the breadth of the sinus. In *B. hordeaceus* the lemma is merely notched at the tip and the awn is clearly dorsal, but frequently the lemma will tear at the apex from the base of the notch right down to the awn. In side-view this 'false sinus' is not so easily visible because its margins are contiguous; furthermore, when viewed from the ventral side (the sinus is obscured by the awn in dorsal view), the 'false sinus' is clearly Y-shaped, with the notch supported on a torn stem.

The species usually has glabrous spikelets, but occasionally they may be thinly to densely pubescent (var. *micromollis* (Krösche) C.E.Hubb.). The latter are sometimes considered to represent introgression from *B. hordeaceus* but this is probably not the case; it is more likely to be the result of the natural variation that is found in the spikelets of many species of *Bromus*.

Reports that *B. lepidus* hybridizes with *B. hordeaceus* are grossly exaggerated. Hybrids in grasses are rarely as fertile or as common as that referred to here, and certainly do not occur so abundantly in the absence of their parents. Sterile hybrids between these two species have not been reported. For further discussion of this subject see *B. hordeaceus*.

154. **Bromus hordeaceus** L. Illustration, page 477

Soft-brome   New Atlas: 787

Annual; culms usually erect, sometimes geniculately ascending, up to 120cm; lower sheaths densely pubescent (rarely thinly pubescent), the upper often glabrous; ligule blunt, 0.4 – 1.8(2.7)mm, finely toothed; blades flat, up to 7mm wide, softly hairy. Panicle erect and loose to very loose at first, becoming somewhat denser and nodding with maturity, 2 – 12.5(18)cm, the primary branches pubescent, the longest with up to 5 spikelets. Spikelets narrowly ovate to oblong, (9)11 – 21(24)mm (excluding the awns), 5- to 13-flowered; lower glume ovate to oblong, 3- to 7-nerved, (4)5 – 9(10)mm, subacute, usually pubescent, sometimes glabrous; upper glume elliptic, 5- to 7-nerved, (5.5)6 – 9.5(11)mm, subacute, usually pubescent, sometimes glabrous; lemmas ultimately with overlapping margins and not inrolled about the grain, 7- to 9-nerved, (6)6.7 – 11(12.7)mm, papery with conspicuous raised nerves (especially when dry), the margins scarcely broadening above into a barely perceptible angle, usually thinly to densely pubescent on the back, rarely glabrous, shallowly notched at the tip; awn ± straight to somewhat curved, (3.5)6 – 10(12)mm, terete or flattened at the base, arising from the back of the lemma 0.7 – 1.9mm below the tip; palea shorter than the lemma (4/5 as long or more); anthers 0.5 – 1.7(2.3)mm. Caryopsis shorter than the palea, sometimes as long or almost as long as it, shallowly concavo-convex to almost flat, the terminal appendage concealed by the palea or at least not visible beyond the tip of the lemma. $2n = 28$. Flowering and fruiting early or mid-May to late August.

B. hordeaceus is very common in most of lowland Britain, especially in England and Wales, and is widespread throughout the British Isles, being rare or absent only in central and northern parts of mainland Scotland. It is somewhat scattered in central Ireland but common elsewhere. It is found in a range of grassy open habitats including hay meadows (where populations are often persistent), sown pastures (where they rarely persist), lawns and road verges, and in more disturbed habitats such as arable fields, waste ground, path edges, dockland and spoil tips. It also occurs on dry rocky outcrops within grassland, on coastal cliffs, shingle beaches, fixed sand-dunes and other sandy places near the sea. Many, if not most, of the species' habitats are associated with human activity and usually have moderately fertile neutral soils. It is more or less absent from acidic soils of pH >5.0 and from aquatic habitats. *B. hordeaceus* has a large number of associates across this wide range of habitats. It occurs from sea-level to 550m (at Kilhope, Co Durham).

This extremely variable grass is the most widespead of our annual bromes. Its wide ecological amplitude has undoubtedly exposed it to diverse selective environments, and this is likely to have produced the distinctive ecotypes recognized at subspecies level (see below). These environments will have ranged from artificial selection by man for seed size, optimizing the species' dispersal with forage-grass seed, to selection for early flowering and seed set in severely droughted coastal sands. Thus, modern populations may comprise of individuals or subpopulations which, now sympatric, are the result of past evolutionary divergence, possibly including hybridization with a range of taxa (Smith, 1968a), a fact reflected in their various degrees of interfertility. Genetic variation in this grass is often masked by phenotypic plasticity (Graves, 1822) noted that "it is subject to great variety in its appearance according to the soil and situation in which it grows"), and the tiny plant with a single spikelet seen on a dry bank hardly seems the same species as the tall plant of hayfields with its many inflorescences. All this variation is on the theme of a winter annual with mainly autumn germination, of seed set from May to early August with little or no dormancy and with no persistent seed bank (in one test only 5% of buried seed were viable after one year). Soft-brome is intolerant of heavy grazing, frequent mowing and trampling and thus rarely persists in pastures and lawns. It is highly inbreeding but occasional rounds of outbreeding may occur; studies in California indicated an average of less than 5% outcrossing (CPE: 164).

B. hordeaceus is native and part of the European Southern Temperate element in the British flora. It is widely naturalized outside its native range including in Australia (where colonist populations have been shown to be less genetically variable than their source populations in England) and N America (extensive studies in California, where it was introduced in the late 1860s and now dominates large areas of grassland, have demonstrated population differentiation in relation to coastal and valley environments). It was not always regarded as a weed, having been grown for hay in Ireland in the early 19th century and cultivated at one time in Scotland. Its distribution in the British Isles appears to be stable.

B. hordeaceus is very similar to *B. lepidus*, but differs in length of lemma, length of caryopsis in relation to the palea, and position of insertion of the awn (see under *B. lepidus* for further details). Specimens with lemma length at the lower end of the range (c.6.5 – 7.5mm), and particularly those that are glabrous, have been considered variously as a distinct species (*B. thominei* auct. non Hardouin) or, more recently, as a hybrid between *B. hordeaceus* and *B. lepidus* (*B. ×pseudothominei* P.M.Sm.). There is no significant correlation between lemma size and pubescence in *B. hordeaceus*, nor is there any indication of bimodality in lemma length; it seems that a hybrid origin for the intermediates can safely be discounted. The two species may well hybridize in the wild, but specimens that have been called *B. ×pseudothominei* are not necessarily this hybrid. Specimens with lemmas over 8mm but with glabrous spikelets have been known as *B. mollis* var. *leiostachys* Hartm.

The species is extremely variable and several local or widespread ecotypes have been accorded rank of subspecies. This probably exaggerates their importance since there is little to indicate that they represent a significant ecological or geographical partitioning of the species and the segregates always seem to grow alongside the typical form. Those that occur in our area, other than the typical variant subsp. *hordeaceus,* are illustrated on plate on page 479.

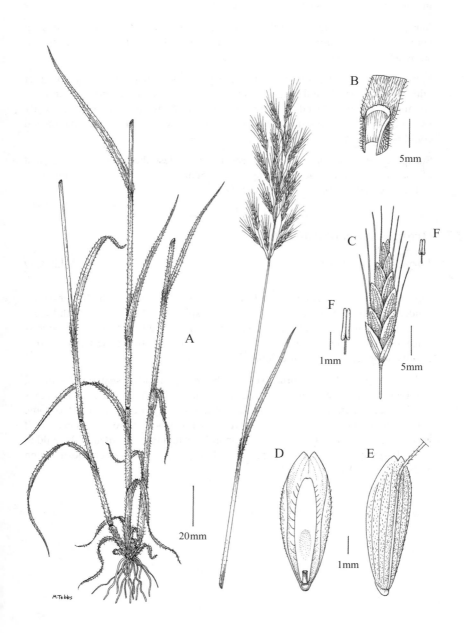

Bromus hordeaceus: A, habit; B, ligule; C, spikelet; D, floret from the front; E, floret from the back; F, anthers from bottom (left) and top (right) of a single spikelet.

Subsp. *thominei* (Hardouin) Braun-Blanq. is a procumbent to ascending plant mainly of sandy places on the coast. New Atlas: 787.

Subsp. *ferronii* (Mabille) P.M.Sm. is an erect to ascending plant with stiff erect panicle and outwardly curving awns, usually found on cliff-tops and sandy or stony ground by the sea. New Atlas: 787.

Subsp. *divaricatus* (Bonnier & Layens) Kerguélen is similar to *ferronii* but is taller with a richer panicle and longer lemmas; the latter are often woolly-pubescent. An alien taxon introduced from Europe originally in wool but nowadays mostly as a contaminant of grass-seed. This taxon may be worthy of re-examination and could prove to be a distinct species.

Subsp. *longipedicellatus* Spalton has recently been described, but is only a variant of *hordeaceus* with panicle branches over 6.5cm. It occurs throughout the range of the type and completely intergrades with it.

155. **Bromus lanceolatus** Roth

Large-headed Brome   New Atlas CD

Belongs near *B. hordeaceus*, but has a dense erect panicle with shorter, stout, rigidly upright branches bearing fewer larger spikelets (20 – 50mm) with longer (12 – 20mm) lemmas covered in dense long hairs (rarely glabrous). The awn is conspicuously flattened below, arises c.4mm below the tip of the lemma and is usually strongly recurved or contorted at maturity.

B. lanceolatus has been recorded very rarely, and from widely scattered localities, in Great Britain as a casual in waste places and rubbish tips. It usually occurs as a birdseed alien but sometimes as an escape from gardens where it has some horticultural merit. Introduction as a wool alien has now more or less ceased. It was introduced into cultivation in Britain in 1798 and first recorded in the wild in 1902. Large-headed Brome is a native of Europe and the Mediterranean region eastwards to C Asia.

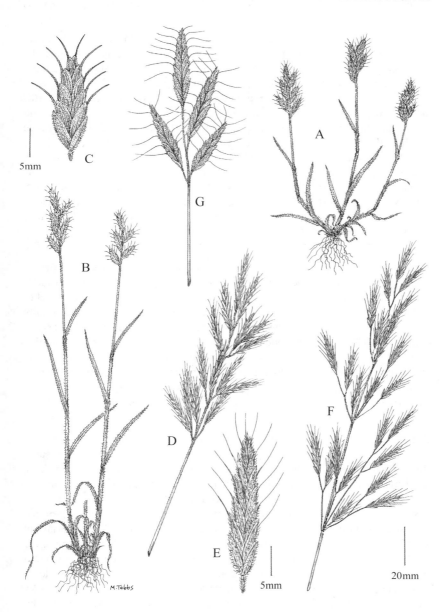

Bromus hordeaceus 'subsp. *thominei*': A, habit. *Bromus hordeaceus* 'subsp. *ferronii*':
B, habit; C, spikelet. *Bromus hordeaceus* 'subsp. *divaricatus*': D, panicle; E, spikelet.
Bromus hordeaceus 'subsp. *longipedicellatus*': F, panicle. *Bromus lanceolatus*: G, panicle.

156. **Elymus farctus** (Viv.) Runemark ex Melderis

Sand Couch   New Atlas: 795 (as *Elytrigia juncea*)

Glaucous, extensively rhizomatous perennial forming loose tufts or mats; culms up to 70cm, erect, slender to stout; leaves glaucous; sheaths glabrous, the outer margin glabrous, with falcate deciduous auricles at the summit; ligule a membranous rim 0.3 – 1.2(1.4)mm; blades sometimes flat and 2 – 6.5mm wide but usually inrolled and 0.5 – 2mm across, prominently ribbed above, the ribs minutely pubescent. Raceme stout, (4)6 – 20cm, straight or curved, fragile and readily breaking just above each spikelet, the latter falling with the internode attached, the internodes smooth on the edges, glabrous and smooth on the back. Spikelets sessile, wedge-shaped, (14)18 – 25(28)mm, 4- to 8(10)-flowered, breaking up between the florets, often reluctantly and seldom before the axis breaks up; glumes narrowly oblong, very tough and rigid, smooth, blunt at the tip, the lower (8.5)11 – 16.5(19)mm, the upper about 1mm longer; lemmas oblong or lanceolate-oblong, (11)13.5 – 19.5(21)mm, thick and tough, smooth, blunt or emarginate at the tip and with a hard apical mucro; anthers (4.5)6 – 8.5mm. $2n = 28$. Flowering and fruiting mid-June to early September.

Sand Couch is common in suitable habitats around the entire coast of the British Isles, including the Channel Islands, the Isles of Scilly and the northern islands north to Shetland. It is largely confined to a narrow zone at the top of sandy beaches including the strandline and the low foredunes to landward, but occasionally occurs on shingle ridges. It grows in a wide range of loose, unconsolidated sands (which may be highly calcareous) and nutrient conditions, the strandline being a patchy environment in this respect. In foredunes it may be found with *Leymus arenarius* and, usually to seaward, with a number of strandline plants such as *Atriplex laciniata, A. littoralis, Cakile maritima, Honckenya peploides* and *Salsola kali*. To landward it may grow with *Ammophila arenaria* and *Festuca rubra* (as 'subsp. *arenaria*').

The ability of *E. farctus* to survive and flourish in its disturbed and hazardous environment is dependent on its perennial lifecycle, extensive rhizome system, ability to grow vertically through accreting sand, tolerance of saline conditions, and capacity to establish new plants from seed and fragments of rhizome. In one study, seed and rhizome fragments were found to be equally important in colonizing the strandline from a nearby foredune, and both seedlings from buried seed and shoots from single-noded fragments emerged from 127mm burial but not 178mm (Harris & Davy 1986). Many-noded fragments emerge from greater depths and are probably the main organs of regeneration. Able to tolerate about 60cm of sand accretion per year, Sand Couch is often the main stabilizer of blown sand just above high water mark where it characteristically builds low hummocky foredunes to seaward of the Marram grass dunes. It may be outcompeted by Marram, more easily buried, or unable to reach the water table in higher dunes. New plants produce short rhizomes at first and longer horizontal rhizomes after

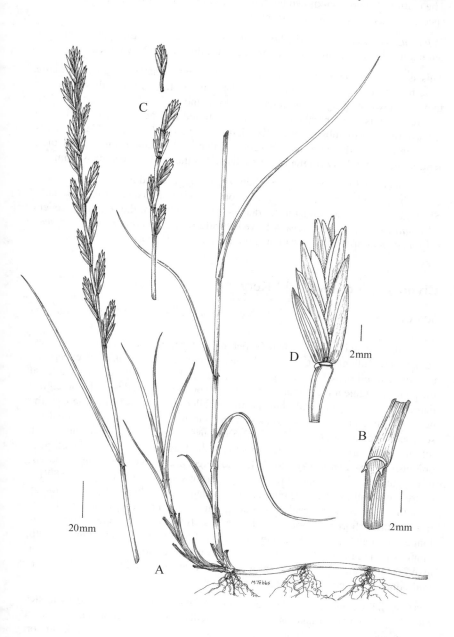

Elymus farctus: A, habit; B, ligule with auricles; C, raceme showing disarticulation;
D, spikelet with internode attached.

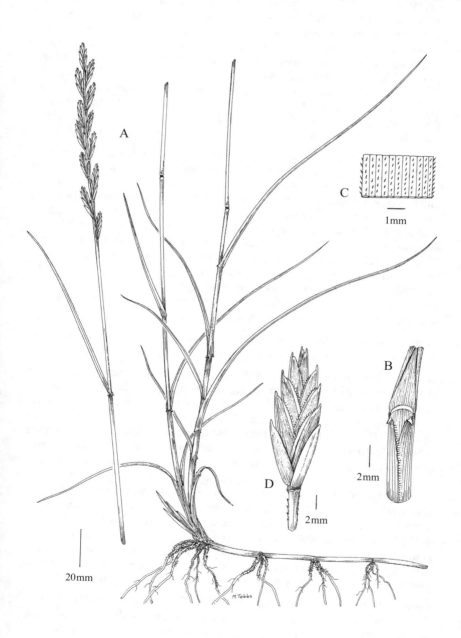

Elymus athericus: A, habit; B, ligule with auricles; C, upper surface of blade; D, spikelet.

to be replaced in its typical habitats by *E. repens*, is uncertain following the recent discovery that most populations in the northwest (and all modern records in Vc 60, W Lancs) are actually hybrids – mostly between *E athericus* and *E. repens* but including other hybrid couch grasses – or *E. repens* (Halliday, 1997; Greenwood, 2004). The main habitat of *E. athericus* is the most landward zone of intertidal saltmarshes where it often forms dense stands and extends to lower elevations along the banks of saltmarsh creeks. It is also found on shingle banks, in the zone between saltmarsh and sand-dune, the seaward faces of sea walls, in coastal grazing marsh and along the banks of tidal rivers. Soils in these habitats range from sands and gravelly mud to fine clays. *E. athericus* has a range of associates but is very commonly found in saltmarsh with *Atriplex portulacoides*.

Once established in the upper reaches of a saltmarsh, Sea Couch may produce dense stands of tall, coarse, unpalatable grass which excludes most other plant species. With the extensive withdrawal of grazing by sheep and cattle on British and European saltmarshes in the last 20 years the grass has become very invasive, even reducing plant diversity at lower elevation than on traditionally grazed marshes. Most expansion is vegetative but new populations may establish from seed which can float for at least 30 days and are probably dispersed by the tides. There is no seed bank and germination in the field is a rare event, especially in older marshes. However, seedling survival is high and new plants must be established since older stands have sometimes been shown to have more genets (genetically different individuals) per unit area than younger ones. *E. athericus* is probably usually outcrossing but is self-compatible.

A native species in the British Isles, *E. athericus* has a European Southern-temperate distribution as a native, and has been introduced to N America.

It is very similar to coastal ecotypes of *E. repens*, differing by scarcely more than the presence of cilia on the outer margin of the leaf-sheath. In coastal situations *E. repens* usually occurs on the landward side and *E. athericus* on the seaward; between the two, extensive patches of hybrids can form and these are usually clearly visible in the field. The hybrid (hitherto erroneously called **E. ×oliveri** (Druce) Melderis & D.C.McClint.; it was recently renamed *Elytrigia ×drucei* Stace (see Stace, 2001) but there is not, as yet, an available combination in *Elymus*), is always male-sterile and is intermediate in most characters; it always has cilia on the sheath-margin but these may be very few in number and hard to find. *E. athericus* also hybridizes with *E. farctus*; likewise, the hybrid (**E. ×obtusiusculus** (Lange) Melderis & D.C.McClint., but this has recently been renamed as *Elytrigia ×acuta* (DC.) Tzvelev nothosubsp. *obtusiuscula* (Lange) Kerguélen, and, again, there is no currently available epithet in *Elymus*) is male-sterile, the plants are intermediate and the sheath-margin is inconspicuously ciliate. The influence of *E. farctus* is clearly visible in the tendency for the raceme-axis to disarticulate (New Atlas: 795).

Plants in the far northern part of the range often fail to set seed and can be mistaken for hybrids. The abundance of cilia on the sheath margins, the toughness of the raceme axis and the thickness of the nerves of the leaves are useful guides, but it can be difficult to assess the true nature of some individuals.

158. **Elymus repens** (L.) Gould

Illustration, page 487

Common Couch

New Atlas: 794 (as *Elytrigia repens*)

Green or sometimes glaucous, extensively rhizomatous perennial forming loose tufts or patches; culms up to 110(160)cm, erect, slender; leaves usually green, sometimes glaucous; sheaths glabrous, or the lower shortly hairy, glabrous on the outer margin, with falcate auricles at the summit; ligule a membranous rim 0.2 – 0.5mm; blades soft, usually flat and 3 – 9(12)mm wide but sometimes inrolled and 0.5 – 2mm across, the nerves thin, more than their own width apart, round-topped and smooth, the upper leaf-surface usually loosely pilose, rarely the nerves thicker and the leaf glabrous. Raceme stiff, (4.5)7.5 – 13.5(21.5)cm, usually straight, tough, the internodes scabrid on the edges and smooth, scabrid, pubescent or pilose on the back. Spikelets sessile, elliptic-oblong, (10)12 – 18(22)mm, 4- to 7(9)-flowered, breaking up between the florets, often reluctantly so and the florets falling in groups, sometimes the spikelet falling entire including the glumes; glumes similar, lanceolate-oblong, rigid and tough, smooth on the back, scabrid on the keel, apiculate or mucronate at the tip, sometimes shortly (up to 4mm) awned, the lower (7)8.5 – 14mm (including the awn), the upper 0 – 1mm longer; lemmas lanceolate-oblong, (8)9 – 13.5mm, rigid and tough, smooth, apiculate or mucronate at the tip with a point 0.5 – 1mm, sometimes awned with an awn up to 5.5(7)mm; anthers (4)4.5 – 6(7)mm. $2n = 42$. Flowering and fruiting late June to early August, sometimes to late August, rarely beyond.

Widespread throughout the British Isles, Common Couch is particularly abundant in areas of arable farming in the lowlands, and becomes rarer only in the uplands and especially in parts of NW Scotland. It occurs on a wide range of cultivated and waste ground including road verges, rough grassland and railway embankments, and is a particularly noxious weed of gardens, orchards, allotments and other agricultural land. (Druce (1932) described it as "too common throughout the British Isles"). Other habitats from which *E. repens* has been recorded include coastal sands and cliffs, shingle, sea walls and saltmarshes (especially in the north), river margins, meadows, hedgerows and spoil heaps. It occurs on a wide range of soil types, except acid peat, and is associated particularly with fertile clay arable land of pH >7.0. It is common in disturbed soils and is found with a wide range of associates occurring up to 430m in Cumbria and, exceptionally, 845m on Great Dun Fell, Westmorland.

Considered to be one of the world's worst perennial weeds, and arguably *the* worst in the cooler N Temperate Zone, *E. repens* mainly persists and spreads due to the production of numerous long stout sharply-pointed rhizomes, small pieces of which can develop into new plants making the grass difficult to eradicate. Rhizome growth is prodigious. In one experiment single tillers produced, after only 20 weeks, an average of around 5m of rhizome per plant bearing 215 buds (but only about 30 seeds compared to 260 seeds of *E. caninus* in the same conditions). Rhizomes vary between 20cm and 1m in length before turning towards the surface and can grow at a depth of 40cm in alluvial soils. They begin to develop in late March or April following vigorous spring growth of the aerial shoots which were produced the previous autumn and require exposure to low temperatures during the dormant period (probably accounting for the species' absence from the tropics). Rhizome production continues to mid-August or mid-October and mature shoots senesce in the autumn, but this phenology is frequently disturbed in arable land. Shade and repeated defoliation inhibit rhizome growth but the species is both frost and drought tolerant. Seed production is generally low but variable and, since the species is self-incompatible, may be affected by large clone size or the establishment of populations from single clones. Seed may germinate immediately, germinating to a higher percentage in the light, and there appears to be a short-lived seed bank. However, regeneration is largely vegetative, and may be encouraged by cultivation without killing or removing rhizomes. There is genetic variation for the partitioning of biomass between above- and below-ground growth and for other traits including growth habit, flowering time, colour and spikelet morphology. *E. repens* is thus an extremely variable species. (Biol. Flora: Palmer & Sagar 1963; CPE: 264).

E. repens is native in the British Isles and in the European Wide-temperate zone, although it has a Circumpolar Wide-temperate distribution following extensive naturalization. It has been introduced to the temperate zones of the southern hemisphere in S America, South Africa, Australia and New Zealand.

Its reputation not entirely bad, Common Couch was once valued for herbal remedies, used for bread flour in famines, is much liked by pigs, and appears to be the favourite emetic of cats and dogs.

E. repens is an extremely variable plant, with awned or awnless spikelets, flat or inrolled blades and green or glaucous colouration. It is represented by two elements which are usually recognized at subspecies level:

158a. subsp. **repens** has flat green blades with slender nerves.

158b. subsp. **arenosus** (Spenn.) Melderis has glaucous inrolled blades with broader nerves. New Atlas p.794.

The latter appears to be rather rare in the British Isles and is found only in coastal sand, but many intermediates are found in other coastal habitats. It closely resembles forms of *E. athericus* from which it differs by scarcely more than the glabrous outer sheath margin.

The species hybridizes with *E. athericus* (see under that species for details) and with *E. farctus*. The latter hybrid (**E. ×laxus** (Fr.) Melderis & D.C.McClint.) is male-sterile, intermediate between the parents and has a tardily fragile raceme axis (New Atlas p.795). *E. repens* (particularly the awned form) hybridizes also with *Hordeum secalinum*. This hybrid (×**Elyhordeum langei** (K.Richt.) Melderis) exists in two forms: the first, known only from W Gloucs (Vc 34), is reasonably distinctive in having a fragile raceme axis and awned glumes and lemmas, and by being male-sterile. The presence of *Hordeum* is also indicated

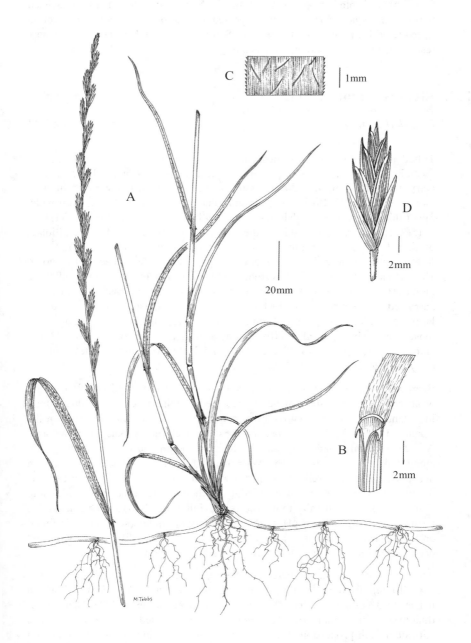

Elymus repens subsp. *repens*: A, habit; B, ligule with auricles; C, upper surface of blade; D, spikelet.

by the fact that often the glumes are more or less collateral with the back of the first lemma visible between them; above the first lemma the rhachilla is twisted to bring subsequent florets into the expected orientation. The second form, found in scattered localities from the Isles of Scilly to Northumberland, more closely resembles its *Elymus* parent, but has a fragile rhachis; it is not always sterile.

159. Elymus caninus (L.) L.

Bearded Couch   New Atlas: 793

Tufted perennial without rhizomes; culms up to 100(140)cm, erect or geniculately ascending, slender; leaves bright green; sheaths glabrous or the lower shortly hairy, the outer margin glabrous, with falcate auricles at the summit; ligule a membranous rim (0.2)0.4 – 0.9(1.1)mm; blades soft, flat, 4 – 10(13)mm wide, rather thin, finely nerved, glabrous or loosely hairy above. Raceme slender, (7)8 – 15(22)cm, curved or nodding, the axis with internodes scabrid or ciliolate on the edges, scabrid or almost smooth on the face, tough or rarely fragile and disarticulating at the base of the internode. Spikelets sessile, lanceolate to oblong, 10 – 18mm, (2)3- to 5(6)-flowered, readily breaking up between the florets; glumes similar, lanceolate to narrowly oblong, rounded on the back, rigid, usually narrowed above into an awn, the body 6 – 10(11)mm, the awn 0 – 4mm; lemmas lanceolate-oblong, 8.5 – 13(14)mm, rigid, minutely hairy below, glabrous or loosely hairy above, usually narrowed into a straight or flexuous awn 0 – 22mm; anthers 2 – 3(3.5)mm. $2n = 28$. Flowering and fruiting mid-June to late August or early September.

Bearded Couch is widespread and locally common in England and Wales, rare or absent from large areas of Scotland, especially the north, and is uncommon in Ireland where it has been recorded mainly in the north. It is absent from the Channel Islands, The Isle of Man and the Outer Hebrides, Orkney and Shetland. A grass of mainly shaded habitats, it occurs in and around woodland and scrub, along hedgerows, on tree-lined riverbanks and on road verges. It can occur in unshaded places as a relic of former woodland, and in mountainous areas it is found in rocky gullies and on cliff ledges. Although often associated with damp shady places it is generally found on free-draining mainly base-rich soils and is most common on soils of pH >6.0. The variety *donianus* (see below) is found on limestone rocks. It has a range of associates across the different habitats and occurs from sea-level to 810m (Creag na Caillick, M Perth).

Although it is a polycarpic perennial, the reproductive strategy of *E. caninus* is very different from that of other *Elymus* species, especially *E. repens* with which it has been compared experimentally (Tripathi & Harper, 1973). Being non-rhizomatous, new plants of *E. caninus* are all established from seed and adults allocate a high proportion of their resources to flowering and seed production (producing around 260 seeds in one experiment compared to 30 seeds of *E.*

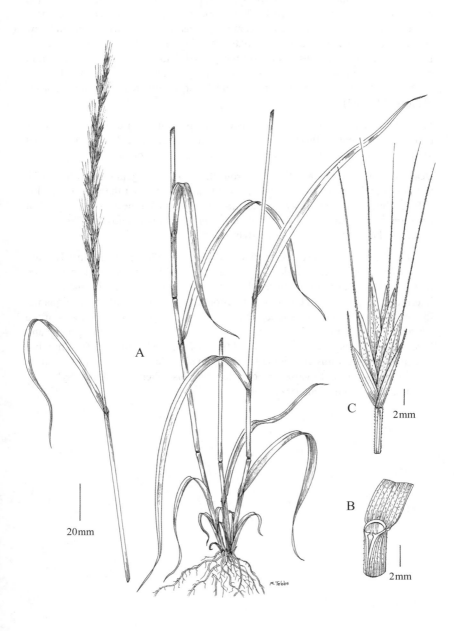

Elymus caninus: A, habit; B, ligule with auricles; C, spikelet.

489

repens). Florets are protogynous and although it is probably mostly outbreeding there is no self-incompatibility. Seed are set from September to October and mainly germinate in early spring. There appears to be no long term seed bank. Plants continue to grow as the tree canopy begins to close in woodland and new shoots appear in the autumn. The plant remains green throughout the winter. Like several other grasses with a similar growth habit, *E. caninus* is intolerant of grazing and mowing, and its shade tolerance and ability to grow in relatively infertile soils probably enable it to avoid being dominated by more vigorous plants (CPE: 262).

E. caninus is native in the British Isles and part of the Eurosiberian Boreo-temperate element in the flora. It has been introduced into N America. Don's Twitch (var. *donianus*) is also found in Iceland and E Greenland.

Bearded Couch stands a little apart from the rest of the genus by virtue of its tufted rather than rhizomatous habit. Most texts indicate that the raceme rhachis is tough but this is not always so; several specimens have been seen in which it fractures in the same way as that of *E. farctus*, but this is unusual. There is no evidence that the two species form hybrids.

Bearded Couch is represented by two fairly distinct elements in Great Britain; these were at one time regarded as species, but now they are viewed as no more than varieties. Beyond our shores they are even less distinct, with many more intermediates, and the value of a distinction at any level is rather questionable. In var. *caninus* the glumes and lemmas are distinctly awned and the awns of the lemmas are 8 – 22mm. In var. *donianus* (Buch.-White) Melderis the glumes and lemmas are inconspicuously awned and the awns of the lemmas are 0 – 3mm but seldom completely absent. The latter is confined to Scottish mountains in Great Britain, but where both varieties occur together elsewhere they freely hybridize forming a spectrum of intermediates.

two years. Tillers require vernalization and normally flower in their second year. The mating system is unknown but the degree of hybridization with other *Elymus* species points to extensive outcrossing.

E. farctus is a native of the British Isles and is part of the large European Southern-temperate element in our flora. It has been introduced into N America.

This is the only member of the genus in our flora to have a regularly fragile axis, but in addition to the fragility of the axis the florets also fall separately; they are, however, very often reluctant to do so and seldom begin to disarticulate before the axis itself breaks up. The plants found around the British Isles are usually referred to subsp. **boreoatlanticus** (Simonet & Guin.) Melderis; this is characterized by the extensive rhizomes, palea-keels ciliolate throughout their length, the particularly fragile raceme axis and anthers not exceeding 8.5mm.

Sand Couch readily hybridizes with both *Elymus repens* and *E. athericus*. In both cases the hybrids are male-sterile and combine characteristics of their parents. See under those species for further details. Should either of the segregate genera *Elytrigia* Desv. or *Thinopyrum* Á.Löve be preferred, the epithet reverts to *juncea* (or *junceum* as appropriate) which is not available in *Elymus*.

157. **Elymus athericus** (Link) Kerguélen

Sea Couch   New Atlas: 794 (as *Elytrigia atherica*)

Glaucous, extensively rhizomatous perennial forming loose tufts or patches; culms up to 100cm, erect, slender; leaves glaucous; sheaths glabrous except for the ciliate or ciliolate outer margin (rarely this glabrous), with falcate auricles at the summit; ligule a membranous rim 0.3 – 0.6(0.8)mm; blades stiff, sometimes flat and 2.5 – 5(7)mm wide but usually inrolled and 0.5 – 1.5mm across, the nerves prominently ribbed above, less than their own width apart, flat-topped and scabrid. Raceme stiff, (3.5)6.5 – 12(13.5)cm, usually straight, the axis tough with internodes scabrid on the edges, smooth on the back. Spikelets sessile, elliptic-oblong, (10)12 – 21mm, (4)5- to 10(12)-flowered, breaking up between the florets, often reluctantly so and the florets falling in groups, sometimes the spikelet falling entire including the glumes; glumes similar, lanceolate-oblong, rigid and tough, smooth on the back, scabrid on the keel, bluntly pointed to apiculate at the tip, rarely with a short awn-point, the lower 7 – 11(13)mm, the upper about 1 mm longer; lemmas lanceolate-oblong, (8.5)9.5 – 12.5mm, rigid and tough, smooth, blunt or pointed at the tip, sometimes with a mucro up to 1.5mm, rarely with an awn 3 – 6mm; anthers (3)4.5 – 7mm. $2n = 42$. Flowering and fruiting late June to mid-August, sometimes as late as early October.

Sea Couch is common around the coastline of the southern part of the British Isles including the Channel Islands, the Isles of Scilly, southern Ireland and the coast of mainland Britain as far north as the Solway on the west coast and Yorkshire on the east. Its exact distribution, particularly near its northern limits where it tends

160. **Leymus arenarius** (L.) Hochst.

Lyme-grass

New Atlas: 796

Robust strongly rhizomatous perennial forming dense tufts or stands, up to 140(200)cm; sheaths smooth and glabrous, with falcate auricles at the summit; ligule a firmly membranous rim (0.4)0.5 – 1(1.2)mm, minutely ciliate on the edge; blades flat or inrolled, 7 – 13(20)mm wide, rigid, scabrid on the prominent nerves above, smooth beneath, sharply pointed at the tip. False raceme stout, rigid, 14 – 30(70)cm, short and dense with the spikelets overlapping by about half their length, or much longer and looser with the spikelets not or scarcely overlapping. Spikelets paired, sessile, 3- to 6-flowered; glumes collateral, narrowly lanceolate, 17 – 27(46)mm, as long as or almost as long as the spikelet, laterally compressed and keeled, 3- to 5-nerved, thinly hairy especially on the keel; lemmas rounded on the back, rapidly decreasing in size upwards, the lowermost 16 – 25mm, tough, 7-nerved, shortly and densely hairy all over, sharply pointed but scarcely awned at the tip; palea as long as the lemma; anthers very variable, mostly 6.5 – 8mm, but often as little as 4.5mm. $2n = 56$. Flowering and fruiting mid-June to late August or even early October.

Lyme-grass occurs around most of the British coast, being more common in the north and absent from the Channel Islands, the Isles of Scilly and long stretches of the south coast of England. It occurs mainly on the north and east coasts of Ireland. Confined to coastal sands, and occasionally fine shingle, it is also a rare casual or a garden escape inland. The coastal distribution of Lyme-grass may be affected by widespread planting to prevent dune erosion. It occurs in loose mobile sand, mostly in the pH range 6.5 – 8.0, and can be a dominant species in the foredune, excluding other plants. It is commonly found with *Ammophila arenaria* and *Elymus farctus*, and with a range of other dune and strandline plants (see *E. farctus*).

A grass easily recognized by its rigid growth habit and attractive bluish waxy bloom, *L. arenarius* is an efficient stabilizer of mobile sand, spreading by extensive creeping rhizomes and able to build small dunes. It is often found between *E. farctus* on the seaward strandline and *A. arenaria* in the landward dunes although more salt-tolerant than either. However, it may be more susceptible to damage from strong winds than these two grasses. It can survive in high *A. arenaria* dunes in the north where rainfall and spray are high compared to more southerly dunes, suggesting that moisture, and perhaps even nutrient, limitation is as important as competition from Marram in fixing its landward limits. A northern species extending into the Arctic Circle, *L. arenarius* can grow through the cold months of the year. Flowering is generally erratic and sparse, except in the far north, but will occur in cultivation after two years from seed. Regeneration from seed is probably much less common than from rhizome fragments. Seed, which often remain on the plant over winter, germinate to a higher percentage in the dark and seedlings are unable to withstand more than 7.5cm of sand burial. (Biol. Flora: Bond, 1952).

L. arenarius is native and is a European Boreo-arctic species, occurring also in E Asia and N America. Its distribution in Britain appears stable but some populations have been lost in southern England. It was once protected here by act of parliament, initially in Scotland, for its sand-binding properties, and it has also been used as a source of grain in Iceland.

Typically, plants have a stout, dense inflorescence with overlapping spikelets, but occasionally there are plants with a highly elongated axis and the spikelets scarcely overlapping; these plants tend to have larger spikelets and often shorter anthers, but the two extremes completely intergrade. Occasionally large stands fail to flower in some years and invariably these plants have been infected by a stem smut fungus, *Ustilago hypodytes*. The overall bluish colour of the plant lends it some horticultural merit and it is often grown as a feature of the herbaceous border; it is propagated by division of the rhizomes.

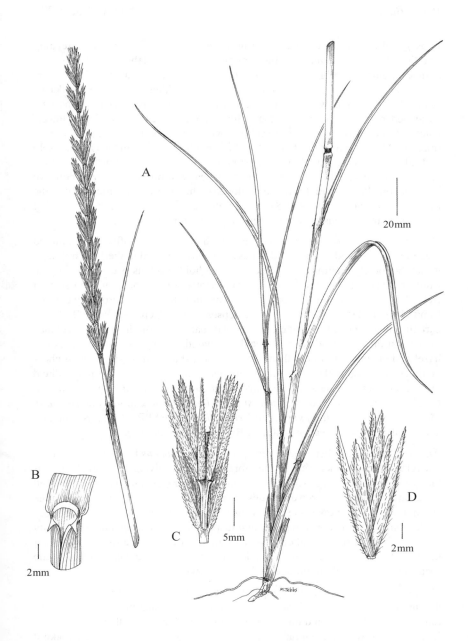

Leymus arenarius: A, habit; B, ligule with auricles; C, portion of inflorescence; D, spikelet.

161. **Hordelymus europaeus** (L.) Jess. ex Harz

Wood Barley   New Atlas: 796

Loosely tufted, short-lived perennial up to 90(120)cm; sheaths with spreading or reflexed hairs, particularly at the summit, and falcate, glabrous or thinly hairy auricles; ligule a membranous rim (0.4)0.5 – 0.7mm; blades flat, 5 – 13mm wide, loosely and thinly hairy. False raceme erect or nodding, 5.5 – 9.5cm, dense. Spikelets 1-flowered with rhachilla-extension 2.5 – 4mm, this often bearing an awned rudiment or rarely a male floret; glumes (12)14 – 17.5mm, linear-lanceolate below, narrowed to a scabrid awn above; lemma (8.5)10 – 11.5mm (measured from tip of callus to tip of palea), broadly rounded on the back, loosely scabrid-hispid especially above, imperceptibly narrowed to a fine scabrid awn 15 – 25mm (measured from tip of palea); palea with prominent keels, concave between the keels (and these often dorsal), the groove accommodating the rhachilla-extension; anthers (1.8)2.8 – 3.5mm. $2n = 28$. Flowering and fruiting late June to mid-August, sometimes persisting until mid-October.

H. europaeus is a scarce grass in the British Isles now confined to scattered localities in mainland England and Wales northwards to Northumberland, although it may be locally plentiful in traditional strongholds such as beechwoods in the Chilterns. There is one recent record from Scotland but it has not been seen in Ireland since 1949 – and only once before that in 1889 – and is probably extinct. Limited to shaded habitats in woods, copses and hedgerows, Wood Barley is particularly associated with ancient boundary banks and old hedgerows. It tends to occur at the woodland edge, in deciduous woodland with a high canopy, or in hazel and elder scrub, rather than in the deepest shade. Most sites are on chalk or limestone soils with a few on calcareous boulder clay. Common woodland plant associates include *Anthriscus sylvestris, Galium aparine, Geum urbanum, Glechoma hederacea, Heracleum sphondylium, Hyacinthoides non-scripta, Mercurialis perennis, Rubus* spp. and *Urtica dioica* (see SPB: 207). It is generally a lowland species but reaches 440m at Brough (Westmorland).

An interesting and rather specialized species, *H. europaeus* bears short rhizomes but relatively few tillers and is therefore fairly short-lived. Individuals appear rarely to last more than 2 – 3 years and populations regenerate mainly from seed which are produced in large quantities in some years. The seeds germinate in the autumn and plants flower the following year. The species has a transient seed bank. Plants often occur in patches and display the contrast in stomatal density and leaf reversal seen in other woodland grasses (an average of 5 stomata per mm^2 on the lower surface and around 80 per mm^2 on the upper surface). Little seems to be known about the species' breeding system.

H. europaeus is a European Temperate species native in Britain and patchily distributed in Europe, N Africa and W Asia. It has declined in Britain due to the removal of hedgerows and the replacement of deciduous woodland by conifers. Its association with ancient habitats and inability to colonize new areas make it dependent on the conservation of its traditional locations.

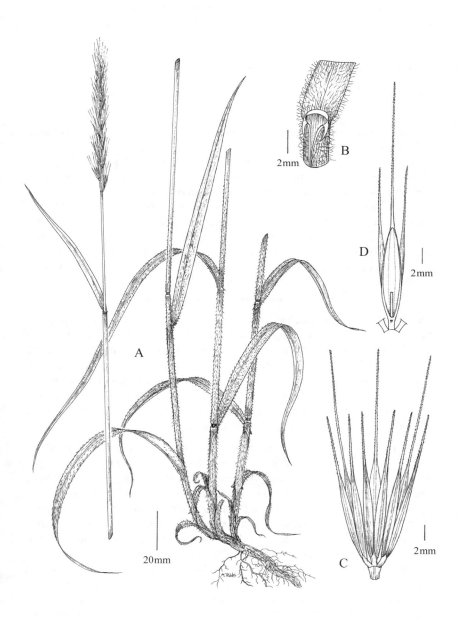

Hordelymus europaeus: A, habit; B, ligule with auricles; C, spikelet triad from the back; D, central spikelet from the front.

It is likely only to be confused with a species of *Hordeum*, but its habit, tough rhachilla and fertile lateral spikelets will distinguish it. Confusingly, there are, on rare occasions, only two spikelets at each node of the inflorescence but even under this circumstance its similarity to *Hordeum* is quite obvious.

162. Hordeum secalinum Schreb.

Meadow Barley   New Atlas: 798

Tufted perennial up to 95cm, the culms usually erect, occasionally geniculate; sheaths not inflated, the lower softly hairy, the upper glabrous, with minute falcate auricles at the summit; ligule a membranous rim 0.3 – 0.6(0.8)mm; blades flat, (1.5)2.5 – 5(6)mm wide, or inrolled, hairy or glabrous, the underside smooth or scabrid. False raceme erect or inclined, dense, laterally compressed, 2.5 – 8cm, the spikelets unequal to very unequal. Central spikelet sessile; glumes bristle-like and long-awned, 9 – 16mm, scabrid; lemma lanceolate, passing gradually into the awn, the body (5.5)7 – 9(10)mm (measured to tip of palea), the awn (4.5)7.5 – 12(14)mm; anthers (2.5)3.3 – 4.4(4.8)mm; lateral spikelets smaller than the central, pedicelled (0.7 – 1.3mm), the glumes awn-like and scabrid throughout; lemma, including the awn but excluding the basal stipe (this up to 1.3mm), 3 – 10mm, male or barren. $2n = 14, 28$. Flowering and fruiting late May to mid-August.

Meadow Barley is common and often locally abundant in the southeast of England below a line from Flamborough Head to the Severn Estuary. North and west of this line it is more scattered, being rare and probably introduced in Scotland, and very local and mainly coastal in Ireland, where it is included in the Irish Red Data Book (Curtis & McGough 1988). Its characteristic habitats are lowland meadows, pastures and coastal grazing marsh, most commonly in unimproved grassland on heavy, often calcareous, clay soils. It also occurs on roadsides and sea walls and can tolerate brackish conditions. It has a wide range of associates.

H. secalinum is generally regarded as a short-lived perennial although plants in a translocation experiment have survived for a minimum of six years, some flowering every year (Dr J.Martin, *pers. comm.*). Most new plants are likely to be established from seed, populations producing large numbers of seed each year, but some may grow from plant fragments transported by cattle, especially in moist soils. *H. secalinum* is essentially a subdominant component of grazed grassland, decreasing significantly if grazing is withdrawn when it tends to be outcompeted by more vigorous species. Whilst it is often plentiful in old pasture it is itself of little agricultural value. It is said to withstand modest improvements of grassland but rarely survives drainage and re-seeding of new leys. Although protandrous and mainly outbreeding, the overall amount of genetic diversity found in some European (Cronberg *et al.,* 1997) and Irish (J.Martin, *pers. comm.*) populations appears to be low.

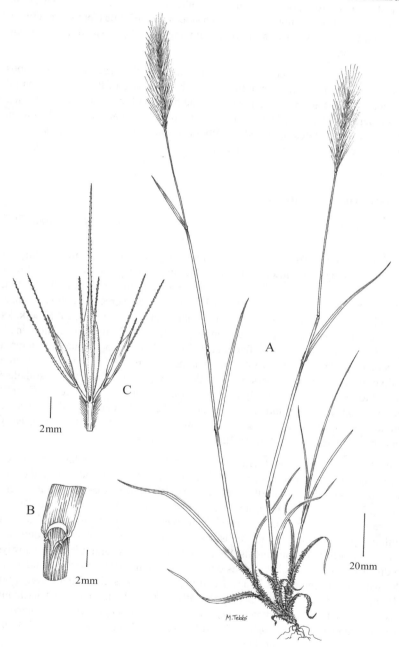

Hordeum secalinum: A, habit; B, ligule with auricles; C, spikelet triad.

H. secalinum is native in Britain and Ireland and is part of our European Temperate flora. It occurs throughout western and southern Europe and in NW Africa. Its general distribution has not changed much since the 1962 Atlas, but it is declining in some areas because of loss of coastal grazing marsh, grassland improvement and conversion to arable.

The lateral florets are much smaller than the central and borne on a conspicuous stipe. They may be male with anthers about half the size of those of the central spikelet or quite barren. In the latter case the palea and male flower are missing and the lemma itself is reduced to little more than the expanded base of its awn. The species can be distinguished from both *H. murinum* and *H. marinum* by its perennial habit and non-inflated sheaths.

163. Hordeum murinum L.

Wall Barley   New Atlas: 797

Annual up to 50(70)cm, the culms erect or geniculate; sheaths slightly to markedly inflated, the lower usually hairy, the upper glabrous, with glabrous falcate auricles at the summit; ligule a membranous rim 0.4 – 1mm; blades flat, 2.5 – 6.5mm wide, glabrous or thinly hairy. False raceme erect or inclined, dense, laterally compressed, 4 – 8.5(10.5)cm, the spikelets all ± equal. Central spikelet subsessile (pedicel not exceeding 0.6mm); glumes bristle-like and long-awned, (15)18 – 27(30)mm, slightly flattened below, ciliate on both margins; lemma lanceolate, passing gradually into the awn, the body (6.5)9 – 12.5mm (measured to tip of palea), the awn 2 – 4(4.5)cm; anthers 0.8 – 1.2(1.4) mm; lateral spikelets similar to the central but shortly pedicelled (0.7 – 1.6mm), inner glume wider at the base than the outer and shortly ciliate on the outer margin, and floret male (anthers as above) or barren. 2*n* = 28. Flowering and fruiting late May or early June to mid-August, sometimes as late as early October.

Wall Barley is common and widespread throughout lowland England and Wales, including the Isles of Scilly and the Channel Islands. It extends along the east coast of Scotland as far north as E Ross (vc 106) but is absent from the west, most of the British uplands, and from most of Ireland except around Dublin where it is increasing. It is associated exclusively with ruderal habitats including building plots, waste ground, roadsides, pavements, the base of buildings and walls, and railway embankments. Where it occurs in grassland it is almost always in disturbed and open sites such as open paths or bare patches in parkland, or in sheep and cattle enclosures in pasture. It requires fertile soils of moderately high pH (mostly 6.5 – 8.5) and open, frequently disturbed habitats where its many associates include *Lolium perenne, Poa annua, Plantago major, Matricaria discoidea* and *Taraxacum officinale*. Although a lowland grass, it reaches 450m on Kirkstone Pass (Westmorland).

Hordeum murinum: A, habit; B, ligule with auricles; C, spikelet triad.

H. murinum is a self-pollinating winter annual, the seed germinating from mid-August onwards and sometimes continuing into December, usually in a single burst of rapid and complete germination following a very short primary dormancy. Spring germination is uncommon and plants from seedlings which appear in August flower and ripen earlier than, and produce around twice as many seed as, those from November seedlings. The species is susceptible to shading and to competition from perennial plants, when seed output is considerably reduced. It thus requires the creation of new open patches within its habitat, and populations fluctuate greatly in size from year to year. Davison (1977, and earlier papers referred to therein) showed that, whilst the requirement for low competition, high nutrients and high light intensity appear to restrict *H. murinum* to ruderal habitats, it is as much limited by climatic conditions to areas of low altitude and low rainfall rather than by the distribution of suitable habitats. The knock-on effects of delayed germination, growth and seed production and poor dispersal gradually eliminate populations in upland areas or where rainfall exceeds around 1000mm per year, although urban sites within these areas provide some suitable habitat.

Classed as an archaeophyte, *H. murinum* has a stable distribution in Britain. It is widely naturalized and has a Circumpolar Southern Temperate distribution. It has been introduced in N & S America, Australia and New Zealand where it has become a serious weed of sheep pasture and lucerne crops. The specific name *murinum* does not evidently derive from *muris*, recognizing its liking for walls, but from *mus*, for mouse, a reference to its hairy spikelets.

Three subspecies occur in the British Isles, only one of them native:

163a. subsp. **murinum**. The description and habitat notes above apply to this, the 'native' subspecies. Notable characters are the overall green colour of the foliage, the triad of subequal spikelets and the relatively long anthers.

163b. susbp. **leporinum** (Link) Arcang. differs from subsp. *murinum* by the unequal spikelets with the laterals noticeably longer than the central; the central spikelet itself borne on a distinct pedicel not less than 0.6mm and often almost as long as that of the laterals. $2n = 28, 42$. A grass of mesic habitats from the Mediterranean region eastwards to C Asia and China, widely scattered in England and Scotland on waste ground where it sometimes persists for a short time.

163c. subsp. **glaucum** (Steud.) Tzvelev has an overall glaucous tinge to the foliage, but otherwise differs from subsp. *leporinum* only by the much smaller anthers of the central spikelet (0.2 – 0.5mm) and chromosome number. $2n = 14$. A plant of xeric habitats with overall distribution similar to that of subsp. *leporinum*. It is much rarer in Britain than subsp. *leporinum* but is found in similar habitats.

164. Hordeum marinum Huds.

Sea Barley   New Atlas: 798

Annual up to 40cm, the culms usually geniculate; sheaths slightly to markedly inflated, glabrous or the lower minutely pubescent, with small rounded auricles at the summit; ligule a membranous rim 0.3 – 0.6mm; blades flat or inrolled, 1.5 – 3(4)mm wide, glabrous or minutely hairy. False raceme erect, dense, laterally compressed, 2 – 5cm, the spikelets unequal. Central spikelet sessile; glumes bristle-like and long-awned, 10 – 18(22)mm, scaberulous; lemma lanceolate, passing gradually into the awn, the body 5.5 – 7.5(8.5)mm (measured to tip of palea), the awn (6)9 – 17(22)mm; anthers 0.8 – 1.4mm; lateral spikelets much reduced, barren, pedicellate (0.7 – 1.1mm); glumes 10 – 23mm, the inner expanded on the outer edge into a conspicuous wing; lemma 2 – 5mm with an awn (1)2 – 5.5(7)mm. $2n = 14$. Flowering and fruiting late June to late August, but sometimes beginning in early June.

Sea Barley is largely confined to the south coast of Wales, the Bristol Channel, and the south and east coasts of England as far north as the Wash. It is patchily distributed within this stretch of coastline and is locally common in the Thames Estuary and along the Essex coast. It was formerly more widespread (see below) and is occasionally found inland along salt-affected roadsides. It is absent from Ireland. It is a grass of bare soils along the coast, being commonly found at the edges of dried-up, brackish pools and ditches or on the landward side of sea walls in vehicle tracks or cattle-trampled ground. It is less commonly found in the upper parts of saltmarshes, especially where these are trampled by cattle or sheep. It favours fertile, often brackish muds but is found now and then on sandy or stony substrates. In those habitats to landward of sea walls it typically occurs with *Aster tripolium, Puccinellia distans, P. fasciculata, P. rupestris* and *Spergularia marina*, whilst common high saltmarsh associates include *Festuca rubra, Glaux maritima, Juncus gerardii, Parapholis strigosa, Plantago coronopus* and *Puccinellia maritima*.

A self-pollinating annual reproducing entirely by seed, *H. marinum* requires open sites for establishment and growth, and particularly favours mud which dries out in spring and is baked hard by mid-summer. Seedlings have been observed in autumn and spring but it is not known which of these cohorts contributes most to population regeneration. The mature spikes are very brittle and spikelets tend to disperse in small clusters. Their dispersal is probably assisted by flooding as winter flood-lines around pools are often marked the following year by narrow banks of *H. marinum* seedlings. Like other annual species of *Hordeum, H. marinum* is susceptible to competition from perennial plants and particularly in this case the grass *Elymus athericus* which eventually colonizes these brackish habitats. The continuous creation of open ground is therefore essential for populations to survive. (SPB: 209).

H. marinum is native in Britain where it is at the northern limit of its Mediterranean-Atlantic distribution. It grows on disturbed ground away from the coast in the Mediterranean, is also found in C Asia, and is widely naturalized outside its native range. Its disappearance from parts along the English south coast and from the east coast north of the Wash (including former sites in Scotland) is probably because in many areas pools and ditches within coastal grazing marshes have been filled in, the grazing marshes have been improved or converted to arable, saltmarsh grazing has decreased or new sea defences no longer provide the open ground for Sea Barley to thrive. It is designated as **vulnerable** by Cheffings & Farrell (2005).

Sea Barley is readily distinguished from *H. murinum* by the glabrous awns of the central spikelet and the reduced lateral spikelets. Two subspecies occur in the British Isles, one of them introduced:

164a. susbp. **marinum**. The description and habitat notes above apply to this, the native subspecies. It is characterized by the expanded wing-like base of the inner glume of the lateral spikelet.

164b. subsp. **gussoneanum** (Parl.) Thell. (*Mediterranean Barley*). Differs from subsp. *marinum* only by the less broadened and quite wingless inner glume of the lateral spikelet, and by the more variable chromosome number ($2n = 14, 28$). A native of the Mediterranean region eastwards to C Asia sometimes recognized as a distinct species (*H. geniculatum* All.), but the minor differences between it and *H. marinum* sensu str. scarcely warrant so high a rank. It is widely scattered as a casual over much of Britain, but has been naturalized in Guernsey for well over a hundred years. It arrives as a contaminant of cereals, esparto, fenugreek and grass-seed, and was once commonly introduced with wool.

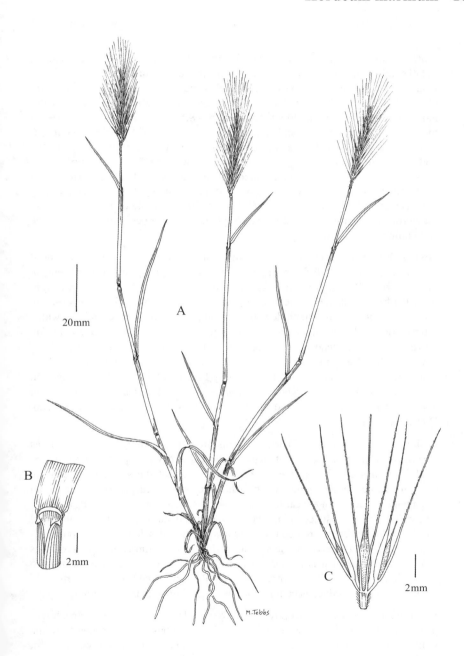

Hordeum marinum: A, habit; B, ligule with auricles; C, spikelet triad.

165. Hordeum jubatum L.

Foxtail Barley   New Atlas: 797

Tufted, short-lived perennial up to 65(90)cm, the culms erect or geniculate; sheaths lightly inflated, the lower retrorse- or spreading-hairy, the upper glabrous, with small blunt auricles at the summit; ligule a membranous rim 0.3 – 0.7(1)mm; blades flat, (1)1.5 – 3(4.5)mm wide, or inrolled, scabrid above, smooth beneath. False raceme eventually nodding, dense, (4)5 – 8.5(10)cm, the spikelets unequal to very unequal. Central spikelet sessile; glumes awn-like throughout, 40 – 65(80)mm, scabrid; lemma lanceolate, passing gradually into the awn, the body 4.5 – 6mm (measured to tip of palea), the awn (25)35 – 75mm; anthers 0.9 – 1.4mm; lateral spikelets smaller than the central, pedicelled (0.5 – 1mm), the glumes awn-like and scabrid throughout; lemma, including the awn but excluding the basal stipe (this up to 1.5mm), (1)2.5 – 8(20)mm, male or barren. $2n = 28$. Flowering and fruiting mid-July to late September, rarely beginning in early June and ending in late October.

Foxtail Barley has been recorded from locations scattered throughout central and eastern Britain as far north as C Scotland. It is rarely found, or absent, in the southwest, Wales, northern Scotland and Ireland. It has become increasingly recorded from roadsides in the last 30 years especially those affected by de-icing salt, and its other habitats include waste ground, newly sown grassland, sea walls, rubbish tips and docklands. On roadsides it seems to be particularly common on roundabouts. It occurs on a wide range of soils although most are likely to have a high pH and many are saline, and is associated with numerous ruderal plant species. On trunk roads it is frequently found with halophytic species such as *Cochlearia danica, Hordeum marinum, Puccinellia distans* and *Spergularia marina*. It is mainly a lowland grass but reaches 410m at Devil's Beef Tub, Dumfries.

In flower, this unmistakable barley with its attractive feathery inflorescence has become a distinctive feature of many waysides and waste places. Populations establish from seed which arrives either as a contaminant of grass-seed and oilseed, or from birdseed, or as a garden escape (the species is increasingly cultivated as an ornamental), but do not appear to persist for more than 3 or 4 years. In its native N America it is an early successional species invading disturbed or saline ground, and would probably require frequent disturbance to establish long-lived populations here. It is a prolific seed producer. Both spring and autumn cohorts of seedlings can be observed and it is thought that the first of these may contribute most to population growth in this country. It is a troublesome weed in many parts of N America, the dry seedheads being injurious to grazing animals and ruining hay.

H. jubatum is classed as a neophyte in the New Atlas. Unlikely as it seems, it was probably introduced as a fodder grass (in 1782) and has been recorded from the wild since 1890. It now arrives mostly as a seed contaminant or as an escape from gardens but was formerly introduced as a wool alien. It is native in N America

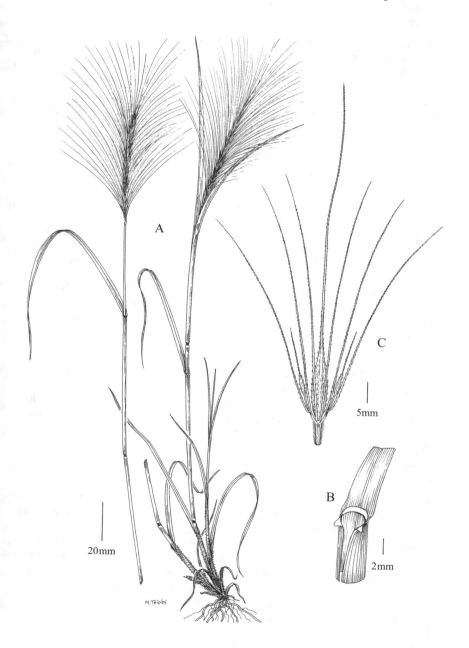

Hordeum jubatum: A, habit; B, ligule with auricles; C, spikelet triad.

and E Asia. Indigenous in the western states of the USA it has become widely naturalized and weedy in the east. It is also widely naturalized in northern and western Europe.

As with *H. secalinum*, the lateral spikelets are much smaller than the central and borne on a conspicuous stipe. They are usually quite barren with the lemma as scarcely more than the slightly expanded awn base, but rarely they are male with well developed palea and small anthers. The species is otherwise distinct in having small spikelets but exceedingly long glumes (and central awn); those of the central spikelet are often conspicuously recurved and the false raceme is often as wide as it is long.

166. Hordeum vulgare L.

Barley   New Atlas: 797

Annual up to 130cm, usually erect; sheaths with conspicuous falcate auricles at the summit; ligule a membramous rim 0.7 – 1.5mm; blades flat, 4 – 15mm wide, smooth or scabrid above. False raceme 4 – 12cm, with tough rhachis, the spikelets unequal or rarely equal. Central spikelet sessile, fertile; glumes linear-oblong or linear-lanceolate, tapering to a fine awn, up to 20mm including the awn; lemma-body 9 – 12mm, tapering to a stout awn up to 18cm; anthers 2 – 3mm; lateral spikelets sometimes similar to the central but usually much reduced, shortly pedicelled and with lemma awnless and barren. $2n = 14$.

Barley has been recorded growing outside fields of the crop in many areas of England and Wales, central and northeastern Scotland and in scattered locations in Ireland. Six-rowed barley is much less commonly recorded than the two-rowed type (and is mapped separately in the New Atlas). Both are generally found on the margins of agricultural land, mostly in barley-growing districts, in fields of other crops, waysides, around farm buildings and in other waste places. Populations along lanes and roadsides are likely to have originated from spilled grain. Many populations arise from birdseed. Few, if any, appear to persist for more than one or two years.

Barley is an important cereal grown throughout the temperate zone and on mountains in the tropics. It is unknown as a wild plant and its origins in cultivation are obscure but were probably in SW Asia. Barley of one type or another has been grown in Britain since the 4th millenium BC although the two-rowed form was not grown in northern Europe until the Middle Ages. It was not recorded from the wild before 1905 and is often ignored by recorders now. British Barley is grown in most parts of the country, especially on lighter soils, and is used to produce malt, as animal feed, and for processing into pearl barley and barley flour (Francis, 2005). The straw is used for animal feed and bedding.

Cultivated barley (*H. vulgare* s. lat.) is represented by numerous strains that fall into 2 main groups:

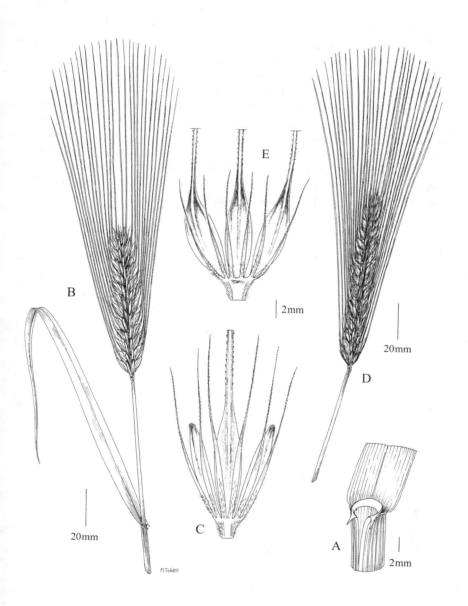

Hordeum vulgare: A, ligule; B, inflorescence of two-rowed barley;
C, spikelet triad of two-rowed barley; D, inflorescence of six-rowed barley;
E, spikelet triad of six-rowed barley.

Two-rowed barley (often under the name *H. distichon* L.) has only the central spikelet of each triad fertile; these are superimposed on either side of the rhachis to give the two rows. The lateral spikelets are reduced to a scale-like barren lemma and palea. This is the usual barley cultivated in the British Isles.

Six-rowed barley (*H. hexastichon* L; *H. vulgare* s. str.) has all three spikelets of a triad fertile. These triads are adjacent with the laterals forming two ranks on either side of the head (thus with the central 2 ranks forming the six rows). Sometimes the head is less dense and the lateral spikelets in opposite rows alternate in the same line, producing just two rows of lateral spikelets. These, with the two rows of central spikelets give a four-rowed barley (*H. tetrastichum* Stokes). Four- and six-rowed barleys are now rarely cultivated in the British Isles, but still occur as relics in waste places and often arise from birdseed. A form of four-rowed barley in which the central spikelet is barren and the laterals fertile is not deliberately grown anywhere and is probably a mutant or sport. Such a configuration of spikelets is known only from one or two rare wild barleys.

167. Secale cereale L.

Rye

Illustration, page 511

New Atlas: 798

Annual; culms up to 150cm, smooth, glabrous throughout or hairy beneath the raceme; blades glabrous or rarely sparsely hairy. Raceme erect at first, usually nodding at maturity, (5)10 – 16(20)cm; rhachis tough, the internodes 3 – 4mm, densely ciliate. Spikelets 13 – 15mm; glumes subequal, 8 – 20mm, puberulous, scabrid-ciliate on the keel, the awn up to 3mm; lemma firmly compressed, 14 – 15(18)mm, smooth or faintly scaberulous on the back, the awn (1.5)3.5 – 5cm. $2n = 14$.

Rye has been recorded in the wild, or as a contaminant of other cereal fields, from many widely scattered localities in the British Isles. It is most frequent in England with a cluster of more recent records in the counties of Dorset, Devon and Somerset. Outside arable land it occurs on waste ground, roadsides, manure heaps, rubbish tips and in other ruderal habitats. It is usually found on infertile sandy soils and is both a relic of cultivation and a grain, grass-seed and birdseed alien. It is confined to the lowlands.

Perhaps the least ancient of our cereals, Rye is believed to have been a weed of primitive wheat and barley crops. Its general vigour, cold and drought tolerance and ability to grow on poorer sandy soils enabled it to oust primitive wheat, especially in the north, and it was then widely grown as a crop in its own right. It was more important than wheat for bread-making throughout northern Europe in the Middle Ages and by the end of the 18th century was the food of most people in this part of the world. The process was reversed, wheat supplementing Rye, with improving agriculture, plant breeding and the use of fertilizers. A versatile plant, Rye can be used as a green manure, for early pasturage, as a grain crop mainly for making black bread and crisp breads or for malting, and its straw can be used for thatching. Varieties particularly suited to one or more of these uses have been selected to produce quite a variable species. Unlike barley and wheat, it is largely self-incompatible and failure to 'breed true' would have been a problem for early farmers. Arber (1934) states that "it runs wild more readily than any of the other cereals and is able to maintain itself for some time if circumstances happen to be favourable", but there is no evidence that this is true of feral populations in the British Isles; these appear to be short-lived.

S. cereale is only known in cultivation. Widely grown in temperate regions in both hemispheres, it is grown on a rather small scale today in Britain, mostly for animal feed and thatch. Some grain crops are grown on sandy land in S and SE England and East Anglia. It was recorded from the wild by 1865, but current distributional trends are unclear.

The inability to separate wheat and rye grain in early agriculture, which with rye's winter hardiness allowed it to replace wheat in colder climates and poorer soils, also led to a widely held belief that wheat crops 'degenerated' or were changed into rye. Rye in turn was believed to metamorphose into Rye Brome, *Bromus secalinus*, which was a weed of rye crops (another 'cheat' grass). Such beliefs, it seems, survived in some quarters into the early part of the 20th century.

Much interest has been shown recently in an artificial hybrid between *Secale cereale* and *Triticum aestivum* (×**Triticosecale**). The plants in question do not appear to have a valid epithet although several distinct cultivars are being investigated. These are being grown on a field scale, particularly in East Anglia, and already some are being found as relics. They vary a great deal in height, some achieving 180cm, and are intermediate in spikelet characters between their parents. The raceme is often long awned and usually nodding; the glumes are broad and obtuse or somewhat apiculate (truncate in *Triticum*, narrow and pointed in *Secale*) and the distal florets are sterile. Chromosome numbers reported are $2n = 42$ and 56.

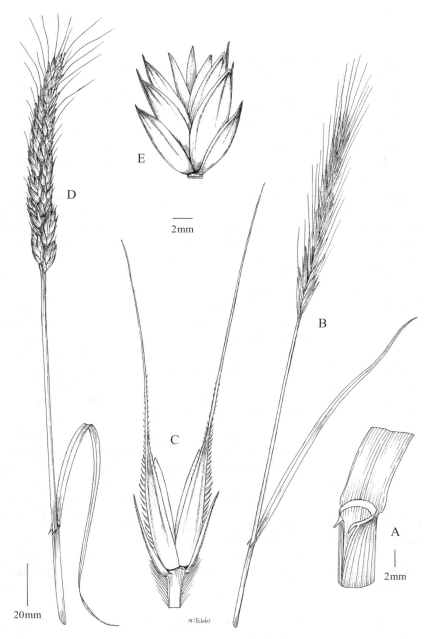

Secale cereale: A, ligule with auricles; B, inflorescence; C, spikelet.
× *Triticosecale*: D, inflorescence; E, spikelet.

511

168. Triticum aestivum L.

Bread Wheat   New Atlas: 799

Culms up to 150cm, smooth and glabrous throughout or faintly puberulous at the nodes, thin-walled and hollow; blades scaberulous, puberulous or glabrous. Raceme erect, 4 – 18cm, lax to dense; rhachis tough, glabrous, the internodes (3)4 – 8mm. Spikelets 3- to 9-flowered, usually only the (2)3 lowermost florets fertile; glumes broadly ovate, 6 – 10(11)mm, coriaceous, glabrous, pubescent or villous, keeled in the upper part only, rounded below, the keel terminating in a 2 – 3mm apical tooth or a 4 – 10mm scabrid awn; fertile lemma (10)12 – 15mm; awn scabrid throughout, 4 – 10(12)cm, or lemma awnless. Grain naked with mealy (to flinty) endosperm. $2n = 42$.

Bread Wheat is found as a common casual scattered throughout lowland Britain, its distribution reflecting the current wheat growing areas in England and Wales and in C & NE Scotland. It is scattered in Ireland. It is found in fields as a relic of recent cultivation and on waste ground, around farms, on roadsides and on rubbish tips. It is a major component of birdseed and is found wherever seed is offered at bird tables or feeders.

Its long history of domestication has left *T. aestivum* with several traits that prevent its survival in the wild, and casual populations almost never persist beyond their year of establishment. Most are escapes from the crop and are therefore likely to be winter wheat (about 98% of the current British crop) and 'beardless' (only one variety of bearded wheat is currently grown in Britain). Selection of modern high-yielding varieties has also seen a reduction in the number of varieties, and hence genetic diversity. For example, half the wheat harvest in 1995 comprised just two varieties ('Riband' and 'Brigadier') and only nine varieties, many with shared ancestry, made up nearly 90% of the total yield (Hindmarch & Pienkowsky, 1998).

Wheat is globally the most widely grown food crop and, with rice, is one of the two most important food crops in the world. It is the staple food of more than a third of the human population. The modern hexaploid Bread Wheat, *T. aestivum*, originated in cultivation during a process of wheat domestication which began some 10,000 years ago in SW Asia. The large-seeded annual wild grasses adapted to hot summers provided excellent portable sources of food. Originating from hybridization between an ancestral cultivated tetraploid *Triticum* (Emmer Wheat) and a wild diploid species *Aegilops tauschii* Coss., *T. aestivum* has replaced most other wheat species during the last 2,000 years. The mealy endosperm with high gluten content produces high quality flour ideal for bread-making and Bread Wheat is grown almost throughout the world up to latitude 69.5° in the northern hemisphere.

Introduced to Britain some 6,000 years ago, Bread Wheat was not recorded from the wild until 1927 and cereal relics were rarely recorded at all before 1970, and are often ignored today.

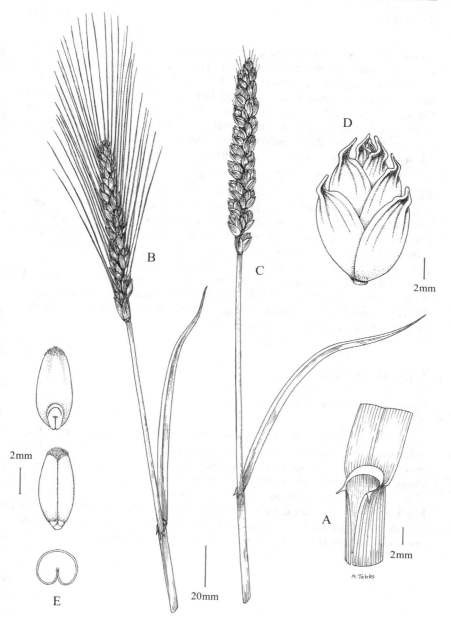

Triticum aestivum: A, ligule with auricles; B, inflorescence of bearded wheat;
C, inflorescence of beardless wheat; D, spikelet of beardless wheat;
E, grain in dorsal view (top), ventral view (middle) and transverse section (bottom).

169. Triticum turgidum L.

Rivet Wheat

Culms up to 150cm, smooth and glabrous throughout, thick-walled and ± solid; blades velutinous (but this rubbing off with age). Raceme nodding, (4.5)7 – 12cm, ovate-cylindrical, sometimes branched below; rhachis tough, densely ciliate, the internodes (2.5)3 – 4mm. Spikelets 5- to 7-flowered, the lowermost 2 – 5 florets fertile; glumes broadly ovate, 8 – 10mm, coriaceous, glabrous, puberulous or velutinous, keeled throughout with 2 keels, one of them prominent, ciliolate, terminating in a 1 – 2mm tooth, the other less developed; fertile lemma 10 – 13(14)mm, glabrous or villous towards the margins; awn scabrid throughout, 8 – 18cm. Grain naked with mealy endosperm. $2n = 28$.

Rivet Wheat has been recorded as a relic, as a contaminant of other grains or as a casual from birdseed mixes. It has become very scarce and the few recent records have mainly been in southern and eastern England, usually on waste land, roadsides or rubbish tips. Populations do not persist. It was formerly grown in parts of Great Britain (especially the north and east) and Ireland as a cereal crop and was first recorded in the wild in 1908. It is rarely grown here today, and then for animal feed or as a speciality crop. The mealy endosperm is low in gluten and produces a rather poor flour best used for biscuit- rather than bread-making. Rivet Wheat is grown in the Mediterranean region eastwards to Siberia and C Asia and in South Africa, Australia and the Americas.

170. Triticum durum L.

Pasta or *Macaroni Wheat*

A rare casual very similar to *T. turgidum* but with glabrous leaves and flinty endosperm. The grain has a prominent hump or ridge on the back not present in either *T. turgidum* or *T. aestivum*. Pasta Wheat has been found as a casual in waste places and on rubbish tips and can also be cultivated from birdseed. As with other wheat species, populations do not persist in the wild. It was trialed in eastern England in the 1970s but remains a niche crop in Britain (Francis, 2005). The flour derived from the flinty endosperm is of high quality and is ideal for making pasta. It is traditionally grown in Spain, Portugal, Italy and Greece.

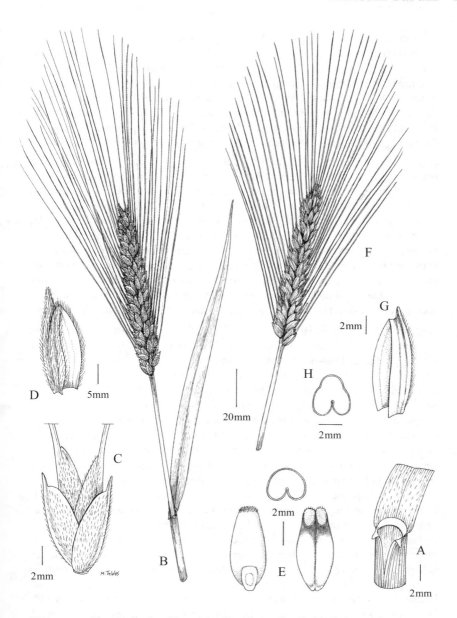

Triticum turgidum: A, ligule with auricles; B, raceme; C, spikelet; D, lower glume;
E, grain in dorsal view (left), ventral view (right) and transverse section (middle).
Triticum durum: F, raceme; G, lower glume; H, grain in tranverse section.

515

171. **Danthonia decumbens** (L.) DC.

Heath-grass　　　　　　　　　　　　　　　　　　New Atlas: 799

Densely tufted perennial up to 45(70)cm; ligule a line of hairs; blades stiff, flat or inrolled. Panicle narrow, often racemose, (2.5)3 – 5.5(6.5)cm, bearing only (3)4 – 9(11) spikelets. Spikelets (6.5)8 – 11(13)mm, the florets usually cleistogamous (see note below); glumes as long as the spikelet or almost so, ± equal, lanceolate or narrowly ovate, blunt; lemmas 5 – 6.7(7)mm, rounded on the back, broadly elliptic, 3-toothed at the tip, the central tooth shorter than the laterals, shortly hairy at the base and on the margins below; anthers 3, 0.2 – 0.5mm. $2n = 24, 36$. Flowering and fruiting mid-June to mid-August or early September.

D. decumbens is widespread and frequent in suitable habitats throughout Great Britain and Ireland. It is generally more common in the west and is absent from arable farming areas of eastern England. It occurs on grassland, heaths and moorland, especially hill and mountain pastures, including habitats such as grassy paths, rock outcrops and mires. It is most commonly found on infertile, damp, sandy or peaty soils which are mildly acidic (in the pH range 4.0 – 6.0) but also occurs on leached chalk and limestone grassland (pH >6.5), especially in the north and west. Often growing in rather species-poor vegetation containing grasses such as *Agrostis capillaris, Molinia caerulea* and *Nardus stricta*, Heath-grass can also be found in species-rich communities in calcareous pasture. It occurs from sea-level to 595m (Tal-y-fan, Caerns.) and up to 1040m in S Kerry.

This small tufted perennial grass has a very distinctive life history strategy and may be regarded as somewhat of a 'tortoise' among grasses. It grows rather slowly, producing long-lived leaves and small panicles with few, relatively large seed which it additionally furnishes with elaiosomes aiding their dispersal by ants (and which are eagerly sought by waterfowl on peaty heaths in July and August). Although probably long-lived, individual plants have limited capacity for lateral expansion and seed provide the means of population growth. Seedlings are mostly found in autumn and some may come from a persistent seed bank. Buried seed have been found to occur in clumps, probably reflecting the storage behaviour of ants. Heath-grass's tolerance of, or adaptation to, nutrient-stressed or oligotrophic situations renders it vulnerable to competition from faster-growing, more productive species when nutrients are added to poor grassland. It is replaced, especially, by *Agrostis capillaris* under such conditions and is never found in fertile or newly established grassland. Its winter greenness and slow replacement of leaves also make it vulnerable to intensive grazing (it is reported to be more palatable than *Agrostis capillaris* and *Festuca ovina*). The species is highly inbreeding (see below). Little seems to be known about the extent to which populations from acidic and calcareous soils may be different, although Hubbard's 1984 edition suggests that the latter may be a different subspecies with $2n = 24$ (subsp. *decipiens* O.Schwartz & Bässler has been coined, but this is an invalid name because it has no type). The ecological distribution of the two forms requires further investigation (CPE: 244).

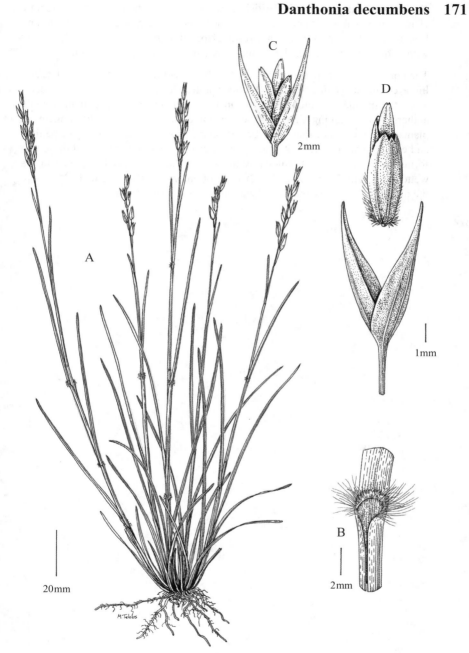

Danthonia decumbens: A, habit; B, ligule; C, intact spikelet;
D, spikelet with florets detached from glumes.

D. decumbens is native in the British Isles and is part of the European Temperate element in our flora. It appears to have declined in many areas of England and Ireland since 1950, presumably as a result of loss of permanent pasture and possibly with widespread use of fertilizers and increasingly eutrophic conditions.

The combination of sparse panicle with only a few relatively large spikelets and ligule comprising a line of hairs is unmistakable. Cleistogamy is the rule in Heath-grass, the spikelets – which are carried in a contracted panicle – producing minute anthers and remaining tightly closed at anthesis. Very rarely, chasmogamous plants may be found; these can be recognized by a rather more open panicle and extruded anthers 1.4 – 2.2mm long. The ecological preferences of these two forms are obscure but chasmogamy has mostly been observed in plants in the wetter soils (Hubbard, 1954). Either form often has cleistogenes tucked away in the older basal sheaths and these bear anthers in the smaller size range.

172. **Cortaderia selloana** (Schult. & Schult.f.) Asch. & Graebn.

Pampas-grass

Illustration, page 521

New Atlas: 799

Culms 1 – 3m; sheaths eventually curling up and fracturing horizontally into short segments; blades up to 2.7m, the lower surface usually green, the upper usually glaucous, with conspicuous midrib and numerous closely-spaced inconspicuous nerves, the margins serrated and saw-like. Panicle 40 – 100(120)cm, maturing to creamy white or tinged with red, pink, purple, silver or gold, usually not drooping to one side. Spikelets 3- to 6-flowered, 15 – 25mm; glumes 12 – 20mm, c.4/5 the length of the spikelet, glabrous; lemmas 12 – 20mm, glabrous or sparsely hairy below with hairs 2 – 5(7)mm in bisexual spikelet, densely hairy all over with hairs 8 – 10mm in female spikelet, narrowly ovate below but tapering to a long narrow tail; anthers of bisexual spikelet 3 – 4.5mm, those of female spikelet represented by minute staminodes. Flowering August to November.

Pampas-grass now occurs outside of cultivation from the Channel Islands to NE Scotland but is most common in southern England and especially in the southwest where it is increasing. It is found on waste ground, roadsides, railway embankments, rubbish dumps, abandoned gardens and on coastal cliffs and sand-dunes. In practically all of these places individuals have arrived as escapes or rejects from gardens or have been deliberately planted, although seedlings occur in some populations and new plants may have become established (see below).

Classed as a neophyte, *C. selloana* has been cultivated in Britain since 1848 and is now widely grown in parks and gardens. It was first recorded from the wild in 1925 and some naturalized plants are known to be long-lived and persistent, a fact that will not surprise anyone who has tried to remove an overgrown and well-established individual from their garden! (AGB: 70). It is a native of S America.

At least a dozen named cultivars of Pampas-grass are grown, varying in stature, winter hardiness, colour of panicle and coloration of leaves (some are variegated). Although structurally the plants are gynodioecious, the bisexual plants have such low fertility that they function as little more than pollen parents and the species is to all intents and purposes dioecious. The bisexual plants are far less decorative than the female, lacking much of the silky hairiness of the spikelet, and were therefore less commonly grown. As a result, Pampas-grass rarely set seed in gardens but there are records of it doing so in 'wild' populations. It now seems that imported seed is becoming more available and an increasing volume of Pampas-grass is being grown from this seed. As a consequence both female and bisexual plants are equally available and in places the species is freely self-seeding. In its native S America it grows in rocky gullies, on riverbanks and along roads, as well as being widely cultivated. 'Pampas-grass' is something of a misnomer, derived doubtless from the misconception that if something occurs in Argentina then it must grow in the pampa; the pampa is quite unsuitable for plants of the habit and stature of *C. selloana*.

173. **Cortaderia richardii** (Endl.) Zotov

Early Pampas-grass

New Atlas CD

Similar to *C. selloana* but differs in the following important ways: sheaths remaining intact and not fracturing; blades dark green on both sides with strong midrib and numerous inconspicuous lateral nerves as above, but also with strong intermediate nerves on either side; panicle usually drooping to one side; spikelets mostly 3-flowered; glumes hairy on the margins below; lemmas deeply bifid with linear lobes, awned between the lobes, hairy only at the base; flowering late June to August.

Early Pampas-grass has become established at a number of mainly coastal sites including Dorset, the Welsh coast around Aberystwyth, in the Isle of Man, the west coast of Scotland and in NE Scotland. At these scattered locations it is found on sea cliffs and waste ground.

C. richardii is genuinely dioecious and both sexes are in cultivation. As the name suggests, it flowers much earlier than *C. selloana* and self-seeding is not unusual.

A neophyte, first recorded from the wild on cliffs at Lyme Regis, Dorset in the 1980s, *C. richardii* is a native of South Island, New Zealand where it grows on riverbanks and in other wet places. It has not been consistently recorded in Britain as it is sometimes confused with *C. selloana*.

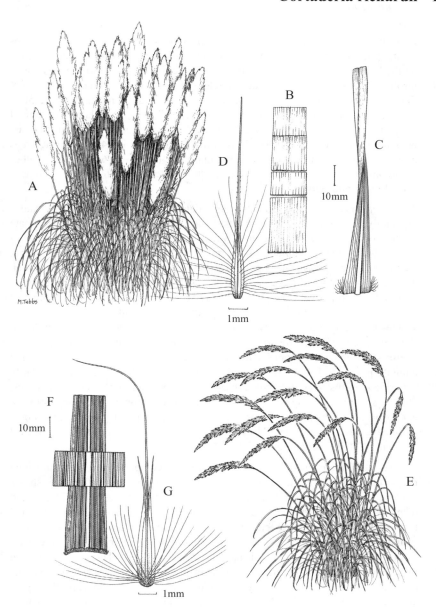

Cortaderia selloana: A, habit; B, sheath showing horizontal fractures;
C, part of blade showing venation; D, lemma.
Cortaderia richardii: E, habit; F, blade showing venation; G, lemma.

174. Molinia caerulea (L.) Moench

Purple Moor-grass   New Atlas: 800

Densely tufted perennial, sometimes with shortly creeping rootstock; culms erect, up to 120(150)cm, the swollen basal internode up to 5cm; sheaths rounded on the back, hairy at the summit; ligule a ciliate rim 0.2 – 0.6mm; blades flat or inrolled, 6 – 60cm × 2.5 – 7mm. Panicle extremely variable, dense and spike-like to loose and open, 5 – 40(60)cm with the longest branches 0.5 – 12.5cm, green or tinged with yellow, brown or purple. Spikelets lanceolate to oblong, 4 – 7.5mm (to tip of second lemma), the rhachilla rough; glumes lanceolate to ovate or oblong, the lower (1.6)1.9 – 3.5(4)mm, the upper 2.5 – 4.5(5)mm; lemmas narrowly lanceolate to narrowly oblong in profile, (3.7)4 – 6(6.4)mm, pointed or blunt; anthers 1.8 – 3.3mm. $2n = 18, 36, 90$. Flowering and fruiting late June or early July to mid-September.

M. caerulea is widespread and locally abundant throughout the British Isles and is especially common in the north and west where it has been estimated to dominate around 10% (600,000ha) of upland vegetation. It is absent or rare in parts of central and eastern England. Its wide range of habitats includes open moorland, heaths, montane grassland, bogs, mires, fens, lake shores and open woodland. The common feature of these habitats, at least the parts where Purple Moor-grass is found, is the permanently or seasonally wet ground. The wide range of soil types is dominated by infertile, acidic, peaty or sandy soils of pH <4.0, but the species has been known to have a bimodal pH distribution (see also *Danthonia decumbens* and *Festuca ovina*), also occurring in calcareous mires and fens and in grassland over limestone at pH levels around 7.0 (CPE: 406). Its optimal habitat appears to be the transitional zones between more or less permanently waterlogged substrates and higher, drier ones (where on moorland one often finds *Nardus stricta*). Although *M. caerulea* frequently dominates large areas to the exclusion of other plants, it does occur in a wide range of plant communities; these have been listed in detail by Taylor *et al.*, (2001). It is found from sea-level to 870m at Meikle Kilrannoch, Angus.

A very variable species, *M. caerulea* in Britain comprises three chromosome races (diploids, tetraploids and decaploids), is an obligate outbreeder, shows evidence of ecotypic differentiation, especially in response to soil type, and displays high phenotypic plasticity. This variation, often habitat based, has led to the recognition of subspecific taxa (see below). The growth and expansion of individual tussocks, which may include more than one genotype, is the main means of reproduction, although many seed are produced. The swollen storage internodes at the base of the stems remain green over winter and new shoots elongate in April or May. Although individual leaves are deciduous, producing an abundance of persistent litter in unmanaged swards, the roots are more long-lived and often very extensive, penetrating deeper than 80cm. Plants are vulnerable to damage in cold spring weather, especially in the uplands, but tolerate moderate shade in birch and oak woodland or willow scrub, where they are shy to flower.

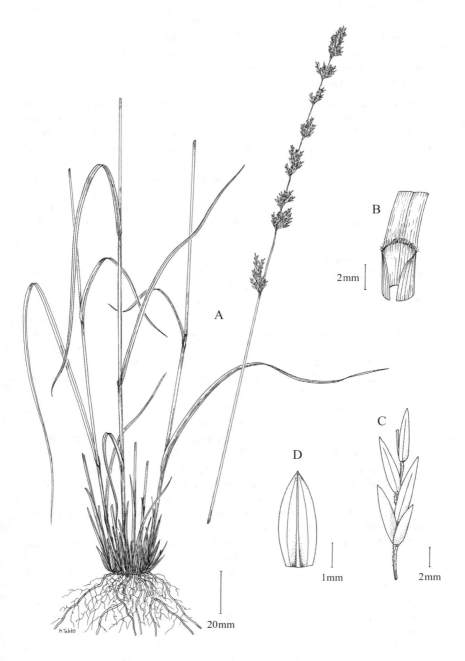

Molinia caerulea: A, habit; B, ligule; C, spikelet; D, lemma.

Seed are set from August to October and germinate in the spring following a chilling to break dormancy. There is a persistent seed bank. Seedlings can often be found in cracks in drying mud around pools, ditches or cattle-poached areas, but few establish to be recruited to the adult population. The species tolerates burning and grazing, both of which are used to manage moors and heathlands for particular purposes (e.g. grouse moors, pasture or ericaceous heathland). (CPE: 434; Biol. Flora: Taylor *et al.*, 2001).

M. caerulea is native in the British Isles and has a Eurosiberian Boreo-temperate distribution, occurring in most of Europe but the extreme south, NE Asia Minor and Siberia. It has been introduced to N America. Since the Industrial Revolution there has been a considerable increase in *M. caerulea* in the uplands of England and Wales and parts of Scotland at the expence of heather, *Calluna vulgaris* (a trend generally attributed to changes in grazing regime or to increased atmospheric nitrogen or sulphur). Similarly, in lowland Europe, notably the Netherlands, the grass's more recent invasion of heathland dominated by *C. vulgaris* or *Erica* spp. has been linked to nutrient enrichment. Conversely, the species has declined in parts of lowland Britain due to habitat loss.

The species is often divided into two subspecies, *caerulea* and *arundinacea* (Schrank.) K.Richt. (subsp. *altissima* (Link) Domin, *M. litoralis* Host) but there is little agreement about their limits. For example, Stace (1997), following Trist & Sell (1988), placed the height of subsp. *caerulea* at below 65cm, compared with subsp. *arundinacea* at above 65cm. Tutin in Tutin *et al.*, (1980) set the transition at 90cm, and Hubbard (1984) at 120cm. Distinctions are also quoted by Stace for panicle length (*caerulea* <30cm, *arundinacea* 30 – 60cm), panicle-branch length (<5cm and often >10cm respectively), spikelet length (3.5 – 5mm and (3)4 – 7.5mm), lemma length (3 – 4mm and (3.2)3.5 – 5.4(5.7)mm) and chromosome number ($2n = 36$ and $2n = 90$). After close examination of a great deal of material it has become apparent that the relationships between the characters – beyond taller plants having longer panicles, and longer spikelets having longer lemmas (although spikelet length is a function of both lemma length and number of florets) – are tenuous, and the association between morphology and habitat (*arundinacea* mostly in fens, *caerulea* mostly absent from fens) is equally tenuous. Trist (1998a) realised that the two subspecies were not very distinct and invoked a third element, subsp. *caerulea* var. *viridiflora* Lej. to bridge the gap between them. Multiple collections from single localities demonstrate quite clearly that the species is variable wherever it grows, and often *arundinacea* occurs as isolated plants within large populations of *caerulea*, and the latter usually grows on the drier, more trampled rides between the wetter fens which may be dominated by the former. It is extremely doubtful if the variation of *M. caerulea* can be accommodated in formal infraspecific taxa and there is little to support the view that recognizing distinct subspecies, differing in both morphology and ecology, is either practicable or worthwhile. Suffice it to say that fens and the more basic wetlands tend to select for the taller, more robust plants with looser panicles, but this is by no means a rule. Little use can be made of an apparent difference in chromosome numbers without reliable supporting morphological characters.

175. **Phragmites australis** (Cav.) Trin. ex Steud. Illustration, page 527

Common Reed New Atlas: 800

Culms up to 3.5m, robust, usually simple but sometimes branched; leaves cauline; ligule 0.5 – 1mm; blades mostly 20 – 50(60)cm × 10 – 40mm (smaller on sterile shoots), long-attenuate at the tip, this curved or flexuous and often fragile. Panicle 15 – 40(60)cm, loose to dense, very soft at maturity, tinged with purple or brown. Spikelets (8)10 – 15mm, with 2 – 5(6) fertile florets, the uppermost usually vestigial or aborted, and callus-hairs 7 – 10mm; glumes elliptic-oblong, subacute at the tip, the lower 3 – 5mm, the upper 4.5 – 8.5(9.5)mm; lowest lemma (8)9 – 13mm; fertile lemmas as long as the spikelet, narrower and thinner than the lowest and more finely pointed but the tip fragile and easily breaking away; anthers 1.3 – 1.8mm. $2n = $ c.48 (but varying from 36 to 96). Flowering and fruiting late July to mid-October, but panicle not mature much before mid-August.

Widespread and common in suitable habitats throughout the British Isles, *P. australis* is especially frequent in the lowlands and in the south. It occurs in a wide range of wetland habitats including the edges of rivers, lakes and ponds, in ditches, marshes, swamps and fens and at the upper limit of saltmarshes and the banks of tidal rivers. In many places it is the dominant and defining occupant of the reed-bed habitat. It also occurs in smaller stands in wet flushes in coastal cliffs and in a range of apparently terrestrial habitat-types such as railway embankments, roadsides, moorland and industrial spoil heaps and waste ground. It often forms dense monospecific stands on mud and in shallow water in transitional habitats, from open water to willow and oak/alder carr, or from intertidal saltmarsh to brackish and freshwater marsh. However, these successions are often actively managed to maintain the reed-bed either for nature conservation or for thatching reeds (see below). Common Reed is most frequent over nutrient-rich substrates and on soils with a pH >4.5. It is confined to flushes in poor soils and is absent from the most oligotrophic and most acidic habitats and from areas of swift flowing water or where water level fluctuates wildly. Dense reeds contain few associates but some fens containing the grass may be very species-rich. It is generally a lowland plant but reaches 470m on Brown Clee Hill (Salop).

Common Reed is quite unmistakable. Our tallest non-woody native plant, it has an extensive system of rhizomes and dense tough long-lasting culms which enable it to dominate its environment, and have also been of considerable utility to mankind. It grows best in shallow water but can survive depths of up to 2m in still water where it often produces floating rafts. Shoot densities of more than 100 per m^2 are not uncommon in the most nutrient-rich reed-beds, although beds tend to be thinner, shorter and with less accumulated litter as one goes further north. Rhizomes may penetrate down to 2m and occasionally, particularly in brackish-water stands, plants produce remarkable surface runners or 'legehalme' which can be 10m long. Individual populations may be very long-lived, perhaps 1,000 years, and most expand and are established by vegetative reproduction.

Fragments of shoot or rhizome may be transported to new sites during periods of flooding or of dredging and maintenance of ditches. Establishment of new populations by seed is thought to be much rarer. British plants have generally low levels of seed set and viability, and young seedlings, which must establish on bare mud or in shallow water, are very vulnerable to flooding (some biotypes of reed have been selected in the Netherlands for higher germination for aerial sowing of reed-beds in newly reclaimed polders). Ripe seed is dispersed from November onwards, the basal tuft of long silky hairs on the light 'seed' aiding its dispersal by wind. It has been claimed that the 'seed' can travel for 40km before falling; certainly Common Reed was one of the first grasses to reach Krakatau (Ridley, 1930). Reed-beds which are managed for thatching are likely to have selected particular biotypes and the wide range of habitats is also likely to have led to inter-population genetic differentiation. However, we are unaware of published studies on genetic variation in *P. australis* in Britain, although peat and river ecotypes have been recognized in the Netherlands. The species contains several ploidy levels and includes aneuploids. (CPE: 464; Biol. Flora: Haslam, 1972).

P. australis is native in the British Isles and is a Circumpolar Wide-temperate species. It is said by Ridley (1930) to be the most widely distributed of all flowering plants in the world, and is widely exploited for human benefit. In addition to being cut for thatching, fencing and fodder, reeds have been used for cellulose production, stabilizing river and lake margins and preventing erosion and, as mentioned above, to stabilize drying out land reclaimed from the sea before it was converted to arable land. More recent uses of reed-beds have been as filters for sewage water (the so-called 'root-zone' method of sewage treatment) or pollutants. Reed-beds are now much prized habitats for wildlife conservation, including several rare birds which depend on them for nesting sites and shelter. There has been concern that reed-beds in some areas, notably the Norfolk Broads, have been lost in the last 50 years (through a combination of nutient enrichment weakening the stems and increasing wash from boats) and are declining generally throughout Europe. Although greatly valued and exploited, Common Reed has also, paradoxically perhaps, been classed as one of the world's worst weeds (because it can block up drainage canals and waterways).

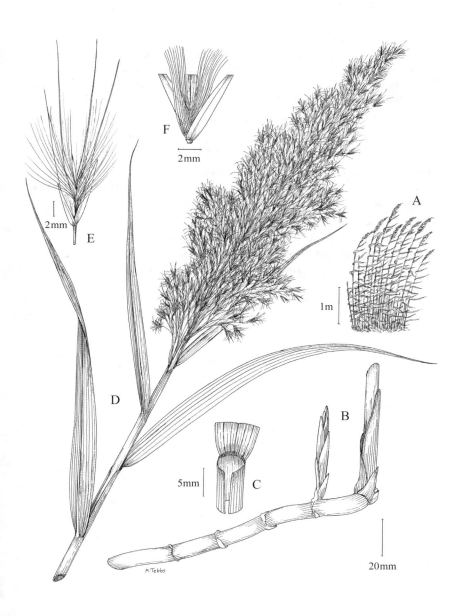

Phragmites australis: A, habit; B, rhizome; C, ligule; D, panicle and uppermost leaves;
E, intact spikelet; F, lower part of florets with glumes removed.

176. **Leptochloa fusca** (L.) Kunth

Brown Beetle-grass   New Atlas CD

Perennial up to 100cm; blades linear, finely tapered. Inflorescence 20 – 40cm, composed of 10 – 30 racemes each 7 – 15cm and bearing loosely arranged, indistinctly secund spikelets. Spikelets 6 – 15mm, 7- to 11-flowered, subterete; lower glume 1.4 – 2.2mm; upper glume 2 – 3.4mm; lemma 2.2 – 4mm, rounded on the back, pilose on the nerves below, tipped with a short mucro 0.1 – 0.3mm.

L. fusca has been recorded in the past from scattered localities, mostly in southern England, but does not appear to have been seen in recent times. It is a casual of fields, waste places and rubbish tips where it is reported to behave as an annual.

Once introduced with wool shoddy, *L. fusca* was first recorded from the wild in Britain in 1948. It is native throughout the tropical and subtropical Old World, usually in aquatic or semi-aquatic habitats.

The species is represented by two subspecies: subsp. **fusca** in which the mucro exceeds the teeth at the tip of the lemma; and subsp. **muelleri** (Benth.) N.Snow in which the teeth exceed the mucro. The latter was formerly accorded species rank (*L. muelleri* (Benth.) Stace) and was always much the rarer.

Leptochloa fusca: A, habit; B, spikelet; C, lemma.

177. Eragrostis pilosa (L.) P.Beauv.

Jersey Love-grass   New Atlas CD

Annual up to 70cm; sheaths glabrous; blades flat. Panicle 4 – 25cm, delicate and open. Spikelets purplish green, 3 – 7 × 0.7 – 1.2mm, linear, 4- to 14-flowered, the florets falling from the persistent rhachilla; glumes very unequal, the lower minute, 0.5 – 0.7mm, obtuse, the upper 0.7 – 1mm, subacute; lemmas 1 – 1.6(1.8)mm, narrowly ovate in profile, thinly membranous with distinct lateral nerves, subacute to obtuse; paleas deciduous with or soon after the lemmas; anthers 0.2 – 0.3mm. Grain elliptic but with one straight side, slightly laterally compressed, 0.6 – 1mm. $2n$ = 20, 30, 36, 40, 50, 60, 72. Flowering and fruiting late August to early October, occasionally from July until November.

Widely scattered as a casual in England and Wales, *E. pilosa* appears to be naturalized in Jersey. It occurs on waste ground, rubbish tips, and – in Jersey – on cultivated land.

A neophyte, this species was cultivated in Britain in 1804 and first recorded in the wild in 1926 (although possibly naturalized in Jersey since 1921). Introduced in birdseed, oilseed and grain (and formerly wool) it is a native of the tropical and warm temperate Old World and has been widely naturalized in South Africa, N & S America and elsewhere.

It is a delicate plant with an open panicle of small spikelets that have a minute lower glume. The mode of disarticulation of the spikelet is quite different from that of *E. curvula* and its allies in that the palea is deciduous with or soon after the lemma, leaving behind a characteristic naked, zig-zag rhachilla.

178. Eragrostis tef (Zucc.) Trotter

Tef   New Atlas CD

A cereal derived from a close relative of *E. pilosa*. It is very similar to *E. pilosa* in habit but is often taller (up to 90cm), with slightly larger spikelets (5.5 – 9 × 1.5 – 2mm), longer glumes (lower 1.2 – 2.5mm, upper 1.7 – 3mm) and longer lemmas (2 – 2.7mm). Its main characteristics, however, are the turgid, non-deciduous grain and persistent florets, both of which would be expected in a grass grown as a cereal crop.

Tef is a rare casual recorded in England from waste places and rubbish tips, but never persisting.

It was cultivated in Britain in the 18th century and recorded in the wild by 1961, but is now very rare. A native in Ethiopia, where it is a staple cereal, it has been grown experimentally as a forage crop in several other tropical areas of Africa, India and Australia and has become widely naturalized there. It arrives here in birdseed and formerly from wool shoddy and has occurred as a garden escape.

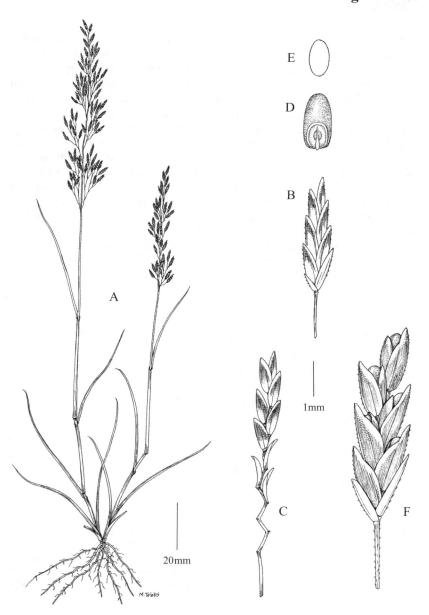

E

D

B

1mm

C

F

A

20mm

M.Tebbs

Eragrostis pilosa: A, habit; B, whole spikelet; C, partially disarticulated spikelet; D, caryopsis, E, transverse section through caryopsis. *Eragrostis tef*: F, spikelet.

179. **Eragrostis mexicana** (Hornem.) Link

Mexican Love-grass

Very much like *E. pilosa* but has a very characteristic squarish grain with a prominent ventral groove. It shares with *E. pilosa* the deciduous palea although its dehiscence is sometimes a little tardy and several of those in a spikelet may be retained for some time after the lemmas have fallen. However, the slightest pressure will cause them to detach (cf. those of *E. curvula* and its allies that cannot be so easily knocked off the rhachilla). The species is a complex of intergrading variants in its native range of southern USA and Mexico. Some authorities (e.g. Ryves *et al.*, 1996) recognize at least three segregates, *E. mexicana, E. neomexicana* Vasey ex L.H.Dewey and *E. virescens* J.Presl. Koch & Sánchez Vega (1985), however, recognize only two, *E. mexicana* subsp. *mexicana* and *E. mexicana* subsp. *virescens* (J. Presl) S.D.Koch & Sánchez Vega, and for now this does seem to be the most satisfactory solution. Subsp. **mexicana** has ovate to oblong spikelets more than 1.4mm wide and a lower glume 1.2 – 2.3mm. Subsp. **virescens** has narrower linear to linear-lanceolate spikelets not more than 1.5mm wide, and a lower glume 0.7 – 1.7mm. Both subspecies have been introduced in birdseed, but only subsp. *virescens* is still found on tips and around docks in scattered localities in southern England.

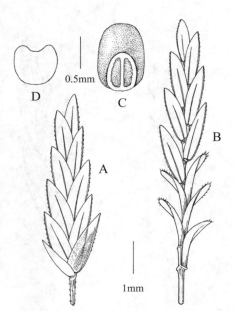

0.5mm

D

C

B

A

1mm

Eragrostis mexicana:
A, whole spikelet;
B, partially disarticulated spikelet;
C, caryopsis;
D, transverse section through caryopsis.

180. **Eragrostis curvula** (Schrad.) Nees

African Love-grass

Densely tufted perennial up to 120cm; basal sheaths silky-pilose below, yellow and horny, the nerves forming close prominent ridges; blades filiform to flat. Panicle 6 – 30cm, spreading or contracted. Spikelets greyish green, 4 – 10 × 1 – 1.5mm, linear to narrowly oblong, 4- to 13-flowered, the lemmas falling from the persistent rhachilla; glumes unequal, acute, the lower 1 – 1.8mm, the upper 1.5 – 2.5mm; lemmas 1.4 – 2.6mm, narrowly ovate-elliptic in profile, membranous with indistinct lateral nerves, subacute; paleas persistent; anthers 0.8 – 1.1mm. Grain elliptic, 0.7 – 1mm. $2n = 20, 40, 50, 54, 60, 70 (80)$. Flowering and fruiting late May to mid-October or even into December, often failing altogether in poor seasons.

Scattered as a rare casual in England and Wales, *E. curvula* seems to be naturalized in two sites in southern England (AGB: 75). Here it is found on waste ground beside disused railways, and has also been recorded from tips and docks. It sets viable seed in at least one of its established locations, and sometimes behaves as an annual.

Classed as a neophyte here, and a native of tropical and South Africa, this grass was probably introduced originally in wool and ballast. It was first recorded in the wild in Britain in 1915 and is occasionally grown in gardens.

An exceedingly variable species sometimes partitioned into numerous varieties or even species, most of them of doubtful practical value. Variation is expressed in several characters, including habit, leaf form, panicle form and spikelet size, but these are quite uncorrelated. '*E. chloromelas* Steud.' is one such variant, recorded in Great Britain, poorly distinguished by its filiform, flexuous blades and shorter lemmas (1 – 1.4mm rather than 2 – 2.6mm in *E. curvula* proper).

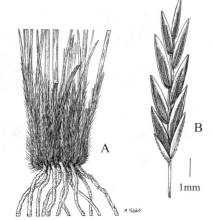

Eragrostis curvula:
A, base of plant;
B, spikelet.

1mm

181. **Eragrostis cilianensis** (All.) Vignolo ex Janch.

Stink-grass   New Atlas CD

An annual up to 90cm with characteristic crateriform glands along the leaf-margins, on the pedicels and sometimes also on the glume and lemma keels (those along the leaf-margins sometimes missing); panicle 4 – 30cm, stiffly branched; spikelets 3 – 20 × 2 – 4mm, the lemmas falling from the persistent rhachilla; lemmas (1.7)2 – 2.8mm; anthers 0.3 – 0.4mm; paleas persistent; grain subrotund, 0.4 – 0.6mm in diameter.

Widely scattered in Britain, mainly in SE England but including records north to lowland Scotland, *E. cilianensis* occurs on waste ground and rubbish tips.

A native of the warm temperate Old World, the species was grown in Britain in 1776 and recorded in the wild by 1908, and is now introduced in grain, birdseed and oilseed (and formerly wool). It is widely naturalized in South Africa, N & S America, Australia and elsewhere.

Eragrostis cilianensis:
A, panicle; B, whole spikelet;
C, partially disarticulated spikelet;
D, lemma; E, caryopsis.

182. **Eragrostis minor** Host

Small Love-grass   New Atlas CD

Very similar to *E. cilianensis* and shares the crateriform glands, deciduous lemma and persistent palea. It differs by its generally smaller spikelets (4.8 – 9mm), shorter lemmas (1.4 – 1.8mm) and distinctly oblong grain (0.5)0.6 – 0.8mm long.

E. minor has been recorded from a small number of widely scattered localities in central and southern Britain on waste ground and rubbish tips and around docks.

The species is a native of the subtropical and warm temperate Old World and was introduced as a casual with grain, birdseed and probably wool. It was cultivated in Britain in 1776 and recorded from the wild in 1898 from Jersey. It has not been recorded recently.

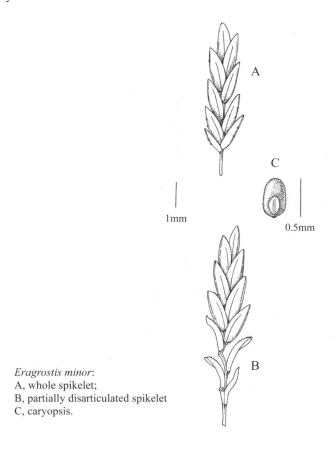

1mm

0.5mm

Eragrostis minor:
A, whole spikelet;
B, partially disarticulated spikelet
C, caryopsis.

183. **Sporobolus africanus** (Poir.) A.Robyns & Tournay

African Dropseed

Resembles a species of *Eragrostis* but has a 1-flowered spikelet. It is a perennial up to 100cm with narrow, spike-like panicle which has short ascending branches. The spikelets are 2.1 – 2.5mm and the pericarp, on wetting, swells and ejects the seed.

Rare and widely scattered in England on rubbish tips and rough ground and formerly more common as a wool alien, *S. africanus* is a native of tropical and southern Africa and Arabia. It was recorded in the wild in Britain in 1958 but does not appear to have been seen recently.

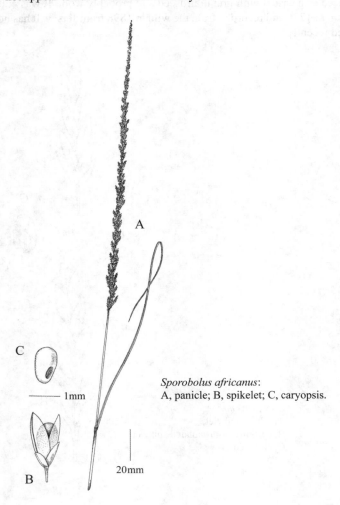

Sporobolus africanus:
A, panicle; B, spikelet; C, caryopsis.

1mm

20mm

536

184. **Eleusine indica** (L.) Gaertn.

Indian Yard-grass   New Atlas CD

Slender annual up to 85cm; ligule sparsely and minutely ciliolate. Inflorescence composed of 1 – 14 digitate racemes (1 or more racemes may be set a little below the rest); racemes linear, slender, 2.5 – 15.5cm × 3 – 5.5mm, the rhachis wingless. Spikelets elliptic, 4.3 – 5.2mm; lower glume 1-nerved, 1.1 – 2.3mm; upper glume 3-nerved, 1.8 – 2.9mm; lemmas lanceolate in profile, 2.4 – 3.6(4)mm, the keel with subsidiary nerves, acute to aubacute at the tip. Grain obliquely striate and with fine close lines perpendicular to the striae. $2n = 18$.

E. indica has been recorded as a casual from a few widely scattered localities, mainly in SE England, but its exact status, distribution and abundance are unsure because of confusion with the following species (although it seems to be much the less common). It is found on rubbish tips and waste ground where it is introduced with birdseed, cotton and oilseed, and around docks where it has arrived in ballast.

Native in Africa and India and found in the tropics and subtropics throughout the world, *E. indica* was recorded in the wild in Britain in 1905. A plant described as *E. indica* which may have been *E. africana* (see below) was recorded from the wild in 1872 and the species was cultivated in Britain by 1714. It occurs as a greenhouse weed in Guernsey (AGB: 79).

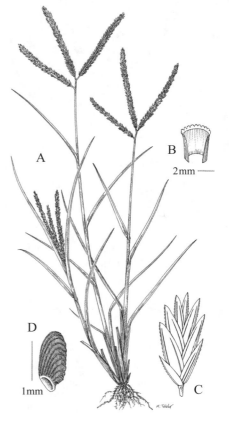

Eleusine indica: A, habit; B, ligule; C, spikelet; D, grain.

537

185. **Eleusine africana** Kenn.-O'Byrne

African Yard-grass   New Atlas CD

Robust annual up to 100cm; ligule with a definite ciliate fringe. Inflorescence composed of 3 – 17 racemes (1 or more may be set a little below the rest); racemes linear, stout, 3.5 – 15.5cm × 4 – 7mm, the rhachis wingless. Spikelets elliptic, 4.6 – 7.8mm; lower glume often 2- or 3-nerved, 2 – 3.2(3.9)mm; upper glume 3-nerved, 3 – 4.7mm; lemmas lanceolate in profile, 3.7 – 4.9mm, acute or subacute at the tip. Grain uniformly granular and obliquely ridged. $2n = 36$.

E. africana is widely scattered in Britain with most records being from SE England but confusion with the preceding species makes it difficult to be certain about the exact distribution. It likewise occurs on rubbish tips and waste ground where it is introduced from birdseed and formerly wool.

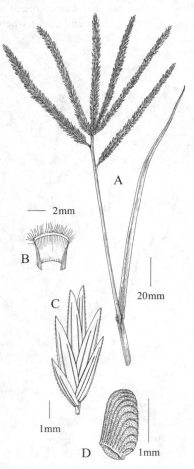

Native in the uplands of eastern & southern tropical Africa and in Arabia, *E. africana* was first recorded in the wild in Britain by 1926 (as *E. indica* subsp. *africana*). It is probably under-recorded. Formerly considered a subspecies (*E. indica* subsp. *africana* (Kenn.-O'Byrne) S.M.Phillips) but distinct enough morphologically and cytologically to be worthy of specific rank; it is the wild progenitor of Finger Millet (*E. coracana* (L.) Gaertn.).

A

2mm

B

20mm

C

1mm

D   1mm

Eleusine africana: A, inflorescence; B, ligule; C, spikelet; D, grain.

186. Cynodon dactylon (L.) Pers.

Illustration, page 541

Bermuda-grass   New Atlas: 800

Mat-forming perennial with profusely branching surface stolons and deep rhizomes; culms mostly erect, sometimes ascending, up to 30cm, but mostly less than 20cm; ligule membranous with conspicuous ciliate fringe, 0.2 – 0.3mm; blades 3 – 8(13)cm × 2 – 3(4)mm, greyish green, glabrous or loosely hairy. Racemes 3 – 5(6) in a single whorl, 2.5 – 5(6.5)cm, erect at first, eventually spreading, straight or curved. Spikelets 2.1 – 2.7mm, the fertile floret usually accompanied by a rhachilla extension, this often bearing a minute rudiment, very rarely a well developed male floret; glumes narrowly lanceolate, subequal, (1.5)1.8 – 2.2(2.4)mm, the upper slightly exceeding the lower; lemma minutely hairy on the keel and sometimes also on the margins; palea as long as the lemma; anthers 1 – 1.5mm. 2n = 36. Flowering and fruiting late July to early October.

Bermuda-grass occurs mainly in the south of England and Wales, especially along the coast, and in the Channel Islands. Elsewhere it may occur as a very rare casual but is absent from Scotland and Ireland. Its habitats include sandy shores and foredunes, where it is arguably native (see below), and short grassland, often in seafront gardens and lawns and on road verges near the sea. It is found inland on lawns and managed verges and may occur on tips and around docks as a casual. Soils are usually dry, infertile and sandy although it persists in amenity areas which may be watered and fertilized. In dunes it occurs with a range of foredune associates and in amenity grassland it can produce dense pure colonies or may be admixed with species such as *Bellis perennis, Elymus repens, Plantago coronopus* and *Poa annua* (a list of associates is given in RDB: 110).

Although quite a rare grass in Britain close to its northern limits, *C. dactylon* forms persistent populations in many sites both in eroding foredunes and in mown and trampled lawns. Its extensive stolons give good ground cover, enabling it to stabilize moving sand, and its deep rhizomes aid drought tolerance, so much so that it is often bright green and highly visible in dry summers when other grasses are parched brown. It is tolerant of low pH and high salinity. Although not especially tolerant of low temperatures over most of its global range, our northern populations seem surprisingly frost tolerant and, like *Spartina* (the only other possibly native grass genus we have which has the C_4 mode of photosynthesis), may be partially adapted to growing in more northerly climates. Populations persist and spread vegetatively but it is not known whether new plants are established from seed except for those introduced with wool or birdseed. The grass is shy to flower in mown and heavily trampled areas and new plants near existing colonies may be from detached stolons. (RDB: 110).

Most populations of *C. dactylon* in Britain are likely to be introductions, although it was first recorded in its foredune habitat in 1688 from the shoreline between Penzance and Marazion in W Cornwall (where it still occurs) and several authorities argue that it is native there and probably in the Channel Islands.

Uncertainty over its native status has led Cheffings & Farrell (2005) to place the species on the **Waiting List**.

It occurs in the tropics and warm temperate regions worldwide and is said to be one of the commonest grasses in the world. It is certainly favoured as a lawn grass in many parts of the tropics such as India, where European settlers soon discovered the virtue of the native 'Doob' grass's robust low growth and tolerance of mowing. It is also a nuisance on arable land in some parts of the world.

187. Cynodon incompletus Nees

African Bermuda-grass   New Atlas CD

Extensively introduced in the past but seldom persisted for very long. With the cessation of manuring with wool shoddy it now enters the country very rarely and is on the decline. It differs from *C. dactylon* by its lack of rhizomes and by the hyaline ligule 0.4 – 1mm lacking a ciliate fringe. Native of South Africa.

188. Chloris virgata Sw.

Feathery Rhodes-grass   New Atlas CD

Superficially similar to species of *Cynodon* but has well developed male or barren florets above the single fertile floret. The fertile lemma is obliquely obovate in profile, slightly gibbous on the keel, has a crown of long spreading hairs just below the tip and an awn 2.5 – 8.5mm; the second lemma is male with an oblong glabrous awned lemma; and the third (if present) is a minute clavate awnless scale.

Once introduced with wool, it was found mostly as a casual of docks and rubbish tips and occasionally as a weed of fields, but there appear to be no recent records. Native of the tropics of both the Old World and the New.

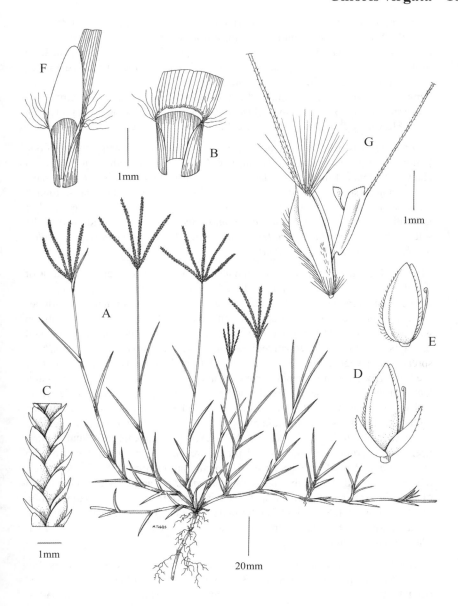

Cynodon dactylon: A, habit; B, ligule; C, segment of raceme; D, intact spikelet; E, floret.
Cynodon incompletus: F, ligule. *Chloris virgata*: G, cluster of florets.

541

189. Spartina alterniflora Loisel.

Smooth Cord-grass

New Atlas CD

Culms up to 120(170)cm; ligule (0.6)1.1 – 2mm; blades flat, up to 50(85)cm × 5 – 10(12)mm, persistent on the sheath. Inflorescence comprising (3)5 – 9(12) racemes on an axis 5 – 17(23)cm; racemes (4)5.5 – 10(15)cm, terminating in a bristle 1.5 – 3.3cm. Spikelets (8.5)10 – 15mm; glumes usually glabrous, sometimes sparsely ciliolate on the keel, very rarely thinly pubescent on the flanks, the lower 5 – 8.5(9.5)mm, the upper as long as the spikelet; lemma 7.5 – 12mm; anthers (3)3.5 – 7mm, dehiscent and usually producing good pollen. $2n$ = 62. Flowering & fruiting mostly mid-July to early October.

S. alterniflora is now an extremely rare grass in Britain, known only from one 'natural' site (i.e. not a known planting) at Marchwood in Southampton Water (S Hants). It occurs at three other places (as var. *glabra*) where it is known to have been planted (see below). It is found in the lowest zone of intertidal saltmarsh on unconsolidated silty clay, where it forms dense pure stands on open mud or is admixed with *Bolboschoenus maritimus, Spartina anglica* and, within the saltmarsh, *Aster tripolium, Atriplex portulacoides, Limonium vulgare, Puccinellia maritima* and *Triglochin maritima.*

The Marchwood population is the remnant of a once extensive series of swards of this grass in Southampton Water and the Rivers Itchen, Test and Hamble which flow into it. Surveys in recent years have shown that its population continues to decline in size, probably due to a combination of habitat loss, competition with *S. anglica* and changes in tidal action, sedimentation and pollution (Maskell & Raybould, 2001). In its native area, and where it is invasive, *S. alterniflora* spreads both vegetatively by means of tillers and extensive rhizomes and by seed, but British plants are not expanding and do not set viable seed. This latter fact is probably because the Marchwood population appears to be a single clone, and some clones of *S. alterniflora* are known to be self-incompatible. However, pollen fertility is also low in these plants, as it is in the single patch of var. *glabra* at Goldhanger on the R. Blackwater, N Essex, which appears to be maintaining itself vegetatively. The Marchwood plants are particularly important from an evolutionary point of view because they are all that remains of the *S. alterniflora* material involved in the hybridization with *S. maritima* and subsequent evolution of *S. anglica* (see account of that species). It is known from an analysis of variation of the chloroplast DNA, which is inherited maternally, that *S. alterniflora* was the female parent in the original cross-pollination (Ferris *et al.,* 1997). (Biol. Flora: Marchant & Goodman 1969).

A neophyte, *S. alterniflora* was first recorded (in the River Itchen) in 1829, but may have been present there since 1816. Whether it was deliberately introduced (to stabilize mud or to provide thatching straw) or, more likely, arrived with ballast (bails of *Spartina* straw were used to cushion heavy items in the hulls of ships) is not known. Initially it thrived, spreading west to Lymington and east possibly

542

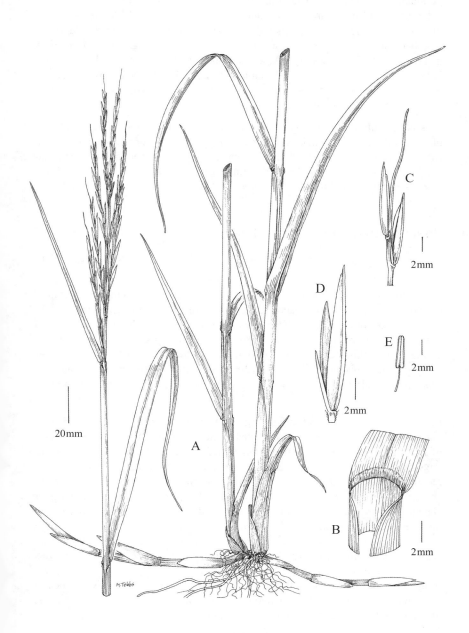

Spartina alterniflora: A, habit; B, ligule; C, terminal part of raceme; D, spikelet; E, anther.

to Thorney Island, but its decline began in the 1920s. The plants at Ealing in Southampton Water, Goldhanger in N Essex, and Udale Bay in E Ross are known to be survivors from deliberate introductions in 1922, 1935 and 1948 respectively, the last one being from cuttings collected at Goldhanger (see Raybould *et al.,* 1991b for details). These are var *glabra.* No other plantings have survived. A native of the Atlantic coast of N America, Canada and Newfoundland, the species is also naturalized in France and Spain. It has become a serious invader on the Pacific coast of the USA, particularly in Washington State and, as a hybrid with the native *S. foliosa,* in San Francisco Bay.

This is the only one of our coastal Cord-grasses to have more or less glabrous glumes and it nearly always has flat leaf-blades. Two varieties are recorded from Britain, var. *alterniflora,* with smaller leaf-blades and looser racemes, and var. *glabra* (Muhl. ex Bigelow) Fernald, with larger leaf-blades and tighter racemes. Most N American authors no longer make the distinction.

190. Spartina maritima (Curtis) Fernald

Small Cord-grass   New Atlas: 801

Culms up to 50cm; ligule 0.3 – 0.8mm; blades flat, up to 16cm × 3 – 5.5mm, or inrolled and 1 – 1.5mm across, ultimately disarticulating from the sheath. Inflorescence comprising 1 – 4(5) racemes on an axis 1 – 4(8)cm; racemes (3.5)5 – 9(10)cm, terminating in a bristle 0.8 – 1.8(2.1)cm. Spikelets (10)11 – 15mm; glumes softly pubescent on keel and flanks, the lower 6.5 – 10.5mm, the upper as long as the spikelet; lemma 9 – 12mm; anthers 3 – 5(6)mm, dehiscent and producing good pollen. $2n = 60$. Flowering & fruiting mostly late July to early October.

Formerly more widepsread in SE England from the River Exe to the Wash, *S. maritima* is now almost entirely confined to the estuarine and coastal saltmarshes of E Suffolk and Essex (from the River Alde south to Osea Island). A fairly large population in Newtown Bay on the Isle of Wight may be the only one remaining on the south coast and the species is probably extinct in Kent, Norfolk and Lincolnshire (see Raybould *et al.,* 1991b). It is typically found in the higher elevations of saltmarsh on firm muds and sandy muds in mixed swards which include *Aster tripolium, Atriplex portulacoides, Limonium vulgare, Plantago maritima, Puccinellia maritima, Salicornia europaea, Suaeda maritima* and *Triglochin maritima.* It often occurs in the lower, wetter parts of such communities and in open areas within the turf or on the edges of creeks and pans. It is known from only one or two sites as a pioneer on bare firm mud. It may be locally common but its distribution is generally patchy and it is absent from large areas of suitable-looking habitat within its core range.

Populations of *S. maritima* in English saltmarshes spread almost entirely vegetatively, by means of tough persistent slender rhizomes. Plants rarely form

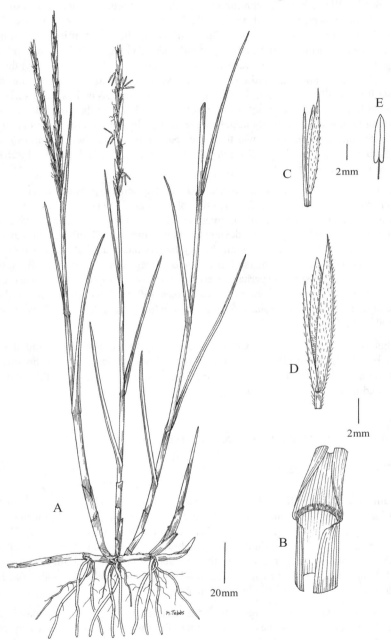

Spartina maritima: A, habit; B, ligule; C, terminal part of raceme; D, spikelet; E, anther.

dense swards, as in other *Spartina* species, but tend to comprise discrete tufts or patches. They are also confined to the shorter swards and open areas of the marsh and are rarely found where taller *Atriplex portulcaoides* or *Puccinellia maritima* occur in high density. In Spain, in the southern part of its range, it is a taller, sward-forming plant and its general lack of vigour in Britain may reflect the fact that it is a grass of warmer climes with a C_4 method of photosynthesis which is at its northern limits here. This may also help to account for the fact that it is usually very late flowering and rarely sets seed. Viable seed have been found but seedlings have not been reported from field populations. The species is protogynous and probably largely outbreeding; there are no records of selfing, cleistogamy or apomixis. It was the pollen parent in the cross with *S. alterniflora* which eventually produced *S. anglica* (see that account). (Biol. Flora: Marchant & Goodman, 1969; SPB: 396).

Regarded as a native in Britain (although thought by some to possibly be an ancient introduction), *S. maritima* is found in suitable habitats from Britain to Spain, in the Adriatic, in northwestern and southwestern Africa and in South Africa. Its decline in this country where it is now designated as **endangered** (Cheffings and Farrell, 2005) may have a number of contributory factors including habitat loss by land claim for agriculture, saltmarsh erosion, and successional changes involving the invasion of taller species (perhaps even stemming originally from the widespread withdrawal of grazing from many east coast saltmarshes). However, as they occupy quite different habitats, *S. anglica* is unlikely to have ousted *S. maritima* in all but a few sites.

This is the smallest of the Cord-grasses, rarely exceeding 50cm, and it has short stiff flat or inrolled leaf-blades that readily disarticulate from the sheath at maturity. It also has the shortest terminal bristle on the raceme, this seldom exceeding the adjacent spikelet.

191. Spartina ×townsendii H.& J.Groves

Townsend's Cord-grass   New Atlas: 801

Culms up to 115cm; ligule 0.6 – 2.2mm; blades flat, up to 45(55)cm × 4 – 10mm, or inrolled and 1 – 2.5mm across. Inflorescence comprising 3 – 7(10) racemes on an axis (4)5 – 12cm; racemes (5)6 – 20cm, terminating in a bristle 1.5 – 3(3.5)cm. Spikelets 12 – 16.5mm; glumes softly pubescent on keel and flanks, the lower 7.5 – 11.5mm, the upper as long as the spikelet; lemma 9.5 – 13.5mm; anthers 5 – 8.5mm, indehiscent or dehiscent but producing barren pollen. $2n = 49 – 66, 76$. Flowering & fruiting mostly late June to early October.

S. ×townsendii has been recorded from mudflats and saltmarshes mainly in southern England along the coast adjacent to the site of its original discovery, but is is also scattered widely northwards to Wales and the west coast of Scotland. There is one confirmed record from Ireland. However, its exact distribution is

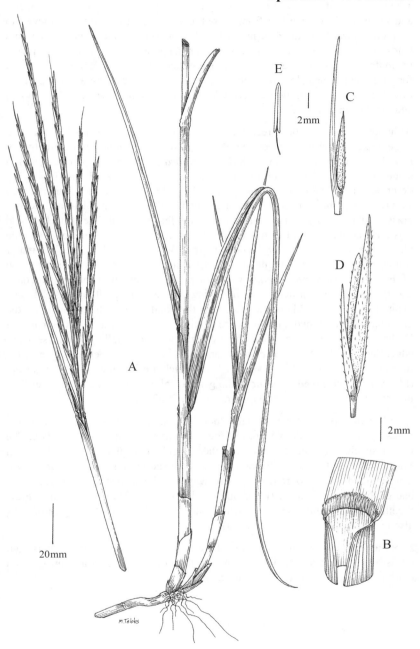

Spartina × townsendii. A, habit; B, ligule; C, terminal part of raceme; D, spikelet; E, anther.

difficult to determine. Widely planted with the fertile *S. anglica* on mudflats around the coast, it was mostly overwhelmed by this more vigorous species and seems to have been lost from all but a few sites. It is easily overlooked in *S. anglica* swards although it has noticeably denser and more erect tillers and tends to occur at the landward edges. The largest population seems to be at Hythe in Southampton Water (S Hants), the site where it was first collected. Here it forms dense patches alongside other saltmarsh plants including *Aster tripolium*, *Atriplex portulacoides*, *Juncus gerardii*, *Puccinellia maritima*, *Spartina anglica* and *Triglochin maritima*.

Although it has never been recreated in the laboratory, *S. ×townsendii* is known to be a natural hybrid between the N American *S. alterniflora* and the native *S. maritima*. The hybridization, with *S. alterniflora* as the female parent, occurred sometime before 1870 when the first plant was collected at Hythe (it was not described until 1880; see Gray *et al.,* 1991). Being sterile, the plants spread slowly at first, but its dispersal was later aided by the deliberate planting of Cordgrass to stabilize mudflats and improve sea defences. Much later (the 1950s) it was realized that such plantings included both the sterile F_1 hybrid and a fertile plant, the allopolyploid *S. anglica*. Since Arne Bay in Poole Harbour was a major source of material for plantings (a *Spartina* 'nursery') and was a mixed sward of the two types, *S. ×townsendii* was transplanted to much of the British coast, and to Europe and further afield, including New Zealand. Although sterile, the plant flowers freely. Many swards along the south coast which contained the grass have been eroded and subject to extensive dieback, although the marsh at Hythe is to some extent protected by a shingle ridge and shell bank at its seaward edge. Ecologically, *S. ×townsendii* is somewhat intermediate between its parents, forming dense stands (like *S. alterniflora*) which are intermediate in height but (like *S. maritima*) tend to occur in the general saltmarsh community rather than the lower zones. (Biol. Flora: Goodman *et al.,* 1969).

Clearly native (since it was actually 'born' here), *S. ×townsendii* represents the first stage in the remarkable story of the origin and evolution of *S. anglica*. The parent species may have grown together in only two places in Southampton Water, and then for about 50 years, before they started to retract. *S. alterniflora* is now found only at Marchwood, 7km away, and the nearest *S. maritima*, which had gone from Hythe by 1913, is on the Isle of Wight. These species also grew together in SW France/NE Spain where an F_1 hybrid (named *S. ×neyrautii*) was also produced (Raybould *et al.,* 1990).

S. ×townsendii is usually recognized by its barren, indehiscent anthers, but occasionally these are dehiscent although the pollen is barren and mis-shapen (for those with a microscope, it is usually less than 45μ in diameter).

192. **Spartina anglica** C.E.Hubb.

Illustration, page 551

Common Cord-grass   New Atlas: 801

Culms up to 100(115)cm; ligule (1)1.4 – 3.2mm; blades flat, up to 50cm × 6 – 11mm, or inrolled and 1 – 3mm across. Inflorescence comprising 2 – 8 racemes on an axis 2 – 15cm; racemes (6)8 – 20(24)cm, terminating in a bristle 1.8 – 5(5.5)cm. Spikelets 13 – 19.5mm; glumes softly pubescent on keel and flanks, the lower 9 – 15mm, the upper as long as the spikelet; lemma 11 – 17mm; anthers 6.5 – 11mm, dehiscent and producing good pollen. $2n = 120 – 124$. Flowering and fruiting early July to early October.

S. anglica is abundant, and often locally dominant, on saltmarshes and intertidal mudflats around the coasts of England and Wales, in southern Scotland and in scattered locations around the coast of Ireland. It is most common as a pioneer plant on open mud or sandy mud in the lowest zone of saltmarshes, but can be found scattered throughout the marsh, especially in pans or creeks, on muddy shingle, and in drainage ditches and brackish areas in grazing marshes to landward of sea walls. It may form extensive pure stands on mudflats, produced by the coalescence of expanding pioneer clumps. Saltmarsh species most commonly found with *S. anglica* include *Aster tripolium* (especially the rayless form), *Atriplex portulacoides, Puccinellia maritima, Salicornia europaea* and *Suaeda maritima*, but it can be found alongside most saltmarsh plants and those of brackish or freshwater habitats such as *Bolboschoenus maritimus* and *Phragmites australis*.

Arguably our best-studied example of plant evolution by allopolyploidy (hybridization between two different species followed by chromosome doubling and the restoration of fertility), *S. anglica* is known to be derived from *S. ×townsendii*, the sterile hybrid of *S. alterniflora* and *S. maritima* (see accounts of those species). It arose some time before 1892 (the first confirmed record at Keysworth) in Southampton Water and, helped by the production of fertile seed, spread naturally along the south coast and to the north coast of France. Its spectacular growth and the ability of the extensive system of roots and rhizomes to stabilize soft mud and prevent the re-suspension of tide-borne sediments, soon convinced coastal engineers that it could be used as an aid to sea defence and land reclamation. First planted outside the area of natural spread in 1907, in Norfolk, most plantings occurred in the 1920s and 1930s when thousands of cuttings and seed batches were introduced around the British coast, many from a single source in Poole Harbour. By the mid-1960s around 12,000ha, approximately a quarter of the saltmarsh in Great Britain, was dominated by this species. Studies of its distribution in relation to mudflat elevations have demonstrated that its success is largely due to an ability to grow to seaward of all other perennial plants (notably *Puccinellia maritima*) and thus to exploit a largely unoccupied niche (Gray *et al.,* 1991). Today, in most south coast harbours and in eastern England below the Wash, *S. anglica* swards are regressing, a process which began in the 1920s, and many plants are infected with Ergot fungus (*Claviceps purpurea*). By contrast, in the north (roughly north of 53°N latitude) where the *S. anglica* invasion was generally later, swards are gradually being replaced by other species, especially *Puccinellia maritima*. Here, *S. anglica* appears only to set seed in warm late summers which facilitate seed ripening and perhaps the breakdown of the self-incompatibility mechanism. It is also at a competitive disadvantage in the north to the cold temperate species, *Puccinellia maritima*. Being a C_4 grass *S. anglica* cannot grow as quickly as *P. maritima* in cool spring conditions (Gray & Mogg, 2001).

S. anglica is endemic as a native to Britain but has been widely planted around the world. Particularly spectacular invasions resulting from its introductions have occurred in N America, Tasmania and China (where by 1980 more than 35,000ha of marsh had resulted from a single batch of seed exported in 1963). Although a successful invader, *S. anglica* displays hardly any genetic variation and it is entirely possible that this is because it originated from a single doubling event (this is difficult to determine since its progenitors have little (*S. maritima*) or no (*S. alterniflora*) variation) (Raybould *et al.,* 1991a).

Putative backcrosses to *S. alterniflora* have been reported, as well as sterile polyhaploids that somewhat resemble *S. ×townsendii*, but it is unlikely that either of these could be recognized as such in the field. The abundance of the species, along with its longer ligule, longer lemmas and longer, fertile anthers are the best means of identifying it.

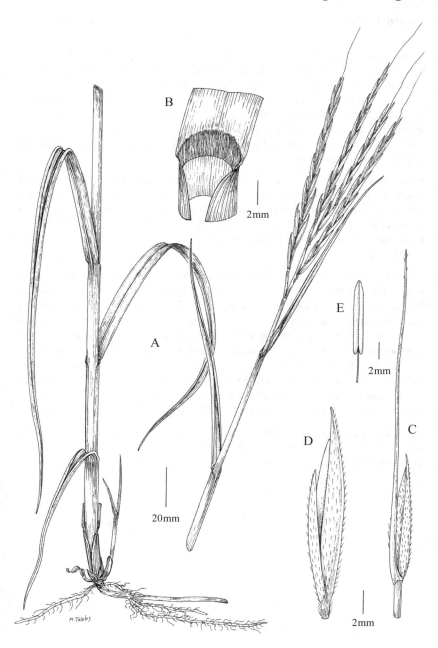

Spartina anglica: A, habit; B, ligule; C, terminal part of raceme; D, spikelet; E, anther.

193. **Spartina pectinata** Bosc ex Link

Prairie Cord-grass   New Atlas CD

Culms up to 180cm; ligule 0.5 – 3mm; blades flat at first, up to 90cm × 15mm, but becoming inrolled on drying. Inflorescence comprising (5)10 – 20(30) racemes on an axis 15 – 30cm; racemes 4 – 8(10)cm, terminating in a bristle 6 – 10mm. Spikelets 8 – 12mm (excluding the awns); glumes coarsely pectinate-scabrid on the keel, glabrous to sparsely pubescent on the flanks, the lower 5 – 10mm, the upper as long as the spikelet and with an awn 3 – 8(10)mm; lemma 7 – 9mm; anthers 5 – 7mm, dehiscent and producing good pollen. $2n = 40$. Flowering and fruiting July to September.

S. pectinata is known from only a handful of scattered sites in Britain and Ireland where it has been introduced and become established as an escape from garden cultivation. First reported from Costelloe Lodge, W Galway (vc H16) where it persists by a freshwater lake, it is also found at Seaton Burn, S Northumb (vc 67), by a quarry in N Hants (vc 12) and at one or two other places in southern England. (AGB: 85).

Prairie Cord-grass, as the name indicates, is a plant of prairies in N America where it grows in wet depressions, on the banks of sluggish streams and around ponds. It produces tall clumps of woody unpalatable tillers supported by an extensive rhizome system. It appears to tolerate a wide range of soil types from fine clays to silty loams and, although mostly found in freshwater conditions, is known to be salt tolerant. It will tolerate high water tables but not prolonged flooding. Where seed are produced they require wet soils for germination and seedlings will only etablish in bare areas. In N America it is sometimes planted to prevent erosion on the banks of drainage channels and has recently been used in this country in biomass trials as a potential energy crop (it has the C_4 mode of photosynthesis).

Classed as a neophyte in the New Atlas, *S. pectinata* was reported from the wild at its W Galway site in 1967. It is a native of N America and is sometimes grown as an ornamental grass here in Britain.

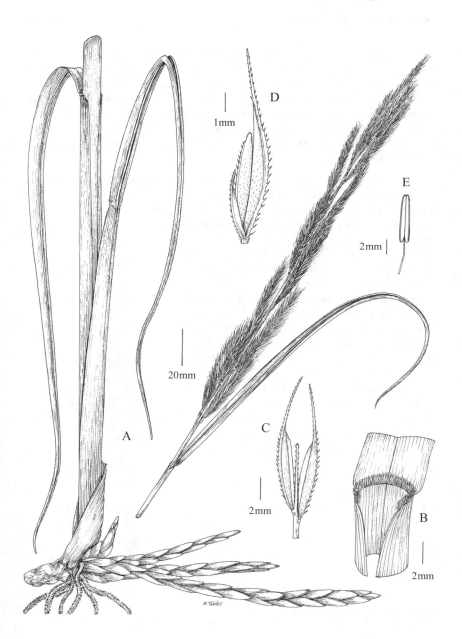

Spartina pectinata: A, habit; B, ligule; C, terminal part of raceme; D, spikelet; E, anther.

194. Panicum miliaceum L.

Broomcorn Millet, Proso New Atlas: 802

Robust annual up to 100cm; sheaths and blades sparsely to densely hispid with long spreading hairs. Panicle open, up to 30cm, usually nodding and bearing the spikelets mostly towards the tips of the branches and branchlets. Spikelets (4)4.5 – 5.5(6.5)mm; lower glume 1/2 – 2/3 the length of the spikelet, 5-nerved, acuminate, separated from the rest of the spikelet by a short internode; upper glume 11- to 17-nerved, acuminate; lower lemma 9- to 13-nerved, acuminate, its palea absent or much reduced; upper lemma orange or yellowish, smooth and shining, usually persistent.

P. miliaceum is now widespread and fairly common in lowland Britain, including the Channel Islands and the Isle of Man, but is rare in Scotland and Ireland. It is found as a casual on tips and waste ground and occasionally in cultivated land as a grain contaminant or in woodland where it is associated with game cover and feeding areas. Introduced mainly as a component of birdseed, it was cultivated here by 1596 and first recorded in the wild in 1872. It is apparently still occasionally cultivated, especially in southern England, for forage, grain or game cover (Francis, 2005; AGB: 88). Probably originating in northern India, but nowhere known as a truly wild plant, *P. miliaceum* is widely cultivated in Asia as a hot-weather crop and in warm temperate and tropical areas around the world. It was grown in some regions of southern Europe before wheat. It may be increasing as a casual in Britain and is probably under-recorded, not least because, until the unmistakable and beautiful panicles appear, it can be mistaken for Maize (*Zea mays*) or Great Millet (*Sorghum bicolor*).

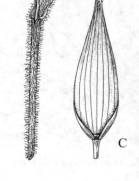

A

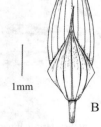

Panicum miliaceum: A, panicle;
B, spikelet, ventral view;
C, spikelet, dorsal view.

1mm

B

C

195. Panicum capillare L.

Witch-grass New Atlas: 802

Annual up to 80cm; sheaths and underside of blades with long spreading hairs. Panicle diffuse, up to 40cm, breaking off at the base at maturity and falling entire. Spikelets 2 – 3.5mm; lower glume 2/5 – 1/2 the length of the spikelet, 1-nerved, acute; upper glume 5- to 7-nerved, acuminate; lower lemma similar to the upper glume, its palea absent or much reduced.

Recorded as a casual from scattered locations in Great Britain and the Channel Islands, *P. capillare* is generally found on waste ground and rubbish tips, often around docks. It arrives mainly in birdseed or as an oilseed and grass-seed contaminant, but some plants may have originated from gardens where its striking panicles make it an attractive ornamental. A native of N America, it was first cultivated here by 1758 and first recorded from the wild in 1867. It is widely naturalized in central and southern Europe.

Panicum capillare: A, panicle; B, spikelet, ventral view; C, spikelet, dorsal view.

20mm

A

B

C

1mm

M.Tebbs

196. Panicum schinzii Hack.

Transvaal Millet   New Atlas CD

Annual up to 100cm; sheaths and blades glabrous. Panicle open, up to 35cm, the branches and branchlets bare of spikelets below. Spikelets 2 – 2.8mm; lower glume up to 1/5 the length of the spikelet, 1-nerved, cuff-like; upper glume 7- to 9-nerved, obtuse to bluntly pointed; lower lemma similar to the upper glume, enclosing a male flower with well developed palea.

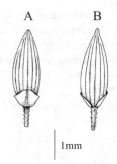

Panicum schinzii:
A, spikelet, ventral view;
B, spikelet, dorsal view.

Recorded from scattered localities mainly in England in the south and Midlands, but with some older records from lowland Scotland, *P. schinzii* is found on rubbish tips, waste ground and dockland. Introduced to Britain as a birdseed alien (formerly also with wool shoddy) it was recorded in the wild in 1918 but there have been few records since 1970. It is a native of southern tropical Africa and South Africa and is naturalized in India and Australia.

197. Panicum dichotomiflorum Michx.

Autumn Millet   New Atlas CD

Annual up to 100cm; sheaths and blades glabrous. Panicle open with the spikelets subcontracted about the upper part of the primary branches, the lower part bare, up to 40cm. Spikelets 2.7 – 3.5mm; lower glume up to 1/3 the length of the spikelet, 1- to 3-nerved, truncate; upper glume 5- to 7-nerved, acuminate; lower lemma similar to the upper glume, its palea absent or much reduced.

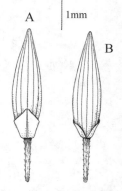

P. dichotomiflorum is found as a casual scattered in southern England on railway sidings, docks, waste land and tips. It regularly occurs in soya-bean waste but can be introduced with birdseed and from other sources. First recorded from the wild in England in 1945, it is native in N America and widely naturalized in southern Europe, Asia and Australia.

Panicum dichotomiflorum:
A, spikelet, ventral view;
B, spikelet, dorsal view.

198. **Echinochloa crusgalli** (L.) P.Beauv.

Cockspur   New Atlas: 802

Coarse annual up to 120cm; ligule absent; blades 7 – 35cm × 4 – 20mm. Inflorescence linear to ovate, 6 – 22cm, strongly tinged with purple; racemes untidily 2- to several-rowed, the longest 2 – 10cm, usually with short secondary branchlets below. Spikelets ovate-elliptic, mostly 3 – 4mm, hispid; lower lemma acuminate or drawn out into an awn up to 5cm; upper lemma 2 – 3mm.

Cockspur has a similar general distribution to Proso Millet, being widespread and quite common in lowland Britain including the Channel Islands and the Isle of Man, and rare in Scotland and Ireland. It is recorded both from cultivated land and from ruderal habitats such as waste ground, roadsides and rubbish tips. Introduced in birdseed, soya bean waste and other materials, formerly including wool, *E. crusgalli* was also widely introduced during the Second World War as a contaminant of carrot seed and other root crops imported from N America (where it is known as 'Barnyard Millet').

Classed as a neophyte and known in Britain since the 17th century, it is able to establish persistent, if rather short-lived, populations in the warmer parts of southern England and the Channel Islands. It is sometimes cultivated as food for game birds. A native of warm temperate and tropical regions throughout the world, it has been widely introduced as a fodder crop. Its success as a weed has been attributed to its high seed production, efficient dispersal, possession of seed dormancy and ability to grow rapidly in a wide range of conditions (Maun & Barrett, 1986).

The species is recognised by its untidily crowded racemes with, usually, awned spikelets, but it is a polymorphic weed whose numerous intergrading races are apparently the consequence of cleistogamous self-pollination. Some of these races have been considered worthy of recognition at species level, but there is no general agreement on this.

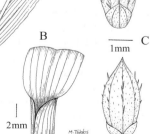

Echinochloa crusgalli: A, panicle; B, junction of sheath and blade; C, spikelet in dorsal view (top) and ventral view (bottom).

557

199. Echinochloa esculenta (A.Braun) H.Scholz

Japanese Millet   New Atlas: 803

A cultivated derivative of *E. crusgalli* that arose in Japan and is grown as a cereal in warm temperate E Asia. It is distinguished by its plump purple-tinged spikelets, 3 – 4mm, in a dense crowded head of simple or branched several-rowed racemes. Similar to and often confused with *E. frumentacea* (see opposite).

E. esculenta has been recorded from scattered localities in southern Britain mainly in SE England but as far north as C Scotland (not in the Channel Islands or Ireland). It is a casual on rubbish tips and waste ground, where it arrives as a component of birdseed, but does not persist. It is sometimes grown as food for game. Confusion with White Millet has obscured its history and status in Britain but it was known by 1971. It may be increasing.

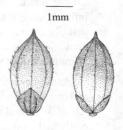

1mm

Echinochloa esculenta: spikelet in dorsal view (left) and ventral view (right).

200. Echinochloa colona (L.) Link

Shama Millet   New Atlas CD

Closely resembles *E. crusgalli* but the spikelets are neatly 4-rowed in the racemes and these seldom exceed 3cm; the spikelets are smaller (1.5 – 3mm) and pubescent rather than hispid; the lower lemma is usually no more than acute, sometimes minutely apiculate, and never awned.

A casual recorded from widely scattered localities in lowland Britain, but not from Scotland or the Channel Islands, *E. colona* is found on waste ground, rubbish tips and similar ruderal habitats. It is usually introduced in birdseed, oilseed, grain, cotton or soya bean waste. Populations do not persist. Grown in Britain by 1699 it was recorded from the wild by 1906 and may be increasing. *E. colona* is native in the tropics and subtropics generally but may be an introduction in N America.

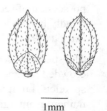

1mm

Echinochloa colona: spikelet in dorsal view (left) and ventral view (right).

201. **Echinochloa frumentacea** Link

White Millet

A cultivated derivative of *E. colona* that arose in India and is widely grown as a cereal in the hotter parts of Africa and Asia. It is distinguished by its plmup pallid spikelets, 2.5 – 3.5mm, in a dense crowded head of short, unbranched, several-rowed racemes. The lower lemma is less sharply pointed than that of *E. esculenta* and the spikelets are slightly smaller, but otherwise the two are very similar and are often confused.

E. frumentacea has been reported from southern Britain including the Isles of Scilly (but not from the Channel Islands, Scotland or Ireland) where it is found mainly on rubbish tips and similar habitats. It is a casual of birdseed first recorded in the wild here in 1930. White Millet is widely naturalized in warmer climates by virtue of its cultivation as a cereal.

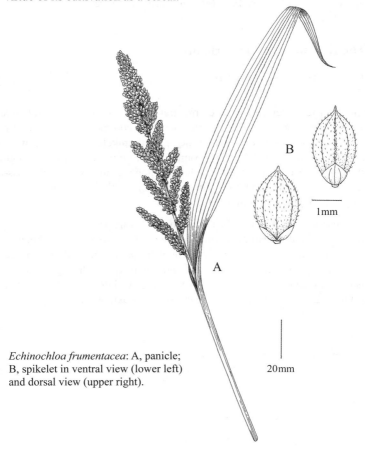

Echinochloa frumentacea: A, panicle;
B, spikelet in ventral view (lower left)
and dorsal view (upper right).

559

202. **Brachiaria platyphylla** (Griseb.) Nash

Broad-leaved Signal-grass   New Atlas CD

Annual; culms decumbent and rooting at the lower nodes, finally erect and up to 50cm. Inflorescence of (2)4 – 6 racemes distant (3 – 8cm apart) on a central axis, embraced below by the uppermost leaf-sheath; racemes 3 – 8cm, bearing single spikelets on a winged rhachis. Spikelets 3.5 – 4.5mm; lower glume up to 1/3 the length of the spikelet, clasping, nerveless, obtuse; upper glume and lower lemma 3- to 5-nerved (often with cross-nerves), obtuse; upper lemma c. 3mm, rugose.

B. platyphylla is a rare casual recorded from southern England on waste ground and rubbish tips. It is characterized by its broad, short leaves and decumbent growth habit. It arrives here as a contaminant of birdseed, oilseed or soybean waste. A native of Cuba and N America, where it is a serious weed of arable agriculture in parts of southeastern USA (especially in cornfields), it was recorded in the wild in England by 1970 (at Guildford Tip, Surrey).

203. **Urochloa panicoides** P.Beauv.

Sharp-flowered Signal-grass   New Atlas CD

Annual up to 100cm, sometimes prostrate below, clothed with tubercle-based hairs. Inflorescence of 2 – 7(10) racemes on a common axis 1 – 9cm; racemes 1 – 7cm, bearing single or sometimes paired spikelets on a narrowly winged rhachis. Spikelets (2.5)3.5 – 4.5(5.5)mm; lower glume 1/4 – 1/2 the length of the spikelet, 3- to 5-nerved, obtuse to subacute; upper glume often with cross-nerves, acute; lower lemma sometimes with a fringe of bristly hairs, acute; upper lemma faintly rugose and with a mucro 0.3 – 1mm.

A rare casual confined mostly to the south of England (apart from the earliest record in 1955 from Humberstone, N Lincs), *U. panicoides* has been found on cultivated ground, waste ground and rubbish tips. Introduced in birdseed and as a seed impurity, it is native in tropical and South Africa, through Arabia to India. It is naturalized in Australia and C America as well as the southern USA where, known as 'Liverseed Grass', it is regarded as a noxious weed.

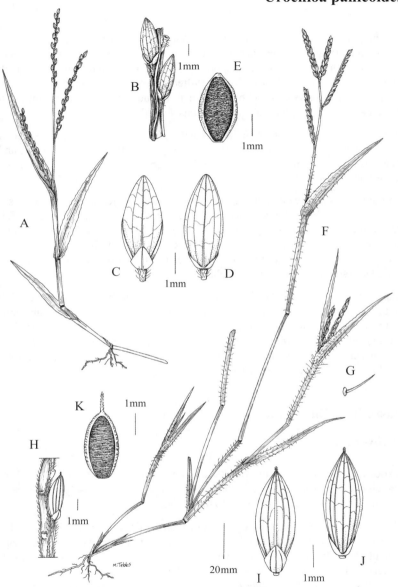

Brachiaria platyphylla: A, habit; B, portion of raceme; C, spikelet, ventral view;
D, spikelet, dorsal view; E, upper floret, ventral view.
Urochloa panicoides: F, habit; G, tubercle-based hair; H, portion of raceme;
I, spikelet, ventral view; J, spikelet, dorsal view; K, upper floret, ventral view.

204. **Paspalum distichum** L.

Creeping stoloniferous perennial; culms up to 50cm. Inflorescence composed of 2(4) conjugate (subdigitate) racemes; racemes 2 – 7cm, the spikelets in 2 rows on a flattened rhachis 1 – 2mm wide. Spikelets ovate, 2.5 – 3.5mm, elliptic, relatively plump, abruptly pointed; lower glume often present as a minute scale; upper glume minutely pubescent, with a prominent midnerve; lower lemma similar to the upper glume, but glabrous; upper lemma smooth, pallid.

P. distichum is a rare grass in Britain which has managed to establish small colonies persisting for some years at a few scattered locations, mainly in England. The best-known are in W Cornwall and E London (AGB: 93). It occurs in damp, sometimes saline, soils.

Throughout its native range this species has a general preference for brackish and saline habitats, although it also occurs in freshwater marshland. It spreads mainly vegetatively and appears to produce relatively few seed (possibly because of the presence of self-incompatible clones). It tolerates flooding in coastal saltmarsh and because of its high salt tolerance has been used in Australia and elsewhere as a fodder grass on salt-affected rangeland and as a coastal sand binder.

Classed as a neophyte in the New Atlas, *P. distichum* was first grown here in 1776 and first recorded in the wild in 1924. It is a native of the tropics and subtropics of the Old World and the New, but is largely absent from the equatorial belt. Introduced into England with birdseed, and formerly with wool, cotton and soya bean waste, it has been naturalized in Cornwall since 1971, and in London since 1984 where it manages to survive our winters.

205. **Paspalum dilatatum** Poir.

Dallis-grass

A robust tufted perennial up to 180cm, with several racemes, each 4 – 11cm, scattered along a central axis 2 – 20cm. The upper glume is densely ciliate on the margins imparting a distinct fringe to the spikelet.

The few widely scattered locations from which this tropical fodder grass has been reported in Britain include waste ground, urban streets, a car park and around docks. It may survive our winters in cultivation but is otherwise unlikely to persist. Its natural habitat is moist grassland on a range of soils, but it has some disadvantages as a fodder crop being very susceptible to ergot. An obligate apomict, it seeds freely but the seed shatter and are difficult to harvest. It is native in S America and has been widely introduced elsewhere. Its very occasional introductions to Britain have been with grain and birdseed (and also formerly with wool). (AGB: 93).

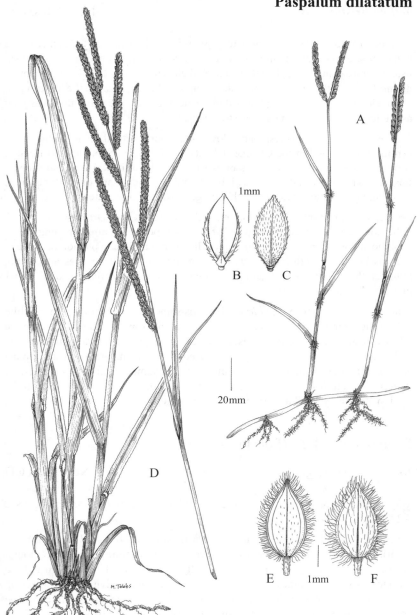

Paspalum distichum: A, habit; B, spikelet, ventral view; C, spikelet, dorsal view.
Paspalum dilatatum: D, habit; E, spikelet, ventral view; F, spikelet, dorsal view.

206. **Setaria pumila** (Poir.) Roem. & Schult.

Yellow Bristle-grass   New Atlas: 803

Annual up to 75cm. Panicle contracted, spike-like, cylindrical, up to 15cm; rhachis hairy; bristles 3 – 12mm, antrorsely scabrid, commonly brownish or yellowish, usually more than 5 per spikelet cluster. Spikelets ovate, (2.5)2.8 – 3.3mm; lower glume 1/3 – 1/2 the length of the spikelet; upper glume similar to the lower, up to 2/3 the length of the spikelet; lower floret male or barren, the palea almost as long as the lemma; upper lemma rugose to corrugate.

S. pumila is now quite widespread in lowland Britain, particularly in southern and central England and in the Channel Islands, but is rare in Scotland and Ireland. It occurs as a casual in open sites on waste ground, cultivated land and rubbish tips, and is probably under-recorded. It is found in a wide range of soil types from sands and gravels to clays, and with a range of ruderal associates.

A strictly summer annual, germinating in the spring, Yellow Bristle-grass is self-pollinating and produces seed which requires a period of after-ripening under cool moist conditions to break dormancy. It is very variable in phenotype in traits such as height, growth habit, leaf width, number of inflorescences and so on, although the plant tends to retain the golden yellow panicle colour and the rather glaucous hue of the leaves.

Classed as a neophyte, *S. pumila* populations sometimes persist for a short while before succumbing to our climate. It is native in the tropical and warm temperate Old World and arrives here in birdseed, oilseed, soya bean waste, agricultural seed and formerly in wool. It is widely naturalized in warm temperate and subtropical areas around the world and is a common weed in some countries, e.g. eastern N America, where it is a serious weed in spring-sown crops. It was known in the wild in Britain by 1867 and appears to be increasing.

207. **Setaria parviflora** (Poir.) Kerguélen

Knotroot Bristle-grass   New Atlas CD

Very similar to *S. pumila* but a perennial with short rhizomes and spikelets 2 – 2.5(3)mm.

A very occasional introduction to southern Britain with birdseed (and formerly wool), *S. parviflora* has rarely been recorded in recent times. It has been found on waste ground and rubbish tips, especially near ports, where it often fails to produce its short rhizomes, instead behaving as an annual dying after flowering in its first year (nevertheless, its still quite distinctive habit is not likely to be confused with *S. pumila*). A native of N America, it was cultivated in Britain in 1805 and first recorded in the wild in 1913.

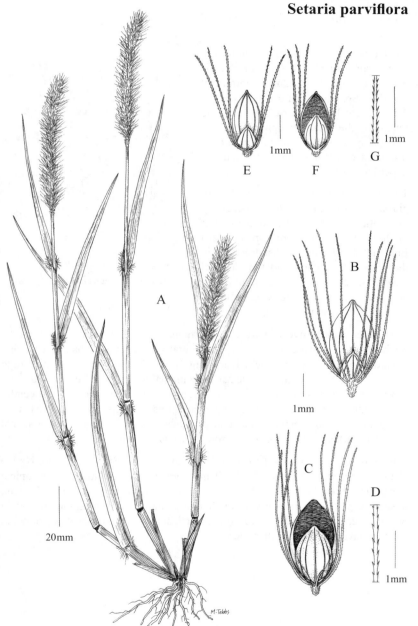

Setaria pumila: A, habit; B, spikelet, ventral view; C, spikelet, dorsal view; D, part of a bristle.
Setaria parviflora: E, spikelet, ventral view; F, spikelet, dorsal view; G, part of a bristle.

208. Setaria viridis (L.) P.Beauv.

Green Bristle-grass New Atlas: 804

Annual up to 100cm. Panicle contracted, neatly spike-like, up to 12cm; rhachis hairy; bristles 3 – 12mm, antrorsely barbed. Spikelets elliptic, (1.8)2 – 2.5(2.7)mm; lower glume 1/4 – 1/3 the length of the spikelet; upper glume as long as the spikelet; lower floret barren, the palea c. 1/2 as long as the lemma; upper lemma finely rugose.

The most widespread of the Bristle-grasses in the British Isles, occurring in Scotland (rarely), the southern half of Ireland, and scattered in northern England, *S. viridis* is most frequent in the south of England and the Channel Islands. It occurs as a weed in cultivated and waste ground, road verges, urban pavements and on rubbish tips.

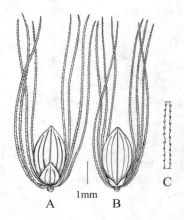

Setaria viridis:
A, spikelet, ventral view;
B, spikelet, dorsal view;
C, part of a bristle.

A summer annual overwintering as dormant seed, *S. viridis* appears to be established in some areas, persisting for several years, and is probably increasing (an indicator of climate change?). It is a major weed in several countries, including Spain, the USA, Canada, Iran and Japan, principally because of its rapid growth to flowering, high seed production and high phenotypic plasticity. It especially infests late-sown spring crops in these countries (Douglas *et al.,* 1985). It is self-pollinating and sometimes agamospermous (producing seed without sexual reproduction), as one might expect from a successful annual weed.

A neophyte, *S. viridis* was first recorded in the wild in Britain in 1666. Native in the warm temperate Old World, it has spread to temperate and subtropical areas throughout the northern hemisphere, and arrives here with birdseed, grain, oilseed, esparto and formerly wool. It is a somewhat polymorphic species in which several varieties have been recognized, some based on bristle colour, and we may have a number of them here.

209. Setaria verticillata (L.) P.Beauv.

Rough Bristle-grass   New Atlas: 803

Very similar to *S. viridis* but with retrorsely barbed bristles and untidily lobed panicles (these often entangled).

S. verticillata has been recorded from widely scattered locations in Britain and in recent times mainly from southern England and the Channel Islands. It is absent from Ireland. It occurs in ruderal and urban habitats including waste ground, docklands, road verges, car parks, garden centres and rubbish tips. It is rare as an arable weed where it sometimes appears in sandy fallow ground. It has a wide range of ruderal associates.

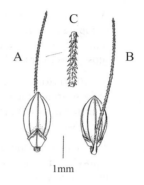

Setaria verticillata:
A, spikelet, ventral view;
B, spikelet, dorsal view;
C, portion of a bristle.

This grass is a summer annual with a very similar population biology and ecology to *S. viridis* and *S. pumila*. It is less successful as an arable weed than these last two species, probably because it is more affected by shading (Steel *et al.,* 1983). It produces dormant seed mainly by self-pollination, but which often develop before the inflorescence emerges and which are readily dispersed in the fur of animals.

Classed as a casual in Britain, *S. verticillata* was first recorded in the wild in 1666. It is native in warm temperate and tropical regions generally (its exact native range is obscured by its spread as a weed) and arrives here in birdseed, oilseed, cotton and esparto (and formerly wool). Populations sometimes persist for a few years, especially in the south.

The species is recognised by the retrorsely barbed bristles that tenaciously cling to fur or clothing. Plants with antrorsely barbed bristles are occasionally found. These are distinguished from *S. viridis* by their untidily lobed panicles (in *S. viridis* these are usually quite neat and smooth in outline) and were formerly taken to represent a hybrid between the two (*S.* ×*verticilliformis* Dumort.; *S. ambigua* Guss.). They are now known not to be a hybrid, but merely a variant of *S. verticillata*. Plants with smaller spikelets and glabrous rather than pubescent leaf-sheaths occur in the more tropical part of the range of the species and are sometimes segregated as a distinct species, *S. adhaerens* (Forssk.) Chiov. The characters do not seem to warrant separation at this rank; variety is probably more appropriate although in tropical Floras the tendency is not to recognize it as distinct at any rank.

210. Setaria italica (L.) P.Beauv.

Foxtail Bristle-grass   New Atlas: 804

A cultivated derivative of *S. viridis*. It is a robust plant up to 150cm with broad drooping panicles up to 30 × 3cm. The bristles scarcely exceed the spikelets and, unusually for a member of the Paniceae, the upper lemma, which is smooth and glossy, drops from the persistent glumes and lower lemma.

S. italica is found as a casual in scattered localities, mainly across southern England but also from time to time further north to the Isle of Man and lowland Scotland. It occurs on waste ground, in gardens and on rubbish tips, and commonly around docks where it has a range of ruderal associates.

This annual Bristle-grass is the familiar 'millet' fed to caged birds, usually as a 'spray', and is unknown as a wild plant. It is thought to have arisen in China more than 5,000 years ago and is grown as a cereal crop in southern Europe (especially Italy, hence the name) and in warm temperate, subtropical and tropical countries throughout the world. It is a quite variable species, with many varieties exhibiting different coloured seed, and at least three cultivated races have been recognized. It is widely naturalized but populations are not established in Britain. It was being cultivated here by 1739 and was recorded in the wild in the early 20th century. It arises from birdseed and as a grain contaminant.

211. Setaria faberi Herrm.

Nodding Bristle-grass   New Atlas CD

Very similar to both *S. pumila* and *S. viridis*, differing from the former by having usually fewer than 5 bristles per spikelet cluster and from the latter by the slightly shorter upper glume that exposes the apical 1/4 of the upper lemma and the nodding rather than erect panicle.

An infrequent casual in southern Britain, *S. faberi* has been recorded from docklands, waste ground and rubbish tips. A handsome grass with nodding panicles it may nonetheless be overlooked in these habitats. It is a regular contaminant of soya bean waste but also arrives in grain, birdseed and oilseed. Native in E Asia, *S. faberi* is naturalized in W Asia, and in N America where it arrived in the 1920s and from where it came to Britain by 1975.

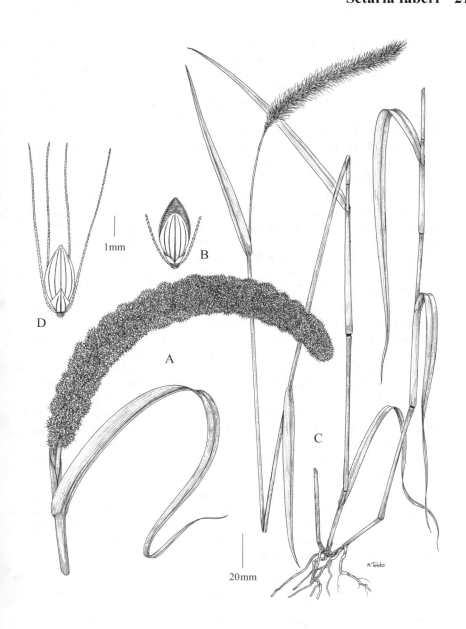

Setaria italica: A, panicle; B, spikelet, dorsal view.
Setaria faberi: C, habit; D, spikelet, ventral view.

212. **Digitaria ischaemum** (Schreb. ex Schweigg.) Schreb. ex Muhl.

Smooth Finger-grass   New Atlas CD

Annual; culms prostrate to erect, up to 40cm; ligules 0.7 – 2.4mm; blades glabrous except at the mouth of the sheath. Racemes 2 – 6, subdigitate on an axis 1.5 – 2cm, the longest 2.5 – 7.5cm; rhachis narrowly winged, 1 – 1.5mm wide, bearing spikelets in groups of 3, at least in the middle part of the raceme. Spikelets 1.9 – 2.4mm, elliptic, obtuse; lower glume an obscure hyaline rim; upper glume nearly as long as the spikelet, 3-nerved, shortly hairy with warty hairs between the nerves; lower lemma as long as the spikelet, flat on the back, 5- to 7-nerved, shortly hairy with warty hairs between the nerves; upper lemma brown, purplish brown or almost black; anthers 0.35 – 0.65mm. $2n = 36, 45$. Flowering and fruiting late July to late September.

A grass of open, disturbed habitats, *D. ischaemum* has been recorded in recent times from only a small number of scattered sites in southern England. Its habitats include cultivated ground, where it has sometimes become established, waste ground, railway sidings and rubbish tips. Its long-established arable populations are generally on sandy soils, and associates in the best known of these (in Surrey) include *Crepis capillaris, Elymus repens, Erodium cicutarium, Geranium molle, Poa annua* and *Stellaria media*. It has occurred as a weed of maize crops.

Smooth Finger-grass and the two following species are strict summer annuals capable under warm conditions of producing large numbers of seed, and have become weeds of cultivation and of managed turf in warmer climates. The seed germinate in the spring, with a higher germination rate in the light than in the dark and, in all three species, buried viable seed banks have been recorded. Seed are probably spread by birds and small rodents which consume them with relish. *D. ischaemum*'s often prostrate growth gives it an advantage as a lawn weed in warmer climates where it invades open ground and dies back leaving seed to establish in the same space the following year, rather like the ecological niche of *Poa annua* in our lawns. It is resistent to trampling and has evolved a number of herbicide-resistent genotypes (as have *D. sanguinalis* and *D. ciliaris*). It is probably inbreeding.

Classed as a neophyte in Britain, *D. ischaemum* was first recorded in the wild here in 1829 (from Weybridge, Surrey). It is a native of warm temperate Eurasia and is extensively naturalized in N America, Australasia and elsewhere. It arrives here in birdseed, soya bean waste and cotton (and formerly with wool shoddy) and hence has tended to be found near ports.

The species is recognised by the dark-coloured 'fruit' and spikelets in groups of three. Two of the spikelets in a group are on short, but unequal, pedicels, the third on a long pedicel. The arrangement thus appears to be pairs of spikelets alternating with solitary spikelets, but the true situation becomes obvious once the spikelets have started to drop. Towards the top and bottom of the raceme

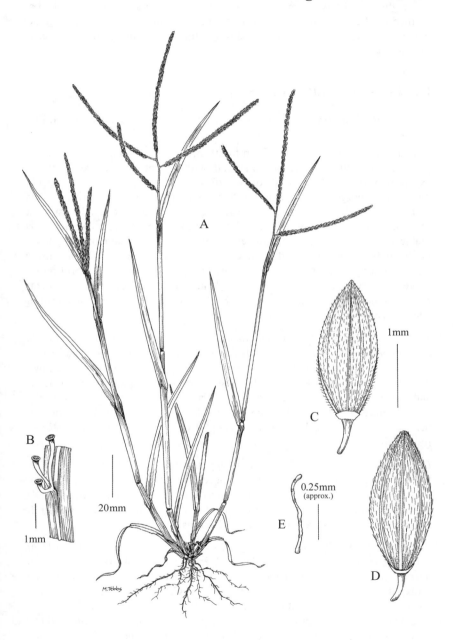

Digitaria ischaemum: A, habit; B, portion of raceme showing group of pedicels;
C, spikelet, ventral view; D, spikelet, dorsal view; E, lemma hair.

571

the third spikelet is usually vestigial or completely suppressed. The hairs on the upper glume and lower lemma are covered in little warts, and are described as verrucose. They also appear to be clavate at the tip but this is an illusion; in fact they are crozier-shaped with curled tips, but this is something only a powerful microscope can reveal.

213. Digitaria sanguinalis (L.) Scop.

Hairy Finger-grass   New Atlas: 804

Annual; culms prostrate to erect, up to 50cm; ligules 1 – 2mm; blades mostly pubescent to stiffly hairy, the hairs smooth with tubercle bases, rarely glabrous except at the mouth of the sheath, often suffused with purple. Racemes 4 – 10(12), digitate or subdigitate on an axis 1 – 2.5cm, the longest 6 – 17cm; rhachis very narrowly winged, 0.8 – 1mm wide, bearing spikelets in pairs, one subsessile, the other pedicellate. Spikelets (2.3)2.5 – 3.1(3.3)mm, ovate-elliptic, subacute; lower glume a minute triangular scale; upper glume 1/3 – 1/2 the length of the spikelet, rarely slightly more, 3-nerved, minutely hairy, especially on the margins; lower lemma as long as the spikelet, flat on the back, 5- to 7-nerved, scabrid on the nerves, sometimes obscurely hairy; upper lemma pallid or grey, often tinged with purple; anthers 0.45 – 0.8mm. $2n = 18, 28, 36 – 48, 54, 76$. Flowering and fruiting late August to late October, sometimes from mid-July.

The most frequent of the three *Digitaria* species described here, *D. sanguinalis* is established in the Channel Islands and the Isles of Scilly as a weed of bulb fields and waste places, and appears to be spreading in southern Britain in a range of habitats including waste ground, garden centres, urban pavements, roadsides and railway sidings. It also occurs as a casual in warm rubbish tips and docks. It has been recorded (rarely) in Scotland and Ireland. Established populations in the south are mostly on light sandy soils but it will grow in a range of disturbed ruderal sites.

D. sanguinalis is very simlar in its biology and ecology to *D. ischaemum* (see that account) and is a widespread and successful weed in warm temperate and subtropical regions. It is probably more tenacious as a lawn weed as, unlike *D. ischaemum*, it roots at the nodes and cannot be pulled easily as an entire plant. In this country the seeds are probably spread in topsoil.

A neophyte in Britain, Hairy Finger-grass was first recorded in the wild in 1690. It is a native of southern Europe, the Mediterranean and SW Asia and has been introduced here and around the world with agricultural seed, grain, oilseed, birdseed and wool. Plues (1867) gives some insight into a possible origin of its name, describing "a less attractive use to which it is applied by those ingenious misappliers of nature's gifts, boys. In some parts of Germany, according to [Mr London's] account, boys prick each others noses with its sharp spikes until they bleed; to this use, or rather abuse, he traces its specific name *sanguinale*".

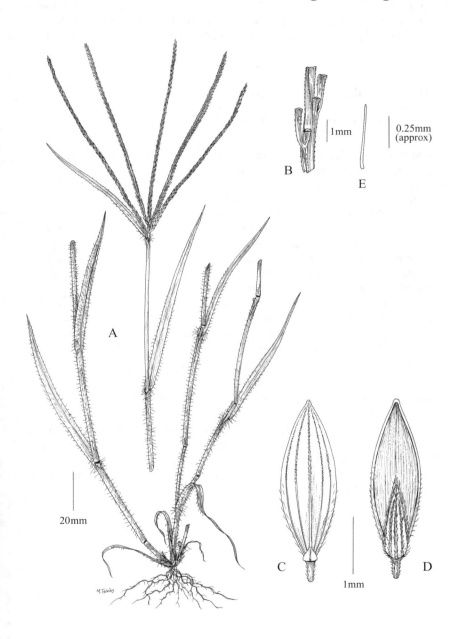

Digitaria sanguinalis: A, habit; B, portion of raceme showing pairs of pedicels;
C, spikelet, ventral view; D, spikelet, dorsal view; E, lemma hair.

The species is recognized by the combination of paired spikelets, sometimes suffused with purple, and hairy leaves and sheaths. The nerves of the lower lemma are characteristically scabrid, but the prickles can be extremely hard to see without high magnification. It is most likely to be confused with the following species.

214. **Digitaria ciliaris** (Retz.) Koeler

Tropical Finger-grass New Atlas CD

Remarkably similar to the above but is generally distinguished by its perfectly smooth nerves on the lower lemma and relatively longer upper glume (2/3 – 3/4 the length of the spikelet, rarely less). Neither character is absolutely reliable and under these circumstances the overall appearance of the plant is helpful. *D. ciliaris* is usually the more robust and luxuriant of the two and seldom has any purple tint in either the leaves or the spikelets; the hairs on the upper glume and lower lemma are usually more prominent. It is the more tropical of the two and is unlikely to become naturalized.

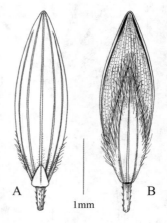

Digitaria ciliaris:
A, spikelet, ventral view;
B, spikelet, dorsal view.

The Tropical (or Southern) Finger-grass seems to have declined in frequency in Britain in recent years, having been recorded from only a handful of sites since 1987, nearly all in southern England. It is found on rubbish tips and occasionally on waste or cultivated ground where it is introduced from the Old World tropics in birdseed, oilseed, soya bean waste and cotton (and formerly wool shoddy). It was recorded in the wild in 1859 (in Surrey) having been cultivated in Britain since the beginning of the 19th century.

215. **Cenchrus echinatus** L.

Illustration, page 577

Spiny Sandbur   New Atlas CD

Annual up to 100cm; panicle 2.5 – 12cm; burs 5 – 10mm; outer bristles terete, mostly not more than half as long as the inner; inner bristles $2 – 5 \times 0.6 – 1.5$mm, flattened, connate for at least half their length into a globose cupule, shortly pubescent; spikelets $2 – 3(4)$ per cupule, 5 – 7mm.

This and the following two species of *Cenchrus* have been recorded as rare or infrequent casuals at locations in southern Britain. They occur on waste ground and rubbish tips.

All three species are summer annuals (although in some climates *C. incertus* may be a biennial or short-lived perennial) and are invasive and often noxious weeds of warm temperate, subtropical and tropical parts of the world. Particularly found in well-drained sandy soils, hence the common name, they invade cultivated land, especially orchards, vineyards, cultivated crops such as maize and alfafa and open grassland. Most *Cenchrus* species are self-pollinating (or apomictic) and the burs are readily dispersed in the fur of animals, in clothing and by flowing water, e.g. in irrigation canals. The burs create a problem in wool and in the hides of animals, affecting the quality of both, and can be injurious to grazing stock. Seeds are inhibited from germinating in the light and can emerge from more than 10cm depth. Plants emerging early in the year can produce several thousand burs (each with 2 – 4 seeds). They require open areas created by disturbance to establish and rarely persist in perennial grassland.

C. echinatus was cultivated in Britain by 1691 and was first found in the wild in 1969. There do not appear to be any recent records. It is native in N & S America and is widely naturalized in tropical regions around the world. It arrived here with wool shoddy, birdseed and soya bean waste.

216. **Cenchrus incertus** M.A.Curtis

Common Sandbur

Annual or short-lived perennial up to 100cm; panicle 3 – 5(8.5)cm; burs 5.5 – 10mm; bristles 8 – 40; outer bristles, when present, mostly flattened; inner bristles 2 – 6 × 1 – 2mm, flattened, connate for at least half their length into an ovoid to globose cupule, their tips diverging from the cupule at irregular intervals, shortly pubescent; spikelets 2 – 4 per cupule, 3.5 – 6mm.

C. incertus is a native of S and C America and southern USA, and has occurred here as a casual of birdseed on tips and waste ground.

217. **Cenchrus longispinus** (Hack.) Fernald

Longspine Sandbur

Annual up to 90cm; panicle 1.5 – 8(10)cm; burs 8.5 – 12mm; bristles 45 – 75; outer bristles numerous, shorter and finer than the inner, terete, often reflexed; inner bristles 3.5 – 7 × 0.5 – (1.5)mm, flattened, connate for at least half their length into a globose cupule, their tips diverging from the cupule at irregular intervals, pubescent to minutely pubescent; spikelets 2 – 3(4) per cupule, 6 – 8mm.

C. longispinus is a native of the Americas and has been introduced into Britain in wool, birdseed and pheasant food (AGB: 101). Each bur of this species has two types of seed, those from the upper spikelets typically germinating within one year, and those from the lower spikelets remaining dormant for longer periods.

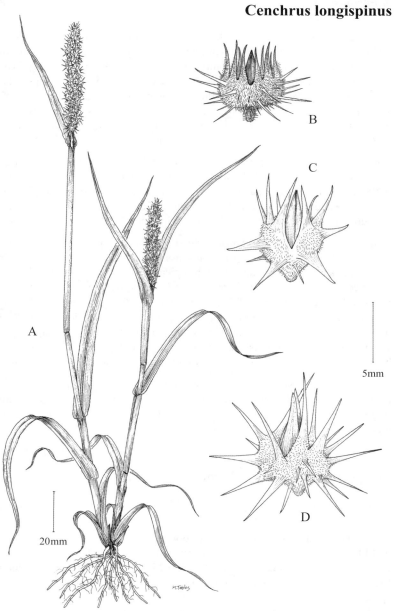

A

B

C

5mm

D

20mm

Cenchrus echinatus: A, habit; B, bur.
Cenchrus incertus: C, bur. *Cenchrus longispinus*: D, bur.

218. **Sorghum halepense** (L.) Pers.

Johnson-grass New Atlas: 805

Rhizomatous perennial ; culms slender to rather stout, up to 1.5m; leaf-sheaths glabrous; leaf-blades up to 90 × 4cm. Panicle lanceolate to pyramidal in outline, 10 – 55cm; primary branches compound, bare at the base, ultimately bearing racemes of 1 – 5 spikelet-pairs. Sessile spikelet 4.5 – 5(5.5)mm, elliptic; lower glume keeled above, the wings of the keels widening upwards to end in minute teeth, forming with the apex a distinctly 3-toothed tip, pilose on the back; upper lemma acute and minutely mucronate to bidentate and with a geniculate awn 10 – 16mm. Pedicelled spikelet 4.5 – 6.5mm, lanceolate, male. $2n = 20, 40$.

Johnson-grass has been recorded from scattered locations in southern England (as far north as S Yorks), Wales and the Channel Islands. It occurs as a casual on rubbish tips and waste ground where it arrives in birdseed, oil-seed, grain, soya bean waste and formerly wool. It has persisted for a few years at one or two sites in southern England but usually disappears in time (AGB: 103).

Considered to be one of the world's worst weeds, the high seed production and extensive rhizome system of Johnson-grass make it difficult to eradicate from cultivated land in warm temperate, subtropical and tropical zones. Its history has involved hybridization with *S. bicolor* and the aggressive weedy tetraploid is likely to have evolved in the USA from crossing between a diploid *S. halepense* introduced for forage from the native Mediterranean populations (from Turkey in 1830 by a Mr Johnson, hence the name) and the primitive sorghum crop. The weedy species readily hybridizes with the crop today and derivatives of this hybridization are widespread. It is classed as a noxious weed in many countries.

Classed as a neophyte in Britain, *S. halepense* was cultivated here by 1691 and recorded from the wild by 1924. It may be increasing (warmer winters?) although it is suggested in the New Atlas that this could reflect an increased interest in recording aliens.

219. **Sorghum bicolor** (L.) Moench

Sorghum, Great Millet New Atlas CD

Annual without rhizomes; culms often robust, up to 2.5m; leaf-sheaths glabrous; leaf-blades usually exceeding 2.5cm in width. Panicle very variable, loose to very dense, erect or with a curved peduncle, up to 25cm; primary branches compound, long or short, bearing stout compound racemes of 2 – 4 spikelet-pairs. Sessile spikelet 4 – 6mm, elliptic to obovate, indehiscent; glumes subequal, pale yellow to chestnut brown or almost black; upper lemma with a weak awn to 10mm. Caryopsis large, broadly obovoid or globular, exposed between the gaping glumes. Pedicelled spikelet 3 – 4mm, lanceolate, barren, persistent. $2n = 20$.

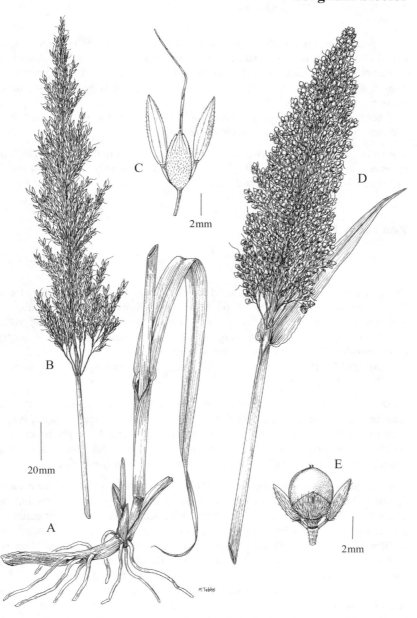

Sorghum halepense: A, base of plant showing rhizome; B, panicle; C, spikelet triad.
Sorghum bicolor: D, panicle; E, spikelet triad.

Scattered in southern Britain and the Channel Islands, Great Millet occurs as a fairly rare casual on rubbish tips, waste ground and, rarely, on cultivated land. Most records are from docklands where it is imported with birdseed and other grains.

Widespread as a cereal in the tropics and on a world scale the 4th most important cereal after wheat, rice and maize, *S. bicolor* is extremely variable, comprising a large number of cultivars (and possibly several subspecies). It is an important crop in Africa, India, SW Asia, the USA and Mexico. It is grown in southern Europe for forage, fodder or to produce grains for animal feed. As a casual here it may not flower and then it may resemble both *Panicum miliaceum* and *Zea mays*. It differs from both by its glabrous leaf-sheaths.

S. bicolor was cultivated in Britain by 1596 and recorded in the wild by 1890. It appears to be increasing as a casual. The species was probably first domesticated in Africa where wild relatives still occur.

220. Zea mays L.

Maize   New Atlas: 805

Robust annual up to 2(4)m; culm solid, erect, 2 – 6cm in diameter, rooting from the lower nodes; leaf-sheaths shortly hairy above; ligule a truncate membrane 3 – 5mm, with short ciliate fringe; leaf-blades clasping the culm, up to 90 × 12(15)cm, flat with undulating margins. Male inflorescence up to 20 × 20cm, erect; spikelets 6 – 15mm. Female inflorescence c.20cm, the spikelets in 8 – 16 rows; styles 15 – 25(40)cm. Caryopsis 5 – 10mm, dorsiventrally flattened, usually cuneiform. $2n = 20$.

Maize has been recorded outside cultivated crops in Britain from scattered locations, mainly in S & E England but as far north as southern Scotland. It has been reported from the Channel Islands and from Ireland. It occurs either as a relic or escape from cultivation on field margins, waste ground and tips or as a casual from grain, birdseed or food refuse, usually on rubbish dumps.

Maize is an extraordinary member of the genus whose other species bear their female spikelets in a single distichous fragile raceme. The permanent attachment of the caryopses to the rhachis and the enclosing leaf-sheaths mean that maize is unable to disperse its seed and persist outside of cultivation. It is quite unknown in the wild and seems to have been domesticated about 7000 years ago in Mexico. It is now the 3rd most important crop in the world (after wheat and rice) and is said to be included in the diet of half the human race. Originally selected by native Americans to grow in environments from Chile to southern Canada, its spread around the world has involved further extensive cultivar selection and breeding, and the displacement of many native crops. Worldwide it is grown for a great variety of products including cereals, animal feed, oils, syrup, alcohol and

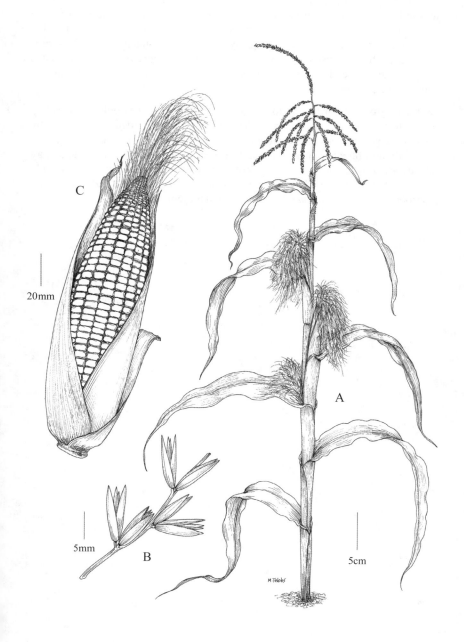

20mm

5mm

5cm

Zea mays: A, habit; B, portion of male raceme; C, cob.

other substances used in industry. In Britain, Maize is grown mainly for animal feed, using the whole plant for silage (mainly in southern Britain but as far north as southern Scotland), but is grown in the south on a smaller scale to produce grain for animal feed or for sweetcorn (cultivars containing genes which delay the conversion of sugar to starch), usually in gardens, allotments, and 'pick-your-own' farms. It is also used for game cover and even in recent years to create maize mazes! The species has been extensively studied by geneticists, including the sequencing of its genome.

A casual, grown in Britain as long ago as 1562, *Z. mays* has only been widely grown here, as forage maize, in the last thirty years. Recorded 'in the wild' by 1876, it may be increasingly seen outside the crop as its use increases. It is likely to remain an obligate cultigen and not become established. As a casual it may not always flower (and the cobs rarely ripen fully) and then it can resemble both *Sorghum* species and *Panicum miliaceum*. In *Sorghum* the leaf-sheaths are glabrous and in *P. miliaceum* they have abundant long-patent hairs.

GLOSSARY

(words in *italics* are cross-referenced within the glossary)

Achene. A fruit in which the hardened pericarp can be separated from the seed (cf. *caryopsis*, *utricle*).

Acuminate. Tapering gradually to a point.

Adnate. Unlike organs which are tightly linked or fused.

Allopolyploid. Taxa originating following hybridisation and chromosome doubling (cf. *autoployploid*).

Amphimitic. Involving true sexual reproduction through fusion of gametes.

Antrorse. Bent or curved forward or upward (cf. *retrorse*).

Apiculate. With a small abruptly ending point.

Appressed. Lying flat against another structure.

Apomixis. Reproduction by seed but without fertilization. Its meaning has varied with time but its use in this book is that defined here.

Aristulate. In the form of a long bristle.

Asperulous. A surface with short, hard projections.

Auricle. Small *falcate* or ear-like outgrowths at the junction of the *sheath* and *blade*.

Autopolyploid. Chromosome multiplication within a single species. (cf. *allopolyploid*)

Awn. Slender, bristle-like projection from the back or tip of a *glume* or *lemma*; often divided into two parts, *column* and *limb*, and may be conspicuously bent (*geniculate*) between the two.

Blade. Sometimes called the *lamina*, that part of the leaf above the *sheath*; often flat, but sometimes folded, involute (the margins rolled inwards) or convolute (rolled-up longitudinally).

Bulliform cells. Clear, thin-walled cells of the epidermis that allow light penetration to the *mesophyll*. They are not, as frequently supposed, actively concerned with the rolling of the leaf to conserve moisture.

C_3 grasses. Mostly temperate species in which CO_2 is taken up by a ribulose diphosphate (5-carbon) receptor molecule which then splits into two molecules of phosphoglycerate, a 3-carbon molecule.

C_4 grasses. Mostly tropical species in which CO_2 is initially taken up by phosphoenol pyruvate (a 3-carbon compound) to form a 4-carbon compound which, after migration to the bundle sheath, is stripped of its CO_2 and fed into the normal photosynthetic cycle.

Callus. A hard projection at the base of a *floret* or *spikelet*, ranging from barely perceptible to elongate and *pungent*.

Capitate. Head-like.

Caryopsis. A form of fruit, characteristic of the grasses, in which the thin fruit wall (*pericarp*) is fused to the seed (cf. *achene*, *utricle*).

Cauline. Attached to the stem.

Chartaceous. Having a parchment or paper-like texture.

Chasmogamous. The condition in which a *floret* opens normally for extrusion of anthers and stigmas.

Chlorenchyma. The chlorophyll-bearing cells of the *mesophyll*.

Ciliate. Fringed with hairs.

Ciliolate. Minutely *ciliate*.

Clavate. Club-shaped.

Cleistogamy. The condition in which fertilization occurs within the unopened *floret*. Such florets are described as cleistogamous.

Cleistogenes. Specialized cleistogamous spikelets on a normally *chasmogamous* plant; they are usually restricted to the lower part of the plant.

Coleoptile. A specialized sheath that protects the plumule during soil penetration.

Coleorhiza. A specialized sheath that protects the radicle during soil penetration.

Collar. A whitish, yellowish or purplish zone at the junction of *sheath* and *blade* visible from the adaxial side. The location of the *plate meristem*.

Collateral. Located side by side.

Column. The basal, or proximal, part of an *awn*; often twisted and capable of untwisting with changes in humidity (and described as hygroscopic).

Connate. Similar structures which are closely joined or united.

Convolute. Rolled up along the longitudinal axis of the structure.

Coriaceous. Having a leathery texture.

Costal zone. The region of the epidermis directly above a vascular bundle.

Crispate. Irregularly curled and twisted.

Crustaceous. Having a hard and brittle texture.

Culm. The flowering stem of a grass.

Cuneate. Wedge shaped, tapering to a narrow base.

Cytotypes. Members of the same taxa with different chromosome complements.

Decurrent. A structure that extends down the stem below its point of insertion.

Deflexed. Turned abruptly downward (cf. *reflexed*)

Digitate. Finger-like.

Disarticulate. To break at a fixed predetermined point.

Ear. The flowerhead of a grass, usually restricted in meaning to that of cultivated cereals.

Elaiosomes. Fleshy structures attached to the seed.

Endosperm. The nutritive content of the seed surrounding the embryo.

Epiblast. A projection of the shoot within the embryo opposite the *scutellum* and sometimes taken to represent a vestigial second cotyledon. Alternatively, it may be viewed as part of the scutellum itself.

Erose. Having an irregularly notched or toothed margin as though chewed.

Excurrent. A structure that extends beyond the margin of that which it is initially part of.

Extravaginal. In which the young vegetative shoot (*innovation*) grows up outside the *sheath* as a result of the bud penetrating the base of the sheath (cf. *intravaginal*).

Falcate. Sickle- or scythe-shaped.

Floret. A structure within the grass *spikelet* comprising *lemma*, *palea* and flower.

Filiform. Wire- or thread-like.

Fimbriate. Fringed.

Fusiform. Spindle-shaped with a thick middle that tapers equally towards the ends.

Geniculate. Abruptly bent, like a knee.

Gibbous. Irregularly rounded, bulging.

Glabrous. Hair-less, Smooth.

Glaucous. Bluish-white in colour.

Glume. One of (usually) two empty scales at the base of the *spikelet*; the outer is the lower glume and the inner is the upper glume.

Hatch-Slack pathway. The typical photosynthetic pathway of tropical (C_4) grasses.

Hilum. The point of attachment of the ovule to the ovary wall and visible in the ripe fruit as a round, oval or linear mark opposite the embryo.

Hispid. With stiff coarse hairs or bristles (cf. *pilose*).

Hyaline. Transparent or translucent.

Imbricate. Overlapping, where the lower structure covers the base of the higher structure.

Indumentum. Covering of fine hairs

Indurated. Hardened.

Innovation. A basal vegetative shoot of a grass; may be *intravaginal* or *extravaginal*.

Intercalary meristem. Meristematic tissue at the *node*.

Intercostal zone. The region of the epidermis between vascular bundles and may contain *long cells*, *short cells*, *microhairs* and stomata.

Internode. The interval between two successive *nodes* of, for example, the *culm*, the *rhachis* or the *rhachilla*.

Intravaginal. In which the young vegetative shoot grows up within the enveloping *sheath*.

Junciform. Rush-like, resembling *Juncus* spp.

Kranz syndrome. The anatomical structures associated with the photosynthetic pathways of C_4 *grasses*.

Lamina. The *blade* of the leaf.

Lanceolate. Long and slender, much longer than wide, with the widest part lower than the middle and ending in a pointed apex.

Lemma. The lower (outer) of the two bracts that enclose the grass flower (cf. *palea*).

Ligule. An outgrowth at the adaxial junction of *sheath* and *blade*, often membranous but sometimes a line of hairs.

Limb. The upper, or distal, part of an *awn*; usually bristle-like.

Lodicule. One of usually two (rarely three) minute scales outside the androecium and probably vestiges of the perianth. They frequently inflate during flowering forcing the *lemma* and *palea* apart to allow extrusion of the anthers and stigmas.

Long cells. Typical elongated cells of the epidermis; they may or may not be interspersed with *short cells*.

Mesocotyl. An interpolated node in the seedling that separates the *coleoptile* from the *scutellum*.

Mesophyll. The ground tissue of the leaf. The vascular bundles are embedded in the mesophyll.

Mestome sheath. A sheath of tissue surrounding the vascular bundle and derived from vascular tissue.

Microhairs. Specialized two-celled hairs in the *intercostal zone* of the epidermis and which may be taxonomically useful at subfamily level.

Moniliform. Cylindrical with contractions at regular intervals, resembling a string of beads.

Monocarpic. Flowering once, then dying (cf. *polycarpic*).

Motor cells. Specialized thin-walled cells within the *mesophyll* that aid light penetration to the *chlorenchyma*.

Mucro. Short, small abrupt tip.

Mucronate. Structure ending suddenly with a stiff spine, tipped with a *mucro*.

Muticous. Not pointed.

Nerve. A vein or rib.

Node. The point at which two successive *internodes* meet, and from whose meristematic tissue (*intercalary meristem*) leaves, adventitious roots and branches arise.

Obovate. Egg shaped with the broader end towards the tip (cf. *ovate*).

Ovate. Egg-shaped with the broader end at the base (cf. *obovate*).

Palea. The upper (inner) of the two bracts that enclose the grass flower. Usually two-keeled and probably a *prophyll* in origin (cf. *lemma*).

Panicle. The classic grass inflorescence derived from a compound *raceme*; varying from open and diffuse to contracted and deceptively *spike*-like.

Parenchyma sheath. A sheath of tissue around the vascular bundle derived from the *mesophyll*. If a *mestome sheath* is present this will be between the vascular bundle and the parenchyma sheath.

Pectinate. Comb-like, having very narrow parallel segments borne at a right angle to the main axis.

Pedicel. The stalk of the *spikelet*.

Pericarp. Carpel tissue that surrounds the solitary ovule.

Pilose. Covered with fine soft hairs (cf. *hispid*).

Plate meristem. Meristematic cells in the *collar* from which tissues of the *blade* are derived.

Plumose. Looking like a feathery plume.

Polycarpic. Flowering more than once, usually in different years (cf. *monocarpic*).

Proliferation. The condition in which the *glumes* and *lemmas* return to their ancestral form of foliage leaf and develop a *blade* at their distal end, the body of the glume or lemma being derived from a sheath. Commonly seen in montane species where it may be obligate, but can occur in many species of lowland grass especially late in the season.

Prophyll. The first leaf of a branch and usually pale in colour and two-keeled in form. It occurs on the adaxial side of the branch and varies considerably in size with location on the plant. The *palea* is likely to be a prophyll in origin.

Protandrous. Pattern of floral development where the pollen is released before the stigmas are receptive (cf. *protogynous*).

Protogynous. Pattern of floral development where the stigmas are receptive before the pollen is released (cf. *protandrous*).

Pruinose. Covered with a pale powdery coating.

Puberulous. Minutely pubescent.

Pungent. Of a *callus*; hard, sharp tips to the leaves.

Raceme. Technically, an indeterminate inflorescence capable of unlimited extension, but in practice its growth is limited. In grasses the term applies to an unbranched inflorescence bearing pedicelled *spikelets*.

Reflexed. Turned abruptly backward.

Retrorse. Bent or curved backward or downward (cf. *antrorse*).

Rhachilla. The axis of a multi-flowered *spikelet*; a one-flowered spikelet may bear a short rhachilla extension beyond the *floret*.

Rhachis. The axis of a *panicle* or *raceme*.

Rhizanthogenes. Highly modified *spikelets* produced on specialized underground rhizomes.

Rugose. Ridged or wrinkled.

Secund. Twisted or turned to one side.

Setaceous. Bristle-like.

Scaberulous. Slightly *scabrid*.

Scabrid. Covered with minute prickles or bristly hairs.

Scarious. Thin, dry and membranaceous.

Sclerenchyma. Lignified cells without protoplasts, commonly associated with the vascular bundles in the *blade*.

Scutellum. A flat haustorial cotyledon.

Scutellum cleft. A space separating the *scutellum* from the *coleorhiza*.

Sessile. Unstalked.

Sheath. The lower part of the grass leaf surrounding the *internode*; its margins may be adjacent, overlapping, contiguous or fused into a cylinder.

Short cells. More or less equidimensional cells of the epidermis, often interspersed among *long cells*.

Silica-bodies. Opaline crystals of silicon dioxide (SiO_2) within the epidermal tissues, often characteristic in shape and sometimes taxonomically useful.

Sinus. Space or indentation.

Spiciform. Spike-like.

Spiculate. Covered with small sharp structures.

Spike. A form of *raceme* in which the *spikelets* are sessile.

Spikelet. The unit of the grass inflorescence comprising (usually) two *glumes* and the enclosed *floret(s)*.

Staminode. Typically modified, sterile stamen.

Sub-. Almost (as in sub*terete*).

Subulate. Tapering regularly from a narrow base to a fine point.

Terete. Rounded in cross-section.

Tiller. An alternative term for *innovation*.

Truncate. Straight or flat.

Tuberculate. Surface covered in small spherical/ellipsoid structures.

Utricle. A fruit in which the soft *pericarp* can be separated from the seed (cf. *caryopsis*, *achene*)

Velutinous. Covered in fine hairs, imparting the appearance of velvet.

Verticillate. Arranged in a whorl.

Villous. Covered with soft, long hairs.

Vivipary. In which the seed germinates while still attached to the parent plant, but in grasses it is frequently used in error for vegetative *proliferation*.

REFERENCES

Arber, A. (1934). *The Gramineae*. Cambridge. Cambridge University Press.

Armstrong, S.F. (1943). *British Grasses and their Employment in Agriculture*. Cambridge. Cambridge University Press.

Aston, J.L. & Bradshaw, A.D. (1966). Evolution in closely adjacent plant populations II. *Agrostis stolonifera* in maritime habitats. *Heredity* **21**: 649-664.

Baldini, R.M. (1995). Revision of the genus *Phalaris* L. (Gramineae). *Webbia* **49**: 265-329.

Barling, D.M. (1962). Studies in the biology of *Poa subcaerulea* Sm. *Watsonia* **5**: 163-173.

Beddows, A.R. (1959). Biological Flora of the British Isles No. 68. *Dactylis glomerata* L. *Journal of Ecology* **47**: 223-239.

Beddows, A.R. (1961). Biological Flora of the British Isles No. 77. *Holcus lanatus* L. *Journal of Ecology* **49**: 421-430.

Beddows, A.R. (1967). Biological Flora of the British Isles No. 107. *Lolium perenne* L. *Journal of Ecology* **55**: 567-587.

Beddows, A.R. (1973). Biological Flora of the British Isles No. 131. *Lolium multiflorum* Lam. *Journal of Ecology* **61**: 587-600.

Blunt, A.G. & Blunt, M.E. (2000). *Corynephorus canescens* (L.) P.Beauv. (Poaceae) at Kinver Edge, Staffordshire; a re-assessment. *Watsonia* **23**: 335-338.

Bolòs, O. de, Masalles, R.M. & Vigo, J. (1988). Notes sobre monocotiledònies. *Collectanea Botanica (Barcelona)* **17**: 95-96.

Bond, T.E.T. (1952). Biological Flora of the British Isles No. 35. *Elymus arenarius* L. *Journal of Ecology* **40**: 217-227.

Bradshaw, A.D. (1959). Population differentiation in *Agrostis tenuis* I. Morphological differentiation. *New Phytologist* **58**: 208-227.

Bradshaw, A.D. & McNeilly, T. (1981). *Evolution and Pollution*. London. Edward Arnold.

Callaghan, T.V. & Lewis, M.C. (1971a). The growth of *Phleum alpinum* L. in contrasting habitats at a sub-antarctic station. *New Phytologist* **70**: 1143-1154.

Callaghan, T.V. & Lewis, M.C. (1971b). Adaptation in the reproductive performance of *Phleum alpinum* L. at a sub-antarctic station. *British Antarctic Survey Bulletin* **26**: 59-75.

Callow, R.S. & Parker, J.S. (1979). Breeding behaviour and population differentiation in the hexaploid grass *Koeleria vallesiana* (Honck.) Bertol. *New Phytologist* **83**: 537-547.

Chadwick, M.J. (1960). Biological Flora of the British Isles No. 73. *Nardus stricta* L. *Journal of Ecology* **48**: 255-267.

Chao, C.S. (1989). *A Guide to Bamboos Grown in Britain*. Royal Botanic Gardens Kew.

Chapman, M.A. & Stace, C.A. (2001). Tor-grass is not *Brachypodium pinnatum*! *BSBI News* **87**: 74.

Chater, A.O. (1993). *Avena strigosa*, Bristle Oat, and other cereals as crops and casuals in Cardiganshire V.C. 46. *BSBI Welsh Bulletin* **55**: 7-14.

Cheffings, C. & Farrell, L. (eds.), (2005). *The Vascular Plant Red Data List for Great Britain,* JNCC Peterborough.

Cheplick, G.P. (ed.) (1998). *Population Biology of Grasses.* Cambridge. Cambridge University Press.

Clark, S.C. (1974). Biological Flora of the British Isles No. 136. *Catapodium rigidum* (L.) C.E.Hubbard. *Journal of Ecology* **62**: 937-958.

Clarke, W.A. (1990). *First Records of British Flowering Plants, ed.2.* London. West, Newman & Co.

Clayton, W.D. & Renvoize, S.A. (1986). *Genera Graminum.* London. HMSO.

Clegg, M.T. & Allard, R.W. (1972). Patterns of genetic differentiation in the slender wild oat species *Avena barbata. Proceedings of the National Academy of Sciences USA* **69**: 1820-1824.

Cope, T.A. (1998). A synopsis of *Eragrostis* Wolf (*Poaceae*) in the Flora Zambesiaca area. *Kew Bulletin* **53**: 129-164.

Crackles, F.E. (1994). *Calamagrostis stricta* (Timm) Koeler, *C. canescens* (Wigg.) Roth and their hybrids in S.E.Yorks., v.c.61, northern England. *Watsonia* **20**: 51-60.

Crackles, F.E. (1995). A graphical analysis of the characters of *Calamagrostis stricta* (Timm) Koeler, *C. canescens* (Wigg.) Roth and their hybrid populations in S.E.Yorks. v.c.61, northern England. *Watsonia* **20**: 397-404.

Crackles, F.E. (1997). Variation in some populations of *Calamagrostis stricta* (Timm) Koeler in the British Isles and the putative past hybridization with *C. canescens* (Wigg.) Roth. *Watsonia* **21**: 341-354.

Cronberg, N., Widén, B. & Bothmer, R. von (1997). Genetic diversity and phenotypic variation in marginal populations of the locally endangered species *Hordeum secalinum* (*Poaceae*). *Plant Systematics and Evolution* **206**: 285-294.

Curtis, T.G.F. & McGough, H.N. (1988). *The Irish Red Data Book I. Vascular Plants.* Dublin. Stationery Office.

Curtis, W. (1805). *Practical Observations on the British Grasses, ed.4.* London. H.D. Symonds.

Cussans, J. & Morton, A. (1990). The distribution of the subspecies of *Arrhenatherum elatius. BSBI News* **55**: 18-19.

Davison, A.W. (1977). The ecology of *Hordeum murinum* L. III. Some effects of adverse climate. *Journal of Ecology* **65**: 523-530.

Davy, A.J. (1980). Biological Flora of the British Isles No. 149. *Deschampsia caespitosa* (L.) Beauv. *Journal of Ecology* **68**: 1075-1096.

Dixon, J.M. (1982). Biological Flora of the British Isles No. 151. *Sesleria albicans* Kit. ex Schultes. *Journal of Ecology* **70**: 667-684.

Dixon, J.M. (1988). Notes on *Avenula pratensis* (L.) Dumort. in Britain. *Watsonia* **17**: 159-162.

Dixon, J.M. (1991). Biological Flora of the British Isles No. 173. *Avenula pratensis* (L.) Dumort. (pp. 829-846), *Avenula pubescens* (Hudson) Dumort. (pp. 846-865). *Journal of Ecology* **79**: 829-865.

Dixon, J.M. (1995). Biological Flora of the British Isles No. 187. *Trisetum flavescens* (L.) Beauv. *Journal of Ecology* **83**: 895-909.

Dixon, J.M. (2000). Biological Flora of the British Isles No. 212. *Koeleria macrantha* (Ledeb.) Schultes. *Journal of Ecology* **88**: 709-726.

Dixon, J.M. (2001). On the status of the genus *Koeleria* Pers. (Poaceae) in Britain. *Watsonia* **23**: 377-390.

Dixon, J.M. (2002). Biological Flora of the British Isles No. 224. *Briza media* L. *Journal of Ecology* **90**: 737-752.

Doğan, M. (1999). A concise taxonomic revision of the genus *Alopecurus* L. (*Gramineae*). *Turkish Journal of Botany* **23**: 245-262.

Douglas, B.J., Thomas, A.G., Morrison, I.N. & Marr, M.G. (1985). The biology of Canadian weeds, 70. *Setaria viridis* (L.) Beauv. *Canadian Journal of Plant Science* **65**: 669-690.

Druce, G.C. (1932). *The Comital Flora of the British Isles*. Arbroath. T.Buncle & Co.

Easy, G.M.S. (1992). 'Breckland bent' in Cambridgeshire. *Nature in Cambridgeshire* **34**: 43-45.

Ennos, R.A. (1985). The mating system and genetic structure in a perennial grass, *Cynosurus cristatus* L. *Heredity* **55**: 121-126.

Ernst, W.H.O. & Malloch, A.J.C. (1994). Biological Flora of the British Isles No. 181. *Phleum arenarium* L. *Journal of Ecology* **82**: 403-413.

Ferris, C., Callow, R.S. & Gray, A.J. (1992). Mixed first and second division restitution in male meiosis of *Hierochloe odorata* (L.) Beauv. (Holy Grass). *Heredity* **69**: 21-31.

Ferris, C., King, R. & Gray, A.J. (1997). Molecular evidence for the maternal parentage in the hybrid origin of *Spartina anglica* C.E.Hubbard. *Molecular Ecology* **6**: 185-187.

FitzGerald, R. (1989). 'Lost and found' – *Alopecurus bulbosus* Gouan in S.E.England. *Watsonia* **17**: 425-428.

Fletcher, R. & Stace, C.A. (2000). A new section and species of *Festuca* (Poaceae) naturalized in England. *Watsonia* **23**: 173-177.

Foley, M.J.Y. & Porter, M.S. (2006). *Calamagrostis scotica* (Druce) Druce (Poaceae), a Red Data Book Plant: its history, taxonomy, ecology and genetics. *Watsonia* **26**: 51-55.

Francis, S.A. (2005). *British Field Crops*. Bury St Edmunds. Sally Francis.

Fryxell, P.A. (1957). Mode of reproduction of higher plants. *Botanical Review* **23**: 135-233.

Gibson, D.J. & Newman, J.A. (2001). Biological Flora of the British Isles No. 217. *Festuca arundinacea* Schreber (*F. elatior* L. ssp. *arundinacea* (Schreber) Hackel). *Journal of Ecology* **89**: 304-324.

Gibson, D.J. & Taylor, I. (2003). Performance of *Festuca arundinacea* Schreber (Poaceae) populations in England. *Watsonia* **24**: 413-426.

Gibson, D.J. & Taylor, I. (2005). Biological Flora of the British Isles No. 238. *Festuca longifolia* Thuill. (*F. glauca* auct. non Vill., *F. glauca* var. *caesia* (Sm.) Howarth, *F. caesia* Sm.). *Journal of Ecology* **93**: 214-226.

Goodman, P.J., Braybrooks, E.M., Marchant, C.J. & Lambert, J.M. (1969). Biological Flora of the British Isles No. 116. *Spartina* × *townsendii* H. & J.Groves sensu lato, *Spartina alterniflora* × *Spartina maritima*. *Journal of Ecology* **57**: 293-313.

Gordon, W.J. (undated, possibly 1907). *Manual of British Grasses*. London. Simpkin, Marshall, Hamilton, Kent & Co.

Grass Phylogeny Working Group (2001). Phylogeny and subfamilial classification of the grasses (Poaceae). *Annals of the Missouri Botanical Garden* **88**: 373-457.

Graves, G. (1822). *A Monograph on the British Grasses*. London. W. & S.Graves.

Gray, A.J. (1986). Do invading species have definable genetic characteristics? *Philosophical Transactions of the Royal Society London B* **314**: 655-675.

Gray, A.J. (1988). Demographic and genetic variation in a post-fire population of *Agrostis curtisii*. *Acta Oecologica* **9**: 31-41.

Gray, A.J. (1993). The vascular plant pioneers of primary succession: persistence and phenotypic plasticity. *Primary succession on land* (ed. J.Miles & D.W.H.Walton), pp. 179-191. Oxford. Blackwell Scientific Publications.

Gray, A.J. & Mogg, R.J. (2001). Climate impacts on pioneer saltmarsh plants. *Climate Research* **18**: 105-112.

Gray, A.J. & Scott, R. (1977). Biological Flora of the British Isles No. 140. *Puccinellia maritima* (Huds.) Parl. *Journal of Ecology* **65**: 699-716.

Gray, A.J., Marshall, D.F. & Raybould, A.F. (1991). A century of evolution in *Spartina anglica*. *Advances in Ecological Research* **21**: 1-62.

Greenwood, E.F. (2004). Coastal *Elytrigia* species and hybrids in north-western England and northern Wales. *BSBI News* **95**: 15-19.

Grime, J.P., Hodgson, J.G. & Hunt, R. (2007). *Comparative plant ecology, ed.2*. London. Unwin Hyman.

Halliday, G. (1995). Two subspecies of *Festuca rubra* L. new to England. *Watsonia* **20**: 412.

Halliday, G. (1997). *A Flora of Cumbria*. Centre for North West Regional Studies. Lancaster. University of Lancaster.

Harberd, D.J. (1961). Observations on population structure and longevity of *Festuca rubra*. *New Phytologist* **60**: 184-210.

Harberd, D.J. (1962). Some observations on natural clones in *Festuca ovina*. *New Phytologist* **61**: 85-100.

Harberd, D.J. (1967). Observations on natural clones in *Holcus mollis*. *New Phytologist* **66**: 401-408.

Harmer, R. & Lee, J.A. (1978a). The growth and nutrient content of *Festuca vivipara* (L.) Sm. plantlets. *New Phytologist* **80**: 99-106.

Harmer, R. & Lee, J.A. (1978b). The germination and viability of *Festuca vivipara* (L.) Sm. plantlets. *New Phytologist* **81**: 745-751.

Harris, D. & Davy, A.J. (1986). Regenerative potential of *Elymus farctus* from rhizome fragments and seed. *Journal of Ecology* **74**: 1057-1067.

Haslam, S.M. (1972). Biological Flora of the British Isles No. 128. *Phragmites communis* Trin. *Journal of Ecology* **60**: 585-610.

Hindmarch, C. & Pienkowsky, M.W. (eds.) (1998). *Land Management: The Hidden Costs*. British Ecological Society. Oxford. Blackwell Scientific Publications.

Holloway, M. (2004). A new site for *Leersia oryzoides* in Surrey. *BSBI News* **96**: 36-37.

Hubbard, C.E. (1954). *Grasses*. Harmondsworth, Middlesex. Pelican Books.

Hubbard, C.E. (1968). *Grasses, ed.2*. Harmondsworth, Middlesex. Pelican Books.

Hubbard, C.E. ed. J.C.E.Hubbard (1984). *Grasses, ed.3*. London. Penguin Books.

Hughes, M.G.B. (1984). *Deschampsia setacea* (Hudson) Hackel new to south-western England. *Watsonia* **15**: 34-36.

Huiskes, A.H.L. (1979). Biological Flora of the British Isles No. 144. *Ammophila arenaria* (L.) Link. *Journal of Ecology* **67**: 363-382.

Hutchinson, C.S. & Seymour, G.B. (1982). Biological Flora of the British Isles No. 153. *Poa annua* L. *Journal of Ecology* **70**: 887-901.

Ivimey-Cook, R.B. (1959). Biological Flora of the British Isles No. 71. *Agrostis setacea* Curt. *Journal of Ecology* **47**: 697-706.

Jones, K. (1958). Cytotaxonomic studies in *Holcus* I. The chromosome complex in *Holcus mollis* L. *New Phytologist* **57**: 191-198.

Kerguelén, M. & Plonka, F. (1989). *Les Festuca de la Flore de France*. Société Botanique du Centre-Ouest. Dignac. La Clef d'Or.

Kik, C. (1987). *On the ecological genetics of the clonal perennial Agrostis stolonifera*. Published PhD thesis. University of Gröningen.

Knapp, J.L. (1804). *Gramina Britannica*. London. T.Bensley.

Koch, S.D. & Sánchez Vega, I. (1985). *Eragrostis mexicana, E. neomexicana, E. orcuttiana* and *E. virescens*: the resolution of a taxonomic problem. *Phytologia* **58**: 377-381.

Lambert, J.M. (1947). Biological Flora of the British Isles No. 17. *Glyceria maxima* (Hartm.) Holmb. *Journal of Ecology* **34**: 310-344.

Leach, S.J. & Pearman, D.A. (2003). An assessment of the status of *Gaudinia fragilis* (L.) P.Beauv. (Poaceae) in the British Isles. *Watsonia* **24**: 469-487.

Lodge, R.W. (1959). Biological Flora of the British Isles No. 70. *Cynosurus cristatus* L. *Journal of Ecology* **47**: 511-518.

Lovatt, G.M. (1981). The history, ecology and status of *Gastridium ventricosum* (Gouan) Schinz & Thell. in the Avon Gorge, Bristol. *Watsonia* **13**: 287-298.

Löve, Á. (1984). Conspectus of the Triticeae. *Feddes Repertorium* **95**: 425-521.

Lyte, B. & Cope, T.A. (1999). Plants in peril: 25 *Bromus interruptus*. *Curtis's Botanical Magazine* **16**: 296-300.

Marchant, C.J. & Goodman, P.J. (1969). Biological Flora of the British Isles No. 116. *Spartina maritima* (Curtis) Fernald (pp. 287-291), *Spartina alterniflora* (pp. 291-295), *Spartina glabra* Muhl. (pp. 295-297). *Journal of Ecology* **57**: 287-297.

Marshall, J.K. (1967). Biological Flora of the British Isles No. 105. *Corynephorus canescens* (L.) P.Beauv. *Journal of Ecology* **55**: 207-220.

Maskell, L.C. & Raybould, A.F. (2001). The decline of *Spartina alterniflora* (Poaceae) in the British Isles. *Watsonia* **23**: 391-400.

Maun, M.A. & Barrett, S.C.H. (1986). The biology of Canadian weeds, 77. *Echinochloa crus-galli* (L.) Beauv. *Canadian Journal of Plant Science* **66**: 739-759.

Naylor, R.E.L. (1972). Biological Flora of the British Isles No. 129. *Alopecurus myosuroides* Huds. *Journal of Ecology* **60**: 611-622.

Nygren, A. (1962). Artificial and natural hybridization in European Calamagrostis. *Symbolae Botanicae Upsaliensis* **17(3)**: 1-105.

Oliver, J. (1998). Vigorous variants of *Brachypodium pinnatum* in N.Wilts and Gloucs. *BSBI News* **79**: 44-49.

Oliver, J. (2001a). Vigour and variably compound inflorescences and profuse seeding in *Brachypodium pinnatum*. *BSBI News* **86**: 31-34.

Oliver, J. (2001b). Hyperfertility and vigorous progeny in three anomalous types of flowering plant. *BSBI News* **88**: 32-36.

Olonova, M.V. (1990, English translation 2001). *Poa* L. in Malyschev, L.I. & Peschkova, G.A. (eds.) *Flora Sibiri* **2**: 165-189. Nauka Publishers, Siberian Division.

Ortiz, S., Rodríguez-Oubiña, J. & Guitián, P. (1999). Taxonomic characterization of littoral sabuline populations of *Mibora minima* (Poaceae) in northwestern Iberian Peninsula. *Nordic Journal of Botany* **19**: 581-586.

Oswald, P. H. (2006) *Anemanthele lessoniana* (*Stipa arundinacea*) in Cambridge *BSBI News* **102**: 50

D'Ovidio, R. & Lucchese, F. (1986). Chromosomal races in the *Brachypodium rupestre* complex in Italy. *Annali di Botanica* **44**: 175-180.

Ovington, J.D. & Scurfield, G. (1956). Biological Flora of the British Isles No. 54. *Holcus mollis* L. *Journal of Ecology* **44**: 272-280.

Palmer, J.H. & Sagar, G.R. (1963). Biological Flora of the British Isles No. 93. *Agropyron repens* (L.) Beauv. *Journal of Ecology* **51**: 783-794.

Pearman, D.A. (1990). *Alopecurus bulbosus* Gouan in Dorset. *Watsonia* **18**: 206-207.

Perring, F.H. & Sell, P.D. (eds.) (1968). *Critical Supplement to the Atlas of the British Flora*. London. Thomas Nelson & Sons.

Perring, F.H., Sell, P.D., Walters, S.M. & Whitehouse, H.L.K. (1964). *A Flora of Cambridgeshire*. Cambridge. Cambridge University Press.

Peterkin, G.F. (1981). *Woodland Conservation and Management*. London. Chapman & Hall.

Pfitzenmeyer, D.C. (1962). Biological Flora of the British Isles No. 81. *Arrhenatherum elatius* (L.) J.& C.Presl. *Journal of Ecology* **50**: 235-245.

Plues, M. (1867). *British Grasses*. London. Reeve & Co.

Portal, R. (1999). *Festuca de France*. Vals-prés Le Puy. Robert Portal.

Preston, C.D. & Croft, J.M. (1997). *Aquatic Plants in Britain and Ireland*. Colchester. Harley Books.

Preston, C.D. & Hill, M.O. (1997). The geographical relationships of British and Irish vascular plants. *Botanical Journal of the Linnean Society* **124**: 1-120.

Preston, C.D., Pearman, D.A. & Dines, T.D. (2002). *New Atlas of the British & Irish Flora*. Oxford. Oxford University Press.

Raybould, A.F., Gray, A.J., Lawrence, M.J. & Marshall, D.F. (1990). The taxonomy and status of *Spartina* × *neyrauti. Watsonia* **18**: 207-209.

Raybould, A.F., Gray, A.J., Lawrence, M.J. & Marshall, D.F. (1991a). The evolution of *Spartina anglica* C.E.Hubbard (Gramineae): origin and genetic variability. *Biological Journal of the Linnean Society* **43**: 111-126.

Raybould, A.F., Gray, A.J., Lawrence, M.J. & Marshall, D.F. (1991b). The evolution of *Spartina anglica* C.E.Hubbard (Gramineae): genetic variation and status of the parental species in Britain. *Biological Journal of the Linnean Society* **44**: 369-380.

Rich, T.C.G. (1997). Wildlife reports: Flowering plants – England. *British Wildlife* **8**: 328.

Rich, T.C.G. & Lockton, A.J. (2002). *Bromus interruptus* (Hack.) Druce (Poaceae) – an extinct English endemic. *Watsonia* **24**: 69-80.

Rich, T.C.G. & Rich, M.D.B. (1988). *Plant Crib*. London. Botanical Society of the British Isles.

Ridley, H.N. (1930). *The Dispersal of Plants Throughout the World*. Ashford. Reeve.

Rihan, J.R. & Gray, A.J. (1991). The distribution of hybrid Marram grass, × *Calammophila baltica* (Flugge) Brand. in the British Isles. *Watsonia* **18**: 369-379.

Roberts, F.J. & Halliday, G (1979). The altitudinal range of *Catabrosa aquatica* (L.) Beauv. *Watsonia* **12**: 342-343.

Ryves, T.B., Clement, E.J. & Foster, M.C. (1996). *Alien Grasses of the British Isles*. London. Botanical Society of the British Isles.

Sales, F. (1993). Taxonomy and nomenclature of *Bromus* sect. *Genea. Edinburgh Journal of Botany* **50**: 1-31.

Sargent, C., Mountford, O. & Greene, D. (1986). The distribution of *Poa angustifolia* L. in Britain. *Watsonia* **16**: 31-36.

Schippmann, U. (1986). Über Brachypodium rupestre (Host) Roemer & Schultes in Bayern. Unterscheidung und Verbreitung. *Berichte der Bayerischen Botanischen Gesellschaft* **57**: 53-56.

Schippmann, U. (1991). Revision der europäischen Arten der Gattung Brachypodium Palisot de Beauvois. *Boissiera* **45**: 1-250.

Scholz, H. (1968). Die Artbestimmung im Brachypodium pinnatum-Komplex. *Willdenowia* **5**: 113-118.

Schouten, Y. & Veldkamp, J.F. (1985). A revision of Anthoxanthum including Hierochloë (Gramineae) in Malesia and Thailand. *Blumea* **30**: 319-351.

Scott, N.E. (1985). The updated distribution of maritime species on British roadsides. *Watsonia* **15**: 381-386.

Scott, N.E. & Davison, A.W. (1982). De-icing salt and the invasion of road verges by maritime plants. *Watsonia* **14**: 41-52.

Scurfield, G. (1954). Biological Flora of the British Isles No. 39. *Deschampsia flexuosa* (L.) Trin. *Journal of Ecology* **42**: 225-233.

Sell, P.D. & Murrell, G. (1996). *Flora of Great Britain and Ireland, 5. Butomaceae – Orchidaceae*. Cambridge. Cambridge University Press.

Skálová, H., Pecháčková, S., Suzuki, J., Herben, T., Hara, T., Hadincová, V. & Krahulec, F. (1997). Within population genetic differentiation in traits affecting clonal growth: *Festuca rubra* in a mountain grassland. *Journal of Evolutionary Biology* **10**: 383-406.

Smith, P. (1968a). The *Bromus mollis* aggregate in Britain. *Watsonia* **6**: 327-344.

Smith, P. (1968b). Serological distinctness of *Bromus pseudosecalinus* P.Smith sp. nov. *Feddes Repertorium* **77**: 61-64.

Smith, R.E.N. & Margetts, L.J. (2001). *Festuca longifolia* Thuill. (Poaceae) in Devon. *Watsonia* **23**: 533-538.

Snaydon, R.W. & Davies, M.S. (1976). Rapid population differentiation in a mosaic environment 2: Morphological variation in *Anthoxanthum odoratum*. *Evolution* **26**: 390-405.

Spalton, L.M. (2002). An analysis of the characters of *Bromus racemosus* L., *B. commutatus* Schrad. and *B. secalinus* L. (Poaceae). *Watsonia* **24**: 193-202.

Stace, C.A. (1961). *Nardurus maritimus* (L.) Murb. in Britain. *Proceedings of the Botanical Society of the British Isles* **4**: 248-261.

Stace, C.A. (ed.) (1975). *Hybridisation and the Flora of the British Isles*. London. Academic Press.

Stace, C.A. (1991). *New Flora of the British Isles*. Cambridge. Cambridge University Press.

Stace, C.A. (1997). *New Flora of the British Isles, ed.2*. Cambridge. Cambridge University Press.

Stace, C.A. (2001). The interspecific hybrids of the rhizomatous couches, *Elytrigia* Desv. (Poaceae). *Watsonia* **23**: 543-547.

Steel, M.G., Cavers, P.B. & Lee, S.M. (1983). The biology of Canadian weeds, 59. *Setaria glauca* (L.) Beauv. and *S. verticillata* (L.) Beauv. *Canadian Journal of Plant Science*. **63**: 711-725.

Stewart, A., Pearman, D.A. & Preston, C.D. (eds.) (1994). *Scarce Plants in Britain*. Peterborough. Joint Nature Conservation Committee.

Taylor, K., Rowland, A.P. & Jones, H.E. (2001). Biological Flora of the British Isles No. 216. *Molinia caerulea* (L.) Moench. *Journal of Ecology* **89**: 126-144.

Tripathi, R.S. & Harper, J.L. (1973). The comparative biology of *Agropyron repens* (L.) Beauv. and *A. caninum* (L.) Beauv. I. The growth of mixed populations established from tillers and seeds. *Journal of Ecology* **61**: 353-358.

Trist, P.J.O. (1981). The survival of *Alopecurus bulbosus* Gouan in former sea-flooded marshes in East Suffolk. *Watsonia* **13**: 313-316.

Trist, P.J.O. (1983). The past and present status of *Gastridium ventricosum* (Gouan) Schinz & Thell. as an arable colonist in Britain. *Watsonia* **14**: 257-261.

Trist, P.J.O. (1986a). A reconsideration of the taxonomic status of *Poa balfourii* Parnell (Gramineae). *Watsonia* **16**: 37-42.

Trist, P.J.O. (1986b). The distribution, ecology, history and status of *Gastridium ventricosum* (Gouan) Schinz & Thell. in the British Isles. *Watsonia* **16**: 43-54.

Trist, P.J.O. (1998a) in Rich, T.C.G. & Jermy, A.C. (eds.). *Plant Crib*. London. Botanical Society of the British Isles.

Trist, P.J.O. (1998b). The distribution and status of *Corynephorus canescens* (L.) P.Beauv. (Poaceae) in Britain and the Channel Islands with particular reference to its conservation. *Watsonia* **22**: 41-47.

Trist, P.J.O. & Butler, J.K. (1995). *Puccinellia distans* (Jacq.) Parl. subsp. *borealis* (O.Holmb.) W.E.Hughes (Poaceae) in mainland Scotland and the Outer Isles. *Watsonia* **20**: 391-396.

Trist, P.J.O. & Sell, P.D. (1988). Two subspecies of *Molinia caerulea* (L.) Moench in the British Isles. *Watsonia* **17**: 153-157.

Trist, P.J.O. & Wilkinson, M.J. (1989). *Alopecurus* × *plettkei* Mattfield in Britain. *Watsonia* **17**: 301-307.

Tutin, T.G., Heywood, V.H., Burges, N.A., Moore, D.M., Valentine, D.H., Walters, S.M. & Webb, D.A. (eds.). (1980) *Flora Europaea 5, Alismataceae to Orchidaceae*. Cambridge. Cambridge University Press.

Tzvelev, N.N. (1976). *Zlaki SSSR*. Leningrad. Academy of Sciences of the USSR.

Tzvelev, N.N. (2004). The new genus *Pseudosclerochloa* and the new species *Puccinellia qinghaica* of the family *Poaceae*. *Botankcheskii Zhurnal* **89**: 839-842.

Van der Putten, W.H. (1993). Soil organisms in coastal foredunes involved in degeneration of *Ammophila arenaria*. In Miles, J. & Walton, D.W.H. (eds.) *Primary Succession on Land*, pp. 273-281. Oxford. Blackwell Scientific Publications.

Vegetti, C. & Anton, A.M. (2000). The grass inflorescence, in Jacobs, S.W.L. & Everett, J. (eds.), *Grass Systematics and Evolution*. Melbourne. CSIRO.

Warren, J.M., Raybould, A.F., Ball, T., Gray, A.J. & Hayward, M.D. (1998). Genetic structure in the perennial grasses *Lolium perenne* and *Agrostis curtisii*. *Heredity* **81**: 556-562.

Watkinson, A.R. (1978). Biological Flora of the British Isles No. 143. *Vulpia fasciculata* (Forskal) Samp. *Journal of Ecology* **66**: 1033-1049.

Watkinson, A.R., Newsham, K.K. & Forrester, L. (1998). Biological Flora of the British Isles No. 201. *Vulpia ciliata* Dumort. ssp. *ambigua* (Le Gall) Stace & Auquier. *Journal of Ecology* **86**: 690-705.

Weimarck, G. (1971). Variation and taxonomy of Hierochloë in the northern hemisphere. *Botaniska Notiser* **124**: 129-175.

Wentworth, J.E., Sieber, V.K. & Ferris, C. (2004). As assessment of the origin of *Alopecurus geniculatus* L. based on 2C DNA amounts, NOR sites, RAPDs and cpDNA analysis. *Watsonia* **25**: 137-155.

Wigginton, M.J. (ed.) (1999). *British Red Data Books I. Vascular Plants, ed.3*. Peterborough. Joint Nature Conservation Committee.

Wilkinson, M.J. & Stace, C.A. (1989). The taxonomic relationships and typification of *Festuca brevipila* Tracey and *F. lemanii* Bastard (Poaceae). *Watsonia* **17**: 289-299.

Wilkinson, M.J. & Stace, C.A. (1991). A new taxonomic treatment of the *Festuca ovina* L. aggregate (Poaceae) in the British Isles. *Botanical Journal of the Linnean Society* **106**: 347-397.

Wilson, A. (1949). *Altitudinal Range of British Plants*. Arbroath. T.Buncle & Co.

INDEX TO GENERA & SPECIES

Numbers refer to species accounts, not pages; numbers prefixed by G refer to generic entries. Accepted names are in **bold**, synonyms are in *italic*. Hybrid formulae are given in Roman and are strictly in alphabetical order of parents.

INDEX TO ENGLISH NAMES

The Botanical Society of the British Isles

The BSBI is for everyone who is interested in the flora of Britain and Ireland. It traces its origins back to 1836, when it was founded as the Botanical Society of London. From its earliest days it has welcomed both professional and amateur members, and it remains the biggest and most active organisation devoted to the study of botany in the British Isles.

Information on the status and distribution of British and Irish flowering plants, ferns and charophytes is gathered through a network of vice-county recorders; this is the basis for plant atlases, county Floras and publications on rare and scarce species and is vital for botanical conservation. The BSBI was a major partner in the production of *New Atlas of the British and Irish Flora* and a related CD-ROM published by Oxford University Press in September 2002. The Society also maintains a varied and useful website at www.bsbi.org.uk.

The BSBI organises plant distribution surveys, publishes handbooks on difficult groups of plants and has national referees available to members to name problematic specimens. Conferences and field meetings are held throughout Britain and Ireland and sometimes abroad. The society also publishes a scientific journal, *Watsonia,* and conference reports. Members are kept informed by a newsletter three times a year.

An education programme supported by the BSBI aims to bring high-quality botanical training within the reach of all, from A Level students to professional development and postgraduate courses.

Details of membership and other information about the BSBI maybe obtained from The Hon. General Secretary, Botanical Society of the British Isles, c/o Department of Botany, The Natural History Museum, Cromwell Road, London SW7 5BD.

The following books are available from the official agents for BSBI publications, Summerfield Books, 3 Phoenix Park, Skelton, Penrith, Cumbria, CA11 9SD (Telephone 01768 484909; Fax 01768 484910; Email: info@summerfieldbooks.com. Full details are available on this website: www.summerfieldbooks.com/bsbi-publications.asp.

BSBI handbooks

Each handbook deals in depth with one or more difficult groups of British and Irish plants.

No. 1   *Sedges of the British Isles* – A. C. Jermy, D. A. Simpson, M. J. Y. Foley & M. S. Porter. Third edition, 2007, incorporating full accounts of the 76 species and subspecies of *Carex* in addition to the other 35 British species of Cyperaceae plus 47 hybrids. 566 pp., with descriptions, line drawings and distribution maps. A5 paperback. [Previous editions 1968 and 1982].

No. 2   *Umbellifers of the British Isles* – T. G. Tutin. 1980, reprinted 2006. 200 pp., with descriptions of 73 species facing line drawings by Ann Farrer. Small paperback.

No. 3   *Docks and knotweeds of the British Isles* – J. E. Lousley & D. H. Kent. 1981. Out of print.

No. 4 **Willows and poplars of Great Britain and Ireland** – R. D. Meikle. 1984, reprinted 2006. 200 pp., with descriptions of 65 species, subspecies, varieties and hybrids of *Salix* and *Populus*, illustrated with line drawings by Victoria Gordon. Small paperback.

No. 5 **Charophytes of Great Britain and Ireland** – Jenny A. Moore. 1986, reprinted 2005 with a new preface and corrections by C. D. Preston. 144 pp., with descriptions of 39 species and varieties of Characeae (stoneworts), line drawings by Margaret Tebbs and 17 distribution maps. Small paperback.

No. 6 **Crucifers of Great Britain and Ireland** – T. C. G. Rich. 1991, reprinted 2006. 344 pp., with descriptions of 148 taxa of Brassicaceae (Cruciferae), 129 of them with line drawings by various artists, and 60 distribution maps. Small paperback.

No. 7 **Roses of Great Britain and Ireland** - G. G. Graham & A. L. Primavesi. 1993, reprinted with corrections 2005. 208 pp., with descriptions, facing line drawings by Margaret Gold, of 13 native and nine introduced taxa of *Rosa,* briefer descriptions of 76 hybrids, and 33 maps. A5 paperback.

No. 8 **Pondweeds of Great Britain and Ireland** – C. D. Preston. 1995, reprinted 2003. 352 pp., with descriptions and line drawings of all 50 species and hybrids of *Potamogeton*, *Groenlandia* and *Ruppia*, most with distribution maps; detailed introductory material and bibliography. A5 paperback.

No. 9 **Dandelions of Great Britain and Ireland** - A. A. Dudman & A. J. Richards. 1997, reprinted with minor alterations 2000. 344 pp., with descriptions of 235 species of *Taraxacum,* most of them illustrated by silhouettes of herbarium specimens; drawings of bud involucres of 139 species by Olga Stewart and 178 distribution maps. A5 paperback.

No. 10 **Sea beans and nickar nuts** – E. Charles Nelson. 2000, reprinted 2003. 156 pp., with descriptions of nearly 60 exotic seeds and fruits found stranded on beaches in north-western Europe (many illustrated by Wendy Walsh) and of the mature plants (some with drawings by Alma Hathway), accounts of their history and folklore, growing instructions, etc. A5 paperback.

No. 11 **Water-starworts (Callitriche) of Europe** – R. V. Lansdown. 2008. 184 pp., with descriptions, line drawings by F. 1. Rumsey and the author, and maps showing distribution in the British Isles and in Europe for all 16 *Callitriche* species and one hybrid reliably recorded in Europe; detailed introductory material, glossary and appendix listing the herbarium material studied. A5 paperback.

No. 12 **Fumitories of Britain and Ireland** – R. J. Murphy. 2009. 121 pp., with descriptions, line drawings, black & white and full colour illustrations of 22 species, subspecies and varieties of fumitory in Britain and Ireland. detailed introductory material, glossary and summary of Vice-counties for which *Fumaria* taxa have been reliably recorded. A5 paperback. The first in a series of full colour handbooks.

Other BSBI publications

Alien grasses of the British Isles – T. B. Ryves, E. J. Clement & M. C. Foster. 1996. 234 pp. A companion volume to the following, listing over 700 non-native grasses; includes keys to bamboos and eight of the larger and more difficult genera and 29 pp. of drawings by G. M. S. Easy. Paperback.

Alien plants of the British Isles – E. J. Clement & M. C. Foster. 1994. 616 pp. Lists 3,586 recorded non-native species (of which 885 are established), with English names, frequency, status, origin, references to descriptions and illustrations, and selected synonyms. Paperback.

Altitudinal limits of British and Irish vascular plants – D. A. Pearman & R. W. M. Corner. 2nd edn 2004. 40 pp. Tables setting out maximum and minimum altitudes for some 1,500 taxa, with vice-county, locality, grid ref., recorder and date for most entries. A5 paperback.

Atlas of British and Irish brambles – A. Newton & R. D. Randall. 2004. 98 pp., with 330 hectad distribution maps of *Rubus* species, summaries of distribution and notes on changes. A5 paperback.

Botanical Links in the Atlantic Arc – S. J. Leach, C. N. Page, Y. Peytoureau & M. N. Sanford (eds). 2006. 336 pp., with colour photograph section, black-and-white photographs, maps and figures. A wide-ranging series of papers on the flora of the Atlantic coastal regions of Europe. Proceedings of an international conference held at Camborne, Cornwall, in 2003, published as BSBI Conference Report No. 24, dedicated to the memory of Dr Franklyn H. Perring. Hardback.

British Alpine Hawkweeds – David Tennant & Tim Rich. 2007. A monograph of British *Hieracium* section *Alpina.* 234 pp., with over 170 drawings and colour photographs and five paintings by Ramond C. Booth. All 39 taxa are described in detail, with their history, distribution maps, a gazetteer, habitats, ecology, biology, origins, cultivation, conservation status and details of relevant herbarium collections. A4 hardback and paperback.

Change in the British Flora 1987-2004 (A report on the BSBI Local Change survey) – M. E. Braithwaite, R. W. Ellis & C. D. Preston. 2006. 390 pp., with colour photographs, distribution maps, tables and graphs. A comparison of the results of two surveys of selected 2 km x 2 km squares. Large paperback.

Current taxonomic research on the British and European Flora – J. P. Bailey & R. G. Ellis (eds). 2006. 156 pp., with colour photographs and text illustrations. Proceedings of a conference held at the University of Leicester in 2003 to mark the retirement of Prof. Clive Stace, published as BSBI Conference Report No. 25. Paperback.

First records of alien plants in the wild in Britain and Ireland – D. A. Pearman & C. D. Preston. 2003. 40 pp. Tables setting out the year(s) in which some 1,600 taxa were first recorded, with details of source, vice-county and some notes for missed entries. A5 paperback.

Illustrations of alien plants of the British Isles – E. J. Clement, D. P. J. Smith & I. R. Thirlwell. 2005. 480 pp., including 444 full-page line drawings of introduced, naturalised and casually occurring alien plants in Britain and Ireland. The drawings are largely from a collection put together by the late David McClintock, originally for publication in his planned Volume 3 of *A New Illustrated British Flora*. A5 paperback.

List of vascular plants of the British Isles – D. H. Kent. 1992. 400 pp. Nomenclature and sequence as in Clive Stace's *New Flora of the British Isles* (1991, 1997), with selected synonyms. Paperback. Supplied with five errata lists. Three supplements (published 1996, 2000 and 2006) are also available.

Plant crib – T. C. G. Rich & A. C. Jermy. 1998, reprinted 2006. 400 pp. An expertly written identification guide for some 325 difficult taxonomic groups, with explanations, keys and illustrations of plant details. A4 paperback.

Vice-county census catalogue of vascular plants of Great Britain, the Isle of Man and the Channel Islands – C. A. Stace, R. G. Ellis, D. H. Kent & D. J. McCosh (eds). 2003. 432 pp. A full listing by species of the vice-counties from which vascular plants have been recorded. A5 paperback.

Other publishers' books

Aquatic plants in Britain and Ireland – C. D. Preston & J. M. Croft. 1997. 365 pp. Accounts and distribution maps of 200 aquatic plants in 72 genera, with 72 line drawings by G. M. S. Easy. Large paperback reprint, published 2001 by Harley Books.

New Atlas of the British and Irish Flora – C. D. Preston, D. A. Pearman & T. D. Dines (eds). 2002. 921 pp. Distribution maps and accompanying text for 2,412 plants, with introductory chapters. Very large hardback with CD-ROM, published by Oxford University Press.

The Vegetative Key to the British Flora – John Poland & Eric Clement. 2009. 526 pp. A striking new approach the identification of nearly 3000 wildflowers, grasses, sedges, trees, shrubs, ferns and fern-allies to be found native, naturalised or casual in the British Isles. With numerous 'thumbnail' line drawings and 24 plates of colour photographs. Softback, privately published by John Poland, Southampton.